INTERNATIONAL ATOMIC WEIGHTS

NAME	SYMBOL	ATOMIC NUMBER	ATOMIC WEIGHT*	NAME	SYMBOL	ATOMIC NUMBER	ATOMIC WEIGHT*
Actinium	Ac	89	227	Mercury	Hg	80	200.61
Aluminum	Al	13	26.98	Molybdenum	Mo	42	95.95
Americium	Am	95	[243]	Neodymium	Nd	60	144.27
Antimony	Sb	51	121.76	Neon	Ne	10	20.183
Argon	Ar	18	39.944	Neptunium	Np	93	[237]
Arsenic	As	33	74.91	Nickel	Ni	28	58.71
Astatine	At	85	[210]	Niobium	Nb	41	92.91
Barium	Ba	56	137.36	Nitrogen	N	7	14.008
Berkelium	Bk	97	[249]	Nobelium	No	102	[253]
Beryllium	Be	4	9.013	Osmium	Os	76	190.2
Bismuth	Bi	83	209.00	Oxygen	O	8	16.0000
Boron	B	5	10.82	Palladium	Pd	46	106.4
Bromine	Br	35	79.916	Phosphorus	P	15	30.975
Cadmium	Cd	48	112.41	Platinum	Pt	78	195.09
Calcium	Ca	20	40.08	Plutonium	Pu	94	[242]
Californium	Cf	98	[249]	Polonium	Po	84	210
Carbon	C	6	12.011	Potassium	K	19	39.100
Cerium	Ce	58	140.13	Praseodymium	Pr	59	140.92
Cesium	Cs	55	132.91	Promethium	Pm	61	[145]
Chlorine	Cl	17	35.457	Protactinium	Pa	91	231
Chromium	Cr	24	52.01	Radium	Ra	88	226.05
Cobalt	Co	27	58.94	Radon	Rn	86	222
Columbium: see Niobium †				Rhenium	Re	75	186.22
Copper	Cu	29	63.54	Rhodium	Rh	45	102.91
Curium	Cm	96	[245]	Rubidium	Rb	37	85.48
Dysprosium	Dy	66	162.51	Ruthenium	Ru	44	101.1
Einsteinium	Es	99	[254]	Samarium	Sm	62	150.35
Erbium	Er	68	167.27	Scandium	Sc	21	44.96
Europium	Eu	63	152.0	Selenium	Se	34	78.96
Fermium	Fm	100	[255]	Silicon	Si	14	28.09
Fluorine	F	9	19.00	Silver	Ag	47	107.880
Francium	Fr	87	[223]	Sodium	Na	11	22.991
Gadolinium	Gd	64	157.26	Strontium	Sr	38	87.63
Gallium	Ga	31	69.72	Sulfur	S	16	32.066§
Germanium	Ge	32	72.60	Tantalum	Ta	73	180.95
Gold	Au	79	197.0	Technetium	Tc	43	[99]
Hafnium	Hf	72	178.50	Tellurium	Te	52	127.61
Helium	He	2	4.003	Terbium	Tb	65	158.93
Holmium	Ho	67	164.94	Thallium	Tl	81	204.39
Hydrogen	H	1	1.0080	Thorium	Th	90	232.05
Indium	In	49	114.82	Thulium	Tm	69	168.94
Iodine	I	53	126.91	Tin	Sn	50	118.70
Iridium	Ir	77	192.2	Titanium	Ti	22	47.90
Iron	Fe	26	55.85	Tungsten	W	74	183.86
Krypton	Kr	36	83.80	Uranium	U	92	238.07
Lanthanum	La	57	138.92	Vanadium	V	23	50.95
Lead	Pb	82	207.21	Xenon	Xe	54	131.30
Lithium	Li	3	6.940	Ytterbium	Yb	70	173.04
Lutetium	Lu	71	174.99	Yttrium	Y	39	88.92
Magnesium	Mg	12	24.32	Zinc	Zn	30	65.38
Manganese	Mn	25	54.94	Zirconium	Zr	40	91.22
Mendelevium	Md	101	[256]				

* A value given in brackets is the mass number of the most stable known isotope.

† The English name of this element has been changed recently, by action of the International Union of Pure and Applied Chemistry.

§ Because of natural variations in the relative abundance of the isotopes of sulfur the atomic weight of this element has a range of ±0.003.

GENERAL CHEMISTRY

A Series of Chemistry Texts

LINUS PAULING, EDITOR

GENERAL CHEMISTRY

An Introduction to
Descriptive Chemistry and
Modern Chemical Theory

by LINUS PAULING

Professor of Chemistry in the California Institute of Technology

Illustrations by ROGER HAYWARD

Second Edition

W. H. FREEMAN AND COMPANY

San Francisco and London

Preface to the Second Edition

Three years ago, in the Preface of my textbook *College Chemistry*, I made the following statement:

"Although *General Chemistry* was written primarily for use by students planning to major in chemistry and related fields, it has been found useful also by students with primary interest in other subjects, including some who have not received instruction in chemistry in high school. Experience has shown, however, that there is need for a book based on the approach of *General Chemistry*, but written in a more slowly paced, less mathematical form. The present book, *College Chemistry*, provides this more gradual introduction to modern chemistry. I propose, in the near future, to revise *General Chemistry* in such a way as to make it especially suited to use by first-year college students who plan to major in chemistry and by other well-prepared students with a special interest in the subject."

The problem of teaching chemistry to students who intend to specialize in this subject or in related fields has become a very difficult one, because of the great increase in chemical knowledge during the past fifty years. The subjects of general chemistry, qualitative analysis and quantitative analysis, physical chemistry, and organic chemistry as they were taught fifty years ago were extensive enough and difficult enough to keep a student busy throughout his four years as an undergraduate. A modern chemist must know a good bit not only about these subjects, but also about mathematics, physics (including atomic physics), colloid chemistry, instrumental analysis, biochemistry, structural chemistry (crystal structure, molecular structure, etc.), statistical mechanics, and other subjects; and in addition the basic chemical subjects themselves, such as physical chemistry and organic chemistry, have developed greatly during the half century since 1900. University and college teachers of chemistry are now facing the difficult situation that has resulted from the progress of science. A decision must be made as to how to solve the problem.

The introduction of new general principles through the development of theoretical chemistry has made it possible to leave out some of the material formerly included in the first-year course. In particular, a smaller amount of time can now be devoted to learning the facts of descriptive chemistry, because many of these facts have been correlated and systematized by new principles. Some of the non-mathematical parts of modern science, especially the descriptive aspects of atomic and molecular structure, can then be introduced during the first year. A part of elementary physical chemistry can also be treated during the first year, leaving time in later years for more advanced parts of this subject to be discussed. Some of these topics may be discussed with such thoroughness in the general chemistry course that they need not be taken up again in later courses, except for review or for amplification by more mathematical treatment.

In preparing the second edition of *General Chemistry* I have attempted to carry out this plan. Two new chapters dealing with atomic physics have been introduced, Chapters 3 and 8. In these chapters there is given a rather thorough discussion of the discovery of X-rays, radioactivity, the electron, and the atomic nucleus, the nature and properties of the electron and the nucleus, the quantum theory, the photoelectric effect and the photon, the Bohr theory of the atom, the somewhat changed picture of the atom provided by quantum mechanics, and related aspects of atomic science. The first-year student may learn how to calculate the amount of energy in a photon of light of given wavelength, and to predict whether or not the absorption of light of this wavelength by a molecule could result in dissociation of the molecule into atoms. A somewhat more detailed discussion of some parts of elementary physical chemistry is presented than was given in the first edition. A chapter on biochemistry has been introduced. The discussion of the chemistry of metals has been extensively revised. This discussion now begins with a chapter on the nature of metals and alloys and the methods of winning and refining metals. There follow three chapters on the chemistry of the transition metals: one on scandium, titanium, vanadium, chromium, and manganese and their congeners, a second on iron, cobalt, nickel, and the platinum metals, and a third on copper, zinc, gallium, and germanium and their congeners. Most of the other chapters have been revised to some extent.

I am indebted for aid in the preparation of this edition to many of my colleagues and to many teachers of chemistry who have written to me or spoken to me about the problems of teaching the first-year chemistry course, and I am glad to express my gratitude to them.

Pasadena, California   LINUS PAULING
28 February 1953

Preface to the First Edition

Chemistry is a very large subject, which continues to grow, as new elements are discovered or made, new compounds are synthesized, and new principles are formulated. Nevertheless, despite its growth, the science can now be presented to the student more easily and effectively than ever before. In the past the course in general chemistry has necessarily tended to be a patchwork of descriptive chemistry and certain theoretical topics. The progress made in recent decades in the development of unifying theoretical concepts has been so great, however, that the presentation of general chemistry to the students of the present generation can be made in a more simple, straightforward, and logical way than formerly.

For example, every boy now knows about atoms, and accepts them as part of his world—they are split in the atomic bomb and in the comic papers, they stare at him from advertisements. In this book I begin the teaching of chemistry by discussing the properties of substances in terms of atoms and molecules. The subject is then developed in as orderly a manner as has seemed possible at the present stage of chemical knowledge.

No previous instruction of the student in chemistry has been assumed, but I believe that the treatment differs enough from that customary in high-school courses to be interesting to a student who has studied chemistry in high school as well as to one who has not.

Descriptive chemistry is presented in limited amount—enough to provide the student with an introduction to the multitude of chemical substances, with their interestingly different properties, but not so much as to confuse him, to bury him under a mass of facts. Chapters 5 and 6 present a survey of the chemical elements and their compounds, in relation to the periodic table, and twelve later chapters are devoted to the chemistry of individual elements or groups of elements.

An order of presentation of topics has been chosen which seems to me to permit the straightforward development of the subject. After the introductory discussion of the properties of substances and of their atomic and molecular structure and the survey of descriptive chemistry in relation to the periodic table of the elements, there are given thorough discussions of weight relations in chemical changes, valence and electronic structure, and oxidation-reduction reactions. The first detailed chapter of descriptive chemistry deals with chromium and manganese and their congeners. These elements have been selected for this prominent place because their chemistry is very interesting, and should hold the attention of the student, and also because they provide excellent examples of oxidation-reduction reactions. The remaining chapters deal with descriptive chemistry and theoretical subjects in a suitable sequence.

The principal theoretical chapters, especially those concerned with the properties of gases, reaction rates, chemical equilibrium, and thermochemistry, are presented in enough detail to provide a satisfactory basic training for students majoring in chemistry. Large parts of these chapters may be omitted in courses for those students not majoring in chemistry.

I am indebted for assistance in various ways in the preparation of the book to Dr. Philip A. Shaffer, Jr., Dr. Norman Davidson, Prof. Ernest H. Swift, Mr. Linus Pauling, Jr., Mr. Peter J. Pauling, Mr. Eugene Maun, and especially Mr. Roger Hayward, the illustrator, and Mr. William H. Freeman, the publisher. I also thank Dr. R. W. G. Wyckoff, Dr. D. S. Clark, Dr. S. Kyropoulos, the Malleable Founders' Society, and the Griffith Observatory for providing figures. The book might well be dedicated to the freshmen students at the California Institute of Technology during the past seven years, who have collaborated with me in putting it to practical test.

LINUS PAULING

Pasadena, California
11 April 1947

Table of Contents

Chapter 1

The Nature and Properties of Matter

1–1. *Matter and Chemistry*

The universe is composed of substances (forms of matter) and radiant energy. Chemistry is the science of substances—their structure, their properties, and the reactions that change them into other substances.

This definition of chemistry is both too narrow and too broad. It is too narrow because the chemist, in his study of substances, must also study radiant energy—light, X-rays, radiowaves—in its interaction with substances. He may be interested in the color of substances, which is produced by the absorption of light. Or he may be interested in the atomic structure of substances, as determined by the diffraction of X-rays (Chap. 3), or even by the absorption or emission of radiowaves by the substances.

On the other hand, the definition is too broad, in that almost all of science could be included within it. The astrophysicist is interested in the substances that are present in stars and other celestial bodies, or that are distributed, in very low concentration, through interstellar space. The nuclear physicist studies the substances that constitute the nuclei of atoms. The biologist is interested in the substances that are present in living organisms. The geologist is interested in the substances, called minerals, that make up the earth. It is, indeed, hard to draw a line between chemistry and other sciences.

The Structure of Matter. The properties of matter are most easily and clearly learned and understood when they are correlated with its structure, in terms of molecules, atoms, and still smaller particles. Structure has to do with the particles that go to make up all matter, and that through their interactions with one another give individuality and variety to matter. We shall launch upon the study of structure in the next chapter.

Kinds of Matter. As we look about us, we observe many different kinds of matter. We see a desk that is constructed mainly of wood, an organic material. The bracket holding up the arm of the desk is of iron; iron is a metal, and it is an elementary substance, one of the ninety-eight known chemical elements. The doorknob on the door is made of brass; brass also is a metal, but it is not an element: it is, instead, an alloy of the two elementary metals copper and zinc. The light fixtures are made of aluminum, copper, brass, tungsten, glass, fluorescent substances, mercury vapor, and several other materials. The student sitting at the desk is composed of matter of a great many different kinds.

With a microscope we can see the cells of plant and animal organisms, such as the red cells of the blood, which are about 0.001 cm in diameter (10^{-3} cm). With the electron microscope virus particles (virus molecules) 10^{-6} cm in diameter can be seen, and by means of the diffraction of X-rays and electron waves molecules and atoms approximately 10^{-8} cm in diameter can be studied. The physicists have, in fact, succeeded in investigating electrons, protons, neutrons, and other particles that are only about 10^{-12} cm in diameter; these are the smallest particles of matter that have as yet been discovered (Fig. 1-1).

The astronomers have obtained much information about matter outside of the earth. They have found that helium, sodium, calcium, hydrogen, and many other elements are present in the sun and other stars, and that ammonia, methane, and other substances are present in the atmospheres of the planets. They have found that matter is present in some stars in a very dense form: the density of one star, the companion of Sirius, is* 61,000 g/cm³, or about one ton per cubic inch. In interstellar space, on the other hand, the concentration of matter is very small: it has been estimated to be about one atom per cubic centimeter, which corresponds to about 10^{-23} g/cm³. We have knowledge about the nature of matter in the very distant nebulae, a billion light-years away—separated from us by what seems to be the radius of the universe, 10^{27} cm.

---

* The symbol *g/cm³* means grams per cubic centimeter. An alternative symbol is *g cm⁻ᵉ*. Either type of symbol may be used for simple combinations of units; for complex ones the symbols with negative exponents are preferred, because they are less liable to be misunderstood.

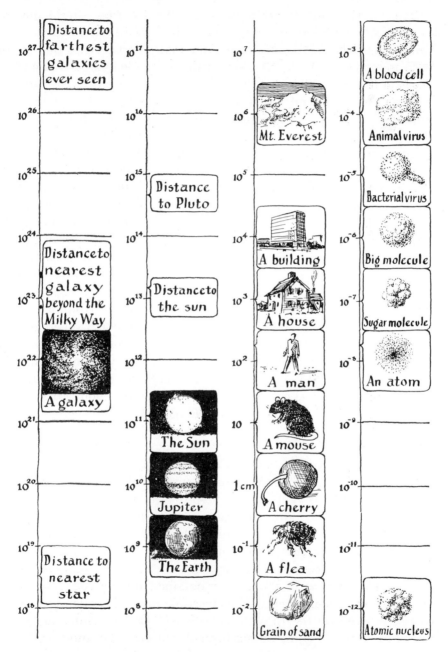

FIG. 1-1   *A diagram showing dimensions of objects, from 10^{-12} cm (the nucleus of an atom) to 10^{27} cm (the radius of the known universe).*

The chemist is interested in matter in all of its forms—in the minerals, drugs, fuels, building materials, and living organisms on earth, in the minute particles 10^{-12} cm in diameter that combine with one another to form atoms and molecules, and in the distant nebulae a million light-years in diameter, that can be studied only by means of the light that reaches the earth and is collected onto a photographic plate by the paraboloidal mirror of a giant telescope.

Matter and Energy.   Matter has mass, and any portion of matter on the earth is attracted toward the center of the earth by the force of gravity; this attraction is called the weight of the portion of matter. In addition to matter, the universe also contains energy, in the form of light (radiant energy). For many years scientists thought that matter and energy could be distinguished through the possession of mass by matter and the lack of possession of mass by energy. Then, early in the present century (1905), it was pointed out by Albert Einstein (born 1879) that energy also has mass, and that light is accordingly attracted by matter through gravitation. This was verified by astronomers, who found that a ray of light traveling from a distant star to the earth and passing close by the sun is bent toward the sun by its gravitational attraction. The observation of this phenomenon was made during a solar eclipse, when the image of the star could be seen close to the sun.

The amount of mass associated with a definite amount of energy is given by an important equation, the *Einstein equation:*

$$E = mc^2 \tag{1-1}$$

In this equation E is the amount of energy, m is the mass, and c is the velocity of light. The velocity of light, c, is one of the fundamental constants of nature;* its value is 2.9979×10^{10} cm/sec.

Until the present century it was also thought that matter could not be created or destroyed, but could only be converted from one form into another. In recent years it has, however, been found possible to convert matter into radiant energy, and to convert radiant energy into matter. The mass m of the matter obtained by the conversion of an amount E of radiant energy or convertible into this amount of radiant energy is given by the Einstein equation (1-1). Experimental verification of the Einstein equation has been obtained by the study of processes involving nuclei of atoms. The nature of these processes will be described in later chapters in this book.

The *units* of the quantities in the Einstein equation as written are

* The symbol c represents the velocity of light in a vacuum (empty space).

those of the metric system (the centimeter-gram-second system). If m is given in g (grams) and c in cm/sec (centimeters per second), then the numerical value of mc^2 is the value of the energy E in ergs.

Until the present century scientists made use of a law of conservation of matter and a law of conservation of energy. These two conservation laws must now be combined into a single one, the **law of conservation of mass,** in which the mass to be conserved includes both the mass of matter in the system and the mass of energy in the system. However, for ordinary chemical reactions we may still make use of the "law" of conservation of matter—that matter cannot be created or destroyed, but only changed in form—recognizing that there is a limitation on the validity of this law: it is not to be applied if one of the processes involving the conversion of radiant energy into matter or matter into radiant energy takes place in the system under consideration.

Let us now consider again the two definitions given at the beginning of this chapter. We see that the statement that matter comprises all the substances of which the universe is composed is not really a definition until we have defined substances. Einstein's theory of relativity, which led to the relation between mass and energy, also provided a satisfactory definition of matter. According to the theory of relativity, matter comprises everything in the universe that has mass when it is standing still— this mass is called its *rest mass.* Additional energy (*kinetic energy*) is required to cause a portion of matter to move. The mass of the moving portion of matter is greater than the rest mass by an amount determined by the kinetic energy, according to Equation 1-1. According to the theory of relativity, it is impossible for any portion of matter to be accelerated to the speed of light. Light itself is considered to consist of bundles (*quanta*) of energy (these quanta of energy are also called *photons*), which can move only at the speed of light, and which have no rest mass. The nature of light will be discussed in detail in Chapter 8.

Example 1.   When 1,000 g of uranium 235 undergoes nuclear fission, as in the detonation of an atomic bomb, the amount 8.23×10^{20} ergs of energy is given off. What is the mass of the material products of the reaction?

> **Solution.**   We can calculate the mass of the energy that is given off (as radiant energy—light, gamma rays, etc.) by the use of the Einstein equation (1-1). Rewriting this equation by dividing each side by c^2, we obtain
>
> $$m = \frac{E}{c^2}$$

The value of c^2 is $(3 \times 10^{10} \text{ cm/sec})^2 = 9 \times 10^{20} \text{ cm}^2/\text{sec}^2$. Hence we obtain

$$m = \frac{8.23 \times 10^{20} \text{ ergs}}{9 \times 10^{20} \text{ cm}^2/\text{sec}^2} = 0.915 \text{ g}$$

Accordingly, the amount of mass sent out in the form of radiant energy is 0.915 g. Subtracting this from the mass 1,000 g of the original material, uranium, we obtain **999.085 g** as the mass of the material products of the reaction. In this nuclear reaction, which will be discussed in detail in the last chapter of the book, nearly 0.1% of the matter has been converted into radiation.

The Einstein relation between mass and energy has been verified by the direct measurement of the mass of the products and of the energy emitted, in nuclear reactions of this sort.

Example 2.   It is found by experiment that when 1,000 g of glyceryl trinitrate (nitroglycerine) is exploded, the amount 8.0×10^{13} ergs of energy is liberated. What is the mass of the products of the explosion?

Solution.   This example is to be solved in exactly the same way as the preceding one. The mass of the radiant energy that is produced by the explosion is obtained by dividing the energy E by the square of the velocity of light, $c^2 = 9 \times 10^{20}$:

$$m = \frac{E}{c^2} = \frac{8.0 \times 10^{13} \text{ ergs}}{9 \times 10^{20}} = 0.89 \times 10^{-7} \text{ g}$$

Thus we calculate that the mass of the products of the explosion is **999.999999911 g.**

Accordingly, the mass of the products of this chemical reaction differs very slightly from the mass of the reactant—so slightly that it is impossible to measure the difference experimentally. The amount of mass that has been converted into energy in the explosion of glyceryl trinitrate is calculated above to be only one ten-billionth of the original mass. This quantity is so small that we may say, for practical purposes, that there is conservation of mass (conservation of matter) in ordinary chemical reactions.

Units of the Metric System.   The *mass* of an object is measured in terms of *grams* (g) or *kilograms* (kg), the kilogram being equal to 1,000 g. The kilogram is defined as the mass of a standard object made of a platinum-iridium alloy and kept in Paris. One pound is equal approximately to 454 g, and hence 1 kg is equal approximately to 2.2 lb. Note that it has become customary in recent years for the abbreviations of units in the metric system to be written without periods.

The metric unit of length is the *meter* (m), which is equal to about 39.37 inches. The meter is defined in terms of a standard meter, of platinum-iridium, kept in Paris. The *centimeter* (cm), which is 1/100 m, is about 0.4 inch, the inch being equal to 2.54 cm. The *millimeter* (mm) is 1/1,000 m or 1/10 cm.

The metric unit of volume is the *liter* (l), which is approximately 1.06 U.S. quarts. The *milliliter* (ml), equal to 1/1,000 l, is usually used as the unit of volume in the measurement of liquids in chemical work. The milliliter is defined as the volume occupied by 1 g of water at 3.98° C (the temperature at which its density is the greatest) and under a pressure of one atmosphere (that is, the normal pressure due to the weight of the air).

At the time when the metric system was set up, in 1799, it was intended that the milliliter be exactly equal to the cubic centimeter (cm³). However, it was later found that the relation between the gram, as given by the prototype kilogram, and the centimeter, one one-hundredth of the distance between two engraved lines on a standard platinum-iridium bar (the prototype meter kept in Paris by the International Bureau of Weights and Measures), is such that the milliliter is not exactly equal to the cubic centimeter, but is, instead, equal to 1.000027 cm³. It is obvious that the distinction between ml and cm³ is ordinarily unimportant.

Units and Dimensions.   We have stated above that the Einstein equation $E = mc^2$ is correct when m is expressed in grams, c in centimeters per second, and E in ergs. These quantities—grams, centimeters per second, and ergs—are called the *units* of m, c, E, respectively.

Other units might be used; for example, the mass might be expressed in pounds, the velocity of light in miles per second, or miles per hour, and the energy in calories or in some other energy unit. However, if other units were to be used for these quantities, it might be necessary to introduce a numerical factor into the equation. The units of the metric system were chosen in such a way as to make the numerical factors in the important equations of physics and chemistry as simple as possible; in this case, the case of the Einstein equation, the numerical factor has the value 1.

It is interesting to note that energy can be expressed in terms of units g cm² sec⁻². There is another well-known equation of physics which involves the same sort of relationship. This is the equation expressing the kinetic energy of a moving particle in terms of its mass and its velocity, as given by Newton's laws of motion. The equation is

$$\text{kinetic energy} = \tfrac{1}{2}mv^2$$

The velocity, v, of a particle may be expressed, in the metric system, in units cm/sec—it is the quotient of the distance traversed by the particle and the time required for traversing this distance. Accordingly, the units of kinetic energy in the metric system are g cm² sec⁻². In the kinetic-energy equation there occurs the numerical factor $\tfrac{1}{2}$.

No matter what units are used, an equation for a quantity of energy must always involve mass, length, and time in the following way, in which the square brackets are used to indicate the *dimensions* of the quantity within the brackets:

$$[\text{energy}] = [\text{mass}][\text{length}]^2[\text{time}]^{-2}$$

This equation says that the dimensions of energy are equal to the dimensions of mass times the dimensions of length squared times the dimensions of time with the exponent −2 (that is, divided by the dimensions of time squared).

It is good to develop the habit of checking the units and dimensions in the equations that you use.

1–2. *Kinds of Matter*

We shall first distinguish between objects and kinds of matter. An object, such as a human being, a table, a brass doorknob, may be made of one kind of matter or of several kinds of matter. The chemist is primarily interested not in the objects themselves, but in the kinds of matter of which they are composed. He is interested in the alloy brass, whether it is in a doorknob or in some other object; and, indeed, his interest is primarily in those properties of the material that are independent of the nature of the objects containing it.

The following sentences indicate the accepted scientific usage of words that designate different kinds of matter.

Materials. *The word **material** is used in referring to any kind of matter, whether homogeneous or heterogeneous.*

A *heterogeneous* material is a material that consists of parts with different properties. A *homogeneous* material has the same properties throughout.

Wood, with soft and hard rings alternating, is obviously a heterogeneous material, as is also granite, in which grains of three different species of matter (the minerals quartz, mica, and feldspar) can be seen.

Substances. *A **substance** is a homogeneous species of matter with reasonably definite chemical composition.*

Pure salt, pure sugar, pure iron, pure copper, pure sulfur, pure water, pure oxygen, and pure hydrogen are representative substances. On the other hand, a solution of sugar in water is not a substance, according to this definition: it is, to be sure, homogeneous, but it does not satisfy the second part of the above definition, inasmuch as its composition is not definite, but is widely variable, being determined by the amount of sugar that happens to have been dissolved in a given amount of water. Similarly, the gold of a gold ring or watchcase is not a pure substance, even though it is apparently homogeneous. It is an alloy of gold with other metals, usually copper, and it consists of a crystalline solution of copper in gold. The word *alloy* is used to refer to a metallic material containing two or more elements: some alloys are substances (intermetallic compounds), but most of them are crystalline solutions or mixtures.

Sometimes (as in the first section of this chapter) the word "substance" is used in a broader sense, essentially as equivalent to material. Chemists usually restrict the use of the word in the way given by the definition above. The chemist's usage of the word substance may be indicated by using the phrase "pure substance."

Our definition is not precise, in that it says that a substance has reasonably definite chemical composition. Most materials that the chemist classifies as substances (pure substances) have definite chemical composition; for example, pure salt consists of the two elements sodium and chlorine in exactly the ratio of one atom of sodium to one atom of chlorine. Others, however, show a small range of variation of chemical composition; an example is the iron sulfide that is made by heating iron and sulfur together. This substance has a range in composition of a few percent. A discussion of substances with variable composition is given in Chapter 7.

Kinds of Definition.   Definitions may be either precise or imprecise. The mathematician may define the words that he uses precisely; in his further discussion he then adheres rigorously to the defined meaning of each word. We have given some precise definitions above. One of them is the definition of the kilogram as the mass of a standard object, the prototype kilogram, that is kept in Paris. Similarly, the gram is defined rigorously and precisely as 1/1,000 the mass of the kilogram.

On the other hand, the words that are used in describing nature, which is itself complex, may not be capable of precise definition. In giving a definition for such a word the effort is made to describe the accepted usage.

Mixtures and Solutions.   A specimen of granite, in which grains of three different species of matter can be seen, is obviously a *mixture*. An emulsion of oil in water (a suspension of droplets of oil in water) is also a mixture. The heterogeneity of a piece of granite is obvious to the eye. The heterogeneity of an emulsion containing large drops of oil suspended in water is also obvious; the emulsion is clearly seen to be a mixture. But as the oil droplets in the emulsion are made smaller and smaller, it may become impossible to observe the heterogeneity of the material, and uncertainty may arise as to whether the material should be called a mixture or a solution.

An ordinary *solution* is homogeneous; it is not usually classified as a substance, however, because its composition is variable. A solution of liquids, such as alcohol and water, or of gases, such as oxygen and nitrogen (the principal constituents of air), may also be called a mixture. The word "mixture" may thus be used to refer to a homogeneous material that is not a pure substance or to a heterogeneous aggregate of two or more substances.

A homogeneous crystalline material is not necessarily a pure substance. Thus natural crystals of sulfur are sometimes deep-yellow or brown in color, instead of light-yellow. They contain some selenium, distributed at random throughout the crystals in place of some of the sulfur, the crystals being homogeneous, and with faces as well formed as those of pure sulfur. These crystals are a *crystalline solution* (or *solid solution*). The gold-copper alloy used in jewelry is another example of a crystalline solution. It is a homogeneous material, but its composition is variable.

Phases.   A material system (that is, a limited part of the universe) may be described in terms of the *phases* constituting it. *A* **phase** *is a*

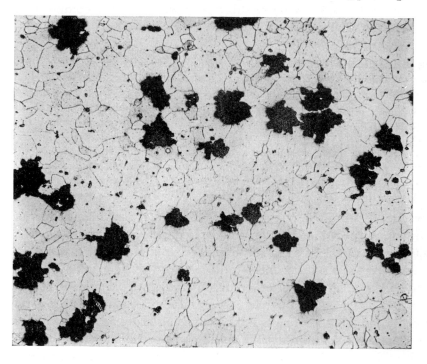

FIG. 1-2   *A photomicrograph (linear magnification* 100 ×—*that is, magnified by a linear factor of* 100) *of a polished and etched surface of a specimen of malleable cast iron, showing small grains of iron and roughly spherical particles of graphite (carbon). (From Malleable Founders' Society.) The grains of iron look somewhat different from one another because of different illumination.*

homogeneous part of a system, separated from other parts by physical boundaries. For example, if a flask is partially full of water in which ice is floating, the system comprising the contents of the flask consists of three phases, the solid phase ice, the liquid phase water, and the gaseous phase air.

A piece of malleable cast iron can be seen with a microscope to be a mixture of small grains of iron and particles of graphite (a form of carbon); it hence consists of two phases, iron and graphite (Fig. 1-2).

A phase in a system comprises all of the parts that have the same properties and composition. Thus, if there were several pieces of ice in the system discussed above, they would constitute not several phases, but only one phase, the ice phase.

Constituents and Components.   Chemists use the words *constituent* and *component* in special ways.

The **constituents** *of a system are the various phases that constitute the system.*

A **set of components** *of a system is a set of substances (the minimum number of substances) from which the phases (constituents) of the system could be made.*

The constituents of the system discussed above are the three phases air, water, and ice. The components of the system may be taken to be either air and water, or air and ice, because the water phase and the ice phase can both be made from a single substance, water (or ice).* In this case the number of components is less than the number of phases. It may be greater; for example, a system consisting just of a solution of sugar in water is constituted of one phase, the solution, but it has two components, sugar and water.

1–3. *The Physical Properties of Substances*

Properties *of substances are their characteristic qualities.*

Sodium chloride, common salt, may be selected as an example of a substance. We have all seen this substance in what appear to be different forms—table salt, in fine grains; salt in the form of crystals a quarter of an inch in diameter, for use in regenerating water-softening minerals or with ice for freezing ice cream; and natural crystals of rock salt an inch or more across. Despite their obvious difference, all of these samples of salt have the same fundamental properties. In each case the crystals, small or large, are bounded by square or rectangular faces, of different sizes, but with each face always at right angles to each adjacent face. The possession of different properties in different directions—in particular the *formation of faces, edges, and corners*—is characteristic of crystals. The *cleavage* of the different crystals of salt is the same: when crushed, the crystals always break (cleave) along planes parallel to the

---

* In the above discussion air has been described as a component of the system. In discussing changes in state of the system in which the air behaves in the same way that nitrogen would behave, this would not lead to any difficulty, but in a rigorous treatment air might have to be described as involving several components (nitrogen, oxygen, argon, etc.).

original faces, producing smaller crystals similar to the larger ones. The different samples have the same salty *taste*. Their *solubility* is the same: at room temperature (18° C) 35.86 g of salt can be dissolved in 100 g of water. The *density* of the salt is the same, 2.163 g/cm³.

Properties of this sort, which are not affected appreciably by the size of the sample or its state of subdivision, are called the *specific properties* of the substance represented by the samples.

There are other properties besides density and solubility that can be measured precisely and expressed in numbers. Such another property is the *melting point*, the temperature at which a crystalline substance melts to form a liquid. The *electric conductivity* and the *thermal conductivity* are similar properties. On the other hand, there are also interesting physical properties of a substance that are not so simple in nature. One such property is the *malleability* of a substance—the ease with which the substance can be hammered out into thin sheets. A related property is the *ductility*—the ease with which the substance can be drawn into a wire. *Hardness* is a similar property: we say that one substance is less hard than a second substance when it is scratched by the second substance, but this test provides only qualitative information about the hardness. A discussion of hardness is presented in Chapter 6.

The *color* of a substance is an important physical property. It is interesting to note that the apparent color of a substance depends upon its state of subdivision: the color becomes lighter as large particles are ground up into smaller ones.

It is customary to say that under the same external conditions all specimens of a particular substance have the same specific physical properties (density, hardness, color, melting point, crystalline form, etc.). Sometimes, however, the word "substance" is used in referring to a material without regard to its state of aggregation; for example, ice, liquid water, and water vapor may be referred to as the same substance. Moreover, a specimen containing crystals of rock salt and crystals of table salt may be called a mixture, even though the specimen may consist entirely of the one chemical substance sodium chloride. This lack of definiteness in usage seems to cause no confusion in practice.

The concept "substance" is, of course, an idealization; all actual substances are more or less impure. It is a useful concept, however, because we have learned through experiment that the properties of various specimens of impure substances with the same major component and different impurities are nearly the same if the impurities are present in only small amounts. These properties are accepted as the properties of the ideal substance.

1–4. The Chemical Properties of Substances

The **chemical properties** of a substance are those properties that relate to
its participation in chemical reactions. **Chemical reactions** are the processes
that convert substances into other substances.

Thus sodium chloride has the property of changing into a soft metal,
sodium, and a greenish-yellow gas, chlorine, when it is decomposed
by electrolysis. It also has the property, when it is dissolved in water,
of producing a white precipitate when a solution of silver nitrate is
added to it; and it has many other chemical properties. Iron has the
property of combining readily with the oxygen in moist air, to form iron
rust; whereas an alloy of iron with chromium and nickel (stainless steel)
is found to resist this process of rusting. It is evident from this example
that the chemical properties of materials are important in engineering.

Most substances have the power to enter into many chemical reactions. The study of these reactions constitutes a large part of the study
of chemistry.

The properties of *taste* and *odor* are closely correlated with the chemical
nature of substances, and are to be considered as chemical properties;
the senses of smell and taste possessed by animals are the *chemical senses.*
There is still complete lack of knowledge as to the way in which the
molecules of tasty and odorous substances interact with the nerve end-
ings in the mouth and nose to produce the sensations of taste and
odor; this problem, like the problem of the molecular basis of the action
of drugs, is one that awaits solution by the younger generation of
chemists.

1–5. The Scientific Method

An important reason for studying science is to learn the scientific method
of attack on a problem. The method may be valuable not only in the
field of science but also in other fields—of business, of law, of government, of sociology, of international relations.

It is not possible to present a complete account of the scientific method
in a few paragraphs. At this point there is given a partial account,
which is amplified at the beginning of the following chapter, and in
later chapters. Here I may say that the scientific method consists, in
part, of the application of the principles of rigorous argument that are
developed in mathematics and in logic, the deduction of sound conclusions from a set of accepted postulates. In a branch of mathematics the
basic postulates are accepted as axioms, and the entire subject is then
derived from these postulates. In science, and in other fields of human

activity, the basic postulates (principles, laws) are not known, but must be discovered. The process of discovering these laws is called *induction*. The first step in applying the scientific method consists in finding some facts, by observation and experiment. In our science these are the facts of descriptive chemistry. The next step is the classification and correlation of many facts by one statement. Such a general statement, which includes within itself a number of facts, is called a *law*—sometimes a *law of nature*.

For example, when it was discovered, early in the nineteenth century, that water could be decomposed into hydrogen and oxygen by electrolysis (the action of an electric current), quantitative measurements of the amounts of hydrogen and oxygen were made. It was found in one experiment that 9 grams of water on electrolysis produced 1 gram of hydrogen and 8 grams of oxygen. This fact, for a particular specimen of water, was then amplified by additional facts, that the same amount of hydrogen, 1 gram, and the same amount of oxygen, 8 grams, were obtained by the electrolysis of 9 grams of water from other sources—rain water, sea water, water obtained by burning hydrogen in oxygen, etc. After many experiments of this sort had been made, all giving the same result, the facts were summarized in a law, that all samples of water give on electrolysis the same relative amounts of hydrogen and oxygen. When similar results were obtained for other chemical substances, this law was generalized into the law of constant composition (or law of definite proportions): in every pure sample of a given compound, the elements are present in the same proportion by weight.

It must be pointed out that the process of induction is never completely reliable. If one hundred analyses of water are made, by weighing the amounts of hydrogen and oxygen obtained by electrolysis of samples of water obtained from different sources, and the same proportion by weight of hydrogen to oxygen is found to within the limits of accuracy of the experiments, it would seem to be reasonably well justified to state that all samples of water have the same ratio of hydrogen to oxygen by weight. If a thousand analyses were made, with the same result, it would seem still more likely that this law is valid. However, if a single reliable analysis were then to be made which gave a different ratio, the law would have to be modified. It might turn out that the law is valid if the weighings of the gases are made with an accuracy of 0.1%, or 0.01%, but not if the weighings are made with still greater accuracy. This has, in fact, been found to be the case for water. In 1929 Professor William F. Giauque of the University of California at Berkeley discovered that there are three different kinds of oxygen atoms, with different masses (these atoms are called isotopes; see Chap. 4), and shortly thereafter Professor Harold C. Urey discovered that there are two kinds of hydrogen atoms, with different masses. Water consisting of molecules made with these different kinds of hydrogen atoms and oxygen atoms contains hydrogen and oxygen in different ratios by weight, and it has been found that the composition by weight of pure water from different natural sources is, in fact, slightly different. It has accordingly become necessary to revise the law of constant composition in such a way as to take into account the existence of these isotopic forms of atoms. The way in which this is done is described in Chapter 4.

One important way in which progress has been made in science is through a *process of successive approximations*. Some measurements are made with a certain precision, such as the measurements of the compositions of substances with accuracy of 1%, and a rough law is formulated that encompasses all of these measurements. It may then happen that, when more precise measurements are made, deviations from the first law are found to exist. A second, more refined but more complicated law may then be formulated to include these deviations. This procedure may have been carried out several times in the course of the formulation of a law of nature in its now accepted state.

It is wise to remember that a law obtained by the process of induction may at any time be found to have limited validity. Conclusions that are reached from such a law by the process of deduction should be recognized as having a probability of being correct that is determined by the probability that the original law is correct.

The application of the scientific method does not consist solely of the routine use of logical rules and procedures. Often a generalization that encompasses many facts has escaped notice until a scientist with unusual insight has discovered it. Intuition and imagination play their part in the scientific method.

As more and more people gain a sound understanding of the nature of the scientific method and learn to apply it in the solution of the problems of everyday life, we may hope for an improvement in the social, political, and international affairs of the world. Technical progress represents one way in which the world can be improved through science. The other way is through the social progress that results from application of the scientific method—through the development of "moral science"; and I believe that the study of science, the learning of the scientific method by all people, will ultimately help the people of the world in the solution of our great social and political problems.

Exercises

1-1. List the names of some chemical substances that you know. Does your present knowledge of chemistry permit you to identify some of these as elements?

1-2. Describe a chemical phenomenon that you have seen in everyday life.

1-3. Give the name of a chemical compound used in medicine. Do you know what elements it is made of? Do you know how it is made or from what natural source it is obtained?

1-4. The sun is 864,000 miles in diameter, and its average density is 1.4 g/cm³. Calculate the mass of the sun, in grams. Also calculate the mass of the interstellar matter in the spherical volume of space about the sun, with radius two light-years (half the distance to the nearest star), assuming the density of matter in interstellar space to be 10^{-23} g/cm³.

1-5. An object with mass 1 g is accelerated until its velocity is 3×10^9 cm/sec (that is, to one-tenth the velocity of light). Using the Einstein equation, calculate the mass of the moving object. Note that the total energy E is equal to the energy of the object when it is standing still (which is m_0c^2, where m_0 is the rest mass, 1 g) plus the quantity $\frac{1}{2}m_0v^2$, the kinetic energy of the moving particle. This expression for the energy of the particle is only approximately correct; a large error would be introduced if the velocity v became close to the velocity of light, c.

1-6. A flask contains a saturated solution of salt and several crystals of salt. (a) How many phases are present in the system contained within the flask? (b) State for each phase whether it is a pure substance or a mixture. (c) What are the constituents of the system? (d) Give a set of components for the system.

1-7. A piece of pure zinc weighing 10 g is placed in a quartz tube with volume 100 ml. The tube is then evacuated (all the air in it is pumped out), and is sealed off. It is then heated until about half of the zinc is melted. Answer questions a, b, c, and d of the preceding exercise, for this system.

1-8. Can you answer questions a, b, c, and d of Exercise 1-6 for the system like that in Exercise 1-7, but made with a 10-g sample of an alloy of copper and gold, instead of a 10-g sample of zinc?

1-9. Are scientific laws in general based on inductive logic or on deductive logic? Explain the difference between inductive and deductive logic.

1-10. What is the limiting factor of the validity of deductions from a scientific law?

1-11. Is the scientific method useful in any endeavor other than the study of the sciences? Can you give an example, if your answer is yes?

1-12. What is meant by "specific property of a substance"? Are odor, shape, density, color, weight, taste, luster, and area specific properties? Which of these are properties that can be quantitatively measured?

1-13. Can a homogeneous mixture be said to have any specific properties? Can a heterogeneous mixture be said to have any specific properties?

1-14. Can you prove by one experiment or one observation that a specimen of material is a mixture? that it is a pure substance?

Reference Books

Further information about descriptive chemistry may be obtained from textbooks and treatises such as the following:

M. C. Sneed and J. L. Maynard, *General Inorganic Chemistry*, D. Van Nostrand Co., New York, **1942.**

F. Ephraim, *Inorganic Chemistry*, Gurney and Jackson, London, **1934.**

J. H. Hildebrand and R. E. Powell, *Principles of Chemistry*, The Macmillan Co., New York, **1952.**

W. M. Latimer and J. H. Hildebrand, *Reference Book of Inorganic Chemistry*, The Macmillan Co., New York, **1951.**

Much useful information is tabulated in the following handbooks. It is suggested that the student majoring in chemistry obtain a copy of one of them:

Charles D. Hodgman (Editor-in-Chief), *Handbook of Chemistry and Physics*, Chemical Rubber Publishing Co., Cleveland, Ohio.

N. A. Lange, *Handbook of Chemistry*, Handbook Publishers, Sandusky, Ohio.

Detailed information about the elements and inorganic compounds may be found in comprehensive treatises; the greatest of these in English is

J. W. Mellor, *A Comprehensive Treatise on Inorganic and Theoretical Chemistry*, Longmans, Green and Co., New York, **1922–1937.**

You may read about the history of chemistry in the following books:

Alexander Findlay, *One Hundred Years of Chemistry*, The Macmillan Co., New York, **1948.**

Mary E. Weeks, *Discovery of the Elements*, Journal of Chemical Education, Easton, Pa., **1945.**

H. N. Smith, *Torchbearers of Chemistry*, Academic Press, New York, **1949.**

Bernard Jaffe, *Crucibles: The Story of Chemistry from Ancient Alchemy to Nuclear Fission*, Simon and Schuster, New York, **1948.**

F. J. Moore (revised by W. T. Hall), *A History of Chemistry*, McGraw-Hill Book Co., New York, **1939.**

James B. Conant, *On Understanding Science: An Historical Approach*, Yale University Press, New Haven, Conn., **1948.**

For the chemistry of stars, planets, comets, interstellar space, etc., see

R. H. Baker, *Astronomy*, D. Van Nostrand Co., New York, **1950.**

Many interesting articles may be found in the *Journal of Chemical Education* and in the *Scientific American*. The chemical articles in the *Encyclopaedia Britannica* are excellent.

Chapter 2

Atoms, Molecules, and Crystals

2–1. *Hypotheses, Theories, and Laws*

Chemistry deals with the properties of many thousands of substances. As the years go by, many new substances are discovered in nature or are made in the laboratory, and many new phenomena are observed. These new discoveries and observations make the science of chemistry broader; nevertheless, the science has not become harder to learn in recent years. It has, indeed, become easier, because the facts of chemistry are being more and more effectively correlated and systematized by theories.

When it is first found that a picture or a mathematical equation explains or correlates a number of empirical facts, the picture or equation, representing a provisional conjecture, is called a *hypothesis*. A hypothesis may be subjected to further tests and experimental checking of deductions that may be made from it. If it continues to agree with the results of experiment, the hypothesis is dignified by the name of *theory* or *law*.

A theory usually involves some idea about the structure of the universe, whereas a law may be a summarizing statement about observed experimental facts. For example, there is a law of the constancy of interfacial angles of crystals. This law states that when the angles between corresponding faces of various crystals of a pure substance are measured, they are found to have the same value. This law simply expresses the fact that the angles between corresponding faces on a crystal of a pure substance are found to have the same value whether the crystal is a small one or a large one, or was grown in England or in California; it does not in any way explain this fact. An explanation of the fact is given by the atomic theory of crystals, the theory that in crystals the atoms are arranged in a regular order (as described later in this chapter).

It may be mentioned that the word "theory" is used in two somewhat different senses by scientists. The first meaning of the word is that de-scribed above—namely, a hypothesis which has been verified to some extent. The second use of the word "theory" is to represent a systematic body of knowledge, compounded of facts, laws, theories in the limited sense described above, deductive arguments, etc. Thus by "atomic theory" we mean not only the idea that substances are composed of atoms, but also all the facts about substances that can be explained and interpreted in terms of atoms, and the arguments that have been developed to explain the properties of substances in terms of their atomic structure.

Theories and laws are of very great value in simplifying science. A knowledge of Newton's laws of motion provides a knowledge of the behavior of countless mechanical systems, such as a falling ball, a moving projectile, the solar system, a derrick or similar machine. This knowledge permits reliable predictions to be made of how a system will behave even before it has been constructed or thoroughly studied and observed in detail. The theories and laws of chemistry are not so precise and exact as those of physics. This fact perhaps makes the sub-ject of chemistry a little more difficult to study than the older branches of physics. On the other hand, this very lack of perfection may account for the interest chemistry can have for the student—there is still great room for discovery in chemistry. Already, however, the theories of chemistry have been found to be of the greatest value in simplifying and ordering the immense body of chemical knowledge.

2–2. *The Atomic Structure of Matter*

The Atomic Theory.   The most important of all chemical theories is the atomic theory. In 1805 the English chemist and physicist John Dalton (1766–1844), of Manchester, advanced arguments in support of the hypothesis that substances consist of small particles of matter. He called these particles **atoms,** from the Greek word *atomos*, meaning indivisible. This hypothesis gave a simple explanation or picture of previously observed but unsatisfactorily explained relations among the weights of substances taking part in chemical reactions with one another (Chap. 7). As it was verified by further work in chemistry and physics, the atomic hypothesis became the atomic theory. *The existence of atoms is now accepted as a fact.*

The rapid progress of our science during the current century is well illustrated by the increase in our knowledge about atoms. In a popular textbook of chemistry written in the early years of the twentieth century atoms were defined as the "imaginary units of which bodies are aggregates." Now, less than half a century later, we have precise knowledge of many properties of atoms and molecules. Atoms and molecules can no longer be considered imaginary.

The Nature of Atoms.   All ordinary matter consists of atoms. The exceptional kinds of matter are the elementary particles from which the atoms are made (electrons, protons, neutrons), and other subatomic particles (positrons, mesons); these elementary particles will be discussed later (Chaps. 3, 8, 33). But atoms are the units which retain their identity when chemical reactions take place; therefore, they are important to us now. Atoms are the structural units of all solids, liquids, and gases. They are very small—only about 2 to 5 Å in diameter.* This is indeed small. If a piece of rock, or anything else, one inch in diameter were to be magnified to the size of the earth, its constituent atoms would become about the size of golf balls or tennis balls. One hundred million atoms side by side make a row about one inch long. A one-inch cube of solid matter thus contains about $(10^8)^3 = 10^{24}$ atoms.

Every atom consists of one **nucleus** *and one or more* **electrons.** (This statement is the modern definition of the word "atom.") The nucleus is a small, heavy particle containing almost all of the mass of the atom. It has a positive electric charge equal in magnitude to the charge of one electron, or to an integral multiple of this charge. The electric charge of nuclei is positive, and that of electrons is negative. Ordinary matter is electrically neutral; that is, it contains equal amounts of positive and negative electric charge.

Nuclei are very small indeed. Their diameter is approximately 1×10^{-12} cm or 1×10^{-4} Å. The nucleus of an atom is accordingly only about one ten-thousandth as great in diameter as the atom itself, and the volume of the nucleus is about 10^{-12}, one million-millionth, of the volume of the atom. If nuclei could be packed together side by side, they would give a form of matter with very great density, of the order of 10^{12} g/cm^3.

---

* The symbol Å stands for a unit of length, the *Ångström unit*, used in the measurement of very minute lengths. It is named after the Swedish physicist A. J. Ångström (1814–1874). One Å is 1×10^{-8} cm (0.00000001 cm); that is, 1 cm is 10^8 Å (1 cm = 100,000,000 Å).

The electron is a particle with small mass, 1/1,836 that of the lightest nucleus, and with a negative electric charge. The electron itself is about as large as a nucleus, its diameter being about 10^{-12} cm. The electrons in an atom are attracted by the nucleus. The electrons move rapidly

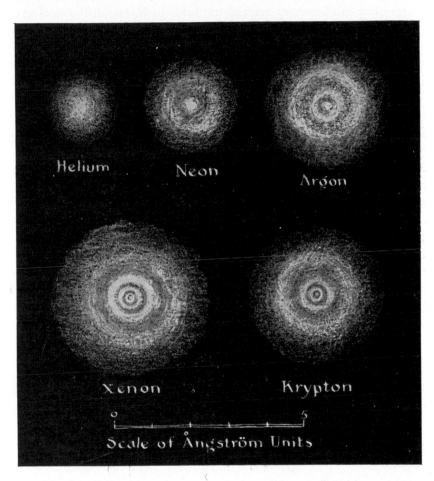

FIG. 2-1 *Drawing of electron distributions in noble-gas atoms, showing successive electron shells.*

around in the space extending over a diameter of a few Ångströms about the nucleus, and, because they move around so fast, they effectively fill this space in such a way as to repel any other atom that approaches to within this diameter.

The evidence for the existence of atoms is now overwhelming. The arguments that led to the original development of the atomic theory were based on chemical facts, described in later sections of this book (especially Chaps. 9 and 10). During the present century the methods of modern physics have provided much straightforward evidence for the existence of atoms and much information about their properties. Most interesting to chemistry are the methods of X-ray diffraction and electron diffraction. These methods are almost equivalent to the preparation of direct photographs of molecules and crystals, showing the atomic arrangement (Chap. 3). Drawings of some of these structures are shown in the figures which accompany this chapter and later chapters.

These experimental methods have also provided us with knowledge of the distribution of electrons around the nucleus of the atom. The indicated structure of some atoms is represented in Figure 2-1.

A Representative Atomic Structure, Copper. Most solid substances are crystalline in nature. Sometimes the particles of a sample of solid substance are themselves single crystals, such as the cubic crystals of sodium chloride in table salt. Sometimes these single crystals are very large; occasionally crystals several yards in diameter of minerals such as beryl are found in nature. Often, however, the individual crystal grains of a crystalline substance are small, and the particles of the substance are aggregates of these grains. The specimen of malleable cast iron of which a photomicrograph is reproduced in Figure 1-2 is seen to contain crystal grains of iron about 0.1 mm in diameter.

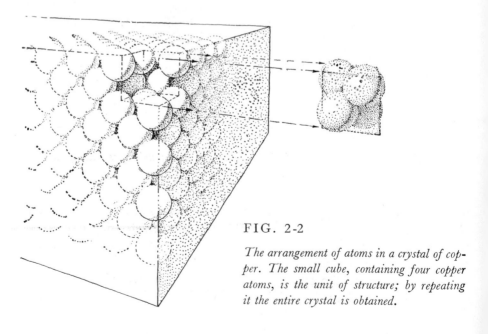

FIG. 2-2

The arrangement of atoms in a crystal of copper. The small cube, containing four copper atoms, is the unit of structure; by repeating it the entire crystal is obtained.

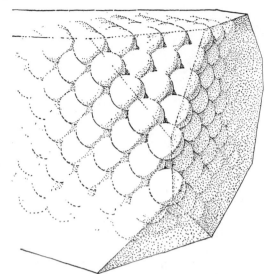

FIG. 2-3

Another atomic view of a copper crystal, showing small octahedral faces and large cubic faces.

It has been found by experiment that *every crystal consists of atoms arranged in a three-dimensional pattern that repeats itself regularly.* In a crystal of copper all of the atoms are alike, and they are arranged in a way called *cubic closest packing,* shown in Figures 2-2 and 2-3. This is the way in which spheres of uniform size may be packed together to occupy the smallest volume.

You must remember while looking at Figures 2-2 and 2-3 that the atoms are shown greatly enlarged relative to the crystal. Even if the crystal were a small one, with edges only about 0.1 mm long, there would still be about 400,000 atoms in a row along each edge.

It was mentioned in the preceding chapter that a crystal is a form of matter with different properties in different directions. We can now see why crystals have this nature. One direction in the copper crystal is that determined by the rows of atoms, and the properties of the crystal in this direction are clearly different from those in most other directions.

It is the *regularity of arrangement* of the atoms in a crystal that gives to the crystal its characteristic properties, in particular the property of growing in the form of polyhedra. The faces of crystals are defined by surface layers of atoms, as shown in Figures 2-2 and 2-3. These faces lie at angles to one another that have definite characteristic values, the same for all specimens of the same substance. The size of the faces may vary from specimen to specimen, but the angles between them remain constant. The principal surface layers shown in Figures 2-2 and 2-3 for copper correspond to the faces of a cube (*cubic faces* or *cube faces*); the smaller surface layer, obtained by cutting off a corner of a

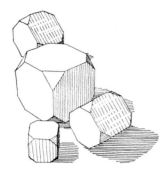

FIG. 2-4

Crystals of native copper.

cube, is called an *octahedral* face (see Fig. 10-5). Native copper, found in deposits of copper ore, is often in the form of crystals with cubic and octahedral faces (Fig. 2-4).

The substance copper crystallizes with this structure because of the tendency of each atom of this metal to attract to itself as many other atoms of copper as can find room about it. The forces that attract atoms to one another and hold them together strongly (the *valence forces,* Chaps. 9 and 10) are said to give rise to the formation of *chemical bonds* between these atoms. These forces are due to the electric interaction of the electrons and nuclei of the atoms, and the nature of the chemical bonds that an atom can form is determined by the electronic structure of the atom.

An ordinary piece of the metal copper does not consist of a single crystal of copper, but of an aggregate of crystals. The crystal grains of a specimen of a metal can be made clearly visible by polishing the surface of the metal, and then etching the metal lightly with an acid or other chemical reagent. Often the grains are very small, and can be seen only with the aid of a microscope (Fig. 2-5), but sometimes they

FIG. 2-5

A polished and etched surface of a piece of cold-drawn copper bar, showing the small crystal grains which compose the ordinary metal. Magnification 200 × (200-fold linearly). The small round spots are gas bubbles. (From Dr. S. Kyropoulos.)

are large, and can be easily seen with the naked eye, as in meteorites (Fig. 2-6) or in brass doorknobs.

Atoms are not hard spheres, but are soft, so that by increased force they may be pushed more closely together (be compressed). This occurs, for example, when a copper crystal becomes somewhat smaller in volume under increased pressure. The approximate sizes which are assigned to atoms correspond to the distance between the nucleus of one atom and the nucleus of a neighboring atom in a crystal under ordinary circumstances. The distance from a copper atom to each of its twelve nearest neighbors in a copper crystal at room temperature and at-

FIG. 2-6   *Polished surface of an iron-nickel meteorite, showing large crystal grains in parallel orientation ("Widmanstätten figures"). About 40% of natural size—the meteorite is about ten inches long. (Courtesy of Griffith Observatory.)*

mospheric pressure is 2.55 Å; one-half of this distance, 1.275 Å, is called the *metallic radius* of the copper atom. Values of radii of atoms are given in later chapters of the book.

Silver and gold, which are similar to copper, crystallize with the same structure. Crystals of these metals are also found in nature. Their atoms are larger than those of copper. It happens that atoms of silver and gold are of nearly the same size, about 1.44 Å in radius.

2–3. *The Description of a Crystal Structure*

The structure of a crystal can be conveniently described in terms of the *unit of structure*. The unit of structure of a cubic crystal is a small cube, which, when repeated parallel to itself in such a way as to fill space, reproduces the entire crystal.

The way in which this is done can be seen from a two-dimensional example. In Figure 2-7 there is shown a portion of a square lattice. The unit of structure of this square lattice is a square; we see that, when this square is repeated parallel to itself in such a way as to fill the plane, we obtain a sort of two-dimensional crystal. In this case there are present a lattice of atoms of one sort, represented by small spheres at the intersections of the lattice lines, and a lattice of atoms of another sort, represented by larger spheres at the centers of the unit squares. We might describe the structure by the use of coordinates x and y, giving the positions of the atoms relative to an origin at the corner of the unit of structure, with x and y taken as fractions of the edges of the unit of

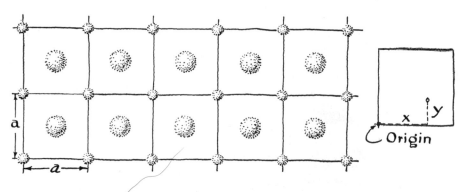

FIG. 2-7   *Arrangement of atoms in a plane. The unit of structure is a square. Small atoms have the coordinates 0, 0 and large atoms the coordinates 1/2, 1/2.*

structure, as indicated in the figure. The atom represented by the small sphere would then have the coordinates $x = 0, y = 0$, and the atom at the center of the square would have the coordinates $x = 1/2, y = 1/2$.

Similarly, for a cubic crystal the unit of structure can be taken as a cube, which when reproduced in parallel orientation would fill space to produce a cubic lattice, as shown in Figure 2-8. The unit of structure could be described, for a cubic crystal, by giving the value of the edge of the unit, a, and the values of the coordinates x, y, and z, for each atom, as fractions of the edge of the unit. Thus, for the cubic closest-packed structure, represented by metallic copper, the unit of structure is cubic, with edge $a = \sqrt{2} \times 2.55$ Å $= 3.61$ Å, and with four atoms per unit, with coordinates $x = 0, y = 0, z = 0; x = 0, y = 1/2, z = 1/2; x = 1/2, y = 0, z = 1/2;$ and $x = 1/2,$

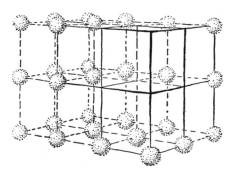

FIG. 2-8

The simple cubic arrangement of atoms. The unit of structure is a cube, with one atom per unit, its coordinates being 0, 0, 0.

FIG. 2-9

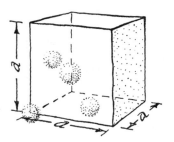

The cubic unit of structure for the face-centered cubic arrangement, corresponding to cubic closest packing of spheres. There are four atoms in the unit, with coordinates 0, 0, 0; 0, 1/2, 1/2; 1/2, 0, 1/2; 1/2, 1/2, 0.

$y = 1/2$, $z = 0$, as shown in Figure 2-9. Often these coordinates are written without giving the symbols x, y, and z; it is then said that there are four copper atoms in the unit, at 0, 0, 0; 0, 1/2, 1/2; 1/2, 0, 1/2; 1/2, 1/2, 0. These are called the *coordinates* of the atoms in the unit cube.

Note that in the unit cube shown in Figure 2-9 an atom is represented at only one of the eight corners. Of course, when this unit cube is surrounded by other unit cubes, atoms are placed at the seven other corners, these atoms being formally associated with the adjacent unit cubes.

The unit of structure of a crystal other than a cubic crystal is a parallelepiped. In the case of the most general sort of crystal, a triclinic crystal (see Sec. 2-4), the parallelepiped is a general one, as shown in Figure 2-10. It can be described by giving the values of a, b, and c, the lengths of the three edges, and also the values of α, β, and γ, the angles between pairs of edges.

Example 1.   The metal iron is cubic, with $a = 2.86$ Å, and with two iron atoms in the unit cube, at 0, 0, 0 and 1/2, 1/2, 1/2. How many nearest neighbors does each iron atom have, and how far away are they?

   Solution.   We draw a cubic unit of structure, with edge 2.86 Å, as shown in Figure 2-11, and we indicate in it the positions 0, 0, 0 and 1/2, 1/2, 1/2. When cubes of this sort are reproduced parallel to one another, we see that we obtain the structure shown in Figure 24-2; this is called the *body-centered arrangement*. It is seen that the atom at 1/2, 1/2, 1/2 is surrounded by eight atoms, the atom at 0, 0, 0 and seven similar atoms. Also, the atom at 0, 0, 0 is surrounded by eight atoms. In each case the surrounding atoms are at the corners of a cube. This situation is described by saying that each atom in the body-centered arrangement has **ligancy 8**, or **coordination number 8.**

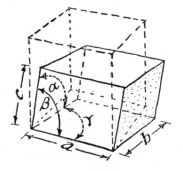

FIG. 2-10

The parallelepiped representing a general unit of structure. It is determined by the lengths of its three edges, and by the three angles between the edges.

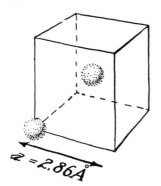

FIG. 2-11

The unit of structure corresponding to the cubic body-centered arrangement. There are two atoms in the unit, with coordinates 0, 0, 0 and 1/2, 1/2, 1/2.

To calculate the interatomic distance, we note that, by the theorem of Pythagoras, the square of the distance is equal to $(a/2)^2 + (a/2)^2 + (a/2)^2$, and hence the distance itself is equal to $\sqrt{3}\,a/2$. Thus the distance between each iron atom and its neighbors is found to be 0.866×2.86 Å $= \mathbf{2.48}$ **Å**. The metallic radius of iron is hence 1.24 Å.

Example 2. The English mathematician and astronomer Thomas Harriot (1560–1621), who was tutor to Sir Walter Raleigh and who traveled to Virginia in 1585, was interested in the atomic theory of substances. He believed that the hypothesis that substances consist of atoms was plausible, and capable of explaining some of the properties of matter. His writings contain the following propositions:

9. The more solid bodies have Atoms touching on all Sydes.

10. Homogeneall bodies consist of Atoms of like figure, and quantitie.

11. The waight may increase by interposition of lesse Atoms in the vacuities betwine the greater.*

12. By the differences of regular touches (in bodies more solid), we find that the lightest are such, where euery Atom is touched with six others about it, and greatest (if not intermingled) where twelve others do touch euery Atom.

Assuming that the atoms can be represented as hard spheres in contact with one another, what difference in density would there be between the two structures described in the above proposition 12?

Solution. The structure where every atom is in contact with six others about it that Harriot had in mind is probably the simple cubic arrangement, shown in Figure 2-12. In this arrangement of atoms the unit of structure is a cube, containing one atom, which can be assigned the coordinates 0, 0, 0. Each atom is then in con-

* This statement describes the structure of interstitial solid solutions and compounds, which we shall discuss briefly in Chapter 26.

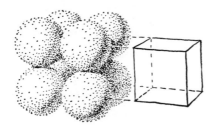

FIG. 2-12

Simple cubic packing of spheres.

tact with six other atoms, which are at the distance d from it. The volume of the unit cube is accordingly d^3. If the mass of the atom is M, the density for this arrangement is M/d^3.

The more dense structure referred to by Harriot, where twelve atoms are in contact with each atom, is the cubic closest-packed arrangement described in the preceding section. (Harriot had apparently discovered, or some earlier investigator had discovered, that there is no way of packing hard spheres in space that gives a greater density than is given by this arrangement.) The cubic unit of structure for this arrangement contains four atoms. Its edge, a, is equal to $2^{1/2}d$, and its volume to $2^{3/2}d^3$. The mass contained in the unit cube is $4M$, and the density is accordingly $4M/2^{3/2}d^3$, or $2^{1/2}M/d^3$.

We thus have found that the dense structure described by Harriot has density $\sqrt{2} = 1.414$ times that of the less dense structure; it is accordingly **41.4%** denser than the less dense structure.

2–4. *Crystal Symmetry; the Crystal Systems*

Symmetry.   The principal classification of crystals is on the basis of their *symmetry*. An object has symmetry if some operation can be carried out on it that converts it into itself. For example, a three-bladed propeller can be rotated about its axis through 120° (one-third of a revolution), and it is then indistinguishable from its original condition,

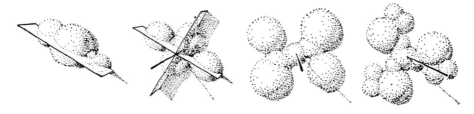

FIG. 2-13   *Groups of atoms with different symmetry: from left to right, a plane of symmetry; two perpendicular planes of symmetry and a twofold axis at their intersection; a twofold axis; a threefold axis.*

provided that the three blades are exactly identical with one another. Similarly, it can be rotated through 240° (two-thirds of a revolution), again becoming indistinguishable from its original condition. These operations of rotation by ⅓ of a revolution and rotation by ⅔ of a revolution, together with the original operation involving no change, constitute the symmetry operations of a *threefold axis* of symmetry. Some other examples of symmetry are given in Figure 2-13.

Only a few symmetry elements are shown by crystals. These include the center of symmetry, twofold axis, threefold axis, fourfold axis, sixfold axis, fourfold inversion axis, threefold inversion axis, and symmetry plane. All of these types of symmetry are illustrated in Figure 2-14.

The fivefold axis does not occur in crystals because the angle of a pentagon, 108°, is not a factor of 360°.

There are thirty-two combinations of these symmetry elements that are represented

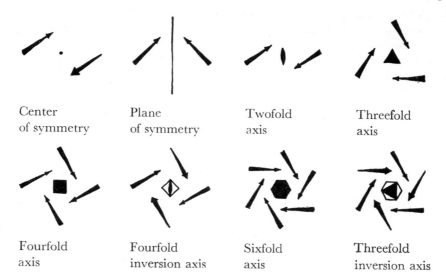

Center   Plane   Twofold   Threefold
of symmetry   of symmetry   axis   axis

Fourfold   Fourfold   Sixfold   Threefold
axis   inversion axis axis   inversion axis

FIG. 2-14   *The symmetry elements that a crystal may have.*

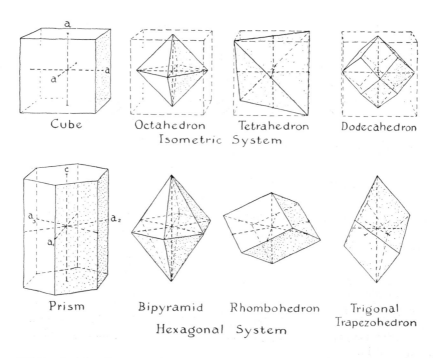

Cube   Octahedron   Tetrahedron   Dodecahedron
                Isometric System

Prism   Bipyramid   Rhombohedron   Trigonal
                                                Trapezohedron
                Hexagonal System

FIG. 2-15   *Representative crystal forms of the cubic and hexagonal systems.*

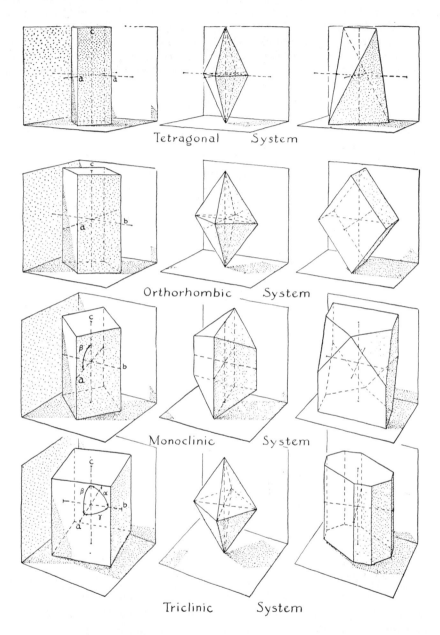

FIG. 2-16 *Representative crystal forms of the tetragonal, orthorhombic, monoclinic, and triclinic crystal systems.*

by crystals. These combinations are called the *thirty-two crystal classes*. Description of the crystal classes can be found in books on the science of crystallography.

The thirty-two crystal classes can be divided into six *crystal systems*, as follows:

Cubic crystals (sometimes called isometric crystals), with both threefold and fourfold symmetry axes (the fourfold axis can be of the rotation-reflection type).

Tetragonal crystals, with one fourfold axis.

Hexagonal or trigonal crystals (including rhombohedral crystals), with one sixfold axis or threefold axis.

Orthorhombic crystals, with two or three planes of symmetry or twofold axes at right angles to each other.

Monoclinic crystals, with one plane of symmetry or one twofold axis, or both.

Triclinic crystals, with either a center of symmetry or no symmetry clements.

The crystals and their unit of structure can be described by axes of symmetry, which in some cases are at right angles with one another, or at 120° for hexagonal or trigonal crystals), or which may be at arbitrary angles. The types of axes required by the different crystal systems are the following:

Cubic crystals: three equal axes with length a, at right angles to one another.

Tetragonal crystals: two equal axes, with length a, and a third axis, with length c, all at right angles.

Hexagonal or trigonal crystals: two equal axes, with length a, at an angle of 120° to each other, and a third axis, with length c, at right angles to the other two.

Orthorhombic crystals: three axes, with lengths a, b, c, at right angles to one another.

Monoclinic crystals: two axes, a and c, at the angle β with one another, and the third axis, b, at right angles to a and c.

Triclinic crystals: three axes, a, b, c, with angles α, β, and γ between them.

The *faces* of a crystal must be related to the axes in a rational way; the intercepts of a face with the three axes are related to the lengths of the axes, a, b, c, in the ratio of integers. Drawings showing crystal axes and faces are given in Figures 2-15 and 2-16.

2–5. *The Molecular Structure of Matter*

Molecular Crystals. The only building stone of a copper crystal is the copper atom; in this crystal there do not exist any discrete groups (distinct groups) of atoms smaller than the crystal specimen itself. On the other hand, crystals of many other substances contain **discrete groups of atoms,** which are called **molecules.** An example of a molecular crystal is shown in the upper left part of Figure 2-17, which is a drawing representing the structure of a crystal of the blackish-gray solid substance iodine, as determined by the X-ray diffraction method. It is seen that the iodine atoms are grouped together in pairs, to form *diatomic molecules* (molecules containing two atoms each).

The distance between the two atoms in the same molecule of a molecular crystal is smaller than the distances between atoms in different molecules. In the iodine crystals the two iodine atoms in each molecule are only 2.70 Å apart, whereas the smallest distance between iodine atoms in different molecules is 3.54 Å.

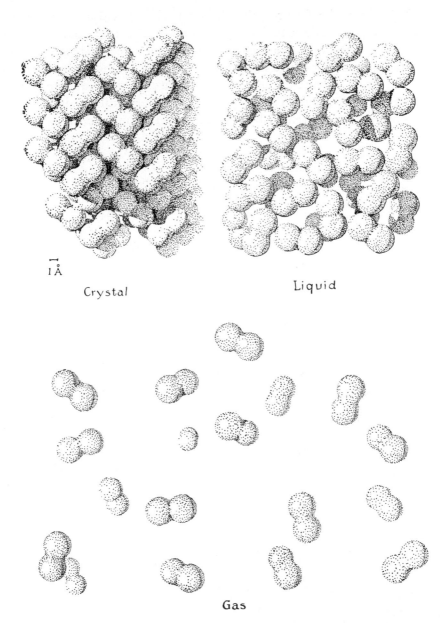

Crystal

Liquid

1 Å

Gas

FIG. 2-17 *Crystalline, liquid, and gaseous iodine, showing diatomic molecules I_2.*

Moreover, the forces acting between atoms within a molecule are very strong, and those acting between molecules are weak. As a result of this, it is hard to cause the molecule to change its shape, whereas it is comparatively easy to change the positions of the molecules relative to one another. For example, under pressure a crystal of iodine decreases in size: the molecules can be pushed together until the intermolecular distances have decreased by several percent; but the molecules them-

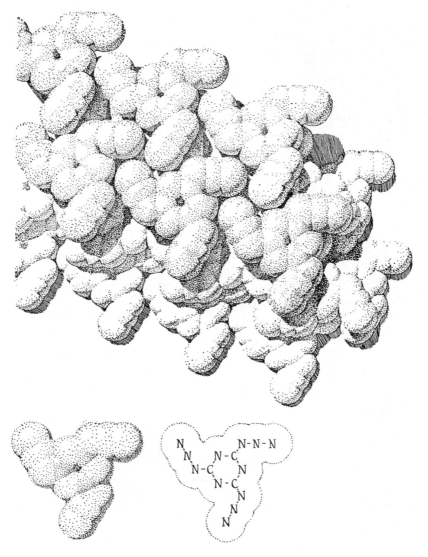

FIG. 2-18   *Above, portion of crystal of cyanuric triazide, C_3N_{12}, showing how the molecules pack together. Below, separate molecules.*

selves retain their original size, with no comparable change in inter-atomic distance within the molecule. When a crystal of iodine at low temperature is heated it expands, so that each of the molecules occupies a larger space in the crystal; but the iodine-iodine distance within the molecule stays very close to the normal 2.70 Å.

The molecules of different chemical substances contain varying num-

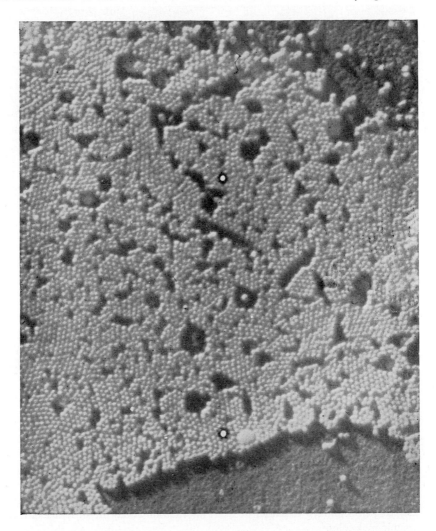

FIG. 2-19   *Electron micrograph of a single layer of tomato bushy stunt virus molecules. The photograph was made to show added contrast by depositing a very thin layer of gold on the specimen at a small angle, giving the impression of shadows cast by the molecules. Linear magnification 55,000. (From Price, Williams, and Wyckoff, Arch. Biochem., 7, 175, 1946.)*

bers of atoms, bonded tightly together. An example of a more complicated molecule is shown in Figure 2-18; this molecule, of the substance cyanuric triazide, contains three carbon atoms and twelve nitrogen atoms. The properties of cyanuric triazide, which is an explosive substance, are determined by the structure of its molecules.

FIG. 2-20   *Electron micrograph of crystals of necrosis virus protein, showing individual molecules in ordered arrangement. Linear magnification 65,000. (From R. W. G. Wyckoff.)*

Crystals Containing Giant Molecules.   Plants and animals have complicated structures, made up of immense numbers of molecules of different kinds. Many of these molecules are very large, containing hundreds of thousands or millions of atoms. Scientists are just beginning to gather detailed information about the structure of these giant organic molecules.

The *viruses* are one kind of giant molecules which have very interesting properties. Some diseases, such as measles, smallpox, infantile paralysis (poliomyelitis), and the common cold, are caused by viruses. Virus molecules have the power of self-duplication —that is, the power of causing other molecules identical with themselves to be formed when they are in the right environment. A disease such as measles results from the formation of a great many measles-virus molecules in the human body which has been infected by a few of these molecules.

Another property which virus molecules have, in common with ordinary small molecules, is the ability to form crystals. The molecules of a virus can form crystals because they are all essentially alike in size and shape, and so can pile together in the regular arrangement which constitutes a crystal.

In the last few years it has become possible to see and to photograph virus molecules. They are too small to be seen with a microscope using ordinary visible light, which cannot permit objects much smaller in diameter than the wavelength of light, about 5,000 Å, to be seen. A wonderful new instrument, the *electron microscope*, has now been developed, which permits objects a hundred times smaller in diameter to be seen. The electron microscope uses beams of electrons in place of beams of light. Its linear magnifying power is about 200,000, as compared with about 1,000 for the ordinary microscope. It is accordingly possible to see objects as small as 25 Å in diameter with the electron microscope.

Two photographs made with the electron microscope are reproduced here, as Figures 2-19 and 2-20. They show molecules of viruses which cause disease in tomato plants. Each "bushy stunt" virus molecule is about 230 Å in diameter. It is made of about 750,000 atoms. The "necrosis" virus molecules are somewhat smaller, about 195 Å in diameter. In each photograph the individual molecules can be clearly seen, and in the photograph of necrosis virus protein molecules the regular way in which the molecules arrange themselves in the crystals is evident.

The Evaporation of a Molecular Crystal.   At a very low temperature the molecules in a crystal of iodine lie rather quietly in their places in the crystal (Fig. 2-17). As the temperature increases, the molecules become more and more agitated; each one bounds back and forth more and more vigorously in the little space left for it by its neighbors, and each one strikes its neighbors more and more strongly as it rebounds from them. This increase in molecular motion with increase in temperature causes the crystal to expand somewhat, giving each molecule a larger space in which to carry out its *thermal oscillation*.

A molecule on the surface of the crystal is held to the crystal by the forces of attraction that its neighboring molecules exert on it. Attractive forces of this kind, which are operative between all molecules when they are close together, are called *van der Waals attractive forces*, this name being used because it was the Dutch physicist J. D. van der Waals (1837–1923) who first gave a thorough discussion of intermolecular forces in relation to the nature of gases and liquids.

These attractive forces are quite weak. Hence occasionally a certain molecule will become so agitated as to break loose from its neighbors, and to fly off into the surrounding space. If the crystal is in a vessel, there will soon be present in the space within the vessel, through this process of evaporation, a large number of these free molecules, each moving in a straight-line path, and occasionally colliding with another molecule or with the walls of the vessel to change the direction of its motion. These free molecules constitute *iodine vapor* or *iodine gas* (Fig. 2-17). The gas molecules are very much like the molecules in the crystal, their interatomic distance being practically the same; it is the distances between molecules that are much larger in a gas than in a crystal.

Iodine vapor has characteristic properties. It is violet in color, and it has a characteristic odor. The odor of tincture of iodine (a solution of iodine in alcohol, used as an antiseptic) is a combination of the odor of iodine vapor and the odor of ethyl alcohol.

It may seem surprising that molecules on the surface of a crystal should evaporate directly into a gas, but in fact the process of slow evaporation of a crystalline substance is not uncommon. Solid pieces of camphor or of naphthalene (as used in moth balls, for example) left out in the air slowly decrease in size, because of the evaporation of molecules from the surface of the solid. Snow may disappear from the ground without melting, by evaporation of the ice crystals at a temperature below that of their melting point. Evaporation is accelerated if a wind is blowing, to take the water vapor away from the immediate neighborhood of the snow crystals, and to prevent the vapor from condensing again on the crystals.

The Nature of a Gas. The characteristic feature of a gas is that its molecules are not held together, but are moving about freely, in a volume rather large compared with the volume of the molecules themselves. The van der Waals attractive forces between the molecules still operate whenever two molecules come close together, but usually these forces are negligibly small because the molecules are far apart. Because of the freedom of molecular motion a specimen of gas does not have either definite shape or definite size. A gas shapes itself to its container. The molecules of a gas exert pressure on the walls of its container by striking the walls and rebounding from them. If the volume occupied by the specimen of gas is decreased, the molecules strike the walls more often, and the pressure accordingly increases. A quantitative study of the properties of gases will be taken up later (Chap. 14).

Gases at ordinary pressure are very dilute: the molecules themselves constitute only about one one-thousandth of the total volume of the gas, the rest being empty space. Thus 1 gram of solid iodine has a volume of about 0.2 cm³ (its density is 4.93 g/cm³), whereas 1 gram of iodine gas at 1 atmosphere pressure and at the temperature 184° C (its boiling point) has a volume of 148 cm³, over 700 times greater. The volume of all of the molecules in a gas is accordingly very small compared with the volume of the gas itself at ordinary pressure. On the other hand, the diameter of a gas molecule is not extremely small compared with the distance between molecules; in a gas at room tem'erature and 1 atmosphere pressure the average distance from a mole cule to its nearest neighbors is about ten times its molecular diameter, as indicated in Figure 2-17.*

The Vapor Pressure of a Crystal.   A crystal of iodine in an evacuated vessel will gradually change into iodine gas by the evaporation of molecules from its surface. Occasionally one of these free gas molecules will again strike the surface of the crystal, and it may stick to the surface, held by the van der Waals attraction of the other crystal molecules. This is called *condensation* of the gas molecules.

The rate at which molecules evaporate from a crystal surface is proportional to the area of the surface, but is essentially independent of the pressure of the surrounding gas, whereas the rate at which gas molecules strike the crystal surface is proportional to the area of the surface and also proportional to the concentration of the molecules in the gas phase (the number of gas molecules in unit volume).

If some iodine crystals are put into a flask, which is then stoppered and allowed to stand at room temperature, it will soon be seen that a quantity of iodine has evaporated, because the gas phase in the flask will be seen to have become violet in color. After a while it will be evident that the process of evaporation has apparently ceased, because the intensity of coloration of the gas phase will no longer increase, but will remain constant. This steady state is reached when the concentration of gas molecules becomes so great that the rate at which gas molecules strike the crystal surface and stay there is just equal to the rate at which molecules leave the crystal surface. The corresponding gas pressure is called the *vapor pressure* of the crystal.

A steady state of such a sort is an example of *equilibrium*. The study of physical equilibrium, such as this equilibrium between the crystal and its vapor, and of chemical equilibrium, representing a steady state among various substances that are reacting chemically with one another, constitutes an important part of general chemistry. It must be recognized that equilibrium is not a situation in which nothing is happening,

---

* You will remember that a cube 1 inch on edge has a diameter one-tenth as great as that of a cube 10 inches on edge, an area one one-hundredth as great, and a volume one one-thousandth as great.

but rather a situation in which opposing reactions are taking place at the same rate, so as to result in no over-all change. This is indicated in Figure 2-21.

The vapor pressure of every crystal increases with increase in temperature. For iodine it has the value 0.20 mm of mercury* at 20° C and 90 mm of mercury at 114° C, the melting point of the crystal. The crystals of iodine which are heated to a temperature only a little below the

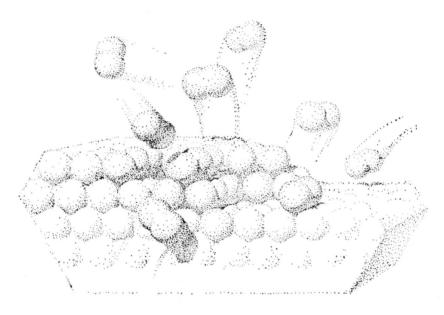

FIG. 2-21 *Equilibrium between molecules evaporating from an iodine crystal and gas molecules depositing on the crystal.*

melting point evaporate rapidly, and the vapor may condense into crystals in a cooler part of the vessel. The complete process of evaporation of a crystal and recondensation of a gas directly as crystals, without apparently passing through the liquid state, is called *sublimation.* Sublimation is often a valuable method of purifying a substance.

* One atmosphere equals the pressure at the surface of the earth that is due to the weight of the air. Pressure is often reported in units equal to the standard atmosphere. The value of this unit is 14.7 pounds per square inch. This is equal to the pressure produced by the weight of a column of mercury 760 mm high. Pressure is also reported in units equal to the height of the corresponding column of mercury. The abbreviation mm Hg is used for mm of mercury. The vapor pressure of iodine at its melting point is 90 mm Hg, which is 90/760 atm or 0.118 atm. The unit of pressure in the metric system is dyne per square centimeter (dyne/cm²). The standard atmosphere is equal to 1.013×10^6 dyne/cm². The dyne is defined as the force that would cause a mass of 1 g to be given an acceleration of 1 cm/sec².

The Nature of a Liquid.   When iodine crystals are heated to 114° C they melt, forming liquid iodine. The temperature at which the crystals and the liquid are in equilibrium—that is, at which there is no tendency for the crystals to melt or for the liquid to freeze—is called the *melting point* of the crystals, and the *freezing point* of the liquid. This temperature is 114° C for iodine.

Liquid iodine differs from the solid (crystals) mainly in its *fluidity*. Like the solid, and unlike the gas, it has a definite volume, 1 g occupying about 0.2 cm³, but it does not have a definite shape; instead, it fits itself to the shape of the bottom part of its container.

From the molecular viewpoint the process of melting can be described in the following way. As a crystal is heated, its molecules are increasingly agitated, and move about more and more vigorously; but this thermal agitation does not carry any one molecule any significant distance away from the position fixed for it by the arrangement of its neighbors in the crystal. At the melting point the agitation finally becomes so great as to cause the molecules to slip by one another and to change somewhat their location relative to one another. They continue to stay close together, but do not continue to retain a regular fixed arrangement; instead, the grouping of molecules around a given molecule changes continually, sometimes being much like the close packing of the crystal, in which each iodine molecule has twelve near neighbors, and sometimes considerably different, the molecule having only ten or nine or eight near neighbors, as shown in Figure 2-17. Thus a liquid, like a crystal, is a *condensed phase*, as contrasted with a gas, the molecules being piled rather closely together; but whereas a crystal is characterized by regularity of atomic or molecular arrangement, a liquid is characterized by randomness of structure. The randomness of structure usually causes the density of a liquid to be somewhat less than that of the corresponding crystal; that is, the volume occupied by the liquid is usually somewhat greater than that occupied by the crystal.

The Vapor Pressure and Boiling Point of a Liquid.   A liquid, like a crystal, is, at any temperature, in equilibrium with its own vapor when the vapor molecules are present in a certain concentration. The pressure corresponding to this concentration of gas molecules is called the *vapor pressure of the liquid* at the given temperature.

The vapor pressure of every liquid increases with increasing temperature. The temperature at which it reaches a standard value (usually 1 atm) is called the *boiling point* (standard boiling point) of the liquid.

At this temperature it is possible for bubbles of the vapor to appear in the liquid and to escape to the surface.

The vapor pressure of liquid iodine at its freezing point, 114° C, is 90 mm Hg. This is exactly the same as the vapor pressure of the crystals at this temperature, as described in the section before the preceding one. That is, iodine gas at a pressure of 90 mm Hg is in equilibrium with the liquid at 114° C, the freezing point of the liquid, and this gas is also in equilibrium with iodine crystals at this temperature, their melting point. The crystals and the liquid are in equilibrium at the freezing point (melting point), and they then have exactly the same vapor pressure. If the two phases had different vapor pressures, the phase with the larger vapor pressure would continue to evaporate, and

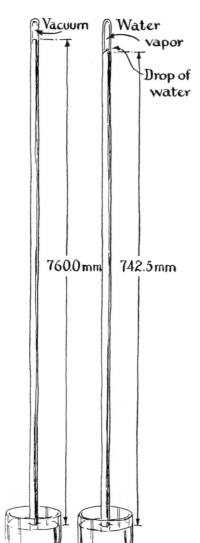

FIG. 2-22

A simple method of measuring the vapor pressure of a liquid.

the vapor would continue to condense as the other phase, until the first phase had disappeared.

The vapor pressure of liquid iodine reaches 1 atm at 184° C, which is the boiling point of iodine.

Other substances undergo similar changes in phase when they are heated. When copper melts, at 1,083° C, it forms liquid copper, in which the arrangement of the copper atoms shows the same sort of randomness as that of the molecules in liquid iodine. Under 1 atm pressure copper boils at 2,310° C to form copper gas; the gas molecules are single copper atoms.

The Dependence of Vapor Pressure on Temperature.   The vapor pressure of a substance can be measured by various techniques, such as that illustrated in Figure 2-22. In this experiment the barometric pressure is measured by measuring the height of a column of mercury in an evacuated tube. If the barometric pressure happened to be exactly normal, the height of the column would be 760.0 mm. The column of mercury is supported by the pressure of the air on the exposed surface of the mercury. Now if a substance, such as a drop of water, were to be introduced into this space in the tube above the column of mercury, by slipping it underneath the open bottom end of the tube and releasing it to permit it to rise to the top of the column, molecules of this substance would evaporate into the space above the column of mercury, until equilibrium between the vapor and the condensed phase was reached. The top of the column of mercury would then be subjected to the pres-

TABLE 2-1   *The Vapor Pressure of Iodine as a Function of Temperature*

TEMPERATURE	VAPOR PRESSURE OF IODINE CRYSTALS	TEMPERATURE	VAPOR PRESSURE OF LIQUID IODINE
30° C	0.471 mm Hg	114.2° C (m.p.)	90.1 mm Hg
40	1.03	120	111
50	2.16	130	157
60	4.31	140	217
70	8.22	150	294
80	15.1	160	394
90	26.8	170	521
100	45.5	180	679
110	74.9	184.35 (b.p.)	760
114.2 (m.p.)	90.1	190	869

sure of this vapor, equal to the vapor pressure of the substance, and the column of mercury would decrease in height.

The results of measurements of this sort on iodine crystals and liquid iodine are given in Table 2-1 (see also Fig. 2-23). By examining the numbers in this table some interesting approximate relations can be discovered. It is seen that for the crystals the vapor pressure does not increase by a constant added amount with each increase of 10° in the

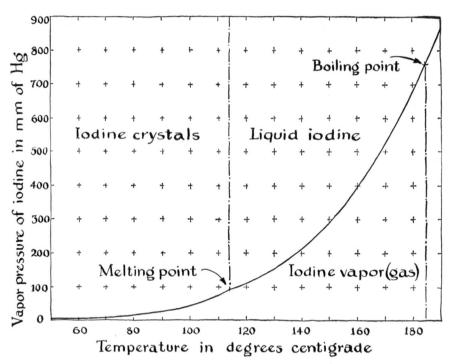

FIG. 2-23 *A graph showing the vapor-pressure curve of iodine crystal and the vapor-pressure curve of liquid iodine. The melting point of the crystal is the temperature at which the crystal and the liquid have the same vapor pressure, and the boiling point of the liquid (at 1 atm pressure) is the temperature at which the vapor pressure of the liquid equals 1 atm.*

temperature, but instead increases by approximately the same factor. When the temperature is changed from 40° (v.p. 1.03 mm Hg) to 50° C (v.p. 2.16), the vapor pressure is approximately doubled, and from 50° to 60° it is again doubled, and so on. Thus, when these experimental data have been obtained, they permit one to formulate an approximate law of nature—namely, that for every increase in temperature of 10° C the vapor pressure of crystalline iodine is approximately doubled. For liquid iodine a similar law can be formulated, but with a different constant. In this case for every 20° increase in temperature the vapor pressure is approximately doubled; the factor by which the vapor pressure increases for a 10° increase in temperature is $\sqrt{2}$, approximately 1.4.

It has indeed been found to be true for substances in general that the vapor pressure increases by a certain constant factor, characteristic of the substance, for every 10° increase in temperature. Such an *exponential increase* in the value of a property of a substance with increase in temperature is often observed.

2–6. *The Meaning of Temperature*

In the preceding discussion the assumption has been made that molecules move more rapidly and violently at any given temperature than at a lower one. This assumption is correct: **the temperature of a system is a measure of the vigor of motion of all the atoms and molecules in the system.**

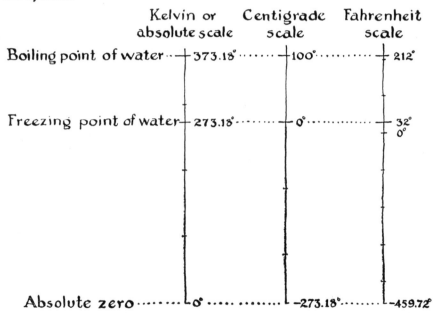

FIG. 2-24   *Comparison of Kelvin, centigrade, and Fahrenheit scales.*

It was recognized by physicists a century ago that the concept that we call temperature is just the concept of vigor of molecular motion. The idea suggested itself of a temperature so low that molecules cease to move. This temperature was named the **absolute zero.** We usually measure temperature by the Fahrenheit scale (f.p. of water 32° F, b.p. 212° F), or, in scientific work, by the *centigrade* or *Celsius scale* (f.p. of air-saturated water at 1 atm pressure 0° C, b.p. of water 100° C). A new temperature scale was devised by Lord Kelvin, a great British physicist (1824–1907). It is called either the *absolute temperature scale* (A) or the *Kelvin scale* (K). The temperature of the absolute zero on this scale, according to the best current determination, is $-273.18°$ on the centigrade scale ($0°$ K $= -273.18°$ C). The scale unit on the centigrade scale, called the centigrade degree, is so selected that the interval between the freezing point of water saturated with air at 1 atm and the boiling point of water at atmospheric pressure is $100°$ C. On the Kelvin scale, with $0°$ K the absolute zero, the freezing point of air-saturated water is $273.18°$ K and the boiling point of water is $373.18°$ K (Fig. 2-24).

The Kelvin scale is so designed that the absolute temperature, measured from the absolute zero, is proportional to the increase of the average kinetic energy of translational motion of the molecules of a gas, kinetic energy being the energy which a moving body has by virtue of its motion, and translational motion being motion in a straight line.

It does not matter which substance is selected. The laws of molecular motion are such that the average kinetic energy of translational motion of the molecules of a gas of any substance is exactly the same as that of the molecules of any other substance at the same temperature—that is, in thermal equilibrium with it.

With increase in temperature there occurs increase in violence of molecular motion of all kinds. Gas molecules move more rapidly, and the atoms within a molecule oscillate more rapidly relative to one another. The atoms and molecules in liquids and solids carry out more vigorous vibrational motions. This vigorous motion at high temperatures may result in chemical reaction, especially decomposition of substances. Thus, when iodine gas is heated to about $1,200°$ C at 1 atm pressure about one-half of the molecules *dissociate* (split) into separate iodine atoms.

You can get a better understanding of many of the phenomena of chemistry by remembering that the absolute temperature is a measure of the vigor of the motion of atoms and molecules.

The Quantitative Relation Between Temperature and Kinetic Energy.   It will be pointed out in the discussion of the kinetic theory of gases (Chap. 14) that the average kinetic energy of the molecules of any gas—that is, the quantity $\frac{1}{2}m(v^2)_{\text{average}}$, where v is the velocity of motion of molecules—is equal to $\frac{3}{2}kT$. In this expression T is the absolute temperature, and k is a fundamental constant, called *Boltzmann's constant*. The value of k is 1.380×10^{-16} erg/deg.

The average velocity of motion of a heavy molecule in a gas at temperature T is accordingly smaller than that of a light molecule at the same temperature. The average velocity of molecules of air at room temperature is about 5×10^4 cm/sec, which is about 1,100 miles per hour.

Exercises

2-1. State the difference between a hypothesis and a theory or law. Give an example of a hypothesis.

2-2. It is stated in the text that atoms are from 2 to 5 Å in diameter. How many Ångströms are there in 1 inch? If the average atom is 3.5 Å in diameter, how many atoms side by side in contact would make a line 1 inch long? How many, in a simple square arrangement, would cover 1 sq. in. of surface? How many, in a simple cubic arrangement (Fig. 2-12), would occupy 1 cu. in.?

2-3. Assuming the average atom to be 3.5 Å in diameter, and the average atomic nucleus to be 3.5×10^{-12} cm in diameter, what would be the diameter of a sphere containing all the nuclei in the earth (diameter 8,000 miles) packed together the way atoms are packed?

2-4. There are about 0.5×10^{24} molecules of water in a cubic inch of water. If a cubic inch of water were poured into the ocean and thoroughly stirred, and a cubic inch of ocean water were then removed, about how many molecules from the original cubic inch would be found in it? Assume the volume of the ocean to correspond to an average depth of 1 mile over the entire surface of the earth.

2-5. If the molecules in a glass of water (say 10 cu. in.) were to be increased in diameter a million-fold, making each molecule the size of a small grain of sand, to what depth could the surface of the earth be covered uniformly with the enlarged molecules?

2-6. Make a two-dimensional drawing representing spherical atoms in closest packing in a single layer. How many neighbors does each atom have in contact with it?

2-7. Arrange marbles, steel balls, or other spheres of the same size in a close-packed layer. Pack a similar layer on top of the first one. Note that a third layer could be put directly above the first layer, or in another position; the second of these alternatives, repeated, leads to the structure of the copper crystal. Repeat this process to build a triangular pyramid. Note that this pyramid is a regular tetrahedron.

2-8. Describe qualitatively the structure of a crystal of iodine, of liquid iodine, and of gaseous iodine.

2-9. Considering what you know about phases and vapor pressure, do you think that there exist a temperature and a pressure at which ice, water, and water vapor can be in equilibrium with one another?

2-10. It has been found that hemoglobin molecules spread on the surface of a solution of ammonium sulfate form a unimolecular layer of hemoglobin, 36 Å thick. Assuming that the density of the hemoglobin in this layer is 1.35 g/cm³, calculate what surface area would be covered by 1 mg of hemoglobin, spread into a unimolecular layer. (Answer: 330 square inches.)

2-11. The metal indium forms tetragonal crystals. The unit of structure is a rectangular parallelepiped, with edges $a_0 = 3.24$ Å, $b_0 = 3.24$ Å, and $c_0 = 4.94$ Å. There are two atoms in the unit of structure, with coordinates 0, 0, 0 and 1/2, 1/2, 1/2. (a) Calculate distances from each atom to its twelve nearest neighbors; note that four are at one distance, and eight at another distance. (b) Show that if the axial ratio c_0/a_0 were equal to 1.414, the twelve distances would be equal. (c) What is the relation between the unit of structure, with this axial ratio, and the cubic unit of structure described in the text for cubic closest packing?

2-12.   Diamond has a cubic unit of structure, with $a_0 = 3.56$ Å. There are eight atoms in the unit, with coordinates 0, 0, 0; 0, 1/2, 1/2; 1/2, 0, 1/2; 1/2, 1/2, 0; 1/4, 1/4, 1/4; 1/4, 3/4, 3/4; 3/4, 1/4, 3/4; 3/4, 3/4, 1/4. How many nearest neighbors does each atom have? What is the distance to each of these neighbors? (Answer: 4; 1.54 Å.)

2-13.   The crystal sodium chloride has a cubic unit of structure, with $a_0 = 5.628$ A. There are four sodium atoms (sodium ions) in the unit of structure, with coordinates 0, 0, 0; 0, 1/2, 1/2; 1/2, 0, 1/2; 1/2, 1/2, 0; and also four chlorine atoms (chloride ions), with coordinates 1/2, 1/2, 1/2; 1/2, 0, 0; 0, 1/2, 0; 0, 0, 1/2. Make a drawing showing the cubic unit of structure and the positions of the atoms. How many nearest neighbors does each atom have, what is the interatomic distance for these neighbors, and what polyhedron is formed by them? This arrangement of atoms, called the sodium chloride arrangement, is a common one for salts.

Chapter 3

The Electron
and the Nucleus

About fifty years ago it was discovered that atoms themselves, which up to that time had been thought to be indivisible, are composed of smaller particles, and that these smaller particles carry electric charges. The discovery of the components of atoms and the investigation of the structure of atoms—the way in which atoms are built of the smaller particles—constitute one of the most interesting stories in the history of science. Moreover, knowledge about the electronic structure of atoms has during recent years permitted the facts of chemistry to be systematized in a striking way, making the subject easier to understand and to remember: it has been discovered that the bonds that hold atoms together in molecules consist of pairs of electrons held jointly by two atoms. The student of chemistry can be helped greatly in mastering his subject by first obtaining a good understanding of atomic structure.

3–1. *The Nature of Electricity*

The ancient Greeks knew that when a piece of amber is rubbed with wool or fur it achieves the power of attracting light objects, such as feathers or bits of straw. The phenomenon was studied by William Gilbert (1540–1603), Queen Elizabeth I's physician, who invented the adjective *electric* to describe the force of attraction, after the Greek word *elektron*, meaning amber. Gilbert and many other scientists, including Benjamin Franklin, investigated electric phenomena, and during the nineteenth century many discoveries about the nature of electricity, and of magnetism, which is closely related to electricity, were made.

It was found that if a rod of sealing wax, which behaves in the same way as amber, is rubbed with a woolen cloth, and a rod of glass is rubbed with a silken cloth, an electric spark will pass between the sealing-wax rod and the glass rod when they are brought near one another. Moreover, it was found that a force of attraction operates between them. If the sealing-wax rod that has been electrically charged by rubbing with the woolen cloth is suspended from a thread, as shown in Figure 3-1, and the charged glass rod is brought near one end of it, this end will turn toward the glass rod. An electrified sealing-wax rod is repelled, however, by a similar sealing-wax rod, and also an electrified glass rod

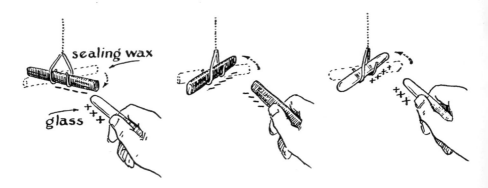

FIG. 3-1 *Experiments showing the attraction of unlike charges of electricity and the repulsion of like charges.*

is repelled by a similar glass rod (Fig. 3-1). The ideas were developed that there are two kinds of electricity, which were called resinous electricity (that which is picked up by the sealing-wax rod) and vitreous electricity (that which is picked up by the glass rod), and that opposite kinds of electricity attract one another, whereas similar kinds repel one another. Franklin assumed that when a glass rod is rubbed with a silken cloth something is transferred from the cloth to the glass rod, and he described the glass rod as positively charged, meaning that it had an excess of the electric fluid that had been transferred to it by the rubbing, with the cloth having a deficiency, and hence being negatively charged. He pointed out that he did not really know whether the electric fluid had been transferred from the silken cloth to the glass rod or from the glass rod to the silken cloth, and that accordingly the decision to describe vitreous electricity as positive (involving an excess of resinous fluid) was an arbitrary one. We now know, in fact, that when the glass rod is rubbed with a silken cloth negatively charged particles, the electrons, are transferred from the glass rod to the silken cloth, and that Franklin thus made the wrong decision.

Careful experiments carried out by Joseph Priestley (1733–1804), by Henry Cavendish (1731–1810), and by the French physicist Charles Augustin de Coulomb (1736–1806) led to the discovery that the force of attraction between two opposite charges of electricity is inversely proportional to the square of the distance between them, and directly proportional to the magnitudes of the charges—that is, to the amount of positive electricity, $+e_1$, and the amount of negative electricity, $-e_2$. This relation can be expressed by the following equation:

$$\text{force of attraction} = \frac{e_1 \times e_2}{r^2} \tag{3-1}$$

In this equation r is the distance between the two charges, considered to be located at points.

The metric *unit* of electric charge is called the *statcoulomb* or esu (electrostatic unit). It is defined as having such a magnitude that the force of attraction between one statcoulomb of positive electricity and one statcoulomb of negative electricity a distance of 1 cm apart is 1 dyne.

In practice there is need for a larger unit of electric charge. The larger unit that has been adopted is the *coulomb*, which is closely equal to 3×10^9 statcoulombs:

1 coulomb $= 3 \times 10^9$ statcoulombs*   (3-2)

According to the inverse-square law of force between electric charges, which is given the name **Coulomb's law,** the force between two unit charges 0.5 cm apart is 4 dynes—that is, four times as great as the force between the charges when they are 1 cm apart.

Force and Potential Energy.   The force of repulsion between two positive charges, each of one statcoulomb, as a function of the distance apart of the charges, is represented in Figure 3-2. With use of Coulomb's law for the force as a function of distance, as represented in this figure, we can calculate the amount of work that must be done to bring the two unit charges from an infinite distance apart to the distance r apart. The relation between work and force is

work = force $\times$ distance   (3-3)

It is found that the work that must be done to bring two unit charges from infinity to the distance r is $1/r$ erg. This work is stored in the system of the two charges the distance r apart; by making use of the force of repulsion between the charges, they would

* The more precise relation is 1 coulomb $= 2.99592 \times 10^9$ statcoulombs.

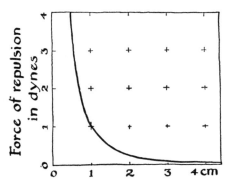

FIG. 3-2

Diagram illustrating the inverse-square law of electrostatic repulsion: the force is inversely proportional to the square of the distance between the charges.

do the amount of work $1/r$ erg as they separate from one another. The stored-up capacity for doing work is called the *potential energy* of the system. It is represented in Figure 3-3.

We see that the potential energy of two unit charges 1 cm apart is 1 erg, and the potential energy of the unit charges ½ cm apart is 2 ergs. Also, it is to be noted that the slope of the curve of potential energy against distance between the charges, as given in Figure 3-3, is equal to the force of repulsion between the charges.

The general expression for the mutual potential energy of two electric charges q_1 and q_2 is

$$\text{potential energy} = \frac{q_1 q_2}{r} \tag{3-4}$$

The potential energy is positive if the charges q_1 and q_2 have the same sign, and negative if they have opposite signs.

The Interaction of an Electric Charge with Electric and Magnetic Fields.   An electric charge is said to be surrounded by an *electric field*, which exercises a force on other electric charges in its neighborhood. (Sometimes the electric field is called the *electrostatic field*.) The strength of an electric field is measured by determining the force that operates on a unit electric charge; the strength of the field in electrostatic units is equal to the force in dynes that operates on a charge of 1 statcoulomb. The field due to a charge q at a distance r from the center of the charge is equal to $\frac{q}{r^2}$, and the field is directed away from the charge (for a positive charge).

The field can be conveniently indicated by a method invented by Michael Faraday (1791–1867), who made many discoveries in electricity and magnetism as well as in

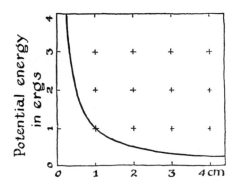

FIG. 3-3

Diagram showing the dependence of the potential energy of two electric charges on the distance between them; the potential energy is inversely proportional to the first power of the distance.

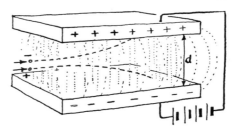

FIG. 3-4

The motion of an electrically charged particle in the uniform electric field between charged plates.

chemistry. Faraday assumed that *lines of force* emanate from every charged body. The direction of the lines of force at any point coincides with the direction of the electric field at that point, and the number of lines of force per square centimeter of cross-section perpendicular to this direction is proportional to the strength of the field.

An important situation is that shown in Figure 3-4, in which two large parallel plates of metal are held a small, constant distance from one another. One of these parallel plates is charged positively and the other is charged negatively. Except near the edges, the lines of force are straight lines between the plates, and with uniform density. Accordingly, in the region between the plates the electric field is constant.

The amount of work, in ergs, required to move a unit positive charge from the negative plate to the positive plate, through the distance d, is equal to the product of the field strength, in electrostatic units, and the distance d, in centimeters. This quantity is called the **potential difference** of the upper plate and the lower plate. The electrostatic unit of potential difference, defined in the preceding sentences, is called the **statvolt.**

It is customary in practice to make use of the **volt** as the unit of potential difference, rather than the statvolt. This practical unit is 1/300 statvolt:

1 volt = 1/300 statvolt   (3-5)

The practical unit of electric field strength is the volt per centimeter. The relation of this unit to the electrostatic unit, the statvolt per centimeter, is

1 volt/cm = 1/300 statvolt/cm   (3-6)

The force exerted on a charged particle by a constant electric field of this sort has the same effect as the force exerted on a mass by the gravitational field of the earth, which is constant in the neighborhood of the surface of the earth. A positively charged particle projected into the region between the plates, as indicated in Figure 3-4, would fall to the bottom plate along the parabolic course represented by the dashed line, in the same way that a projectile fired horizontally would fall toward the surface of the earth.

No force is exerted on a stationary electric charge by a constant *magnetic field*. The force exerted on a moving electric charge by a magnetic field that it is traversing is at right angles to the direction of motion of the charged particle and the direction of the magnetic field. This is illustrated in Figure 3-5. The poles of the magnet are marked *N* (north-seeking pole) and *S* (south-seeking pole); the lines of force are indicated as going from the north-seeking pole to the south-seeking pole. A positively charged particle is shown as moving through the field from the left to the right. The nature of electricity and magnetism is such that a force operates which is proportional to the strength of the magnetic field, the quantity of electric charge on the particle, and the speed of the particle, and the direction of this force is at right angles to the plane formed by the

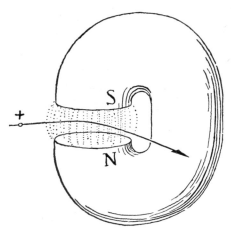

FIG. 3-5

The path of a moving electric charge in a magnetic field.

direction of motion of the moving particle and the direction of the lines of force of the magnetic field, its sense being out of the plane of the paper. This causes the moving charged particle to be deflected to the front, as indicated in the drawing.

The Explanation of Electricity and Magnetism.   You may well ask how scientists explain the fact that an electron is repelled by another electron, or that in general two electrically charged bodies repel or attract one another in accordance with Coulomb's law; or how scientists explain the still more extraordinary and unexpected fact that an electric charge that is moving through a magnetic field is pushed to one side by inter-action of its charge with the field. The answer to these questions is that there is no explanation. These properties of electric charges and of electric and magnetic fields are a part of the world in which we live.

The discovery of the fact that a sideways force is exerted on an electric charge moving through a magnetic field has led to very important practical applications. The ordinary electric generator (dynamo) produces electricity because of this fact. In an electric gen-erator a wire is moved rapidly through a magnetic field, in a direction perpendicular to the lengthwise direction of the wire. Moving the wire (including the electrons in it) through the magnetic field causes the electrons to be set in motion, relative to the atoms in the wire, in the direction toward one end of the wire—namely, the end indicated by the rule of Figure 3-5. In this way a flow of electrons (current of electricity) is produced in the wire. Practically all of the electric power that is used in the world is produced by this method, the energy for operating the electric generators (for moving the wire through the magnetic field) being provided by the fall of water in the earth's gravita-tional field or by the combustion of coal or oil to drive steam engines. A small amount of electric power is produced directly from chemical energy, as will be discussed in Chap-ter 13.

The Electromagnetic Pump.   An interesting new device that makes use of the force that acts on a moving electric charge in a magnetic field is the electromagnetic pump, which has been devised to pump the liquid metal (such as sodium-potassium alloy) that is used as a heat-transfer agent to carry the heat from a nuclear reactor to an external boiler. The liquid metal is in a pipe (made of a nickel-chromium alloy steel) between the poles of a large permanent magnet. An electric current of about 20,000 amperes, at 1 volt potential difference, passes through the liquid metal, as indicated

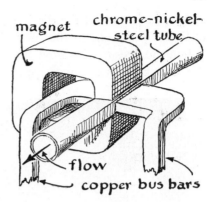

FIG. 3-6

The construction of an electromagnetic pump. When electric current flows through the liquid alloy in the region between the poles of the magnet, a force operates on the moving charges, and hence on the alloy, in the direction indicated.

in Figure 3-6. The sideways force that is exerted on the electrons moving through the magnetic field causes the metal to flow in the indicated direction, at right angles to the direction of the electric current and the direction of the magnetic field.

3–2. *The Discovery of the Electron*

It was discovered in the early part of the nineteenth century that compounds can be decomposed by an electric current, and the quantity of electricity needed to liberate a certain amount of an element from one of its compounds was measured. It was found that, for example, 96,500 coulombs (2.89×10^{14} statcoulombs) of electricity is required to liberate 1 g of hydrogen from water (we shall discuss these matters in detail in Chaps. 8 and 13). After thinking about these phenomena, Dr. G. Johnstone Stoney, an English scientist, stated as early as 1874 that they indicate that electricity exists in discrete units, and that the units are associated with material atoms. In 1891 he emphasized this point and suggested the name *electron* for the postulated unit of electricity.

At that time experiments were being carried on by physicists on the conduction of electricity through gases; these experiments after some years (in 1897) led Sir J. J. Thomson (1856–1940), then director of the Cavendish Laboratory at Cambridge University, to the firm conclusion that the electron exists and to the determination of some of its properties.

If a glass tube about 50 cm long is fitted with electrodes and a potential difference of about 10,000 volts is applied between the two electrodes, as indicated in Figure 3-7, no electric discharge occurs until part of the air or other gas has been pumped out of the tube. Discharge begins to occur when the pressure has become about 10 mm of mercury. The nature of the discharge, which is associated with the emission of light by the gas in the tube, changes as the pressure becomes lower. When the pressure is somewhat less than 1 mm Hg, a dark space, called the Crookes dark space, appears in the neighborhood of the cathode,

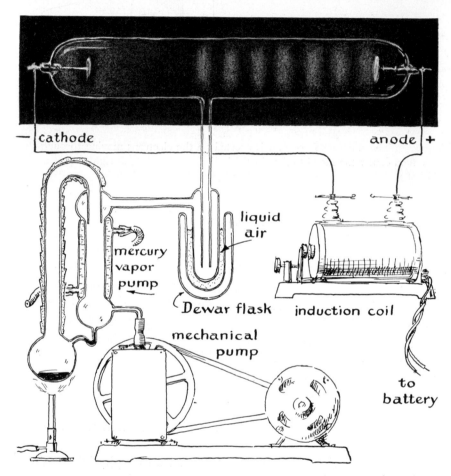

FIG. 3-7 *Apparatus used to observe the discharge of electricity in a gas at low pressure. The dark space around the cathode is called the Crookes dark space; at still lower pressures the Crookes dark space fills the whole tube.*

and striations are observed in the rest of the tube. At still lower pressures the Crookes dark space increases in size, until at about 0.01 mm Hg it fills the whole tube. At this pressure no light is given out by the residual gas within the tube, but the glass of the tube itself glows (fluoresces) with a faint greenish light.

FIG. 3-8

Experiment showing that cathode rays,
starting from the cathode at the left, move
through the Crookes tube in straight lines.

It was discovered that the greenish light is due to bombardment of
the glass by rays liberated at the cathode (called *cathode rays*), and
traveling in straight lines. This was revealed by the experiment illustrated in Figure 3-8; it was observed that an object placed within the
discharge tube casts a shadow on the glass, which fluoresces except in
the region of this shadow.

It was shown by Jean Perrin in 1895 that these cathode rays consist
of negatively charged particles. His experiment is illustrated in Figure
3-9. He introduced in the Crookes tube a shield with a slit, such as to
form a beam of cathode rays. He also placed a fluorescent screen in
the tube, so that the path of the beam could be followed by the trace
of the fluorescence. When a magnet was placed near the tube, in such
a way that the lines of force of the magnetic field were perpendicular
to the direction of motion of the cathode rays, the beam was observed

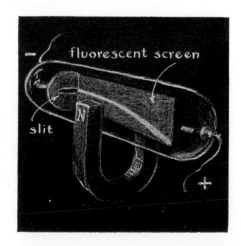

FIG. 3-9

Experiment showing that the cathode rays
have a negative charge.

to be deflected in the direction corresponding to the presence of a negative charge on the particles.

The amount of deflection could not be used to determine the ratio
of charge to mass of the particles, however, because of lack of knowledge
of the speed with which they were moving. J. J. Thomson then carried
out an experiment that permitted him to determine the speed. This
was done with the use of the apparatus shown in Figure 3-10, in which
the cathode rays could be affected simultaneously by a magnetic field
and an electric field. For a fixed value of the magnetic field strength,

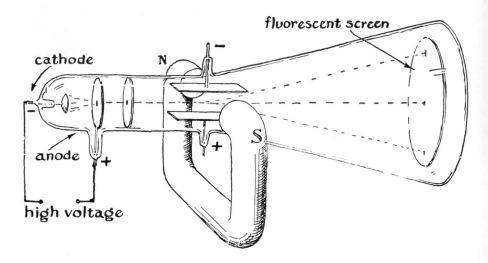

FIG. 3-10   *The apparatus used by J. J. Thomson to determine the ratio of electric
charge to mass of the cathode rays, through the simultaneous deflection of the rays by
an electric field and a magnetic field.*

the strength of the electric field could be varied until the beam struck
the fluorescent screen at the central position, at which it would strike the
screen in the absence of both the magnetic field and the electric field.
Under these conditions the force due to the magnetic field is just balanced by the force due to the electrostatic field. The force due to the
magnetic field is, however, equal in magnitude to Hev, in which H is
the strength of the magnetic field, e the electric charge, and v the velocity. The force due to the electric field is Ee, in which E is the field
strength. When these are equal, we have

$$Hev = Ee$$

The electric charge of the particles, e, cancels out, and v, the velocity of the particles, is then given by the equation

$$v = \frac{E}{H}$$

By inserting the values of E and H Thomson was able to calculate the velocity v. The values that he obtained were found to be dependent upon the voltage at which the Crookes tube was operated; they were of the order of 5×10^9 cm/sec—that is, about ⅙ the velocity of light.

Knowing the velocity of the cathode rays, he could then determine the ratio of charge to mass of the particles by measuring the deflection of the beam produced by either the electrostatic field alone or the magnetic field alone. From these experiments he obtained the value $e/m = 3 \times 10^{17}$ statcoulombs per gram. To within his experimental error (involving a possible factor of about 2) the same value was obtained whether the tube had been filled originally with air, hydrogen, carbon dioxide, or methyl iodide; also, the same value was obtained whether the cathodes were made of platinum, aluminum, copper, iron, lead, silver, tin, or zinc.

The value of e/m obtained from this experiment convinced Thomson that the particles constitute a form of matter different from the ordinary forms of matter. His argument involved comparison with the value of e/m for hydrogen or other substances as obtained by electrolysis (Chap. 13). It was mentioned above that 1 g of hydrogen is produced in the electrolysis of water by 2.89×10^{14} statcoulombs; hence, if Stoney's suggestion that one elementary charge is to be associated with each atom of hydrogen is correct, the ratio e/m for hydrogen is 2.89×10^{14} statcoulombs per gram. If the same electric charge is involved in both cases, then the mass of the particles present in the cathode rays must be about 1,000 times smaller than the mass of a hydrogen atom. Later experiments showed that in his original work in 1897 Thomson had obtained a value too small by a quotient of nearly two, and accordingly that the mass of the cathode-ray particle (the electron) is approximately 1/2,000 of the mass of the hydrogen atom (actually 1/1,837).

Measurement of the Charge of the Electron.   After the discovery of the electron by J. J. Thomson, many investigators worked on the problem of determining either e or m separately. R. A. Millikan, who began his experiments in 1906, was the most successful; by means of his oil-drop experiment he determined the value of e in 1909 to within 1%.

The apparatus that he used is illustrated in Figure 3-11. Small drops of oil are formed by a sprayer, and some of them attach themselves to ions that have been produced in the air by irradiation with a beam of X-rays. The experimenter watches one of the small oil drops through a microscope and measures the rate at which it falls in the earth's gravitational field. Because of the large frictional force of the air, the drops reach a terminal velocity at which the frictional force is just equal to the gravitational force. This terminal velocity depends on the size and

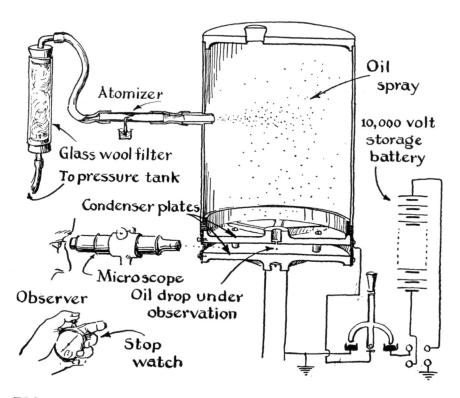

FIG. 3-11   *A diagram of the apparatus used by R. A. Millikan in determining the charge of the electron by the oil-drop method.*

mass of the drop, and the mass can be calculated if the density of the oil is known, and also the viscosity of air. When the electric field is turned on, charging the plates above and below the region where the oil drops are suspended, some of the drops (which carry no electric charge) continue to fall as before; others, carrying electric charges, change their speed and may rise, being pulled up by the attraction of the electric charge for the oppositely charged upper plate in the apparatus. The rate of rise of a drop that has been watched falling is then observed. From this rate, and its rate of fall when the electric field was turned off, the magnitude of the electric charge on the drop can be calculated. In various experiments with different drops, values such as the following were obtained:

$$e = 4.8 \times 10^{-10}$$

$$e = 9.6 \times 10^{-10} = 2 \times 4.8 \times 10^{-10}$$

$$e = 4.8 \times 10^{-10}$$

$$e = 24.0 \times 10^{-10} = 5 \times 4.8 \times 10^{-10}$$

All of these values have a common factor, 4.8×10^{-10}. Millikan accordingly concluded that this is the smallest electric charge that can occur under these conditions. The average value of his measurements was -4.77×10^{-10} statcoulomb. This was accepted as the charge of the electron. It was found later (1935) to be nearly 1% low, mainly because of an error in the value used for the viscosity of air.

3–3. *The Properties of the Electron*

The electron is a particle with negative electric charge of magnitude -4.802×10^{-10} statcoulomb or -1.601×10^{-19} coulomb. Its rest mass is 9.107×10^{-28} g, which is 1/1,837 of that of the hydrogen atom. It is small in size; the radius of the electron cannot be determined exactly, but it is known to be about 1×10^{-12} cm.

It was discovered in 1925 that the electron has angular momentum, as though it were spinning about its own axis. This angular momentum is referred to as the *spin* of the electron. Associated with it is a *magnetic dipole moment;* the electron has the same properties as a small magnet. It is this magnetic moment, due to electron spin, that is responsible for the properties of most paramagnetic substances and ferromagnetic substances.*

Example 1.   If, in one experiment, J. J. Thomson accelerated the electrons in his Crookes tube by applying a potential difference of 10,000 volts between the cathode and the anode, and if an electron that escaped from the cathode was accelerated by falling through the entire field between cathode and anode, with what velocity would it be moving?

   Solution.   The strength of the electric field between the anode and the cathode is $10,000/d$ volt/cm, where d is the distance between the anode and the cathode.

* Paramagnetic substances are those substances that tend to move into a strong magnetic field, such as that between the poles of a magnet; diamagnetic substances tend to move out of the field. Ferromagnetic substances retain their magnetism in the absence of an applied magnetic field.

The electrostatic unit of potential, the statvolt, is equal to 300 v; hence the strength of the field is $33.3/d$ statvolt/cm. The force acting on the electron is the product of the field strength and the charge e, which is 4.80×10^{-10} statcoulomb, and the total energy imparted to the electron is the product of this force times the distance d. Hence the energy of the electron that has been accelerated by 10,000 v is $33.3 \times 4.80 \times 10^{-10}$ erg $= 1.60 \times 10^{-8}$ erg.

This energy is in the form of kinetic energy, and is $\frac{1}{2} mv^2$, where m is the mass of the electron, 9.107×10^{-28} g, and v is its velocity. Hence we write

$$\frac{1}{2} mv^2 = 1.60 \times 10^{-8}$$

or

$$v^2 = \frac{2 \times 1.60 \times 10^{-8}}{9.107 \times 10^{-28}} = 0.352 \times 10^{20}$$

$$v = 5.9 \times 10^9 \text{ cm/sec}$$

Thus we see that the electron that has been accelerated by falling through a potential drop of 10,000 v is moving with a velocity of 6×10^9 cm/sec, which is just $\frac{1}{5}$ of the velocity of light. [There is a small error in this calculation because Newton's equation rather than Einstein's (relativistic) equation has been used for the kinetic energy.]

J. J. Thomson was surprised that all of the particles in the cathode-ray beam were moving with practically the same velocity. The reason for this is that all of the electrons had been liberated at the cathode and had fallen through the same potential difference. If there had been a large amount of gas in the tube many of the electrons might have collided with gas molecules and imparted some of their energy to them, in which case they would not have had the same energy.

The Flow of Electricity in a Metal. A direct current of electricity passing along a copper wire is a *flow of electrons* along the wire. In a metal or similar conductor of electricity there are electrons which have considerable freedom of motion and which move along between the atoms of the metal when an electric potential difference is applied.

Let us call to mind the analogy between the flow of electricity along a wire and the flow of water in a pipe. *Quantity* of water is measured in liters or cubic feet; quantity of electricity is usually measured either in *coulombs* or in statcoulombs. *Rate of flow*, or *current*, of water, the quantity passing a given point of the pipe in unit time, is measured in liters per second, or cubic feet per second; current of electricity is measured in *amperes* (coulombs per second), or in statamperes (statcoulombs per second). The rate of flow of water in a pipe depends on the *pressure difference* at the ends of the pipe, with atmospheres or pounds per square inch as units. The current of electricity in the wire depends on the *electric pressure difference* or *potential difference* or *voltage drop* between its ends, which is usually measured in *volts* or in statvolts. The definitions of the unit of quantity of electricity (the coulomb) and the unit of electric potential (the volt) have been arbitrarily made by international agreement.

An electric generator is essentially an electron pump, which pumps electrons under pressure out of one wire and into another. A generator of direct current pumps electrons continually in the same direction, and one of alternating current reverses its pumping direction regularly, thus building up electron pressure first in one direction and then in the other. A 60-cycle generator reverses its pumping direction 120 times per second.

3–4. The Discovery of X-rays and Radioactivity

The period of ten years beginning in 1895 was a period of great discovery. X-rays were discovered in 1895, radioactivity was discovered in 1896, the new radioactive elements polonium and radium were isolated in the same year, the electron was discovered in 1897, the quantum theory was discovered in 1900, and the light quantum (the photon) was discovered, by Einstein, in 1905, the same year in which he developed the theory of relativity.

Wilhelm Konrad Röntgen (1845–1923), professor of physics at the University of Würzburg, reported in 1895 that he had discovered a new kind of rays, which he called X-rays. He began his paper with a sentence that read essentially as follows: "If the discharge of a large induction coil is allowed to pass through a Crookes tube or similar apparatus, and the tube is covered with a fairly closely fitting mantle of thin, black cardboard, it is seen that light is emitted by a fluorescent screen in the neighborhood." He showed that the X-rays that he had discovered could penetrate matter which is impervious to ordinary light, and could produce fluorescence in various substances, such as glass and calcite. He found that a photographic plate is blackened by the radiation, that the rays are not deflected by a magnet, and that they appear to come from the place in the vacuum tube that is struck by the cathode rays. Within a few weeks after the announcement of this great discovery X-rays were being used by physicians for the investigation of patients.

For nearly twenty years there was doubt as to the nature of X-rays; some scientists thought that their properties could be accounted for best on a corpuscular basis, whereas others thought that X-rays were similar to ordinary light, but with very short wavelengths. The second alternative was shown to be correct when, in 1912, the diffraction of X-rays by crystals was observed (Sec. 3-6).

Soon after the discovery of X-rays the great French mathematician Henri Poincaré suggested at a meeting of the French Academy of Sciences that the X-radiation might be connected with the fluorescence shown by the glass of the Crookes tube at the place where the X-rays are emitted. This suggestion stimulated the French physicist Henri Becquerel (1852–1908) to investigate some fluorescent minerals. He was professor of physics at the Museum of Natural History in Paris, as successor to his father and grandfather. His father had collected many fluorescent minerals, which were available in the museum. Becquerel selected a uranium salt, exposed it to sunlight until it showed strong fluorescence, and then placed it against a photographic plate wrapped in black paper. He found upon developing the plate that it had been blackened, which seemed to confirm Poincaré's idea. However, Becquerel then found that the salts of uranium would blacken a photographic plate wrapped in paper even though they had not been exposed to sunlight to make them fluorescent, and he showed that the effect could be observed with any compound of uranium. He also found that the radiation produced by the uranium compounds could, like X-rays, discharge an electroscope, by ionizing the air and making it conductive.

Marie Sklodowska Curie (1867–1934) then began a systematic investigation of "Becquerel radiation," using the electroscope technique (Fig. 3-12), to see if substances other than uranium exhibited similar properties; this work was the subject of her doctor's dissertation. She found that natural pitchblende, an ore of uranium, is several times more active than purified uranium oxide, and, with her husband, Professor Pierre Curie (1859–1906), she began to separate pitchblende into fractions and to determine their activity. She isolated a bismuth sulfide fraction that was 400 times more active than uranium. Since pure bismuth sulfide is not radioactive, she assumed that a new, strongly radioactive element, similar in chemical properties to bismuth, was present as a contaminant. This element, which she named *polonium*, was the first element discovered through its properties of radioactivity. In the same year, 1896, the Curies isolated an active barium chloride fraction, containing another new element, which they named *radium*.

Becquerel also continued to study the properties of his new radiation, and he was able to make use of the strongly radiating preparations produced by the Curies. In 1899 Becquerel showed that the radiation from radium could be deflected by a magnet. Also in 1899, a young physicist from New Zealand, Ernest Rutherford, working in the Cavendish Laboratory in Cambridge under J. J. Thomson, reported that the radiation from uranium is of at least two distinct types, which he called

FIG. 3-12

A simple electroscope. When an electric charge is present on the gold foil and its support, the two leaves of the foil separate, because of the repulsion of like electric charges.

α (alpha) radiation and β (beta) radiation. A French investigator, P. Villard, soon reported that a third kind of radiation, γ (gamma) radiation, is also emitted.

Alpha, Beta, and Gamma Rays.   The experiments showing the presence of three kinds of rays emitted by natural radioactive materials are illustrated by Figure 3-13. The rays, collimated by passing along a narrow hole in a lead block, traverse a strong magnetic field. They are differently affected, showing them to have different electric charges. Alpha rays are positively charged; further studies, made by Rutherford, showed them to be the positive parts of helium atoms, moving at high speed. Beta rays are electrons, also moving at high speeds—they are similar in nature to the cathode rays produced in a Crookes tube.

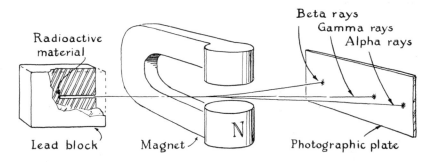

FIG. 3-13   *The deflection of alpha rays and beta rays by a magnetic field.*

Gamma rays are similar to visible light, but with very short wavelengths —they are identical with X-rays produced in an X-ray tube operated at very high voltage.

The identification of the positively charged alpha particles with helium atoms was made by Rutherford by an experiment in which he allowed the alpha particles to be shot through a thin metal foil into a chamber, and later was able to show the presence of helium in the chamber. He could, moreover, correlate the amount of helium in the chamber with the number of alpha particles penetrating the foil.

The nature of the nuclear processes that occur in radioactive elements will be discussed in Chapter 33.

3–5. *The Nuclei of Atoms*

In 1911 Ernest Rutherford (1871–1937), then professor of physics at the University of Manchester, England, carried out some experiments which showed that most of the mass of atoms is concentrated in particles which are very small in size compared with the atoms themselves. The method that he used is very simple, and the arguments involved in drawing conclusions from them are also very simple.

The experiments consisted in bombarding a film of some substance (Rutherford used a piece of metal foil) with a stream of fast-moving alpha particles, and observing the direction in which the alpha particles rebound from the atoms. It is now known that the alpha particles are the nuclei of helium atoms, but this was not learned until after Rutherford had carried out his experiments. The experimental method is indi-

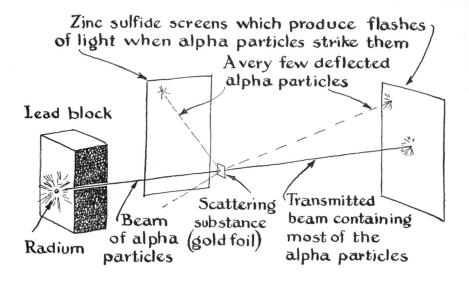

FIG. 3-14   *A diagram representing the experiment carried out by Rutherford, which showed that atoms contain very small, heavy atomic nuclei.*

cated by the drawing in Figure 3-14. A piece of radium emits alpha particles in all directions. A set of slits is constructed to define a beam of the alpha particles. This beam of alpha particles then passes through the metal foil (labeled "scattering substance" in the figure), and the direction in which the alpha particles continue their motion is observed. The direction of motion of the alpha particles can be detected by use of a screen coated with zinc sulfide. When an alpha particle strikes this screen a flash of light is sent out.

If the atoms bombarded with alpha particles were solid throughout their volume, obviously every alpha particle aimed at the cross-sectional area of several square Å should bounce off and change direction slightly.

Practically none would pass through even a film one atom thick without deflection. Actually, however, most of the particles did pass through the foil without appreciable deflection; in one experiment in which the alpha particles were sent through a gold foil 5,000 Å thick, so that they penetrated about 1,000 layers of atoms, only about one alpha particle in 100,000 was deflected. This one usually showed a great deflection, often through more than 90°. When foil twice as thick was taken, it was found that about twice as many alpha particles showed deflection through large angles, with most of them still passing straight through.

It is clear that these experimental results can be understood if the assumption is made that most of the mass of the atom is concentrated into a very small particle, which Rutherford called the *atomic nucleus*. If the alpha particle were also very small, then the chance of collision of these two very small particles as the alpha particle passed through the atom would be small. Since about one particle in 100,000 is deflected on passing through a foil consisting of 1,000 atom layers, only about one atom in 100,000,000 would be deflected by a single layer of atoms. Rutherford concluded from this that the heavy nucleus had a cross-sectional area only 0.00000001 as great as the cross-sectional area of the atoms, and hence that the ratio of the diameter of the nucleus to the diameter of the atom is the square root of this factor— that is, $1/100,000,000^{1/2} = 1/10,000$. Since the diameter of the atom is of the order of a few Ångströms, the diameter of the nucleus is indicated to be approximately 10^{-4} Å or 10^{-12} cm.

The picture of the atom that has been developed from this experiment and similar experiments is indeed an extraordinary one. If we could magnify a piece of gold leaf by the linear factor 10^9—that is, by 1,000,000,000—we would see it as an immense pile of atoms about two feet in diameter, each atom thus being about as big as a bushel basket. Practically the entire mass of each atom would, however, be concentrated in a single particle, the nucleus, about 0.001 inch in diameter, like an extremely small grain of sand. This nucleus would be surrounded by electrons, moving very rapidly about. Rutherford's experiment would consist in shooting through a pile of these bushel-basket atoms a stream of minute grains of sand, each of which would continue in a straight line unless it happened to collide with one of the minute grains of sand representing the nuclei of the atoms. It is obvious that the chance of such a collision would be very small. (Note that in the Rutherford experiment the alpha particles are not deflected by the electrons because they are very much heavier than the electrons.)

The nucleus of the hydrogen atom has the same electric charge as the electron, but with opposite sign, positive instead of negative. The nuclei of other atoms have positive charges that are multiples of this fundamental charge. The structure of these atomic nuclei will be discussed in the following chapter.

3–6. *X-rays and Crystal Structure*

The question of the nature of X-rays remained unanswered until 1912, when Max von Laue (born 1879), at the University of Munich, suggested an experiment, the diffraction of X-rays by crystals, which was successfully carried out, and which showed immediately that X-rays are similar in nature to ordinary light, but have a far smaller wavelength than ordinary light. The diffraction of X-rays by crystals has been of great importance to chemistry, not only through the determination of the wavelengths of X-rays characteristic of different elements, which will be discussed in the following chapter, but also because it has permitted the determination of the atomic arrangement in crystals, and in this way has contributed to the development of modern structural chemistry.

Waves and Their Interference. During the nineteenth century it was recognized that light can be produced by moving an electric charge back and forth in an oscillatory manner. The motion of the electric charge produces an oscillatory change in the electric field surrounding the charge, and this change is transmitted through space, with the velocity of light, 3.00×10^{10} cm/sec.

The nature of the wave motion is represented by the sine curve shown in Figure 3-15. This curve might represent, for example, the instantaneous contour of waves on the surface of the ocean. The distance between one crest and an adjacent crest is called the *wavelength*, usually represented by the symbol λ (Greek letter lambda). The height of the crest, which is also the depth of the trough, with reference to the average level is called the *amplitude* of the wave. If the waves are moving with the velocity c cm/sec, the frequency of the waves, represented by the symbol ν (Greek letter nu), is equal to c/λ; that is, it is the number of waves

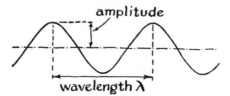

FIG. 3-15

Diagram representing wave motion.

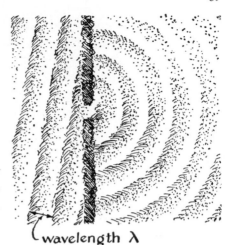

FIG. 3-16

Diagram representing waves on the surface of water, from the left, striking a pier; waves propagated through the opening in the pier then spread out in circles.

wavelength λ

that pass by a fixed point in unit time (1 sec). The dimensions of the wavelength are those of length. The dimensions of frequency, number of waves per second, are [time^{-1}]. We see that the product of wavelength and frequency has the dimensions [length] [time^{-1}]—that is, the dimensions of velocity. The equation connecting wavelength λ, frequency ν, and velocity c is

$$\lambda \nu = c \tag{3-7}$$

In the case of a light wave the sine curve shown in Figure 3-15 is considered to represent the magnitude of the electric field in space. The electric field of a light wave is perpendicular to the direction of motion of the beam of light.

The phenomenon of *interference of waves* is used to determine the wavelength of light waves and X-rays. This phenomenon can be illus-

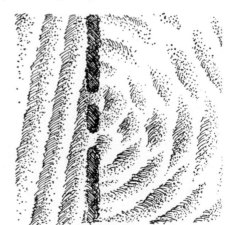

FIG. 3-17

The interference and reinforcement of two sets of circular waves, from two openings.

trated by Figures 3-16 and 3-17. In 3-16 there is shown a set of water waves approaching a jetty in which there is a small opening. The waves that strike the jetty dissipate their energy among the rocks of the jetty, but the part of the waves that strikes the opening causes a disturbance on the other side of the jetty. This disturbance is in the form of a set of circular waves, that spread out from the opening of the jetty. The wavelength of these circular waves is the same as the wavelength of the incident water waves. When light or X-rays strike atoms, part of the energy of the incident light is scattered by the atoms. Each atom scatters a set of circular waves. If two atoms that are excited by the same incident waves scatter light, as illustrated in Figure 3-17, there are certain directions in which the circular waves (spherical waves in the case of atoms in three-dimensional space) from the two scattering centers reinforce one another, producing waves with twice the amplitude of either set, and other directions in which the trough of one set of waves coincides with the crest of the other set, and interference occurs. The directions of reinforcement and interference for two sets of circular waves are shown in the figure.

It is easy to calculate the angles at which reinforcement and interference would occur, in terms of the distance between the two scattering centers and the wavelength of the waves. The way in which the calculation is made is shown in Figure 3-18. Here r_1 is the distance from the first scattering center, and r_2 the distance from the second scattering center. At all points in the median plane these two distances are equal. Accordingly, a crest of a wave of the first set will reach a distant point P at the same time as a crest of a wave of the second set, and there will be reinforcement at this point. The point P'' lies at such distances r_1'' and r_2'' that $r_1''-r_2''$ is just equal to one wavelength of the waves. Accordingly, the crest of a wave from the first scattering center will reach P'' at the same time as the crest of the preceding wave from the second scattering center, and again there will be reinforcement. At the intermediate point P', however, the difference $r_1'-r_2'$ is just one-half of a wavelength. The crest of a wave from one scattering center will coincide with the trough of a wave from another scattering center, and there will be interference.

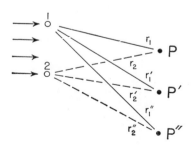

FIG. 3-18

Diagram illustrating the conditions for interference and reinforcement of circular waves from two points, 1 and 2. The incident waves are moving toward the right, as shown by the arrows.

An additional discussion of interference of visible light, and its use in the grating spectroscope, will be given in Chapter 8.

The Bragg Equation for the Diffraction of X-rays by Crystals.   It was shown during the decade after the discovery of X-rays that if these rays were similar to ordinary light their wavelength must be of the order of magnitude of 1 Å—that is, about 1/5,000 of the wavelength of visible light. Then Max von Laue had the idea that crystals, in which atoms are arranged in a regular lattice with interatomic distances of a few Ångströms, might serve to produce diffraction effects with X-rays. The experiment was immediately carried out by two experimental physicists, Friedrich and Knipping, with use of a crystal of copper sul-

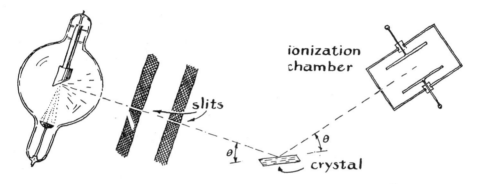

FIG. 3-19   *The Bragg ionization-chamber technique of investigating the diffraction of X-rays by crystals.*

fate pentahydrate. A narrow beam of X-rays from an X-ray tube was passed through the crystal, and photographic plates were placed around the crystal. It was found that on the photographic plate behind the crystal there was a blackened spot representing the position where the direct beam of X-rays had struck the plate, and also several other spots, showing the preferential scattering of the beam of X-rays in certain directions, corresponding to diffraction maxima. This experiment showed at once that X-rays are similar to light, in having a wave nature, and that the wavelength of the X-rays produced by the X-ray tube that was used was of the order of 1 Å.

Sir William Bragg (1862–1942) and his son, Sir Lawrence Bragg (born 1890), then succeeded in determining the structure of many crystals by the use of the phenomenon of X-ray diffraction, and also in determining the wavelengths of the X-rays produced by different X-ray

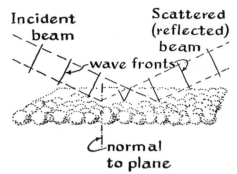

FIG. 3-20

Diagram showing the equality of path lengths when the conditions for specular reflection from a layer are satisfied.

tubes. Their experimental method is shown in Figure 3-19. A beam of X-rays is defined by a slit system, usually slits in a piece of lead. The beam impinges on the face of a crystal, such as the cleavage face of a salt crystal. An instrument for detecting X-rays (in the case of the original experiments by the Braggs an *ionization chamber*, but in modern work a *Geiger counter* may be used) was then placed as shown in the figure. Lawrence Bragg had developed a simple theory of diffraction of X-rays by crystals. This theory is illustrated in Figures 3-20 and 3-21. He pointed out that if the beam of rays incident on a plane of atoms and the scattered beam are in the same vertical plane and at the same angle with the plane, as shown in Figure 3-20, the conditions for reinforcement are satisfied. This sort of scattering is called *specular reflection*— it is similar to reflection from a mirror. He then formulated the conditions for reinforcement of the beam specularly reflected from one plane of atoms and the beam specularly reflected from another plane of atoms separated from it by the *interplanar distance d*. This situation is illustrated in Figure 3-21. We see that the difference in path is equal to $2d \sin \theta$, in which θ is the *Bragg angle* (the angle between the incident beam and the plane of atoms). In order to have reinforcement this difference in path $2d \sin \theta$ must be equal to the wavelength λ or an integral multiple of this

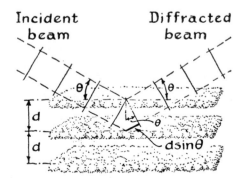

FIG. 3-21

Diagram illustrating the derivation of the Bragg equation for the diffraction of X-rays by crystals.

FIG. 3-22

Spacings between different rows of atoms in a two-dimensional crystal.

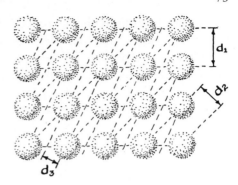

wavelength—that is, to $n\lambda$, in which n is an integer. We thus obtain the *Bragg equation* for the diffraction of X-rays:

$$n\lambda = 2d \sin \theta \tag{3-8}$$

The way in which the structure of crystals was then determined is illustrated in Figure 3-22. Here we show a simple cubic arrangement of atoms, as seen along one of the cube faces. It is evident that there

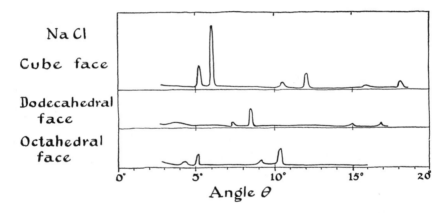

FIG. 3-23   *Experimental data obtained by the Braggs for the diffraction of X-rays by the sodium chloride crystal.*

are layers of atoms, shown by their traces in the plane of the paper, with spacings d_1, d_2, d_3, etc., which are in the ratios $1 : 2^{-\frac{1}{2}} : 5^{-\frac{1}{2}}$, etc. Since the relative values of the spacings d_1, d_2, d_3, etc. could be determined without knowledge of the wavelengths of X-rays, but simply as inversely proportional to their values of $\sin \theta$, the nature of the atomic arrangement could be discovered by the Bragg experiments.

A reproduction of some of the first experimental measurements made by the Braggs is shown as Figure 3-23. It is seen that there occurs a pattern of reflections that is repeated at values of sin θ representing the values 1, 2, and 3 for the integer n, which is called the *order of the reflection*. The pattern that is repeated consists of a weak scattered beam, at the smaller angle, and a stronger scattered beam, at the larger angle. This shows that there were present in the beam of X-rays produced by the X-ray tube a shorter wavelength and a longer wavelength, with greater intensity of the X-rays of longer wavelength than of shorter wavelength.

Within a few months the Braggs had succeeded in determining the wavelengths of X-rays to about 1%, and also in determining the structures of about twenty different crystals. We have already discussed the results of their discovery in the preceding chapter, in which the structures of the copper crystal and of the iodine crystal were described.

Example 2.   The Braggs calculated from the density of salt and Millikan's value of the charge of the electron, by a method which we shall discuss later (Chap. 7), that the spacing d_1 for the cube face of the sodium chloride crystal has the value 2.81 Å. Using the experimental data given in Figure 3-23, find the wavelengths of the two kinds of radiation produced by the X-ray tube that they used.

   Solution.   Let us first calculate the wavelength of the X-rays with shorter wavelength. This is called the $K\beta$ line. The Bragg angle θ for this line in the first order is seen from the figure to be 4°48′. The value of sin θ is accordingly 0.0924. The Bragg equation for $n = 1$ is

$$\lambda = 2d \sin \theta$$

We insert the value 2.81 for d and 0.0924 for sin θ and obtain

$$\lambda = 2 \times 2.81 \times 0.0924 = \mathbf{0.519 \text{ Å}}$$

This is the value of the wavelength for the $K\beta$ line. In the same way we calculate for the other line, using the observed value of θ of 6°0′, the value

$$\lambda = \mathbf{0.587 \text{ Å}}$$

This is the wavelength of the $K\alpha$ line. These two wavelengths correspond to the metal palladium, which was the target (the anode) of the X-ray tube used by the Braggs in this experiment. The two lines are part of the *characteristic X-radiation* of the element palladium.

Exercises

3-1.   State the law of attraction or repulsion between two electrically charged particles. How is the force between the two charged particles changed (a) if the distance between them is doubled? (b) if the charge of one particle is doubled? (c) if the charges of both particles are doubled?

3-2.   According to the law of gravitation, the gravitational force of attraction between two particles with masses m_1 and m_2 a distance r apart is Gm_1m_2/r^2, where

G, the constant of gravitation, has been found by experiment to have the value 6.673×10^{-8}; that is, the force of attraction between two particles each with mass 1 g and the distance 1 cm apart is 6.673×10^{-8} dyne. (a) Calculate the force of electrostatic attraction between an electron and a proton 10 Å apart. (b) Calculate the force of gravitational attraction between an electron and a proton 10 Å apart. What is the relationship of the electrostatic attraction to the gravitational attraction at this distance? (c) What is the dependence on distance of the ratio of electrostatic attraction and gravitational attraction of an electron and a proton?

3-3. Discuss the motion of an electron moving transversely between two parallel plates carrying opposite electric charges. Also discuss the motion of an electron moving transversely between the poles of a magnet.

3-4. Describe the electromagnetic pump, used to pump sodium-potassium alloy in nuclear power plants. Why is the electromagnetic pump not used as a water pump?

3-5. Describe the experiments of Jean Perrin and J. J. Thomson that led to the discovery of the electron.

3-6. Calculate the velocity with which the electrons would move in the apparatus used by J. J. Thomson, operated at an accelerating voltage of 5,000 v. Assume that each electron has kinetic energy equal to eV, where e is the charge of the electron in statcoulombs and V is the accelerating potential in statvolts.

3-7. Describe Millikan's oil-drop experiment. Why is a knowledge of the value of the viscosity of air needed in order for the value of the charge of the electron to be calculated from the measurements?

3-8. Briefly summarize the history of the discovery of X-rays by Röntgen, the discovery of radioactivity by Becquerel, and the discovery of polonium and radium by the Curies.

3-9. Describe the Rutherford experiment, and explain why the observations indicate that most of the mass of an atom is concentrated in a very small particle, the nucleus.

3-10. The principal α particles from radium have an energy of 4.79 Mev (4.79 million electron volts). With what velocity are they moving? What is the ratio of their velocity to the velocity of light? The mass of the α particle is 6.66×10^{-24} g. (Answer: Velocity 1.5×10^9 cm/sec.) (Note that if the velocity of a particle is less than 10% of the velocity of light, the expression $\frac{1}{2}mv^2$ for its kinetic energy can be used with error less than 1%. For larger values of the velocity the theory of relativity must be used to obtain the correct answers.)

3-11. Calculate the energy, in ergs, of α particles of radium, which have energy 4.79 Mev. The nucleus of an atom of gold has the electric charge $79e$, in which e is the magnitude of the charge of the electron. The α particle has the charge $2e$. At what distance is the mutual potential energy of the α particle and the nucleus of an atom of gold (equal, in ergs, to the product of the two charges, in statcoulombs, divided by the distance between them, in centimeters) equal to the kinetic energy of the α particle? This radius may be taken as indicating how closely the α particle must approach the atom of gold in order to experience a large deflection. (Answer: 4.75×10^{-4} Å.)

3-12. Calculate the number of α particles that would be predicted to undergo very large deflection, as a result of approaching to within the distance 4.75×10^{-4} Å from a gold nucleus (as calculated in the preceding problem), when the α particles pass through a single layer of gold atoms. Assume the gold atoms in the layer to be in the triangular close-packed arrangement, with distance 2.88 Å between centers of adjacent atoms.

3-13. A beam of light impinges normally (perpendicularly) upon a ruled grating, with 10,000 rulings per inch. Calculate the angles between which the visible spectrum appears in the first order. Make the calculations for the wavelength 4,000 Å (violet) and 7,500 Å (red).

3-14. Explain, in terms of reinforcement of scattered waves, why there is reinforcement of the X-rays scattered by all of the atoms in a plane of atoms, if the incident beam and the diffracted beam lie in the same vertical plane (perpendicular to the plane of the atoms), and the two beams make the same angle with the plane of the atoms.

3-15. Assuming specular reflection from a plane of atoms (see preceding exercise), derive the Bragg equation for the diffraction of X-rays from a sequence of planes of atoms the distance d apart.

3-16. The distance between layers of atoms parallel to the cube face of a crystal of sodium chloride is 2.81 Å. Using the Bragg equation, calculate the first three angles of reflection of copper $K\alpha$ radiation (that is, of the $K\alpha$ X-ray line from an X-ray tube with a copper target). The wavelength of the $K\alpha$ line of copper is 1.54 Å.

Reference Books

R. F. Humphreys and R. Beringer, *First Principles of Atomic Physics*, Harper & Brothers, New York, **1950.**

H. E. White, *Classical and Modern Physics*, D. Van Nostrand Co., New York, **1950.**

Chapter 4

Elements, Elementary Substances, and Compounds

One of the most important parts of chemical theory is the division of substances into the two classes *elementary substances* and *compounds*. This division was achieved about a century and a half ago, principally through the efforts of the French chemist Lavoisier.

4–1. *The Chemical Elements*

Two Classes of Substances. *The kind of matter represented by a particular kind of atom is called an* **element.**

All pure substances can be divided into two classes: elementary substances, and compounds. *An* **elementary substance** *is a substance that consists of atoms of only one kind. A* **compound** *is a substance that consists of atoms of two or more different kinds.* These atoms of two or more different kinds must be present in a definite numerical ratio, since substances are usually defined as having a definite composition.

Thus an elementary substance is composed of one element. A compound is composed of two or more elements.

Hydrogen, oxygen, carbon, iron, copper, zinc, lead, tin, silver, gold, sulfur, phosphorus are common elements; ninety-eight different elements in all are known at the present time. Common salt, sugar, baking soda, and penicillin are well-known compounds. Common salt contains two kinds of atoms—atoms of sodium and atoms of chlorine. Sugar contains three kinds of atoms—atoms of carbon, hydrogen, and oxygen. Baking soda contains atoms of sodium, hydrogen, carbon, and oxygen; and penicillin contains atoms of carbon, hydrogen, oxygen, nitrogen, and sulfur. Several hundred thousand different chemical compounds are now known, and many new ones are made every year.

The Different Kinds of Atoms.   To avoid confusion, it is necessary for us to state exactly what is meant by *a particular kind of atom* in the above definition of an element. By this expression we mean *an atom whose nucleus has a given electric charge.* All nuclei have positive electric charges which are equal to or are integral multiples of the charge of the

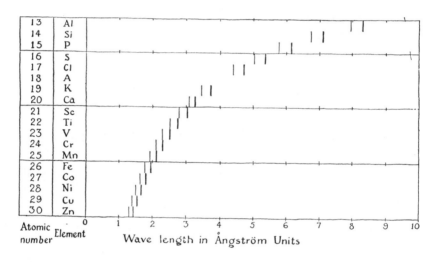

FIG. 4-1   *Diagram showing regular change of wavelength of X-ray emission lines for a series of elements.*

electron (with changed sign). The integer which expresses this relation is called the **atomic number.** It is usually given the symbol Z, the electric charge of a nucleus with atomic number Z being Ze, with the charge of the electron $-e$. Thus the simplest atom, that of hydrogen, has atomic number 1; that is, $Z = 1$ for the hydrogen atom, and the charge of its nucleus is $+e$.

An element is a kind of matter all of whose atoms have the same atomic number. This number can hence be referred to as the *atomic number of the element.*

The one-hundred and two elements that have so far been discovered or made by scientists represent all the atomic numbers from 1 to 102.

The Assignment of Atomic Numbers to the Elements.   Soon after the discovery of the electron as a constituent of matter it was recognized that elements might be assigned atomic numbers, but the way of doing this correctly was not known until 1913. In that year H. G. J. Moseley (1887–1915), a young English physicist working in Manchester, used various elements as targets in an X-ray tube, with the Bragg technique

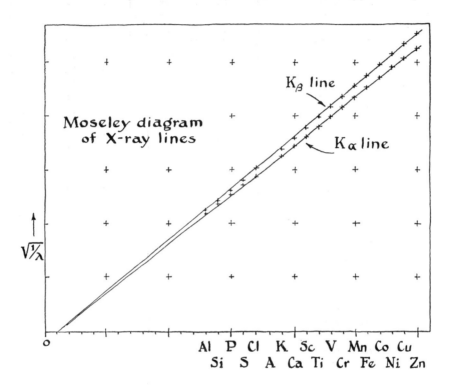

FIG. 4-2   *A graph of the reciprocal of the square root of the wavelengths of X-ray lines, for the Kα line and the Kβ line, of elements, plotted against the order of the elements in the periodic table. This graph, called the Moseley diagram, was used by Moseley in determining the atomic numbers of the elements.*

described in the preceding chapter (Fig. 3-22), and obtained the X-ray emission spectra of a number of the elements. His results are reproduced in Figure 4-1. He found that the reciprocals of the square roots of the wavelengths of the X-ray lines lie nearly on a straight line, when plotted against the order of the elements indicated by their atomic weights, as shown in Figure 4-2. From a diagram of this sort (now called a Moseley diagram) it is easy to assign atomic numbers to the elements.

TABLE 4-1   *The Names, Atomic Numbers, and Symbols of the Elements*

ATOMIC NUMBER	SYMBOL	ELEMENT	ATOMIC NUMBER	SYMBOL	ELEMENT	ATOMIC NUMBER	SYMBOL	ELEMENT
1	H	Hydrogen	35	Br	Bromine	69	Tm	Thulium
2	He	Helium	36	Kr	Krypton	70	Yb	Ytterbium
3	Li	Lithium	37	Rb	Rubidium	71	Lu	Lutetium*
4	Be	Beryllium	38	Sr	Strontium	72	Hf	Hafnium
5	B	Boron	39	Y	Yttrium	73	Ta	Tantalum
6	C	Carbon	40	Zr	Zirconium	74	W	Tungsten*
7	N	Nitrogen	41	Nb	Niobium*	75	Re	Rhenium
8	O	Oxygen	42	Mo	Molybdenum	76	Os	Osmium
9	F	Fluorine	43	Tc	Technetium*	77	Ir	Iridium
10	Ne	Neon	44	Ru	Ruthenium	78	Pt	Platinum
11	Na	Sodium	45	Rh	Rhodium	79	Au	Gold
12	Mg	Magnesium	46	Pd	Palladium	80	Hg	Mercury
13	Al	Aluminum	47	Ag	Silver	81	Tl	Thallium
14	Si	Silicon	48	Cd	Cadmium	82	Pb	Lead
15	P	Phosphorus	49	In	Indium	83	Bi	Bismuth
16	S	Sulfur	50	Sn	Tin	84	Po	Polonium
17	Cl	Chlorine	51	Sb	Antimony	85	At	Astatine*
18	Ar	Argon	52	Te	Tellurium	86	Rn	Radon
19	K	Potassium	53	I	Iodine	87	Fr	Francium*
20	Ca	Calcium	54	Xe	Xenon	88	Ra	Radium
21	Sc	Scandium	55	Cs	Cesium	89	Ac	Actinium
22	Ti	Titanium	56	Ba	Barium	90	Th	Thorium
23	V	Vanadium	57	La	Lanthanum	91	Pa	Protactinium
24	Cr	Chromium	58	Ce	Cerium	92	U	Uranium
25	Mn	Manganese	59	Pr	Praseodymium	93	Np	Neptunium*
26	Fe	Iron	60	Nd	Neodymium	94	Pu	Plutonium*
27	Co	Cobalt	61	Pm	Promethium*	95	Am	Americium*
28	Ni	Nickel	62	Sm	Samarium	96	Cm	Curium*
29	Cu	Copper	63	Eu	Europium	97	Bk	Berkelium*
30	Zn	Zinc	64	Gd	Gadolinium	98	Cf	Californium*
31	Ga	Gallium	65	Tb	Terbium	99	Es	Einsteinium
32	Ge	Germanium	66	Dy	Dysprosium	100	Fm	Fermium
33	As	Arsenic	67	Ho	Holmium	101	Md	Mendelevium
34	Se	Selenium	68	Er	Erbium	102	No	Nobelium

* Several decisions about the names of the elements were made at the 15th Meeting of the International Union of Pure and Applied Chemistry at Amsterdam in September 1949. The names and symbols given in the above table were accepted for the eight new elements discovered during World War II: technetium (43), promethium (61), astatine (85), francium (87), neptunium (93), plutonium (94), americium (95), and curium (96). It was further decided to use the name "wolfram" instead of "tungsten" for element 74, and the name "niobium" instead of "columbium" for element 41. The spelling "lutetium" rather than "lutecium" was accepted for element 71. At the next meeting of the International Union the two names "wolfram" and "tungsten" for element 74 were made optional. We shall use the name "tungsten."

Element 61, promethium, was made as an artificial radioactive isotope. The name "illinium" was formerly used for element 61, when it was thought to exist in nature.

The manufacture of element 97, berkelium, and element 98, californium, was announced early in 1950 by workers in the University of California at Berkeley.

It was also found that when a compound is used as the target in an X-ray tube the X-ray spectrum produced by the tube contains the lines characteristic of all of the elements present in the compound. The X-ray method can accordingly be used not only to determine the atomic number of an element, but also to find out whether a material contains atoms of only one element or atoms of two or more elements.

Although all the atoms of a given element have the same atomic number, they are usually not all exactly alike, but are of several different varieties, called the *isotopes* of the element. Isotopes are discussed in a later section of this chapter.

The Names and Symbols of the Elements.   The names of the elements are given in order of atomic number in Table 4-1. The *chemical symbols* of the elements, used as abbreviations for their names, are also given in the table. These symbols are usually the initial letters of the names, plus another letter when necessary. In some cases the initial letters of Latin names are used: Fe for iron (*ferrum*), Cu for copper (*cuprum*), Ag for silver (*argentum*), Au for gold (*aurum*), Hg for mercury (*hydrargyrum*). The system of chemical symbols was proposed by the great Swedish chemist Jons Jakob Berzelius (1779–1848) in 1811.

The elements are shown in a special arrangement, the *periodic table,* at the front of the book and in Table 5-1, and are also given in alphabetical order in Table 4-2, as well as in the order of their atomic numbers in Table 4-1.

A symbol is used to represent an atom of an element, as well as the element itself. The symbol I represents the element iodine, and also may be used to mean the elementary substance. However, I_2 is the customary formula for the elementary substance, because it is known that elementary iodine consists of diatomic molecules in the solid and liquid states as well as in the gaseous state (except at very high temperature).

The History of the Concept of Elements and of Chemical Symbols.   According to the Greek philosopher Aristotle (384–322 B.C.), there were four elements, earth, water, air, and fire. He presumably used these names to represent the solid, liquid, and gaseous states, and the state of incandescence or burning. Presumably the classification of wood as containing "earth" and "air" meant that heating wood transforms it into solid ash or charcoal and gaseous substances.

Aristotle's "elements" refer to states, rather than to kinds of matter. The Aristotelian concept of elements was thus very remote from the modern concept, and the two seem to have in common only a striving to find simplicity in nature. The modern concept of elements as simple forms of matter was first introduced by the English scientist Robert Boyle (1627–1691), in his book *The Skeptical Chymist*, published in 1662. The first successful application of Boyle's concept was made by the French chemist Antoine Laurent

Lavoisier (1743–1794), who gave an essentially correct table of thirty-three elements (including, however, heat and light!) in his book *Traité Elémentaire de Chimie* in 1789.

There is evidence that gold, iron, copper, silver, lead, and tin were known to man before 3000 B.C., and that arsenic, antimony, and mercury were discovered before 1500 B.C. In a manuscript written in Greek in the tenth or eleventh century and now kept in St. Mark's Library in Venice, the work of an Egyptian alchemist (the early chemists were called alchemists), perhaps of the second century A.D., is described. In this manuscript seven metals are identified with seven celestial bodies—gold with the sun, silver with the moon, lead with Saturn, iron with Mars, copper with Venus, tin with Mercury, and electrum (an alloy of gold and silver) with Jupiter. The signs conventionally used for these bodies were used for the corresponding metals. Other symbols were also used; thus the symbol for iron oxide was a complex symbol containing the symbol for iron.

The second-century alchemist whose work is described in the St. Mark's manuscript was endeavoring to make gold. The endeavor to make gold was continued by alchemists throughout the Middle Ages, together with studies dealing with industrial processes, especially metallurgical processes, and with the manufacture of drugs. In the course of the early work of the alchemists many important chemical discoveries were made.

During the Middle Ages an extensive system, in part secret, of symbols for chemical substances was developed. Toward the end of the eighteenth century chemists began to make use of initial letters of the names of elements and compounds, instead of the older symbols. Berzelius then systematized this procedure, and his scheme was soon adopted by all chemists.

4–2. *The Formulas of Compounds*

Compounds are represented by *formulas* made up of the symbols of the elements contained in the compound. For example, NaCl is the formula for sodium chloride, which consists of equal numbers of sodium and chlorine atoms. When the atoms of the different elements are not present in the compound in equal numbers, their ratios are indicated by the use of subscripts. Thus H_2O is the formula for water, each molecule of which contains two hydrogen atoms and one oxygen atom.

If the true molecular structure of a substance is known, it is proper to indicate it in the formula. Hydrogen peroxide is a compound of hydrogen and oxygen which differs from water in that two hydrogen atoms and two oxygen atoms are contained in its molecule. The formula for hydrogen peroxide is written H_2O_2, and not HO. Similarly, the formula for cyanuric triazide (Fig. 2-6) should be written C_3N_{12}, and not CN_4, because each molecule contains three carbon atoms and twelve nitrogen atoms.

More complex ways of arranging the symbols are often used, especially for organic compounds, in order to indicate how the atoms in the molecules are bonded to one another—that is, to show the details of the structure of the molecules. Acetic acid, the acid of vinegar, has the formula $C_2H_4O_2$. This formula is, however, often written $HC_2H_3O_2$, to indicate that one of the four hydrogen atoms is easily replaced by another atom; salts such as sodium acetate, $NaC_2H_3O_2$, can be made. Sometimes the formula of acetic acid is written CH_3COOH, to indicate that in the molecule there is a group CH_3 attached to a carbon atom C, to which are also attached an oxygen atom O and an OH group.

4–3. *Chemical Reactions*

The gas hydrogen consists of diatomic molecules, H_2. Oxygen also consists of diatomic molecules, O_2. If two flasks, one containing hydrogen and one containing oxygen, are connected together, the two gases mix

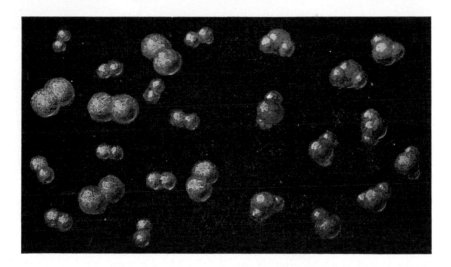

FIG. 4-3   *At the left there is represented a gas containing hydrogen molecules* (H_2) *and oxygen molecules* (O_2), *and at the right the same system after chemical reaction, leading to the formation of water molecules*, H_2O.

with each other quietly, to produce a gaseous mixture. If, however, a flame is brought into contact with the gaseous mixture a violent explosion occurs, and afterward the presence of water can be shown. This explosion is the result of the combination of hydrogen and oxygen to form a new substance, water, with the emission also of heat and light. The difference between a mixture of hydrogen and oxygen and the substance obtained by combination of hydrogen and oxygen in terms of molecular structure is shown in Figure 4-3.

The elementary substance sodium is at ordinary temperatures a soft, white metal. It consists of sodium atoms arranged in a regular structure (Fig. 4-4) similar to that described for copper, but not identical with it. The elementary substance chlorine is a greenish-yellow gas, consisting of diatomic molecules, Cl_2. Sodium metal will burn in chlorine gas, to give a new substance, which is sodium chloride (common salt), with properties greatly different from those of either of the two substances from which it is made. The sodium atoms in the sodium metal which

FIG. 4-4   *At the left there are represented chlorine gas molecules* (Cl_2) *and metallic sodium, and at the right the same system after chemical reaction, with the formation of common salt, sodium chloride.*

reacted and the chlorine atoms in the chlorine gas which reacted are present in the sodium chloride formed by the reaction, but rearranged and ordered in a new way.

This process of converting substances into other substances by the rearrangement of atoms is **chemical reaction.**   The substances which are destroyed* in a chemical reaction are called the **reactants,** and those which are produced are called the **products.**

Many examples of familiar chemical reactions might be mentioned. When gasoline burns, gasoline and oxygen of the air are the reactants, and carbon dioxide and water are the products (small amounts of other substances may also be produced). When an ordinary storage battery

---

* The *atoms* are not destroyed in such a chemical reaction; only their *arrangement* is destroyed.

is discharging, lead dioxide, lead, and sulfuric acid are the reactants, and lead sulfate and water are the products.

In the crystal of sodium chloride there are atoms of two different kinds, arranged in the regular pattern shown in Figure 4-4. The smaller atoms are those of sodium and the larger ones are those of chlorine.* The structure can be described in terms of a cubic unit, with four sodium atoms at 0, 0, 0; 0, 1/2, 1/2; 1/2, 0, 1/2; and 1/2, 1/2, 0; and four chlorine atoms at 1/2, 1/2, 1/2; 1/2, 0, 0; 0, 1/2, 0; and 0, 0, 1/2. The surface layers shown, which are the cube faces of the sodium chloride crystal, contain both kinds of atoms in equal numbers, when the unit is repeated a great number of times.

The numerical ratio of sodium and chlorine atoms in solid sodium chloride is fixed at 1 : 1 by the structure of the crystal, and that for sodium chloride gas is likewise fixed at 1 : 1 by the structure of the gas molecule. Similarly, the numerical ratio of hydrogen atoms and oxygen atoms in water is fixed at 2 : 1 by the structure of the water molecule. *It is the definite structure of crystals and molecules which causes substances in general to contain their component elements in definite atomic ratios.*

It is accordingly the definite structure of crystals and of molecules that is responsible for the experimental observations that led to the formulation of the *law of constant composition*, or *law of definite proportions*.

How to Balance the Equation for a Chemical Reaction.   The chemical reaction of the formation of water from hydrogen and oxygen can be represented by an equation:

$$2H_2 + O_2 \longrightarrow 2H_2O$$

On the left side of this equation we have the formula H_2 for hydrogen and the formula O_2 for oxygen, and on the right side the formula H_2O for water. We use the formulas to indicate relative numbers of atoms, as well as to describe the reactants and the products of the chemical reaction. It is accordingly necessary to introduce the coefficient 2 in front of the symbol for the hydrogen molecule and in front of the formula for water, in order to write the equation representing this chemical reaction correctly.

The process of introducing numerical coefficients before the formulas of the reactants and products until there are exactly the same number of atoms of each element on the left side of the equation as on the right side of the equation is called "balancing the equation."

---

* It will be pointed out later (Chap. 9) that the sodium chloride crystal may be better described as consisting of *ions* (electrically charged atoms): sodium ion, Na^+, and chloride ion, Cl^-.

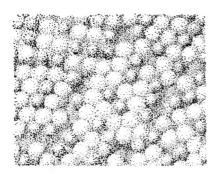

FIG. 4-5

An alloy of gold and copper. The alloy consists of small crystals, each crystal being made of gold atoms and copper atoms in an orderly array, but with the atoms of the two different kinds distributed essentially at random among the atomic positions.

It is a very good practice to check every chemical equation that you write, to be sure that it agrees with the "law of the conservation of atoms of every element."

The Atomic Structure of Materials Other than Pure Substances. In Figure 4-5 there is shown the atomic structure of the gold-copper alloy used in jewelry. This material consists of small crystal grains, held firmly together by the interatomic forces between them, each grain being composed of atoms in a regular arrangement, the cubic closest-packed arrangement described in Chapter 2 for metallic copper. However, the atoms of gold and the atoms of copper are not distributed in a regular way, but instead occupy the atomic positions in the crystalline arrangement largely at random, as shown in the figure. Because of the randomness of the distribution of gold atoms and copper atoms there is no requirement that the ratio of the number of gold atoms and copper atoms in a crystal of this solid solution have any particular value, and accordingly the composition of the alloy is not fixed by the structure of the crystal but is, instead, determined by the relative amounts of copper and gold that are melted together to make the alloy.

The structure of liquid and gaseous solutions is similar (see Fig. 4-3, representing a gaseous mixture of hydrogen and oxygen).

Other materials may consist of a mixture of grains each of which is a pure substance, or a mixture of grains or other phases which are themselves not pure substances but are solutions. In all of these cases the ratio of numbers of atoms of different kinds is not fixed by the structure of the material.

4–4. *The Difference in Chemical Properties of Elements and Compounds*

The Older Definition of an Element. It is only recently that methods (especially the study of the X-ray spectra produced by a substance) have become available for determining directly whether a substance contains atoms of only one kind or of two or more kinds. For two hundred years, since 1741, when M. V. Lomonosov (1711–1765), a great and imaginative Russian poet and chemist, published his new ideas about the nature of matter, and especially since 1789, when Lavoisier published such a clear discussion of the question as to convince nearly all of his fellow chemists, substances had undergone classification as elements or compounds on the basis of chemical reactions. Definite chemical evidence for the compound nature of a substance could be obtained; if it was lacking, the substance was presumed to be an element.

There are two chemical tests for the compound nature of a substance.

First: *If a substance can be decomposed* (that is, if it can be made to undergo reaction in which it alone is destroyed) *to form two or more product substances,* the original substance must be a compound.* For example, molten salt can be decomposed completely into sodium and chlorine by passing an electric current through it; hence it is a compound. Similarly, mercuric oxide, HgO, can be decomposed into mercury and oxygen simply by heating it; hence it is a compound.

The second chemical test for the compound nature of a substance is the following: *If two or more substances react to form a single product substance, that substance is a compound.* Thus sodium and chlorine, in the proper relative amounts, will react completely to form common salt; hence common salt is a compound.

It is interesting to note that until the new physical methods, especially the X-ray method, were developed, there was no way of rigorously proving a substance to be an element. In the early years of the science of chemistry a substance was accepted as an element so long as no reaction showing it to be a compound had been observed. At first some mistakes were made: lime (calcium oxide, CaO) was considered to be an element until the English chemist Sir Humphry Davy (1778–1829) reduced it to calcium metal in 1808; and uranium dioxide, UO_2, was accepted as an element from 1789 to 1841. However, by 1900 all but about a score of the elements which are now known had been recognized and correctly identified as elements.

This chemical method of classifying substances is interesting as an example of logical argument. A single experiment in which a substance is decomposed into two or more other substances or is alone formed from them proves that it is a compound; this conclusion is inescapable.

---

* Here it is assumed that the different products are essentially different, and do not contain the same atoms (as do oxygen and ozone, ice and water, rhombic sulfur and monoclinic sulfur; see Chapters 6 and 17).

The failure of such an experiment, however, does not prove that the substance is an element. It is, indeed, not possible to prove that a substance is an element by tests of this kind, no matter how many are made. It may be convenient to assume it to be an element, if there is no evidence to the contrary; but it should not be forgotten that the assumption is not necessarily true.

Radioactivity and the Transmutation of Elements. For centuries before the development of chemistry as a science, the alchemists strove to carry out the *transmutation of elements*, in particular to change mercury into gold with the aid of the "philosopher's stone." Then, as scientific chemistry developed and success in transmutation eluded the investigators, the opinion gained firm hold that the conversion of one element into another was impossible, and that atoms were immutable and indestructible. The definitions of element and elementary substance accepted during the nineteenth century were based upon this belief.

In 1896 there came the discovery of radioactivity by Henri Becquerel and the discovery of radium by Pierre and Marie Curie (Chap. 3). Soon thereafter it was recognized that radioactive changes involve the spontaneous conversion of atoms of one element into those of another. It then became necessary to change the definition of element; this was done by saying that one element could not be converted into another element by artificial means.

It has now become necessary to make another change in the definition. In 1919 Lord Rutherford and his collaborators at the Cavendish Laboratory in Cambridge, England, where active study of radioactive phenomena was under way, reported that they had succeeded in converting nitrogen atoms into oxygen atoms by bombarding nitrogen with high-speed alpha particles (helium nuclei), which are given off by radium. Since 1930 there has been great progress in this field of artificial radioactivity, which now is the most actively prosecuted research field in physics. Nearly every element has now been rendered radioactive and converted into other elements by bombardment with particles moving at high speed, and a great body of information about the properties of atomic nuclei is being gathered. As a result of this work it is now said that an element cannot be transmuted into another element by ordinary chemical methods. The discovery of these new phenomena might have led to confusion about the validity of the classification of substances as elementary substances and compounds were it not for the fact that our knowledge of the structure and properties of atoms has also increased rapidly in recent years. In this book we have not made use of any variant of the old definition, but have, at the beginning of this chapter, defined an element as the kind of matter represented by a particular kind of atom—namely, atoms with a particular atomic number.

4–5. *The Structure of the Hydrogen Atom and the Hydrogen Molecule*

The smallest and lightest nucleus is the **proton.** The proton carries one unit of positive charge, and with one electron, which carries one unit of negative charge, it forms a hydrogen atom. The proton is about as heavy as a hydrogen atom, since its mass is 1,836 times that of the electron. All but 1/1,837 of the mass of the hydrogen atom is due to the proton, the remainder being due to the electron.

Soon after the development of the concept of the nuclear atom, some idea was gained as to the way in which a proton and an electron are combined to form a **hydrogen atom.** In 1913 the Danish theoretical physicist Niels Bohr (born 1885) developed his orbital theory of the atom and explained with it the positions of the lines in the spectrum of hydrogen. A discussion of the Bohr theory will be given in Chapter 8. Because of the electrostatic attraction of the oppositely charged electron and proton, which corresponds to an inverse-square force similar to the gravitational force between the earth and the sun, the electron might be expected to revolve in an orbit about the much heavier proton in a way similar to that in which the earth revolves about the sun. Bohr suggested that the orbit of the electron in the normal hydrogen atom should be circular, with radius 0.530 Å (he calculated this radius from the frequencies of the lines in the spectrum of hydrogen, as discussed later in Chapter 8); this is a reasonable size for the atom, in comparison with the volume per atom of solid and liquid molecular hydrogen. The electron was calculated to be going around this orbit with the constant speed 2.18×10^8 cm/sec, which is a little less than 1% of the speed of light.

This picture is now thought to be nearly but not quite right. The electron does not move in a definite orbit, but rather in a somewhat random way, so that it is sometimes very close to the nucleus and sometimes rather far away. Moreover, it moves mainly toward the nucleus or away from it, and it travels in all directions about the nucleus instead of staying in one plane. Although it does not stay just 0.530 Å from the nucleus, this is its most probable distance. Actually, by moving around rapidly, it effectively occupies all the space within a radius of about 1 Å of the nucleus, and so gives the hydrogen atom an effective diameter of about 2 Å, as indicated in Figure 4-6. The speed of the electron is not constant; but its average* is the Bohr value 2.18×10^8 cm/sec.

Thus we can describe the free hydrogen atom as having a heavy nucleus at the center of a sphere defined by the space filled by the fast-moving electron in its motion about the nucleus. This sphere is about 1 Å in radius.

The electronic structure of heavier atoms will be discussed in later chapters (Chaps. 8 to 10).

---

* This statement refers to the root-mean-square average, which is the square root of the arithmetic average of the values of the square of the speed.

The **hydrogen molecule** has the structure indicated in Figure 4-6. The two nuclei are firmly held at a distance of about 0.74 Å apart; they oscillate relatively to each other with an amplitude of a few hundredths of an Ångström at room temperature, and with a somewhat larger amplitude at higher temperatures. The two electrons move about very rapidly in the region of the two nuclei, their time-average distribution being indicated by the shading in the figure. It can be seen that the motion of the two electrons is concentrated into the small region just between the two nuclei. We might draw an analogy with two steel balls (the nuclei) vulcanized into a tough piece of rubber (the electrons)

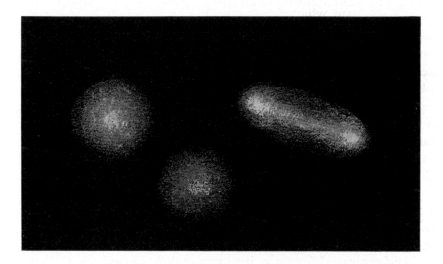

FIG. 4-6   *The electron distribution in two hydrogen atoms (at the left) and a hydrogen molecule (at the right). The two nuclei in the molecule are 0.74 Å apart.*

which surrounds them and binds them together. The electrons may be considered to be moving rapidly, as in the hydrogen atom; but their orbits in the hydrogen molecule include both nuclei. *It is the two electrons held jointly by the two nuclei that constitute the chemical bond between the two hydrogen atoms in the hydrogen molecule.*

4–6. *Isotopes and the Structure of the Nucleus*

In the discussion of the masses of atoms use is made of a very small unit of mass, about 1.660×10^{-24} g. This *atomic mass unit* is defined in the following section.

The mass of the hydrogen atom made from a proton and an electron is 1.0078 atomic mass units. Ordinary hydrogen consists almost entirely of these atoms, but in addition it contains about 1 part in 5,000 of heavier hydrogen atoms. The mass of a *heavy hydrogen atom* or *deuterium atom* is 2.0143 atomic mass units. The nucleus of the deuterium atom is called the *deuteron*. This nucleus has the same charge as the proton, but has about twice the mass of the proton.

Nuclear physicists have observed a particle, the **neutron,*** that has nearly the same mass (about 1.0090 units) as the proton, but is electrically neutral. The deuteron may be described as a nucleus with atomic number 1 and atomic mass 2, which is composed of one proton and one neutron.

The deuterium atom and the light hydrogen atom are the stable isotopes of hydrogen.† It is now thought that all nuclei are built from protons and neutrons, and that *the* **isotopes** *of an element are atoms whose nuclei contain the same number of protons (equal to the atomic number of the element) but different numbers of neutrons.*§

Since the masses of the proton and the neutron are each very near to one atomic mass unit, the integer nearest to the mass of an atom (the *mass number*) is the sum of the number of protons and the number of neutrons in its nucleus.

Hence the **atomic number** *is the number of protons in the nucleus and the* **mass number** *is the number of protons plus the number of neutrons in the nucleus.*

The word *nucleon* is now used to refer to any constituent of the nucleus, either proton or neutron. The mass number of a nucleus is therefore the number of its nucleons.

All known elements have two or more isotopes. In some cases (beryllium, fluorine, sodium, aluminum, etc.) only one isotope occurs naturally, the others being unstable. The maximum number of stable isotopes of any element is 10, possessed by tin.

The chemical properties of all the isotopes of an element are essentially the same. These properties are determined in the main by the atomic number of the nucleus, and not by its mass.

When it is desired to distinguish between isotopes, the approximate

---

* The discovery of the neutron is discussed in Chapter 33.

† An unstable isotope of hydrogen, with mass 3, can be made. Its nucleus consists of one proton and two neutrons. This isotope, which is called *tritium*, is radioactive; its nucleus (the *triton*) decomposes spontaneously.

§ In recent years the word *nuclide* has been used to denote a nuclear species. Nuclides with the same electric charge are isotopes.

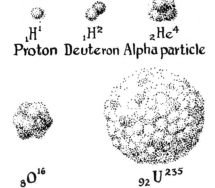

$_1H^1$ $_1H^2$ $_2He^4$
Proton Deuteron Alpha particle

$_8O^{16}$ $_{92}U^{235}$

FIG. 4-7

Hypothetical structures of some atomic nuclei. We do not yet know just how these nuclei are constructed out of elementary particles, but it is known that nuclei are approximately 10^{-12} cm in diameter, and are, accordingly, very small even compared with atoms.

atomic mass is given as a superscript to the symbol: thus H^1 is light hydrogen and H^2 is heavy hydrogen (deuterium). Oxygen consists mainly of O^{16}, with much smaller amounts of O^{17} and O^{18}. When equations for nuclear reactions are written, the atomic number is also often placed as a left subscript, thus: $_1H^1$, $_8O^{17}$.

The detailed structure of nuclei is not known. Hypothetical diagrams of nuclear structure are shown in Figure 4-7.

4–7. *The Atomic Weights of the Elements*

All of the weight relations in chemical reactions depend upon the weights of the atoms of the elements. These weights (or masses), called *atomic weights*, are very important in the study and practice of chemistry.

The Meaning of Atomic Weights.   The fact that many elements consist of a mixture of stable isotopes complicates the discussion of atomic weights.

The chemical atomic weights of elements are the average relative weights (masses) of atoms of the elements, the average being for the usual isotopic composition of each element.

The base of atomic weights is the element oxygen, with its atomic weight arbitrarily taken as 16.00000.

Oxygen was chosen as the base by general agreement of chemists for the reason that it combines with most of the elements, whose atomic weights can then be evaluated by the experimental determination of the weight relations involved in the oxygen compounds. The choice of 16.00000 is due to the facts that with this standard an astonishingly large number of elements have nearly integral atomic weights (carbon, C, 12.010; nitrogen, N, 14.008; sodium, Na, 22.997; etc.) and that none has atomic weight less than one unit (hydrogen, H, 1.0080; helium, He, 4.003; lithium, Li, 6.940). The *atomic mass unit* mentioned in the preceding section, equal to 1.660×10^{-24} g, is defined as exactly 1/16 of the mass of an average oxygen atom. It is called the *dalton*, with symbol d.

Ordinary hydrogen contains about one deuterium atom (mass 2.0143 d) to every 5,000 light hydrogen atoms (mass 1.0078 d). We see that the extra mass, approximately 1 d, of one deuterium atom to every 5,000 light atoms would cause an increase in the average mass of 1/5,000, or 0.0002 d, and that accordingly the average mass, or chemical atomic weight, of ordinary hydrogen is $1.0078 + 0.0002 = 1.0080$.

The chemical atomic weight defined in this way, as the average for the usual isotopic composition of the element, would not be very useful unless the isotopic composition were constant. It is, in fact, found that the isotopic composition of most elements (the proportion of different isotopes) is the same for all natural occurrences of the element, to within the precision of experimental determination of atomic weights. An exception is lead, which is found in certain minerals (where it was formed by radioactive decomposition of thorium) with atomic weight 205.96 and in others (where it was formed by radioactive decomposition of uranium) with atomic weight 208.0. The atomic weight of ordinary lead, from the common mineral galena, PbS, is 207.21. Since galena is the source of almost all the lead that is used, this is the value given in the table of atomic weights.

Another exception is sulfur; it has been found that the isotopic composition of sulfur from different sources varies somewhat, so that the atomic weight is given as 32.066 ± 0.003, the indicated uncertainty corresponding to the observed variation.

The History of the Atomic Weight Scale.   John Dalton, who in 1803 made the old atomic hypothesis into a useful scientific theory by developing the concept of atomic weights, chose as the base the value 1 for hydrogen. Later Berzelius used 100 for oxygen as the base; this was not accepted, and the Belgian chemist J. S. Stas (1813–1891), in his careful work from 1850 on, used the value 16 for oxygen, considering this equivalent to 1 for hydrogen. By 1905 it was recognized that the ratio of atomic weights for hydrogen and oxygen, as determined by measuring experimentally the ratio of weights of hydrogen and of oxygen that combine with one another to form water, differs from 1 : 16 by nearly 1%. Most of the experimental values of atomic-weight ratios had been determined relative to oxygen, for which 16 had been used: by accepting 16.00000 for oxygen as base, no change in the earlier tables was needed, except for hydrogen. It is good that this decision was reached, since only a few years ago (1938) the accepted ratio of atomic weights H : O was revised from 1.0078 : 16 to 1.0080 : 16 as the result of more precise experimental work. If hydrogen were being used as the basis of atomic

TABLE 4-2   *International Atomic Weights*

NAME	SYM-BOL	ATOMIC NUMBER	ATOMIC WEIGHT*	NAME	SYM-BOL	ATOMIC NUMBER	ATOMIC WEIGHT*
Actinium	Ac	89	227	Iodine	I	53	126.91
Aluminum	Al	13	26.98	Iridium	Ir	77	192.2
Americium	Am	95	[243]	Iron	Fe	26	55.85
Antimony	Sb	51	121.76	Krypton	Kr	36	83.80
Argon	Ar	18	39.944	Lanthanum	La	57	138.92
Arsenic	As	33	74.91	Lead	Pb	82	207.21
Astatine	At	85	[210]	Lithium	Li	3	6.940
Barium	Ba	56	137.36	Lutetium	Lu	71	174.99
Berkelium	Bk	97	[249]	Magnesium	Mg	12	24.32
Beryllium	Be	4	9.013	Manganese	Mn	25	54.94
Bismuth	Bi	83	209.00	Mendelevium	Md	101	[256]
Boron	B	5	10.82	Mercury	Hg	80	200.61
Bromine	Br	35	79.916	Molybdenum	Mo	42	95.95
Cadmium	Cd	48	112.41	Neodymium	Nd	60	144.27
Calcium	Ca	20	40.08	Neon	Ne	10	20.183
Californium	Cf	98	[249]	Neptunium	Np	93	[237]
Carbon	C	6	12.011	Nickel	Ni	28	58.71
Cerium	Ce	58	140.13	Niobium	Nb	41	92.91
Cesium	Cs	55	132.91	Nitrogen	N	7	14.008
Chlorine	Cl	17	35.457	Nobelium	No	102	253
Chromium	Cr	24	52.01	Osmium	Os	76	190.2
Cobalt	Co	27	58.94	Oxygen	O	8	16.0000
Columbium: see Niobium †				Palladium	Pd	46	106.4
Copper	Cu	29	63.54	Phosphorus	P	15	30.975
Curium	Cm	96	[245]	Platinum	Pt	78	195.09
Dysprosium	Dy	66	162.51	Plutonium	Pu	94	[242]
Einsteinium	Es	99	[254]	Polonium	Po	84	210
Erbium	Er	68	167.27	Potassium	K	19	39.100
Europium	Eu	63	152.0	Praseodymium	Pr	59	140.92
Fermium	Fm	100	[255]	Promethium	Pm	61	[145]
Fluorine	F	9	19.00	Protactinium	Pa	91	231
Francium	Fr	87	[223]	Radium	Ra	88	226.05
Gadolinium	Gd	64	157.26	Radon	Rn	86	222
Gallium	Ga	31	69.72	Rhenium	Re	75	186.22
Germanium	Ge	32	72.60	Rhodium	Rh	45	102.91
Gold	Au	79	197.0	Rubidium	Rb	37	85.48
Hafnium	Hf	72	178.50	Ruthenium	Ru	44	101.1
Helium	He	2	4.003	Samarium	Sm	62	150.35
Holmium	Ho	67	164.94	Scandium	Sc	21	44.96
Hydrogen	H	1	1.0080	Selenium	Se	34	78.96
Indium	In	49	114.82	Silicon	Si	14	28.09

TABLE 4-2 (*continued*)

NAME	SYM-BOL	ATOMIC NUMBER	ATOMIC WEIGHT*	NAME	SYM-BOL	ATOMIC NUMBER	ATOMIC WEIGHT*
Silver	Ag	47	107.880	Tin	Sn	50	118.70
Sodium	Na	11	22.991	Titanium	Ti	22	47.90
Strontium	Sr	38	87.63	Tungsten	W	74	183.86
Sulfur	S	16	32.066§	Uranium	U	92	238.07
Tantalum	Ta	73	180.95	Vanadium	V	23	50.95
Technetium	Tc	43	[99]	Xenon	Xe	54	131.30
Tellurium	Te	52	127.61	Ytterbium	Yb	70	173.04
Terbium	Tb	65	158.93	Yttrium	Y	39	88.92
Thallium	Tl	81	204.39	Zinc	Zn	30	65.38
Thorium	Th	90	232.05	Zirconium	Zr	40	91.22
Thulium	Tm	69	168.94				

* A value given in brackets is the mass number of the most stable known isotope.

† The English name of this element has been changed recently, by action of the International Union of Pure and Applied Chemistry; see the footnote to Table 4-1.

§ Because of natural variations in the relative abundance of the isotopes of sulfur the atomic weight of this element has a range of ±0.003.

weights, this change would have required changes of almost all atomic weights by 0.02%, instead of only that of hydrogen, because most atomic weights had been determined by comparison with oxygen.

Prout's Hypothesis.   An imaginative physician and chemist, William Prout of Edinburgh and London, in 1816 suggested that all atoms are built of hydrogen, with all atomic weights multiples of the atomic weight of hydrogen. At that time the available rough values of atomic weights showed in general no disagreement with this hypothesis, and Prout rejected as erroneous those few which did. As more accurate values were obtained, it became clear that Prout's hypothesis was contradicted by the facts; chlorine, for example, has the atomic weight 35.457, and boron has the atomic weight 10.82.

Prout's hypothesis was revived by the discovery of isotopes; thus chlorine consists of two natural isotopes Cl^{35} and Cl^{37}, and boron of two isotopes B^{10} and B^{11}, in each case with nearly integral atomic weights and present in such relative amounts as to give the chemical atomic weight. It is now seen that Prout's idea contained an element of truth.

The Einstein Equation and the Masses of Nuclei.   A striking property of nuclei is that *the mass of a heavy nucleus is slightly less than the sum of the masses of the protons and neutrons that combine to form it*. The reason for this is that during the combination of the nucleons a large amount of energy is released in the form of radiation. In consequence of the Einstein equation between mass and energy, $E = mc^2$ (Equation 1-1), this radiation leads to a corresponding decrease in mass of the material products by about 1%.

4–8. *The Values of the Atomic Weights*

The 1955 atomic weights of the elements, as announced by the Commission on Atomic Weights of the International Union of Pure and

Applied Chemistry,* are given in Table 4-2. The use of these values in carrying out chemical calculations is discussed in Chapter 7.

4–9. *Avogadro's Number*

The meaning of atomic weights is closely related to a very interesting number, called *Avogadro's number*. This number is named after the Italian physicist Amedeo Avogadro (1776–1856), who made a very important contribution to the laws describing the behavior of gases (Chap. 14).

The atomic mass unit was defined as 1/16 of the mass of an average oxygen atom. It is evident that if we knew how many oxygen atoms there are in 16.00000 g of oxygen we could evaluate this unit.

The amount of oxygen weighing 16.00000 g is called a *gram-atom* of oxygen. **Avogadro's number N is defined as the number of oxygen atoms in a gram-atom of oxygen.** It is, of course, also the number of atoms of any element in a gram-atom of that element, defined as the amount of the element with weight in grams equal to the atomic weight.

The value of Avogadro's number was known with an accuracy of about 30% in 1875; one way in which it had been estimated, by Lord Rayleigh (1842–1919), was through the consideration of the blue color of the sky.† Avogadro's number was then determined to within about 1% by R. A. Millikan, through his oil-drop experiment, in 1909, and then more accurately (to within 0.1%) in the period between 1930 and 1940 through the work of several experimental physicists. It is §

$$N = 0.6024 \times 10^{24}$$

Avogadro's number is a useful number in chemistry just because atoms are so small. Chemical reactions occur between atoms and molecules,

* Report on the Committee on Atomic Weights of the American Chemical Society and the Commission on Atomic Weights of the International Union of Pure and Applied Chemistry, *Journal of the American Chemical Society*, **78**, 3235 (1956).

† A brief description of this subject is given in the article "Light" in the *Encyclopaedia Britannica* (14th Edition).

§ It may be pointed out that Avogadro's number as written above, 0.6024×10^{24}, differs from the usual convention about writing large numbers, according to which one integer is introduced before the decimal point. With this convention Avogadro's number would be written as 6.024×10^{23}. However, there is great convenience in learning Avogadro's number as 0.6024×10^{24}. An important use of this number involves the conversion of the volume of a gram-atom of an element into the volume per atom. The first volume is expressed in cm^3, and the second in Å^3. The relation between cm^3 and Å^3 involves the factor 10^{24}: 1 cm^3 = 10^{24} Å^3. Accordingly, in case that Avogadro's number has been taken as 0.6024×10^{24}, there is no trouble whatever in deciding on the position of the decimal point, whereas if 6.024×10^{23} is used it is always necessary to decide whether the decimal point should be moved one place to the right or one place to the left.

and the weights of chemical substances which react with one another are, accordingly, determined by the weights of the atoms and molecules. We may say that when the reaction

$$2H_2 + O_2 \longrightarrow 2H_2O$$

occurs, 4×1.0080 d of hydrogen combines with 2×16.0000 d of oxygen to form 2×18.0160 d of water; but the dalton (the atomic-weight unit) is so small that we feel the need to consider a certain very large number of atoms and molecules, whose weight would be of the order of a few grams or pounds. It would, of course, now be possible to decide to take, say, 1.000×10^{24} as the standard number; but during the period of development of chemistry the number called Avogadro's number was accepted as the standard number for this use.

The Determination of Avogadro's Number. Before 1909 rough values of Avogadro's number had been estimated in various ways. Reference has been made to the determination of this number by Lord Rayleigh through the consideration of the blue color of the sky. In Chapter 11 another determination is described, by Jean Perrin, who was able to measure the motion of microscopic particles of a resin suspended in water, and to interpret his observations in such a way as to evaluate Avogadro's number.

The way in which Avogadro's number is calculated from the value of the charge of the electron will be discussed in Chapter 13.

The X-ray method of determining Avogadro's number, which is the most accurate method now known, is the following. The wavelengths of spectral lines in visible light can be determined by measuring the positions of the lines in a spectrum of light produced by a ruled grating (Chap. 8). The wavelengths of X-ray lines are very small, and hence their angles of diffraction by an ordinary ruled grating are very small. During the past fifteen years the angles have, however, been measured accurately, giving accurate values of the wavelengths of the X-ray lines. Accurate measurement of the Bragg angle of diffraction of these X-ray lines by a crystal then permits the determination of the size of the unit of structure of the crystal. The product of the volume of this unit by the density of the crystal is the total mass of the atoms in the unit. By comparing this with the sum of the atomic weights of the atoms the value of Avogadro's number is found.

Reference on methods of determining Avogadro's number: G. P. Harnwell and J. J. Livingood, *Experimental Atomic Physics*, McGraw-Hill Book Co., New York, **1933,** Secs. 1-3 to 3-11.

Exercises

4-1. Define atomic number. Define elementary substance in terms of atoms.

4-2. Describe a chemical experiment which would prove that water is not an element. Can you think of a chemical proof that iron is an element?

4-3. When sugar is strongly heated, water vapor is driven off and a black residue, carbon, is left. Does this experiment prove rigorously that sugar is not an element?

4-4. What are the reasons for the final choice of O = 16.00000 as the base of atomic weights, instead of O = 100.00 or H = 1.0000, both of which were used in the past?

4-5. The atomic weight of aluminum is 26.97. With use of Avogadro's number, calculate the weight in grams of one aluminum atom.

4-6. Define chemical symbol and chemical formula. Explain the purpose of each letter or number in a formula.

4-7. Using your own words, give a definition of chemical reaction.

4-8. Balance the following equations of chemical reactions:

$$Fe + O_2 \longrightarrow Fe_2O_3$$
$$H_2 + N_2 \longrightarrow NH_3$$
$$HgO \longrightarrow Hg + O_2$$
$$CO + O_2 \longrightarrow CO_2$$
$$C_{12}H_{22}O_{11} + O_2 \longrightarrow CO_2 + H_2O$$
$$NaCl + H_2SO_4 \longrightarrow NaHSO_4 + HCl$$
$$KClO_3 \longrightarrow KCl + O_2$$
$$H_2 + O_2 \longrightarrow H_2O$$
$$Zn + H_2SO_4 \longrightarrow ZnSO_4 + H_2$$

4-9. How was the definition of element affected by the discovery of radioactivity in 1896?

4-10. What aspects of the flow of electricity are expressed by the words "coulomb," "ampere," "volt," "watt"?

4-11. Is each of the following materials an element, a compound, or a mixture: naphthalene, sea water, copper, brass, iron rust, egg yolk?

4-12. Exactly what is meant by the statement that the atomic weight of tin is 118.70?

4-13. The atomic weight of light hydrogen (with a proton as its nucleus) is 1.0078. With use of Avogadro's number calculate the weight in grams of a single hydrogen atom. The electron is stated in the text to have a mass only 1/1,846 of that of the hydrogen atom. What is the weight of the electron in grams?

4-14. What are the atomic number and the approximate atomic weight of the element each of whose nuclei contains 79 protons and 118 neutrons? By reference to Tables 4-1 and 4-2 identify this element.

4-15. How many protons and how many neutrons are in the nucleus of the isotope of chlorine with mass 35? of the isotope of chlorine with mass 37? of the isotope of plutonium with mass 239?

4-16. When 1 ampere of direct current is flowing through the filament of an incandescent bulb, how many electrons pass a given point on the filament each minute? Note that the value of the charge of the electron in coulombs is given in the text.

4-17. A molecule of sulfur dioxide consists of a sulfur atom with two oxygen atoms attached to it. Using Avogadro's number and the atomic weight of sulfur, calculate the weight of the sulfur atom, in grams. Also calculate the weight of the two oxygen atoms. What is the weight of the sulfur dioxide molecule, in grams? What percentage of this weight is the weight of the sulfur atom? What would you say about the composition by weight of sulfur dioxide, in terms of sulfur and oxygen?

4-18. By counting the flashes of light produced by alpha particles when they strike a screen coated with zinc sulfide, Sir William Ramsay and Professor Frederick Soddy found that 1 g of radium gives off 13.8×10^{10} alpha particles (nuclei of helium atoms) per second. They also measured the amount of helium gas produced in this way, finding 0.158 cm^3 (at 0° C and 1 atm) per year per gram of radium. At this temperature and pressure 1 1 of helium weighs 0.179 g. Avogadro's number of helium atoms weighs 4.003 g (the atomic weight of helium is 4.003). From these data calculate an approximate value of Avogadro's number.

4-19. An atom of Pd^{101} loses a proton. What are its new atomic number and atomic weight?

4-20. How many neutrons and how many protons may be considered to be present in the nuclide $_{45}Rh^{103}$?

Reference Book

F. Sherwood Taylor, *The Alchemists*, Henry Schuman, New York, **1948.**

Chapter 5

The Chemical
Elements and the
Periodic Law: Part 1

The one-hundred and two known elements include some with which everyone is familiar and many which are rare. Some of the elementary substances are metals, and some are non-metals; at room temperature some are gases, some are liquids, and some are solids.* They show extremely great variety in their chemical properties and in the nature of the compounds which they form. In consequence, the study of chemistry is not simple or easy; to obtain a reasonably broad knowledge of general chemistry it is necessary to learn a great many facts.

The facts of chemistry cannot be completely coordinated by a unifying theory. Nevertheless, the development of chemical theories has now proceeded far enough to be of great aid to the student, who can simplify his task of learning about the properties and reactions of substances by correlating the empirical information with theories, such as the periodic law.

5–1. *The Periodic Law*

One of the most valuable parts of chemical theory is the *periodic law*. In its modern form this law states simply that *the properties of the chemical*

---

* The elements which are gases at standard conditions (0° C and 1 atm) are hydrogen, helium, nitrogen, oxygen, fluorine, neon, chlorine, argon, krypton, xenon, and radon. The only elements which are liquids at standard conditions are bromine and mercury.

elements are not arbitrary, but depend upon the structure of the atom and vary with the atomic number in a systematic way. The important point is that this dependence involves a crude periodicity which shows itself in the periodic recurrence of characteristic properties.

For example, the elements with atomic numbers 2, 10, 18, 36, 54, and 86 are all chemically inert gases. Similarly, the elements with atomic numbers one greater—namely, 3, 11, 19, 37, 55, and 87—are all light metals that are very reactive chemically. These six metals, lithium (3), sodium (11), potassium (19), rubidium (37), cesium (55), and francium (87), all react with chlorine to form colorless salts that crystallize in cubes and show a cubic cleavage. The chemical formulas of these salts are similar: LiCl, NaCl, KCl, RbCl, CsCl, and FrCl. The composition and properties of other compounds of these six metals are correspondingly similar, and different from those of other elements.*

The comparison of the observed chemical and physical properties of elements and their compounds with the atomic numbers of the elements accordingly indicates that, after the first two elements, hydrogen and helium, there are the *first short period* of eight elements (from helium, atomic number 2, to neon, 10), the *second short period* of eight elements (to argon, 18), the *first long period* of eighteen elements (to krypton, 36), the *second long period* of eighteen elements (to xenon, 54), and then the *very long period* of 32 elements (to radon, 86). If enough new elements of very large atomic number are made in the future, it may well be found that there is another very long period of 32 elements, ending in another inert gas, with atomic number 118.

5–2. *The Periodic System*

The periodicity of properties of the elements with increasing atomic number may be effectively shown by arranging the elements in a table, called the **periodic table** or **periodic system** of the elements. Many different forms of the periodic system have been proposed and used. We shall base the discussion of the elements and their properties in this book on the simple system shown as Table 5-1 (it is also reproduced inside the front cover of the book).

The Development of the Periodic System. The differentiation of chemical substances into two groups, elements and compounds, was achieved at the end of the eighteenth century. A long time was required for the recognition of the fact that the

---

* Actually very little is yet known about the sixth of these elements, francium, which has been only recently discovered; but there is little doubt that francium is closely similar to the other alkali metals in its properties.

THE PERIODIC SYSTEM OF THE ELEMENTS

Group O	
H 1	He 2

O	I	II	III	IV	V	VI	VII
He 2							
Ne 10	Li 3	Be 4	B 5	C 6	N 7	O 8	F 9
Ar 18	Na 11	Mg 12	Al 13	Si 14	P 15	S 16	Cl 17

O	I	II	III	IVa	Va	VIa	VIIa	VIII			Ib	IIb	IIIb	IV	V	VI	VII	O
Ar 18	K 19	Ca 20	Sc 21	Ti 22	V 23	Cr 24	Mn 25	Fe 26	Co 27	Ni 28	Cu 29	Zn 30	Ga 31	Ge 32	As 33	Se 34	Br 35	Kr 36
Kr 36	Rb 37	Sr 38	Y 39	Zr 40	Nb 41	Mo 42	Tc 43	Ru 44	Rh 45	Pd 46	Ag 47	Cd 48	In 49	Sn 50	Sb 51	Te 52	I 53	Xe 54
Xe 54	Cs 55	Ba 56	La 57 *	Hf 72	Ta 73	W 74	Re 75	Os 76	Ir 77	Pt 78	Au 79	Hg 80	Tl 81	Pb 82	Bi 83	Po 84	At 85	Rn 86
Rn 86	Fr 87	Ra 88	Ac 89 ◆	Th 90	Pa 91	U 92	Np 93	Pu 94										

* Lanthanons

Ce 58	Pr 59	Nd 60	Pm 61	Sm 62	Eu 63	Gd 64	Tb 65	Dy 66	Ho 67	Er 68	Tm 69	Yb 70	Lu 71

◆ Actinons

Th 90	Pa 91	U 92	Np 93	Pu 94	Am 95	Cm 96	Bk 97	Cf 98	Es 99	Fm 100	Md 101	No 102

elements can be classified in the way now described by the periodic law. The first step was taken in 1817, when the German chemist J. W. Döbereiner (1780–1849) showed that the combining weight of strontium lies midway between the combining weights of the two related elements calcium and barium. Some years later he recognized the existence of other "triads" of similar elements (chlorine, bromine, and iodine; lithium, sodium, and potassium).

Other chemists then showed that the elements could be classified into groups consisting of more than three similar elements. Fluorine was added to the triad chlorine, bromine, and iodine, and magnesium to the triad calcium, strontium, barium. Oxygen, sulfur, selenium, and tellurium had been classed as one family, and nitrogen, phosphorus, arsenic, antimony, and bismuth as another family of elements by 1854.

In 1862 the French chemist A. E. B. de Chancourtois arranged the elements in the order of atomic weights on a helical curve in space, with corresponding points on the successive turns of the helix differing by 16 in atomic weight. He noticed that elements with similar properties appeared near corresponding points, and suggested that "the properties of elements are the properties of numbers." The English chemist J. A. R. Newlands in 1863 proposed a system of classification of the elements in order of atomic weights, in which the elements were divided into seven groups of seven elements each. He termed his relation the *law of octaves*, by analogy with the seven intervals of the musical scale. His proposal was ridiculed, however, and he did not develop it further.

The final and most important step in the development of the periodic table was taken in 1869, when the Russian chemist Dmitri I. Mendelyeev (1834–1907) made a thorough study of the relation between the atomic weights of the elements and their physical and chemical properties, with especial attention to valence (Chaps. 9 and 10). Mendelyeev proposed a periodic table containing seventeen columns, resembling in a general way the periodic Table 5-1 with the noble gases missing (the noble gases had not yet been discovered at that time; see Sec. 5-4). In 1871 Mendelyeev revised this table, and placed a number of elements in different positions, corresponding to revised values of their atomic weights. At the same time, 1871, both he and the German chemist Lothar Meyer (1830–1895), who was working independently, proposed a table with eight columns, obtained by splitting each of the long periods into a period of seven elements, an eighth group containing the three central elements (such as Fe, Co, Ni), and a second period of seven elements. The first and second periods of seven were later distinguished by use of the letters a and b attached to the group symbols, which were the Roman numerals. This nomenclature of the periods (Ia, IIa, IIIa, IVa, Va, VIa, VIIa, VIII, Ib, IIb, IIIb, IVb, Vb, VIb, VIIb) appears, slightly revised, in the present periodic table even when it is written in the extended form.

The periodic table in the second form proposed by Mendelyeev (the "short-period" form) remained very popular for many years, and is only now being replaced by the "long-period" form, used in this book.

The "zero" group was added to the periodic table after the discovery of the noble gases helium, neon, argon, etc., by Lord Rayleigh and Sir William Ramsay in 1894 and the following years. A form of the periodic table closely similar to that shown in Table 5-1 was devised in 1895 by the Danish chemist Julius Thomsen (1826–1909). After the discovery of the electron by the English physicist Sir J. J. Thomson and the development of the theory of the nuclear atom by Ernest Rutherford, it was suggested in 1911 by the Dutch physicist A. van den Broek that the nuclear charge of an element, which we now call its atomic number, might be equal to the ordinal number of the element in the periodic system. The young British physicist H. G. J. Moseley then determined the correct values of the atomic numbers of many elements by the study of their X-ray spectra, as described in Chapter 4. In 1922 Niels Bohr interpreted the periodic table in terms of the electronic structure of atoms in a way similar to that given in Chapters 9 and 10 of this book.

The periodic law was accepted immediately after its proposal by Mendelyeev because of his success in making predictions with its use which were afterward verified by experiment. In 1871 Mendelyeev found that by changing seventeen elements from the positions indicated by the atomic weights which had been accepted for them into new positions, their properties could be better correlated with the properties of the other elements. He pointed out that this change indicated the existence of small errors in the previously accepted atomic weights of several of the elements, and large errors for several others, to the compounds of which incorrect formulas had been assigned. Further experimental work verified that Mendelyeev's revisions were correct.

Most of the elements occur in the periodic table in the order of increasing atomic weight. However, there still remain four pairs of elements in the inverted order of atomic weight; argon and potassium (the atomic numbers of argon and potassium are 18 and 19, respectively, whereas their atomic weights are 39.944 and 39.094), cobalt and nickel, tellurium and iodine, and protactinium and thorium. The nature of the isotopes of these elements is such that the atomic weight of the naturally occurring mixture of isotopes is greater for the element of lower atomic number in each of these pairs than for the element of higher atomic number; thus argon consists almost entirely (99.6%) of the isotope with mass number 40 (18 protons, 22 neutrons), whereas potassium consists largely (93.4%) of the isotope with mass number 39 (19 protons, 20 neutrons). This inversion of the order in the periodic system, as indicated by the chemical properties of the elements, from that of atomic weight caused much concern before the atomic numbers of the elements were discovered, but has now been recognized as having little significance.

A very striking application of the periodic law was made by Mendelyeev. He was able to predict the existence of six elements which had not yet been discovered, corresponding to vacant places in his table. He named these elements eka-boron, eka-aluminum, eka-silicon, eka-manganese, dvi-manganese, and eka-tantalum (Sanskrit: *eka*, first; *dvi*, second). Three of these elements were soon discovered (they were named scandium, gallium, and germanium by their discoverers), and it was found that their properties and the properties of their compounds are very close to those predicted by Mendelyeev for eka-boron, eka-aluminum, and eka-silicon, respectively. Since then the elements technetium, rhenium, and polonium have been discovered or made artificially (in the case of technetium; see Chap. 33), and have been found to have properties similar to those predicted for eka-manganese, dvi-manganese, and eka-tantalum. A comparison of the properties predicted by Mendelyeev for eka-silicon and those determined experimentally for germanium is given below:

Mendelyeev's predictions for eka-silicon (1871):	*Observed properties of germanium (discovered in 1886):*
Atomic weight about 72.	Atomic weight 72.60.
Es will be obtained from EsO_2 or K_2EsF_6 by reduction with sodium.	Ge is obtained by reaction of K_2GeF_6 and sodium.

Mendelyeev's predictions—(Contd.):	*Observed properties*—(Contd.):
Es will be a dark-gray metal, with high melting point and density 5.5.	Ge is gray, with melting point 958° C and density 5.36 g/cm^3.
Es will be slightly attacked by acids, such as hydrochloric acid, HCl, and will resist alkalies, such as sodium hydroxide, NaOH.	Ge is not dissolved by HCl or NaOH, but is dissolved by concentrated nitric acid, HNO_3.
On heating Es, it will form the oxide EsO_2, with high melting point and density 4.7.	Ge reacts with oxygen to give GeO_2, m.p. 1,100° C, density 4.70 g/cm^3.
A hydrated EsO_2 soluble in acid and easily reprecipitated is expected.	$Ge(OH)_4$ dissolves in dilute acid and is reprecipitated on dilution or addition of base.
The sulfide, EsS_2, will be insoluble in water but soluble in ammonium sulfide.	GeS_2 is insoluble in water and dilute acids, but readily soluble in ammonium sulfide.
$EsCl_4$ will be a volatile liquid, with boiling point a little under 100°, and density 1.9.	$GeCl_4$ is a volatile liquid, with b.p. 83° C and density 1.88 g/cm^3.

After helium and argon had been discovered the existence of neon, krypton, xenon, and radon was clearly indicated by the periodic law, and the search for these elements in air led to the discovery of the first three of them; radon was then discovered during the investigation of the properties of radium and other radioactive substances. While studying the relation between atomic structure and the periodic law Niels Bohr pointed out that element 72 would be expected to be similar in its properties to zirconium. G. von Hevesy and D. Coster were led by this observation to examine ores of zirconium and to discover the missing element, which they named hafnium.

5–3. *Description of the Periodic Table*

The horizontal rows of the periodic table are called *periods:* they consist of a very short period (containing hydrogen and helium, atomic numbers 1 and 2), two short periods of 8 elements each, two long periods of 18 elements each, a very long period of 32 elements, and an incomplete period.

The properties of elements change in a systematic way through a period: this is indicated in Figure 5-1, which shows the atomic volume (the atomic weight divided by the density—that is, the volume in cm^3 of 1 g-atom of the element) of the elements at 0° C and 1 atm, as a function of the atomic number.

The vertical columns of the periodic table, with connections between the short and long periods as shown, are the *groups* of chemical elements. Elements in the same group may be called *congeners;* these elements have closely related physical and chemical properties.

The groups I, II, and III are considered to include the elements in corresponding places at the left side of all the periods, and V, VI, and VII the elements at the right side. The central elements of the long periods, called the *transition elements*, have properties differing from those of the elements of the short periods; these elements are discussed

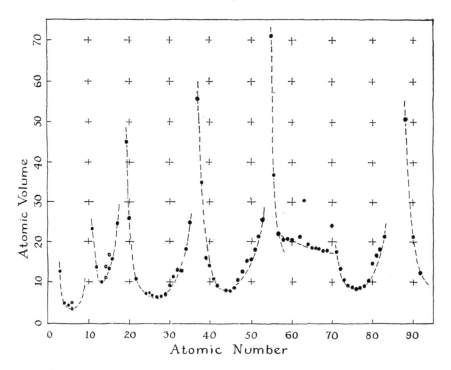

FIG. 5-1   *Curve of gram-atomic volume (the volume containing 1 gram-atom) of the elements as function of atomic number, illustrating periodicity of properties.*

separately, as groups IVa, Va, VIa, VIIa, VIII (which, for historical reasons, includes three elements in each long period), Ib, IIb, IIIb, and IVb.

The very long period is compressed into the table by removing fourteen elements, the *rare-earth metals*, from $Z = 58$ to $Z = 71$, and representing them separately below.

The elements on the left side and in the center of the periodic table are **metals.** These elementary substances have the characteristic properties called *metallic properties*—high electric and thermal conductivity, metallic luster, the ability to be hammered into sheets (malleability) and to be drawn into wire (ductility). The elements on the right side of the periodic table are **non-metals,** the elementary substances not having metallic properties.

The metallic properties are most pronounced for elements in the lower left-hand corner of the periodic table, and the non-metallic properties are most pronounced for elements in the upper right-hand corner. The transition from metals to non-metals is marked by the elements with intermediate properties, which occupy a diagonal region extending from a point near the upper center to the lower right-hand corner. These elements, which are called **metalloids,** include boron, silicon, germanium, arsenic, antimony, tellurium, and polonium.

5–4. *The Noble Gases*

Helium, the element with atomic number 2, is a gas with the very striking chemical property that it forms no ordinary chemical compounds, but exists only in the free state (there are a few exceptional compounds in which atoms of helium are trapped within a crystalline lattice). Its atoms will not even combine with one another to form diatomic molecules, but remain as separate atoms in the gas, which is hence described as containing monatomic molecules. Because of its property of remaining aloof from other elements it is called a "noble" gas.

This lack of chemical reactivity is the result of an extraordinary stability of the electronic structure of the helium atom. This stability is characteristic of the presence of two electrons close to an atomic nucleus.

The other elements of the zero group of the periodic table—neon, argon, krypton, xenon, and radon—are also chemically inert. The failure of these inert elements to form chemical compounds is similarly due to the great stability of their electronic structures. These extremely stable electronic structures are formed by 2, 10, 18, 36, 54, and 86 electrons about a nucleus.

These six gases are called the *noble gases* or *rare gases* or *inert gases*. Their names, except *radon*, are from Greek roots: *helios*, sun; *neos*, new; *argos*, inert; *kryptos*, hidden; *xenos*, stranger. Radon is named after radium, from which it is formed by radioactive decomposition. The properties of the noble gases are given in Table 5-2.

Helium.   Helium is present in very small quantities in the atmosphere. Its presence in the sun is shown by the occurrence of its spectral lines in sunlight. These lines were observed in 1868, long before the element was discovered on earth, and the lines were ascribed to a new element, which was named helium by Sir Norman Lockyer (1836–1920).*

TABLE 5-2   *Properties of the Noble Gases*

	SYMBOL	ATOMIC NUMBER	ATOMIC WEIGHT	MELTING POINT	BOILING POINT
Helium	He	2	4.003	−272.2° C*	−268.9° C
Neon	Ne	10	20.183	−248.67°	−245.9°
Argon	Ar	18	39.944	−189.2°	−185.7°
Krypton	Kr	36	83.80	−157°	−152.9°
Xenon	Xe	54	131.30	−112°	−107.1°
Radon	Rn	86	222	−71°	−61.8°

* At 26 atm pressure. At smaller pressures helium remains liquid at still lower temperatures.

Helium occurs in some uranium minerals, from which it can be liberated by heating. It is also present in natural gas from some wells, especially in Texas and Canada; this is the principal source of the element.

Helium is used for filling balloons and dirigibles and for mixing with oxygen (in place of the nitrogen of the air) for breathing by divers, in order to avoid the "bends," which are caused by gas bubbles formed by release of the nitrogen that had dissolved in the blood under increased pressure.

Neon.   The second noble gas, neon, occurs in the atmosphere to the extent of 0.002%. It is obtained, along with the other noble gases (except helium), by the fractional distillation of liquid air.

When an electrical discharge is passed through a tube containing neon gas at low pressure, the atoms of neon are caused to emit their characteristic spectral lines. This produces a brilliant red light, used in advertising signs (neon signs). Other colors are obtained by the use of helium, argon, and mercury, sometimes in mixtures with neon or with one another.

---

* The ending "ium," which is otherwise used only for metallic elements, is due to Lockyer's incorrect surmise that the new element was a metal. "Helion" would be a better name.

Argon.   Argon composes about 1% of the atmosphere. It is used in incandescent light bulbs to permit the filament to be heated to a higher temperature, and thus to produce a whiter light, than would be practical in a vacuum. The argon decreases the rate at which the metallic filament evaporates, by keeping vaporized metal atoms from diffusing away from the filament.

Krypton, Xenon, and Radon.   Krypton and xenon, which occur in very small quantities in the air, have not found any significant use. Radon, which is produced steadily by radium, is used in the treatment of cancer. It has been found that the rays given off by radioactive substances are effective in controlling this disease. A convenient way of administering this radiation is to pump the radon that has been produced by a sample of radium into a small gold tube, which is then placed in proximity to the tissues to be treated.

The Discovery of the Noble Gases.   The story of the discovery of argon provides an interesting illustration of the importance of attention to minor discrepancies in scientific investigations.

For over a hundred years it was thought that atmospheric air consisted, aside from small variable amounts of water vapor and carbon dioxide, solely of oxygen (21% by volume) and nitrogen (79%). In 1785 Henry Cavendish investigated the composition of the atmosphere. He mixed oxygen with air, and then passed an electric spark through the mixture, to form oxides of nitrogen, which were dissolved in an alkaline solution in contact with the gas. The sparking was continued until there was no further decrease in volume, and the oxygen was then removed from the residual gas by treatment with a sulfide solution. He found that after this treatment only a small bubble of air remained unabsorbed, not more than 1/120 of the original air. Although Cavendish did not commit himself on the point, it seems to have been assumed by chemists that if the sparking had been continued for a longer time there would have been no residue, and Cavendish's experiment was accordingly interpreted as showing that only oxygen and nitrogen were present in the atmosphere.

In 1894 Lord Rayleigh began an investigation involving the careful determination of the densities of the gases hydrogen, oxygen, and nitrogen. To prepare nitrogen he mixed dried air with an excess of ammonia, NH_3, and passed the mixture over red-hot copper. Under these conditions the oxygen reacts with ammonia, according to the equation

$$4NH_3 + 3O_2 \longrightarrow 6H_2O + 2N_2$$

The excess ammonia was then removed by bubbling the gas through sulfuric acid. The remaining gas, after drying, should have been pure nitrogen, derived in part from the ammonia and in part from air. The density of this gas was determined. Another sample of nitrogen was made simply by passing air over red-hot copper, which removed the oxygen by combining with it to form copper oxide:

$$O_2 + 2Cu \longrightarrow 2CuO$$

When the density of this gas was determined it was found to be about 0.1% greater than that from the sample of ammonia and air. In order to investigate this discrepancy, a third sample of nitrogen was made, by use of a mixture of ammonia and pure oxygen. It was found that this sample of nitrogen had a density 0.5% less than that of the second sample. Further investigations showed that nitrogen prepared entirely from air had a density 0.5% greater than nitrogen prepared completely from ammonia or in any other chemical way, as by mixing solutions of ammonium chloride, NH_4Cl, and sodium nitrite, $NaNO_2$:

$$NH_4Cl + NaNO_2 \longrightarrow N_2 + 2H_2O + NaCl$$

Nitrogen obtained from air was found to have density 1.2572 g/l at 0° C and 1 atm, whereas nitrogen made by chemical methods had a density 1.2505 g/l. Rayleigh and Sir William Ramsay then repeated Cavendish's experiments, and showed by spectroscopic analysis that the residual gas was indeed not nitrogen but a new element. They then searched for the other stable noble gases and discovered them.

5–5. *Hydrogen*

Hydrogen, the first element in the periodic table, is unique; it has no congeners. It is a very widely distributed element; there are more compounds of hydrogen known than of any other element, carbon being a close second.

Properties of Hydrogen.   Free hydrogen, H_2, is a colorless, odorless, and tasteless gas. It is the lightest of all gases, its density being about 1/14 that of air. Its melting point ($-259°$ C or 14° K) and boiling point ($-252.7°$ C) are very low, only those of helium being lower. Liquid hydrogen, with density 0.070 g/cm³, is, as might be expected, the lightest of all liquids. Crystalline hydrogen, with density 0.088 g/cm³, is also the lightest of all crystalline substances. Hydrogen is very slightly soluble in water: 1 liter of water at 0° C dissolves only 21.5 ml of hydrogen gas under 1 atm pressure. The solubility decreases with increasing temperature, and increases with increase in the pressure of the gas.

The Preparation of Hydrogen.   In the laboratory hydrogen may be made by the reaction of an acid such as sulfuric acid, H_2SO_4, with a metal such as zinc. The equation for the reaction is

$$H_2SO_4 + Zn \longrightarrow ZnSO_4 + H_2 \uparrow$$

The vertical arrow placed beside the formula of hydrogen in this equation is used to indicate that hydrogen is a gas, which escapes from the region of reaction.

Hydrogen can also be prepared by the reaction of metals with water or steam. Sodium and its congeners react very vigorously with water, so vigorously as to generate enough heat to ignite the liberated hydrogen. An alloy of lead and sodium, which reacts less vigorously, is sometimes used for the preparation of hydrogen. The equation for the reaction of sodium with water is the following:

$$2Na + 2H_2O \longrightarrow 2NaOH + H_2 \uparrow$$

The substance NaOH produced in this way is called *sodium hydroxide.*
    Much of the hydrogen that is used in industry, especially for the hydrogenation of vegetable oils and whale oil to convert them into solid fats, is produced by the reaction of iron with steam. The steam from a boiler is passed over iron filings heated to a temperature of about 600° C. The reaction that occurs is

$$3Fe + 4H_2O \longrightarrow Fe_3O_4 + 4H_2 \uparrow$$

After a mass of iron has been used in this way for some time it is largely converted into iron oxide, Fe_3O_4. The iron can then be regenerated by passing carbon monoxide, CO, over the heated oxide:

$$Fe_3O_4 + 4CO \longrightarrow 3Fe + 4CO_2 \uparrow$$

The carbon monoxide is changed by this reaction into CO_2, carbon dioxide. In this way the iron can be used over and over again.
    Hydrogen can also be made by the reaction of a *metal hydride* (a compound of a metal and hydrogen) with water. Thus calcium hydride, CaH_2, produces hydrogen according to the following reaction:

$$CaH_2 + 2H_2O \longrightarrow Ca(OH)_2 + 2H_2 \uparrow$$

The greatest yield (that is, the greatest ratio of weight of hydrogen produced to weight of reacting material) is obtained by the use of the hydride of the lightest metal, lithium:

$$LiH + H_2O \longrightarrow LiOH + H_2 \uparrow$$

    Hydrogen (together with oxygen) can also be made by the electrolysis of water. Pure water hardly conducts an electric current at all, but it becomes a good conductor if a salt or an acid or a base is dissolved in it. When two electrodes are introduced into such a solution and a suitable potential difference of electricity is applied, hydrogen is liberated at one electrode (the cathode) and oxygen at the other electrode (the anode). The theory of this phenomenon will be discussed in Chapter 8. The over-all reaction is represented by the equation

$$2H_2O \longrightarrow 2H_2 \uparrow + O_2 \uparrow$$

Thus two molecules of hydrogen are formed for each molecule of oxygen. It is interesting to note (see Fig. 5-2) that the volume of hydrogen produced by the passage of a given amount of current is twice as great as the volume of oxygen produced. This fact is related to the fact that in the above equation two molecules of hydrogen are shown as being produced for every molecule of oxygen. After many experiments with chemical reactions in which gases are involved were carried out, it was recognized about a hundred years ago that equal volumes of different gases contain the same number of molecules. This statement, together with the quantitative expression of the fact that gases expand in volume when they are heated and contract in volume when they are subjected to increased pressure, constitutes the *gas laws*, which will be treated in Chapter 14.

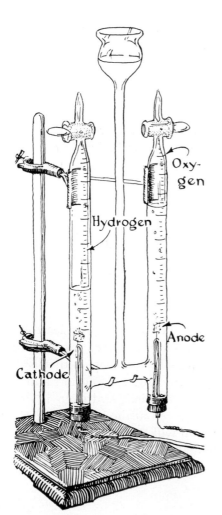

FIG. 5-2

Apparatus for the electrolysis of water.

A large part of the hydrogen used industrially is made by the electrolysis of water.

History of the Discovery of Hydrogen.   It was observed early in the sixteenth century that a combustible gas is formed when sulfuric acid acts upon iron filings. Robert Boyle, of Oxford, noticed that hydrogen would not burn in the rarefied atmosphere produced by his air pump. Henry Cavendish in 1781 showed that water is produced when hydrogen combines with oxygen. He did not recognize that the hydrogen had originally been produced from water or acid, but thought that it had come from the metal that reacted with the acid. Cavendish's name for hydrogen was "inflammable air." Lavoisier named the element hydrogen (water-former, from Greek *hydor*, water, and *genon*, to form).

5–6. *Oxygen*

Occurrence of Oxygen.   Oxygen is the most abundant element in the earth's crust. It constitutes by weight 89% of water, 23% of air (21% by volume), and nearly 50% of the common minerals* (silicates).

TABLE 5-3   *Composition of the Atmosphere*

SUBSTANCE	VOLUME PERCENT IN DRY AIR	SUBSTANCE	VOLUME PERCENT IN DRY AIR
Nitrogen	78.03	Neon	0.0018
Oxygen	20.99	Helium	0.0005
Argon	0.93	Krypton	0.0001
Carbon dioxide	0.03	Ozone	0.00006
Hydrogen	0.01	Xenon	0.000009

The average composition of the atmosphere is given in Table 5-3. The estimated composition of the outer crust of the earth is shown in Table 5-4 and Figure 5-3.

The Discovery of Oxygen.   Joseph Priestley (1733–1804), an English chemist and minister (he moved to the United States in 1794), announced in 1774 the discovery of a gas with the power of supporting combustion better than air. He had prepared the gas by heating some red mercuric oxide which was confined in a cylinder over mercury.

* A *mineral* is any chemical element, compound, or other homogeneous material (such as a liquid solution or a crystalline solution) occurring naturally as a product of inorganic processes. Most minerals are solids. Water and mercury are examples of liquid minerals, and air and helium (from rocks or helium wells) are examples of gaseous minerals. Amalgam (mercury containing dissolved silver and gold) is an example of a solution occurring as a mineral. *Rocks* are simple minerals (*limestone* consists of the mineral calcite, $CaCO_3$) or mixtures of minerals (*granite* is a mixture of three minerals, quartz, feldspar, and mica).

TABLE 5-4   *The Estimated Composition by Weight of the Earth's Crust*

Oxygen	46.5%	Sodium	3 %
Silicon	28	Potassium	2.5
Aluminum	8	Magnesium	2.2
Iron	5	Titanium	0.5
Calcium	3.5	Hydrogen	0.2

K. W. Scheele (1742–1786) of Sweden seems to have prepared and investigated oxygen before 1773, but an account of his work was not published until 1777.

Red mercuric oxide, HgO, is made by heating mercuric nitrate, $Hg(NO_3)_2$, which itself is made by the action of nitric acid (HNO_3) on mercury. Priestley found that when mercuric oxide is heated to a high temperature it decomposes with the liberation of oxygen:

$$2HgO \longrightarrow 2Hg + O_2 \uparrow$$

In order to obtain the oxygen he introduced mercuric oxide into the top of a closed tube which had been filled with mercury, its open lower end being under the surface of a bath of mercury. He then heated the mercuric oxide by use of a burning glass (a large glass lens), and in this way collected the oxygen over mercury. He found that substances burned in the gas more vigorously than in air. In 1775 Lavoisier reported his work on the nature of combustion and the oxidation of metals, and advanced his new theory of combustion. He showed that 1/5 of the volume of air is removed by phos-

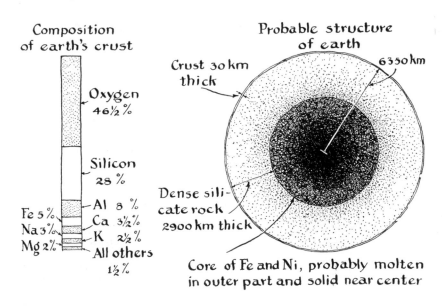

FIG. 5-3   *The composition of the earth's crust, and the probable structure of the earth (as induced mainly from the study of records of earthquake waves that have passed through the earth).*

phorus or by mercury (when heated for a long time), and that by strongly heating the mercuric oxide formed in this way a gas with volume equal to the volume lost from the air could be recovered. He showed that this gas supported combustion vigor-ously, and could support life on inspiration. Lavoisier named the new gas oxygen (Greek, *oxys*, acid, and *genon*, to form) because he thought, mistakenly, that it was a constituent of all acids.

Preparation and Properties.   Ordinary oxygen consists of diatomic molecules, O_2. It is a colorless, odorless gas, which is slightly soluble in water—1 liter of water at $0°$ C dissolves 48.9 ml of oxygen gas at 1 atm pressure. Oxygen condenses to a pale blue liquid at its boiling point, $-183.0°$ C, and on further cooling freezes, at $-218.4°$ C, to a pale blue crystalline solid. The solid, liquid, and gas are all paramag-netic.* This property of paramagnetism is rare, except for the transition metals and their metallic salts; most other substances are diamagnetic.

Oxygen may be easily prepared in the laboratory by heating potas-sium chlorate, $KClO_3$:

$$2KClO_3 \longrightarrow 2KCl + 3O_2 \uparrow$$

The reaction proceeds readily at a temperature just above the melting point of potassium chlorate if a small amount of manganese dioxide, MnO_2, is mixed with it. Although the manganese dioxide increases the rate of evolution of oxygen from the potassium chlorate, it itself is not changed. *A substance with this property of accelerating a chemical re-action without itself undergoing significant change is called a* **catalyst,** *and is said to catalyze the reaction.*

Oxygen is made commercially mainly by the fractional distillation of liquid air. Nitrogen is more volatile than oxygen, and tends to evap-orate first from liquid air. By properly controlling the conditions of the evaporation nearly pure oxygen can be obtained. The oxygen is stored and shipped in steel cylinders, at pressures of 100 atm or more. Some oxygen is also made commercially, together with hydrogen, by the electrolysis of water.

Oxygen forms compounds with all the elements except the inert gases. The compounds formed are called **oxides.** Examples are hydro-

---

* Paramagnetism and diamagnetism are defined in the footnote of Sec. 3-3. The para-magnetism of liquid oxygen can be demonstrated by dipping a strong permanent magnet into liquid oxygen. Part of the liquid will cling to the magnet, and can be lifted out of the container.

There has recently been invented an instrument for the determination of the amount of oxygen in a gas by measurement of the magnetic susceptibility of the gas. Oxygen is the only common gas that is strongly magnetic, and the magnetic susceptibility of a gas mixture is determined nearly entirely by the amount of oxygen in it.

gen oxide, H_2O (water); sodium oxide, Na_2O; magnesium oxide, MgO; aluminum oxide, Al_2O_3; zinc oxide, ZnO; sulfur dioxide, SO_2; arsenic trioxide, As_4O_6. Most of the elementary substances combine so vigorously with oxygen that they will burn, either spontaneously (phosphorus) or after ignition (sulfur, hydrogen, sodium, magnesium, iron, etc.). A few, such as copper and mercury, form oxides only slowly, even when heated; and others, such as iridium, cannot be made to react directly with oxygen, although their oxides can be prepared by indirect methods.

Many compounds of oxygen are discussed throughout this book.

5–7. *Acids, Bases, and Salts*

The alchemists observed that many different substances when dissolved in water give solutions with certain properties in common, such as acidic taste and the property of reacting with metals such as zinc with liberation of hydrogen. These substances were classed as *acids*. It is now known that the acidic properties of the solutions are due to the presence of *hydrogen ion*, H^+, in concentration greater than in pure water.

The usage of the word "acid" is variable. For many purposes it is convenient to say that *an* **acid** *is a hydrogen-containing substance that dissociates on solution in water to produce hydrogen ion.* Examples of acids, in addition to those given earlier in this chapter, are

> hydrobromic acid, HBr (hydrogen bromide)
> hydrosulfuric acid, H_2S (hydrogen sulfide)
> nitric acid, HNO_3
> perchloric acid, $HClO_4$
> chloric acid, $HClO_3$
> carbonic acid, H_2CO_3

In recent years the word "acid" has been used by chemists in much more general ways. These are discussed briefly in a later chapter of this book (Chap. 21). These extensions of the concept of acidity are interesting, but for most purposes it is satisfactory to adhere to the older usage described above.

A **base** *is a substance containing the hydroxide ion, OH^-, or the hydroxyl group, OH, which can dissociate in aqueous solution as the hydroxide ion, OH^-.* Basic solutions have a characteristic brackish taste.

Hydroxides of metals are compounds of metals with the *hydroxyl group*, OH. The hydroxides of the metals are bases. The hydroxides LiOH, NaOH, KOH, RbOH, and CsOH are called *alkalies;* and

$Be(OH)_2$, $Mg(OH)_2$, $Ca(OH)_2$, $Sr(OH)_2$, and $Ba(OH)_2$ are called *alkaline earths*. A basic solution is also called an *alkaline solution*.

Acids and basis combine to form compounds which are called **salts.** Thus the reaction of sodium hydroxide and sulfuric acid produces the salt sodium sulfate, Na_2SO_4, and water:

$$2NaOH + H_2SO_4 \longrightarrow Na_2SO_4 + 2H_2O$$

Similarly, the reaction of calcium hydroxide and phosphoric acid produces water and calcium phosphate, $Ca_3(PO_4)_2$:

$$3Ca(OH)_2 + 2H_3PO_4 \longrightarrow Ca_3(PO_4)_2 + 6H_2O$$

Hydrogen Ion (Hydronium Ion) and Hydroxide Ion.   The hydrogen ion, H^+, has a very simple structure: it consists of a bare proton, without the electron that is attached to it in a hydrogen atom. The hydrogen ion has a positive electric charge of one unit. The bare proton, H^+, does not exist in appreciable concentration in aqueous solutions, but instead exists attached to a water molecule, forming the *hydronium ion*, H_3O^+.

Because of the additional complexity introduced into chemical equations by use of H_3O^+ in place of H^+, it is customary for the sake of convenience to write equations for reactions of acids in aqueous solution with use of the symbol H^+. It is to be understood that this is a shorthand device, and that the molecular species present is the hydronium ion, H_3O^+.

The hydroxide ion, which is present in basic solutions, carries a negative charge: its formula is OH^-.

Nomenclature of Acids, Bases, and Salts.   Acids with one, two, and three replaceable hydrogen atoms are called *monoprotic*, *diprotic*, and *triprotic acids*, respectively, and bases with one, two, and three replaceable hydroxyl groups are called *monohydroxic*, *dihydroxic*, and *trihydroxic bases*. Salts, such as Na_2SO_4, which result from complete neutralization of an acid by a base are called *normal salts;* those containing more acid are called *acid salts*, and those containing more base *basic salts*.

The ways of naming salts are illustrated by the following examples; older names which are now not approved are given in parentheses:

Na_2SO_4:   sodium sulfate, normal sodium sulfate
$NaHSO_4$:   sodium hydrogen sulfate; sodium acid sulfate; (sodium bisulfate)

Na_3PO_4:   normal sodium phosphate; trisodium phosphate; sodium phosphate, tribasic; sodium phosphate, tertiary

Na_2HPO_4:   disodium monohydrogen phosphate; sodium monohydrogen phosphate; sodium phosphate, dibasic; sodium phosphate, binary or secondary

NaH_2PO_4:   sodium dihydrogen phosphate; sodium phosphate, monobasic; sodium phosphate, primary

$Ca(H_2PO_4)_2$:   calcium dihydrogen phosphate; calcium phosphate, monobasic; calcium phosphate, primary

$CaHPO_4$:   calcium monohydrogen phosphate; calcium phosphate, dibasic; calcium phosphate, secondary

Note that the prefixes and adjectives give the relative numbers of equivalents (rather than atoms) of metal and hydrogen, an equivalent of a metal being the amount that takes the place of one atom of hydrogen.

Indicators.   Acids and bases have the property of causing many organic substances to change color. Thus if lemon juice is added to a cup of tea, the tea becomes lighter in color; a dark-brown substance in the tea is converted into a light-yellow substance. That this change is reversible may be shown by adding an alkaline substance, such as common baking soda (sodium hydrogen carbonate, $NaHCO_3$) to the tea; this will restore the original dark color. A substance that has this property of changing color when acid or base is added to it is called an *indicator*.

A very common indicator is *litmus*, a dye obtained from certain lichens. Litmus assumes a red color in acidic solution and a blue color in basic solution. A useful way of testing the acidity or basicity of a solution is by use of paper in which litmus has been absorbed, called *litmus paper*. A solution which gives litmus paper a color intermediate between blue and red is called a *neutral solution*. Such a solution contains hydrogen ions and hydroxide ions in equal (extremely small) amounts.

Acidic Oxides and Basic Oxides.   An oxide such as sulfur trioxide, SO_3, or phosphorus pentoxide, P_2O_5, which does not contain hydrogen but which with water forms an acid, is called an *acidic oxide* or *acid anhydride*. The equations for the reactions of formation of the corresponding acids from these oxides are the following:

$$SO_3 + H_2O \longrightarrow H_2SO_4$$
$$P_2O_5 + 3H_2O \longrightarrow 2H_3PO_4$$

The oxides of most of the non-metallic elements are acidic oxides.

An oxide which with water forms a base is called a *basic oxide*. The oxides of the metals are basic oxides. Thus sodium oxide, Na_2O, reacts with water to form a base, sodium hydroxide:

$$Na_2O + H_2O \longrightarrow 2NaOH$$

Acidic oxides and basic oxides may combine directly with one another to form salts:

$$Na_2O + SO_3 \longrightarrow Na_2SO_4$$
$$3CaO + P_2O_5 \longrightarrow Ca_3(PO_4)_2$$

5–8. *Ozone*

Ozone is a blue gas which has a characteristic odor (its name is from the Greek *ozein*, to smell) and is a stronger oxidizing agent than ordinary oxygen. It is formed when an electric spark or a silent electric discharge is passed through oxygen.

Although its properties are different from those of ordinary oxygen, ozone is not a compound, but is elementary oxygen in a different form— a form with three atoms in the molecule (O_3) instead of two, as in ordinary oxygen (Fig. 5-4).

The existence of an elementary substance in two forms is called **allotropy** (Greek *allotropia*, variety, from *allos*, other, and *tropos*, direction). Ordinary oxygen and ozone are the *allotropes* of oxygen. Allotropy is shown by many elements; it is due either to the existence of two or more kinds of molecules (containing different numbers of atoms) or to the existence of two or more different crystalline forms; that is, of different arrangements of the atoms or molecules in a crystalline array.

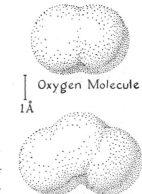

Oxygen Molecule

$1\overset{\circ}{A}$

FIG. 5-4

Molecules of oxygen and ozone. This drawing, like most of the drawings of atoms and molecules in this book, is made with linear magnification about 60.000.000.

Ozone Molecule

Ozone contains more energy than oxygen: the heat evolved when 48 g of ozone decomposes to oxygen is 32,400 cal,* and that amount of energy must have been given to the ozone molecule by the electric discharge when the ozone was formed. Because of its greater energy content, ozone is more reactive than oxygen. It converts mercury and silver into oxides, and it readily frees iodine from potassium iodide, whereas oxygen does not cause these reactions at room temperature.

Like some other oxidizing agents (such as chlorine), ozone has the power of converting many colored organic substances to colorless products; it accordingly finds use as a bleaching agent for oils, waxes, starch, and flour. It is also used instead of chlorine for sterilizing drinking water, by destroying the bacteria in it.

5–9. *The Phlogiston Theory*

During nearly the whole of the eighteenth century chemistry was dominated by a striking theory, the *phlogiston theory*. The phlogiston theory can be traced back to the teachings of the German alchemist Johann Joachim Becher (1635–1682), who believed that combustion of a substance involved the loss of a form of matter, the principle of combustion, which he named *terra pinguin*. The German physician Georg Ernst Stahl (1660–1734), who had been a pupil of Becher's, developed the phlogiston theory in an effort to give a general explanation of chemical reactions. He assumed that there exists a substance *phlogiston* (Greek *phlogizein*, to set on fire, to burn), the material of fire. Metals were supposed to be composed of a calx (Latin *calx*, stone, limestone), combined with phlogiston. There was a characteristic calx for each metal. Candle wax and charcoal were supposed to consist mainly of phlogiston; and when they burned, phlogiston was supposed to be liberated as heat and light, only a small residue remaining. When a metal oxide is heated out of contact with air the oxide is reduced to the metal itself; Stahl described this reaction by saying that when a calx is heated with charcoal out of contact with air the phlogiston of the charcoal combines with the calx, producing the metal. The phlogiston theory thus provided a general explanation of the chemical processes of oxidation and reduction: oxidation was taken to be the liberation of phlogiston, and reduction combination with phlogiston.

It is interesting to consider other ways in which chemical phenomena were accounted for by the phlogiston theory. The success of the theory in providing these explanations explains the fact that it had many strong adherents.

The food ingested by an animal was assumed to consist largely of phlogiston, which when released produced the heat of the animal body. Both combustion and life cease in a confined volume of air—the explanation of this was that a given volume of air could hold only a certain amount of phlogiston, and when it became saturated it could not support combustion or life.

When limestone or chalk (calcium carbonate, $CaCO_3$) is strongly heated, it is converted into quicklime (CaO). According to the phlogiston theory quicklime was a

---

* The calorie (cal) is a unit of heat (a unit of energy). It is defined as the amount of heat required to raise the temperature of 1 g of water by 1° C (more precisely, from 14.5° C to 15.5° C).

compound of limestone with phlogiston, obtained from the heat. Joseph Black (1728–1799), a Scottish professor, showed that the process of conversion of limestone into quicklime is accompanied by a loss in weight, rather than a gain in weight as would be expected from the phlogiston theory. This investigation, carried out in the middle of the eighteenth century, did not cause the supporters of the phlogiston theory to abandon it. Indeed, it seems likely that it was generally known by them that the metals themselves are lighter than their calces. The fact was explained by saying that phlogiston is a form of matter that is repelled in the earth's gravitational field (everyone knows that heat rises).

When Scheele began his studies on phlogiston, he found that when hydrogen (which he considered to be phlogiston) is burned in air contained over water, the volume of air decreases. He also found that the water seemed to be unchanged, and he concluded that the phlogiston had combined with a constituent of air, "fire-air," to form "caloric" (heat), which had escaped through the glass wall of his container. He argued that if caloric could be made to react with a substance with a strong affinity for phlogiston, such as pyrolusite (manganese dioxide), or the red calx of mercury (mercuric oxide), such a substance would remove the phlogiston and combine with it, and liberate the fire-air. He carried out the experiments, and obtained his fire-air (oxygen).

Scheele was the first man to isolate chlorine. He heated pyrolusite with hydrochloric acid, which he called "marine acid," and obtained a greenish-yellow gas. He explained the reaction by saying that the pyrolusite had absorbed phlogiston from the acid, and he named the gas "dephlogisticated marine acid." The equation for the reaction he carried out is

$$MnO_2 + 4HCl \longrightarrow MnCl_2 + 2H_2O + Cl_2 \uparrow$$

Scheele made his discovery of fire-air in 1773, but an account of it was not published until 1777. In 1774 Priestley, in England, made oxygen from mercuric oxide. He was surprised to find that his gas could support combustion very well, and could support the respiration of animals. He explained these facts by saying that ordinary air is partially saturated with phlogiston and cannot make room for much more, whereas his new air, which he named "dephlogisticated air," is free of phlogiston, and can absorb a large amount. The gas that remains after the combustible material is burned in air (nitrogen) he called "phlogisticated air."

It was Lavoisier, in 1775, who recognized that Priestley's experiments could be given another interpretation. He suggested that Priestley's gas, which he named oxygen, could combine with non-metallic elements such as sulfur and phosphorus to form acids (acidic oxides), and with metals to form basic oxides (the calces of the metals). The metallic salts were formed by the union of the two kinds of oxides. The phlogistonists objected to the theory because it did not explain the formation of inflammable air (hydrogen) when metals are dissolved in acids—the same salt is formed when a metal calx is dissolved in acid, but without the liberation of the phlogiston as inflammable air. Lavoisier then learned about Cavendish's proof that hydrogen and oxygen combine to form water, and he recognized that when a metal dissolves in an acid (a non-metal oxide plus water) the oxygen of the water can combine with the metal to produce the metal oxide, which with the non-metal oxide gives the salt, the hydrogen of the water being liberated.

Lavoisier's idea that all acids contain oxygen was not given up for about thirty years. This idea required, of course, that hydrochloric acid contain oxygen. In 1807 Davy showed that hydrogen chloride reacts with potassium to form potassium chloride and hydrogen, and he pointed out that there was no evidence to show that chlorine is not an element. Within a few years the elementary nature of chlorine was accepted by chemists generally (J. J. Berzelius was the last of the great chemists of the time to accept the idea, in 1820), and hydrogen was recognized as the essential constituent of acids.

Exercises

5-1. It is said in the text that one of the most valuable parts of chemical theory is the periodic law. State this law in your own words.

5-2. Define congener, metal, metalloid, transition element.

5-3. Sketch a plan of the periodic table, and fill in from memory the symbols of the first eighteen elements.

5-4. By extrapolation with use of the data given in Table 5-2, predict values of the atomic weight, melting point, and boiling point of element 118. What would you expect its chemical properties to be?

5-5. Where was helium first detected? What is the principal source of this element at present?

5-6. List as many uses as you can for the various noble gases.

5-7. What are the most important metallic properties? In what part of the periodic table are the elements with metallic properties?

5-8. Classify the following elements as metals, metalloids, or non-metals: potassium, arsenic, aluminum, xenon, bromine, silicon, phosphorus.

5-9. The density of calcium is 1.54 g/cm^3. Calculate the gram-atomic volume of calcium.

5-10. What is the lightest gas? the lightest liquid? the lightest crystalline substance? the substance with the lowest known melting point and boiling point?

5-11. What are allotropes? What differences in properties and structure between oxygen and ozone can you mention?

5-12. Do you know any elements other than oxygen which exist in allotropic forms?

5-13. Write the equation for the neutralization of acetic acid, $HC_2H_3O_2$, by sodium hydroxide, NaOH. Write the equation for the neutralization of this acid by calcium hydroxide, $Ca(OH)_2$.

5-14. Write equations to represent the formation from sodium hydroxide and phosphoric acid of normal sodium phosphate, disodium monohydrogen phosphate, and sodium dihydrogen phosphate.

5-15. When sulfur is burned in air, it forms the gas sulfur dioxide, SO_2. What is the formula of the acid of which this gas is the anhydride?

Chapter 6

The Chemical Elements and the Periodic Law: Part 2

The chemistry of the elements lithium, beryllium, boron, carbon, nitrogen, and fluorine and of the congeners of lithium, beryllium, and boron is discussed in the following sections.

6–1. *Lithium, Beryllium, Boron, and Carbon*

The four elements lithium (atomic number 3), beryllium (4), boron (5), and carbon (6) strikingly illustrate the dependence of properties on position in the periodic table. Lithium is a rather soft, very light element with characteristic metallic properties; beryllium is harder and denser, and its metallic properties are less pronounced; boron is still harder and denser, and its properties are not those of a metal, but rather those of a metalloid; carbon (diamond) is extremely hard, denser by 50% than boron, and is a non-metal.

These differences in properties are shown in Table 6-1. It is seen that the density increases steadily from 0.530 g/cm³ for lithium to 3.51 g/cm³ for carbon (diamond). The atomic radius decreases correspondingly from 1.55 Å for lithium to 0.77 Å for carbon. The melting point and the boiling point, which like hardness and related properties may be considered to reflect the strength of the bonds between atoms in the substance, increase steadily, the melting point from 186° C for lithium to 3,500° C for carbon and the boiling point from 1,336° C for lithium to 4,200° C for carbon.

It will be pointed out later (Chap. 10) that the change in properties from lithium to carbon is correlated with the use by atoms of these elements of all their electrons except two in the formation of bonds with adjacent atoms in the elementary substances. Thus lithium, with three electrons per atom, uses one electron per atom in forming bonds between lithium atoms, beryllium uses two electrons per atom, boron three

TABLE 6-1   *Physical Properties of Elements from Lithium to Carbon*

	LITHIUM	BERYLLIUM	BORON	CARBON (DIAMOND)
Atomic number	3	4	5	6
Atomic weight	6.940	9.013	10.82	12.011
Density (g/cm³)	0.530	1.82	2.54	3.51
Gram-atomic volume (cm³/g-atom)	13.1	4.95	4.26	3.42
Atomic radius (Å)	1.55	1.12	0.89	0.77
Melting point (°C)	186°	1,350°	2,300°	3,500°
Boiling point (°C)	1,336°	2,000° (?)	2,550°	4,200°
Heat of sublimation (kcal/g-atom)	39	75	115	141
Electric conductivity (mho/cm) *	11×10^4	6×10^4	1×10^{-6}	2×10^{-13}
Mechanical properties	soft	hard	very hard	extremely hard
	malleable	malleable	brittle	brittle
	ductile	ductile		
Mohs hardness	1	6.5	9.3	10

* The electric conductivity, in mho/cm, is the amount of current, in amperes, flowing through a rod of material with cross-section 1 cm² when there is an electric potential difference between the ends of the rod of 1 volt per cm of length of the rod. (Note that mho is the anagram of ohm, the unit of electric resistance. A wire with conductivity x mho has resistance 1/x ohm.)

electrons per atom, and carbon four electrons per atom. We might accordingly expect that the bonds between the carbon atom and its neighboring atoms would be altogether approximately four times as strong as those between the lithium atom and neighboring atoms, and the properties of the substances support this idea. An interesting example is provided by the heat of sublimation. The values given in the table represent the amounts of energy, in kcal,* necessary to convert one gram-atom of the element from the standard crystalline state to the gaseous monatomic state. It is seen that these values are roughly equal to 37 kcal/g-atom multiplied by the number of binding electrons.

* A kilocalorie (kcal) is 1,000 calories.

The characteristic properties of a metal are high electric conductivity, malleability, and ductility. It is seen that lithium and beryllium have these properties. Boron, on the other hand, has a very small electric conductivity at room temperature, and that of diamond is still smaller. Boron and diamond are also brittle, rather than malleable and ductile.

Boron is called a metalloid rather than a non-metal in part because of its chemical properties, which are discussed below, and in part because of the change in its electric conductivity with temperature. Metals have high electric conductivity, which decreases with increasing temperature. Non-metals have extremely low electric conductivity, which does not increase very much with increasing temperature. Metalloids have low electric conductivity, which increases rapidly with increasing temperature. Thus the electric conductivity of boron increases a million-fold on heating the substance from room temperature to a red heat, whereas that of diamond changes by only a small amount.

The explanation of these phenomena given by the electron theory of metals is that there are present in metals many electrons which are free to move from atom to atom through the metallic crystal. At low temperatures the atoms are arranged in regular rows characteristic of the crystalline state, and the electrons can move easily through the crystal lattice. At high temperatures, however, thermal agitation introduces irregularities in the atomic arrangement, which interfere with the ease of motion of the electrons, and thus cause the electric conductivity to become smaller.

On the other hand, in a metalloid there are only a very few electrons that are free to move through the crystal, and the electric conductivity is correspondingly small. Most of the electrons are held firmly by the atoms. When the temperature is increased, the increasing thermal agitation causes some of the bound electrons to break loose, and to become free electrons. This increases the number of free electrons, and causes the electric conductivity to increase. There is, of course, somewhat less freedom of motion of each free electron at higher temperature than at lower temperature because of the irregularity of the atomic arrangement at higher temperature, but the effect of this in decreasing the conductivity per free electron is more than counterbalanced by the great increase in the number of free electrons in the metalloid with increasing temperature.

6-2. The Alkali Metals

The elements of the first group, lithium, sodium, potassium, rubidium, and cesium,* are soft, silvery-white metals with great chemical reactivity. Some of their physical properties are given in Table 6-2.

The alkali metals are made by electrolysis of the fused hydroxides or fused chlorides. Because of their reactivity, the metals must be kept in an inert atmosphere or under oil. The metals are useful chemical reagents in the laboratory, and they find industrial use (especially sodium)

* The sixth alkali metal, francium (Fr), element 87, has been obtained only in minute quantities, and no information has been published about its properties.

in the manufacture of organic chemicals, dyestuffs, and lead tetraethyl (a constituent of "ethyl gasoline"). Sodium is used in sodium-vapor lamps, and, because of its large heat conductivity, in the stems of valves of airplane engines, to conduct heat away from the valve heads. A sodium-potassium alloy is used as a heat transfer agent in uranium piles. Cesium is used in vacuum tubes, to increase electron emission from filaments (Chap. 8).

The vapors of the alkali metals are monatomic.

Compounds of sodium are readily identified by the yellow color that they give to a flame. Lithium causes a carmine coloration of the flame, and potassium, rubidium, and cesium cause a violet coloration. The elements may be easily identified by use of a spectroscope.

TABLE 6-2   *Properties of the Alkali Metals*

	SYM-BOL	ATOMIC NUMBER	ATOMIC WEIGHT	MELTING POINT	BOILING POINT	DENSITY	METALLIC RADIUS*	RADIUS OF CATION, M^+
Lithium	Li	3	6.940	186° C	1,336° C	0.530 g/cm³	1.55 Å	0.60 Å
Sodium	Na	11	22.991	97.5°	880°	.963	1.90	0.95
Potassium	K	19	39.100	62.3°	760°	.857	2.35	1.33
Rubidium	Rb	37	85.48	38.5°	700°	1.594	2.48	1.48
Cesium	Cs	55	132.91	28.5°	670°	1.992	2.67	1.69

* For coordination number 12—that is, for a structure in which the atom is in contact with twelve neighboring atoms.

The hydroxides of the alkali metals, which are called *alkalies*, all have the formula MOH (M = Li, Na, K, Rb, or Cs), the chlorides the formula MCl, the sulfates the formula M_2SO_4, and the nitrates the formula MNO_3.

Compounds of Lithium.

Lithium chloride, LiCl, is made by fusing a mineral containing lithium with barium chloride, $BaCl_2$, and extracting the fusion with water. Lithium chloride is used in the preparation of other compounds of lithium.

When lithium is heated in a stream of hydrogen, the compound **lithium hydride,** LiH, is formed. This substance reacts with water with the liberation of a large volume of hydrogen, relative to the weight of the substance:

$$LiH + H_2O \longrightarrow LiOH + H_2 \uparrow$$

Lithium occurs in the minerals *spodumene,* $LiAlSi_2O_6$; *amblygonite,* $LiAlPO_4F$; and *lepidolite,* $K_2Li_3Al_5Si_6O_{20}F_4$.

Compounds of lithium have found use in the manufacture of glass and of glazes for dishes and porcelain objects.

Compounds of Sodium.   The most important compound of sodium is **sodium chloride** (common salt), NaCl. It crystallizes as colorless cubes, with melting point 801° C, and it has a characteristic salty taste. It occurs in sea water to the extent of 3%, and in solid deposits and concentrated brines that are pumped from wells. Many million tons of the substance are obtained from these sources every year. It is used mainly for the preparation of other compounds of sodium and of chlorine, as well as of sodium metal and chlorine gas.

Sodium hydroxide (*caustic soda*), NaOH, is a white, hygroscopic (water-attracting) solid, which dissolves readily in water. Its solutions have a smooth, soapy feeling, and are very corrosive to the skin (this is the meaning of "caustic" in the name "caustic soda"). Sodium hydroxide is made either by the electrolysis of sodium chloride (Chap. 13) or by the action of calcium hydroxide, $Ca(OH)_2$, on sodium carbonate, Na_2CO_3:

$$Na_2CO_3 + Ca(OH)_2 \longrightarrow CaCO_3 \downarrow + 2NaOH$$

Calcium carbonate is insoluble, and precipitates out during this reaction, leaving the sodium hydroxide in solution. Sodium hydroxide is a useful laboratory reagent and a very important industrial chemical. It is used in industry in the manufacture of soap, the refining of petroleum, and the manufacture of paper, textiles, rayon and cellulose film, and many other products.

Sodium carbonate (washing soda), $Na_2CO_3 \cdot 10H_2O$, is a white, crystalline substance used as a household alkali, for washing and cleaning, and as an industrial chemical. The crystals of the decahydrate lose water readily, forming the monohydrate, $Na_2CO_3 \cdot H_2O$. The monohydrate when heated to 100° changes to anhydrous sodium carbonate (*soda ash*), Na_2CO_3.

Sodium hydrogen carbonate (*baking soda, bicarbonate of soda*), $NaHCO_3$, is a white substance usually available as a powder. It is used in cooking, in medicine, and in the manufacture of baking powder.

Baking powder is a leavening agent used in making biscuits, cakes, and other food. Its purpose is to provide bubbles of gas, to make the dough "rise." The same foods can be made by use of sodium hydrogen carbonate and sour milk, instead of baking powder. In each case the reaction that occurs involves the action of an acid on sodium hydrogen carbonate, to form carbon dioxide. When sour milk is used, the acid that reacts with the sodium hydrogen carbonate is lactic acid, $HC_3H_5O_3$, the equation for the reaction being

$$NaHCO_3 + HC_3H_5O_3 \longrightarrow NaC_3H_5O_3 + H_2O + CO_2 \uparrow$$

The product $NaC_3H_5O_3$ is sodium lactate, the sodium salt of lactic acid (Chap. 28). Cream-of-tartar baking powder consists of sodium hydrogen carbonate, potassium hydrogen tartrate ($KHC_4H_4O_6$, commonly known as cream of tartar), and starch, the starch being added to keep water vapor in the air from causing the powder to form a solid cake. The reaction that occurs when water is added to a cream-of-tartar baking powder is

$$NaHCO_3 + KHC_4H_4O_6 \longrightarrow NaKC_4H_4O_6 + H_2O + CO_2 \uparrow$$

The product sodium potassium tartrate, $NaKC_4H_4O_6$, has the common name "Rochelle salt." Baking powders are also made with calcium dihydrogen phosphate, $Ca(H_2PO_4)_2$, sodium dihydrogen phosphate, NaH_2PO_4, or sodium aluminum sulfate, $NaAl(SO_4)_2$, as the acidic constituent. The last of these substances is acidic because of the hydrolysis of the aluminum salt (Chap. 21).

The leavening agent in ordinary bread dough is *yeast*, a microorganism. This microorganism produces an *enzyme* (an organic catalyst) that converts sugar into alcohol and carbon dioxide:

$$C_6H_{12}O_6 \longrightarrow 2C_2H_5OH + 2CO_2 \uparrow$$

The formula $C_6H_{12}O_6$ in this equation represents glucose, a simple sugar.

Compounds of Potassium.   Potassium chloride, KCl, forms colorless cubic crystals, resembling those of sodium chloride. There are very large deposits of potassium chloride, together with other salts, at Stassfurt, Germany, and near Carlsbad, New Mexico. Potassium chloride is also obtained from Searles Lake, in the Mojave Desert in California.

Potassium hydroxide, KOH, is a valuable, strongly alkaline substance, with properties similar to those of sodium hydroxide. Other important salts of potassium, which resemble the corresponding salts of sodium, are **potassium sulfate,** K_2SO_4, **potassium carbonate,** K_2CO_3, and **potassium hydrogen carbonate,** $KHCO_3$.

The principal use of potassium compounds is in fertilizers.

The compounds of rubidium and cesium resemble those of potassium closely. They do not have any important uses.

6–3. *The Alkaline-Earth Metals*

The metals of group II of the periodic table, beryllium, magnesium, calcium, strontium, barium, and radium, are called the alkaline-earth metals.* Some of their properties are listed in Table 6-3. These metals are much harder and less reactive than the alkali metals. The compounds of all the alkaline-earth metals are similar in composition.

An interesting deviation from the customary regular increase in density of the elementary substance with increase in atomic number through a group of the periodic table is shown by these metals. The density decreases somewhat from beryllium to magnesium, and again from magnesium to calcium, † and then shows the normal rapid increase.

TABLE 6-3   *Properties of the Alkaline-Earth Metals**

	SYMBOL	ATOMIC NUMBER	ATOMIC WEIGHT	MELTING POINT	DENSITY (g/cm³)	METALLIC RADIUS	RADIUS OF CATION M⁺⁺
Beryllium	Be	4	9.013	1,350° C	1.86	1.12 Å	0.31 Å
Magnesium	Mg	12	24.32	651°	1.75	1.60	0.65
Calcium	Ca	20	40.08	810°	1.55	1.97	0.99
Strontium	Sr	38	87.63	800°	2.60	2.15	1.13
Barium	Ba	56	137.36	850°	3.61	2.22	1.35
Radium	Ra	88	226.05	960°	(4.45) †	(2.46) †	

* The boiling points of these metals are uncertain; they are about 600° higher than the melting points.
† Estimated.

However, the minimum density of calcium does not have great significance. Both the atomic weight and the effective atomic radius in the metal are seen to increase rapidly with atomic number, and it happens that the increase of the radius is the more significant from beryllium to calcium, causing the density (which is proportional to [atomic weight]/[cube of radius]) to decrease.

Beryllium. Beryllium is a light, silvery-white metal, which can be made by electrolysis of a fused mixture of beryllium chloride, $BeCl_2$, and sodium chloride (electrolytic methods of production of metals are discussed in Chap. 13). The metal is used for making windows for X-ray tubes; X-rays readily penetrate elements with low atomic number, and beryllium metal has the best mechanical properties of the very light elements. It is also used as a constituent of special alloys. About 2%

* Their oxides are called the alkaline earths.
† A similar decrease in density occurs from sodium to potassium; see Table 6-2.

beryllium in copper produces a hard alloy especially suited for use in springs.

The principal ore of beryllium is its aluminosilicate, **beryl,** $Be_3Al_2Si_6O_{18}$. *Emeralds* are beryl crystals containing traces of chromium, which gives them a green color. *Aquamarine* is a bluish-green variety of beryl.

The compounds of beryllium have little special value, except that **beryllium oxide,** BeO, is used in the uranium piles in which plutonium is made from uranium (Chap. 33).

Compounds of beryllium are very poisonous. Even the dust of the powdered metal or its oxide may cause very serious illness when inhaled.

Magnesium.   Magnesium metal is made by electrolysis of fused magnesium chloride, and also by the reduction of magnesium oxide by carbon or by ferrosilicon (an alloy of iron and silicon). Except for calcium and the alkali metals, magnesium is the lightest metal known; and it finds use in light-weight alloys, such as *magnalium* (10% magnesium, 90% aluminum).

Magnesium reacts with boiling water, to form **magnesium hydroxide,** $Mg(OH)_2$, an alkaline substance. The metal burns in air with a bright white light, to form **magnesium oxide,** MgO, the old name of which is *magnesia*. Flashlight powder is a mixture of magnesium powder and an oxidizing agent.

Magnesium oxide suspended in water is used in medicine (as "milk of magnesia"), for neutralizing excess acid in the stomach and as a laxative. **Magnesium sulfate,** "Epsom salts," $MgSO_4 \cdot 7H_2O$, is used as a cathartic.

Magnesium carbonate, $MgCO_3$, occurs in nature as the mineral *magnesite*. It is used as a basic lining for copper converters and open-hearth steel furnaces (Chap. 27).

Calcium.   Metallic calcium is made by the electrolysis of fused calcium chloride, $CaCl_2$. The metal is silvery-white in color, and is somewhat harder than lead. It reacts with water, and burns in air when ignited, forming a mixture of **calcium oxide,** CaO, and calcium nitride, Ca_3N_2. Calcium reacts with cold water to form **calcium hydroxide,** $Ca(OH)_2$. The common name of calcium oxide is *quicklime*, and that of calcium hydroxide is *slaked lime*.

Calcium has a number of practical uses—as a deoxidizer for iron and steel and for copper and copper alloys, as a constituent of lead alloys (metals for bearings, or the sheath for electric cables) and of aluminum alloys, and as a reducing agent for making other metals from their oxides.

The most important compound of calcium is **calcium carbonate,** $CaCO_3$. This substance occurs in beautiful colorless crystals as the mineral *calcite* (Fig. 6-1). *Marble* is a microcrystalline form of calcium carbonate, and *limestone* is a rock composed mainly of this substance. Calcium carbonate is the principal constituent also of pearls, coral, and

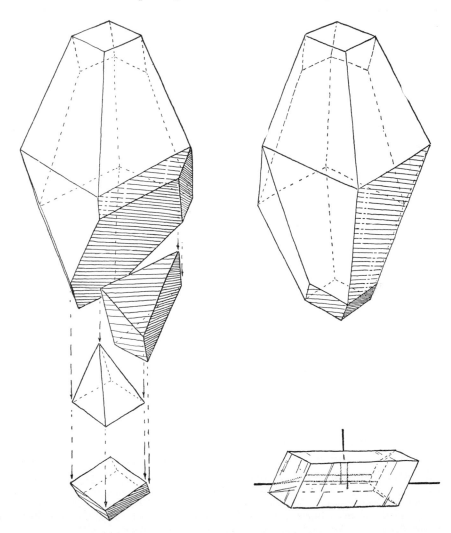

FIG. 6-1   *Natural crystals of calcite, CaCO₃, showing planes of cleavage and how they produce the cleavage rhombohedron (left). The property of birefringence (double refraction) is possessed by calcite (lower right).*

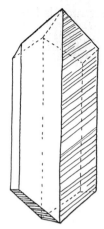

FIG. 6-2

Natural crystal of aragonite, another form of calcium carbonate, CaCO₃.

most seashells. Calcium carbonate also occurs in a second crystalline form, as the mineral *aragonite* (Fig. 6-2; see also Sec. 6-8). When calcium carbonate is heated (as in a lime-kiln, where limestone is mixed with fuel, which is burned), it decomposes, forming quicklime:

$$CaCO_3 \longrightarrow CaO + CO_2 \uparrow$$

Quicklime is slaked by adding water, to form calcium hydroxide:

$$CaO + H_2O \longrightarrow Ca(OH)_2$$

Slaked lime prepared in this way is a white powder which can be mixed with water and sand to form *mortar*. The mortar hardens by forming crystals of calcium hydroxide, which cement the grains of sand together; then on exposure to air the mortar continues to get harder by taking up carbon dioxide and forming calcium carbonate.

Large amounts of limestone are used also in the manufacture of Portland cement, described in Chapter 30.

Calcium sulfate occurs in nature as the mineral *gypsum*,* $CaSO_4 \cdot 2H_2O$. Gypsum is a white substance, which is used commercially for fabrication into wallboard, and for conversion into *plaster of Paris*. When gypsum is heated a little above 100° C it loses three-quarters of its water of crystallization, forming the powdered substance $CaSO_4 \cdot \frac{1}{2}H_2O$, which is

---

* Sometimes the formula of a substance is written in a special way, to give indication of the properties of the substance. The formula of gypsum might be written CaH_4SO_6. Instead, it is written $CaSO_4 \cdot 2H_2O$, because gypsum is closely related to sulfuric acid, H_2SO_4, and might be expected to contain the SO_4 group, and also because, when gypsum is heated, water is very readily driven off. The formula $CaSO_4 \cdot 2H_2O$ indicates that gypsum is easily decomposed into anhydrous calcium sulfate, $CaSO_4$, and 2 molecules of water. A substance such as gypsum is said to contain *water of crystallization*.

plaster of Paris. When mixed with water the small crystals of plaster of Paris dissolve and then crystallize as long needles of $CaSO_4 \cdot 2H_2O$. These needles grow together, and form a solid mass, with the shape into which the wet powder was molded.

Calcium phosphate, $Ca_3(PO_4)_2$, occurs in large deposits in nature (phosphate rock). It is converted into calcium dihydrogen phosphate, $Ca(H_2PO_4)_2$, and is used as a fertilizer.

Strontium.   The principal minerals of strontium are **strontium sulfate,** *celestite,* $SrSO_4$, and **strontium carbonate,** *strontianite,* $SrCO_3$.

Strontium nitrate, $Sr(NO_3)_2$, is made by dissolving strontium carbonate in nitric acid. It is mixed with carbon and sulfur to make red fire for use in fireworks, signal shells, and railroad flares. **Strontium chlorate,** $Sr(ClO_3)_2$, is used for the same purpose. The other compounds of strontium are similar to the corresponding compounds of calcium. Strontium metal has no practical uses.

Barium.   The metal barium has no significant use. Its principal compounds are **barium sulfate,** $BaSO_4$, which is only very slightly soluble in water and dilute acids, and **barium chloride,** $BaCl_2 \cdot 2H_2O$, which is soluble in water. Barium sulfate occurs in nature as the mineral *barite.*

Barium, like other elements with large atomic number, absorbs X-rays strongly, and a thin paste of barium sulfate and water is swallowed as a "barium meal" to obtain contrasting X-ray photographs and fluoroscopic views of the alimentary tract. The solubility of the substance is so small that the poisonous action of most barium compounds is avoided.

Barium nitrate, $Ba(NO_3)_2$, and **barium chlorate,** $Ba(ClO_3)_2$, are used for producing green fire in fireworks.

Radium.   Compounds of radium are closely similar in properties to those of barium. The radioactivity of radium is discussed in Chapter 33.

6–4. *Boron and Aluminum and Their Congeners*

Boron.   Boron can be made by heating potassium tetrafluoroborate, KBF_4, with sodium in a crucible lined with magnesium oxide:

$$KBF_4 + 3Na \longrightarrow KF + 3NaF + B$$

The element can also be made by heating boric oxide, B_2O_3, with powdered magnesium:

$$B_2O_3 + 3Mg \longrightarrow 3MgO + 2B$$

Boron forms brilliant transparent crystals, which are nearly as hard as diamond. The element has found some use in removing oxygen from molten copper before making castings of copper.

Boron forms a compound with carbon, B_4C. This substance, **boron carbide,** is the hardest substance known next to diamond, and it has found extensive use as an abrasive and for the manufacture of small mortars and pestles for grinding very hard substances.

Boron forms several hydrides, the simplest of which is **diborane,** B_2H_6, a poisonous, ill-smelling, spontaneously inflammable gas.

Boric acid, H_3BO_3, occurs in the volcanic steam jets of central Italy. The substance is a white crystalline solid, which is sufficiently volatile to be carried along with a stream of steam. It is a very weak acid, and is used in medicine as a mild antiseptic. It is an excellent preservative for foods, but this use is illegal because of its toxicity.

The principal sources of compounds of boron are the complex borate minerals, including *borax*, sodium tetraborate decahydrate, $Na_2B_4O_7 \cdot 10H_2O$; *kernite*, sodium tetraborate tetrahydrate, $Na_2B_4O_7 \cdot 4H_2O$ (which gives borax when water is added); and *colemanite*, calcium hexaborate pentahydrate, $Ca_2B_6O_{11} \cdot 5H_2O$. The main deposits of these minerals are in California.

These minerals are salts of the complex acids $H_2B_4O_7$, tetraboric acid, and $H_4B_6O_{11}$, hexaboric acid, which, like the acid anhydride boric oxide, B_2O_3, may be made by the dehydration of boric acid:

$$4H_3BO_3 \longrightarrow H_2B_4O_7 + 5H_2O$$

$$6H_3BO_3 \longrightarrow H_4B_6O_{11} + 7H_2O$$

$$2H_3BO_3 \longrightarrow B_2O_3 + 3H_2O$$

Borax is used in making certain types of enamels and glass (such as Pyrex glass, which contains about 12% B_2O_3), for softening water, as a household cleanser, and as a flux in welding metals. The last of these uses depends upon the power of molten borax to dissolve metallic oxides, forming borates. This power is also used in the laboratory for identifying the metal in a metallic oxide. A small amount of borax is melted in a loop of platinum wire, with loss of most of the water. The metallic oxide is then added to the "borax bead," and, on further heating, it dissolves, giving to the bead, which forms a glass on cooling, a color which may be characteristic of the metal (green for chromium, blue for cobalt, etc.).

Aluminum.   The second element in group III, aluminum, is an important metal. Its density is only 2.712 g/cm^3, and it is strong as well as light, and is ductile and malleable. It finds extensive use as a structural metal, especially in airplane construction.

The metal is reactive, and when strongly heated it burns rapidly in air or oxygen. Aluminum dust forms an explosive mixture with air. Under ordinary conditions, however, aluminum rapidly becomes coated with a thin, tough layer of aluminum oxide, which protects it against further corrosion. This protection is so effective that the sixty-inch and hundred-inch telescope mirrors on Mt. Wilson have not had to be re-coated with aluminum (which was deposited as a reflecting layer by evaporation in a vacuum) for several years, whereas the silver coating formerly used tarnished rapidly and was replaced every few months.

Some of the **alloys of aluminum** are very useful. *Duralumin* or *dural* is an alloy (containing 95% aluminum, 4% copper, 0.5% manganese, and 0.5% magnesium) which is stronger and tougher than pure alu-minum. It is less resistant to corrosion, however, and often is protected by a coating of pure aluminum. Plate made by rolling a billet of dural sandwiched between and welded to two pieces of pure aluminum is called *Alclad plate*.

The principal ore of aluminum is *bauxite*, a mixture of hydrated alu-minum oxides ($AlHO_2$, $Al(OH)_3$). The metal is won from the ore by an electrolytic process, described in Chapter 13, and is sometimes further purified by electrolysis.

Aluminum is a constituent of many minerals, including clay, mica, feldspar, sillimanite, and the zeolites. Some of these minerals are dis-cussed under the chemistry of silicon, in Chapter 30.

Aluminum oxide (*alumina*), Al_2O_3, occurs in nature as the mineral *corundum*. Corundum is the hardest of all naturally occurring substances except diamond. Corundum and impure corundum (*emery*) are used as abrasives. Pure corundum is colorless. The precious stones *ruby* (red) and *sapphire* (blue or other colors) are transparent crystalline corundum con-taining small amounts of other metallic oxides (chromic oxide, titanium oxide). Artificial rubies and sapphires can be made by melting aluminum oxide (m.p. 2,050° C) with small admixtures of other oxides, and cooling the melt in such a way as to produce large crystals. These stones are in-distinguishable from natural stones, except for the presence of character-istic rounded microscopic air bubbles. They are used as gems, as bearings ("jewels") in watches and other instruments, and as dies through which wires are drawn. Very finely divided aluminum oxide (*activated alumina*) is used as a dehydrating agent and as a catalyst.

Aluminum sulfate, $Al_2(SO_4) \cdot 18H_2O$, may be made by dissolving alu-minum hydroxide or bauxite in sulfuric acid. It is used in water purification and as a mordant in dyeing and printing cloth (a mordant is a substance which fixes the dye to the cloth, rendering it insoluble). Both of these uses depend upon its property of producing a gelatinous precipitate of **aluminum hydroxide,** $Al(OH)_3$, when it is dissolved in a large amount of neutral or slightly alkaline water (see Hydrolysis, Chap. 21). In dyeing and printing cloth, the gelatinous precipitate aids in holding the dye on the cloth. In water purification it adsorbs* dissolved and suspended impurities, which are removed as it settles to the bottom of the reservoir.

A solution containing aluminum sulfate and potassium sulfate forms, on evaporation, beautiful octahedral crystals of **alum,** $KAl(SO_4)_2 \cdot 12H_2O$. Similar crystals of **ammonium alum,** $NH_4Al(SO_4)_2 \cdot 12H_2O$, are formed with ammonium sulfate. The alums are also used as mordants in dyeing cloth, in water purification, and in weighting and sizing paper (by precipitating aluminum hydroxide in the meshes of the cellulose fibers).

Aluminum chloride, $AlCl_3$ or $AlCl_3 \cdot 6H_2O$, is made by treating aluminum or aluminum hydroxide with hydrochloric acid. The anhydrous salt is used in many chemical processes, including a cracking process for making gasoline.

Scandium, Yttrium, and Lanthanum.   Scandium, yttrium, and lanthanum, the congeners of boron and aluminum, form colorless compounds similar to those of aluminum, their oxides having the formulas Sc_2O_3, Y_2O_3, and La_2O_3. These elements and their compounds have not yet found any important use.

6–5. *Carbon*

Carbon occurs in nature in its elementary state in two allotropic forms: **diamond,** the hardest substance known, which often forms beautiful, transparent, highly refractive crystals, used as gems (Fig. 6-3; poorer stones are used as an industrial abrasive); and **graphite,** a soft, black, crystalline substance, used as a lubricant and in the "lead" of lead pencils. Charcoal, coke, and carbon black (lampblack) are microcrystalline or "amorphous" (non-crystalline) forms of carbon.

Hardness.   The property of *hardness* is not a simple one to define. It has probably evaded quantitative definition because the concept of hardness represents a composite

---

* *Adsorption* is the adhesion of molecules of a gas, liquid, or dissolved substance or of particles to the surface of a solid substance. *Absorption* is the assimilation of molecules into a solid or liquid substance, with the formation of a solution or a compound. Sometimes the word *sorption* is used to include both of these phenomena.

FIG. 6-3

A natural crystal of diamond, with octahedral
faces and smaller faces rounding the edges, and
a brilliant-cut diamond.

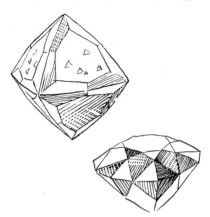

of several properties (tensile strength, resistance to cleavage, etc.). Various scales of hardness and instruments for testing hardness have been proposed. One test consists of dropping a diamond-tipped weight on the specimen and measuring the height of rebound; the softer specimens undergo greater deformation, which uses some of the kinetic energy of the weight and decreases the height of its rebound. In another test (the Brinell test) a hardened steel ball is pressed into the surface of the specimen, and the size of the produced indentation is measured.

A very simple test of hardness is the scratch test; a specimen which scratches another specimen and is not scratched by it is said to be harder than the second specimen. The scratch-test scale used by mineralogists is the **Mohs scale,** with reference points (the *Mohs hardness*) from 1 to 10, defined by the following ten minerals:

1. Talc, $Mg_3Si_4O_{10}(OH)_2$
2. Gypsum, $CaSO_4 \cdot 2H_2O$
3. Calcite, $CaCO_3$
4. Fluorite, CaF_2
5. Apatite, $Ca_5(PO_4)_3F$
6. Orthoclase, $KAlSi_3O_8$
7. Quartz, SiO_2
8. Topaz, $Al_2SiO_4F_2$
9. Corundum, Al_2O_3
10. Diamond, C

Diamond is indeed far harder than corundum, and recent modifications of the Mohs scale have been suggested which assign a much larger hardness number, such as 15, to diamond.

Carbon burns to form the gases **carbon monoxide,** CO, and **carbon dioxide,** CO_2, the former being produced when there is a deficiency of oxygen.

Carbon monoxide is a colorless, odorless gas with only very small solubility in water (35.4 ml per liter of water at 0° C and 1 atm). It is poisonous, because of its ability to combine with the hemoglobin in the blood in the same way that oxygen does, and thus to prevent the hemoglobin from combining with oxygen in the lungs and carrying it to the tissues. Carbon monoxide is a valuable industrial gas, for use as a fuel and as a reducing agent.

Carbon dioxide is a colorless, odorless gas with a weakly acid taste, due to the formation of carbonic acid when it is dissolved in water. It is about 50% heavier than air. It is easily soluble in water, one liter of water at 0° C dissolving 1,713 ml of the gas under 1 atm pressure. It has the very interesting property that its melting point (freezing point) is higher than the point of vaporization at 1 atm of the crystalline form. When solid, crystalline carbon dioxide is heated from a very low temperature, its vapor pressure reaches 1 atm at −79°, at which temperature it vaporizes without melting. If the pressure is increased to 5.2 atm the crystalline substance melts to a liquid at −56.6°. Under ordinary pressure, then, the solid substance is changed directly to a gas. This property has made solid carbon dioxide (Dry Ice) popular as a refrigerating agent.

Carbon dioxide combines with water to form **carbonic acid,** H_2CO_3, a weak acid whose salts are the **carbonates.** The carbonates, especially *calcium carbonate*, $CaCO_3$, are important minerals. Carbon dioxide is used for the manufacture of *sodium carbonate*, $Na_2CO_3 \cdot 10H_2O$, *sodium hydrogen carbonate*, $NaHCO_3$, and *carbonated water*, for use as a beverage (soda water). Carbonated water is charged with carbon dioxide under a pressure of 3 or 4 atm.

Carbon dioxide can be used to extinguish fires by smothering them. One form of portable fire extinguisher is a cylinder of liquid carbon dioxide—the gas can be liquefied at ordinary temperatures under pressures of about 70 atm. Some commercial carbon dioxide (mainly solid carbon dioxide) is made from the gas emitted in nearly pure state from gas wells in the western United States. Most of the carbon dioxide used commercially is a by-product of cement mills, lime-kilns, and iron blast furnaces.

6–6. *Nitrogen*

Nitrogen is the lightest element of the fifth group. The chemistry of nitrogen is very interesting and important. Nitrogen is an essential element in most of the substances which make up living matter, including the proteins. Its important compounds include explosives, fertilizers, and other industrial materials.

Elementary nitrogen occurs in nature in the atmosphere, of which it constitutes 78% by volume. Compounds of nitrogen are made from free nitrogen by the action of lightning, which produces oxides of nitrogen which are carried into the soil by falling rain, and then become constituents of plants and animals. Nitrogen is also removed from the atmosphere by *nitrogen-fixing bacteria*, which live in nodules on the roots of some plants, especially the legumes—beans, peas, alfalfa, clover. In recent decades man has developed methods for the fixation of atmospheric nitrogen.

Nitrogen is a colorless, odorless, and tasteless gas. The elementary substance is composed of diatomic molecules, N_2. At $0°$ C and 1 atm pressure a liter of nitrogen weighs 1.2506 g. The gas condenses to a colorless liquid at $-195.8°$ C, and to a white solid at $-209.86°$ C. It is slightly soluble in water, 1 liter of which dissolves 23.5 ml of the gas at $0°$ C and 1 atm.

Nitrogen is chemically unreactive; it does not burn, and at ordinary temperature does not react with other elements. At high temperatures it combines with lithium, magnesium, calcium, and boron, to form *nitrides*, with the formulas Li_3N, Mg_3N_2, Ca_3N_2, and BN, respectively. In a mixture with oxygen through which electric sparks are passed it reacts slowly to form *nitric oxide*, NO.

Nitrogen is made commercially by the fractional distillation of liquid air. In the laboratory it is conveniently made, in slightly impure form, by removing oxygen from air. It may also be made by the oxidation of ammonia by hot copper oxide:

$$2NH_3 + 3CuO \longrightarrow 3H_2O + 3Cu + N_2 \uparrow$$

Compounds of Nitrogen.   **Ammonia**, NH_3, is an easily condensable gas (b.p. $-33.35°$ C; m.p. $-77.7°$ C), readily soluble in water to produce an alkaline solution. The gas is colorless and has a pungent odor, often detected around stables and manure piles, where ammonia is produced by decomposition of organic matter. The solution of ammonia in water is called **ammonium hydroxide** solution (or sometimes *ammonia water* or *aqua ammonia*). Ammonium hydroxide has the formula NH_4OH. It is a base, which forms salts with the common acids.

Ammonium chloride, NH_4Cl, is a white salt, with a bitter, salty taste. It is used in dry batteries (Chap. 13) and as a flux in soldering and welding (a flux is a material that forms a melt with metal oxides). **Ammonium sulfate**, $(NH_4)_2SO_4$, is an important fertilizer; and **ammonium nitrate**, NH_4NO_3, mixed with other substances, is used as an explosive, and also is used as a fertilizer.

Nitrogen forms six oxides: **nitrous oxide**, N_2O; **nitric oxide**, NO; **dinitrogen trioxide**, N_2O_3; **nitrogen dioxide**, NO_2; **dinitrogen tetroxide**, N_2O_4; and **dinitrogen pentoxide**, N_2O_5. Dinitrogen pentoxide is the anhydride of **nitric acid**, HNO_3. This acid is a colorless liquid with melting point $-42°$ C, boiling point $86°$ C, and density 1.52 g/cm^3. It is a strong and corrosive acid, which attacks the skin and gives it a yellow color. Its potassium salt, **potassium nitrate,** KNO_3 (*saltpeter*), is used in pickling meat (ham, corned beef), in medicine, and in the manufacture of *gunpowder*, which is an intimate mixture of potassium nitrate, charcoal, and sulfur, which explodes when ignited in a closed space. **Sodium nitrate,** $NaNO_3$, is used as a fertilizer, and for conversion into nitric acid and other nitrates. It is found in large quantities in Chile, and has the common name *Chile saltpeter*.

A more detailed discussion of the chemistry of nitrogen and of its congeners is given in Chapter 18.

6–7. *Fluorine*

Fluorine is the most reactive of all the elements, and it forms compounds with all the elements except the inert gases. Substances such as wood and rubber burst into flame when held in a stream of fluorine, and even asbestos (a silicate of magnesium and aluminum) reacts vigorously with it and becomes incandescent.

Platinum is attacked only slowly by fluorine. Copper and steel can be used as containers for the gas; they are attacked by it, but become coated with a thin layer of copper fluoride or iron fluoride which then protects them against further attack. Fluorine was first made in 1886 by the French chemist Henri Moissan (1852–1907), by the electrolysis of a solution of potassium fluoride, KF, in liquid hydrogen fluoride, HF. In recent years methods for its commercial production and transport (in steel tanks) have been developed, and it is now used in chemical industry in moderate quantities.

Fluorine is a pale-yellow gas, which condenses to a liquid at $-187°$ C and freezes at $-223°$ C.

Fluorine occurs in nature in minerals such as **fluorite,** CaF_2; **fluorapatite,** $Ca_5(PO_4)_3F$, which is a constituent of bones and teeth; and **cryolite,** Na_3AlF_6; and in small quantities in sea water. Its name, from Latin *fluere*, to flow, refers to the use of fluorite as a flux.

Hydrogen fluoride, HF, can be made by treating fluorite with sulfuric acid:

$$H_2SO_4 + CaF_2 \longrightarrow CaSO_4 + 2HF \uparrow$$

This method is used industrially. The reaction is usually carried out in the laboratory in a lead dish, because hydrogen fluoride attacks glass, porcelain, and other silicates.

The solution of hydrogen fluoride in water is called **hydrofluoric acid.** This solution, and also hydrogen fluoride gas, may be used for etching glass. The glass is covered with a thin layer of paraffin, through which the design to be etched, such as the graduations on a buret, is scratched with a stylus. The object is then treated with the acid. The reactions that occur are similar to those for quartz, SiO_2:

$$SiO_2 + 4HF \longrightarrow SiF_4 + 2H_2O$$

The product, SiF_4, **silicon tetrafluoride,** is a gas.

Hydrofluoric acid must be handled with great care, because on contact with the skin it produces sores which heal very slowly. The acid is stored in wax bottles.

The salts of hydrofluoric acid are called *fluorides.* **Sodium fluoride,** NaF, is used as an insecticide.

The congeners of fluorine—chlorine, bromine, and iodine—are similar to fluorine in chemical properties but are less reactive. These elements are called *halogens* (from the Greek words meaning *salt-producers*) because many of their compounds are salts.

6–8. *Crystal Form, Polymorphism, and Isomorphism*

Polymorphism, in chemistry, is the assumption of two or more crystalline forms by the same substance. Calcite and aragonite (Figs. 6-1 and 6-2) are different from one another in properties—they have different crystal form, different cleavage, different density (2.71 g/cm^3 and 2.93 g/cm^3, respectively); if they were not subjected to careful chemical analysis,

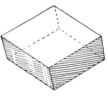

Mn CO_3

FIG. 6-4

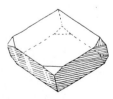

Ca CO_3

Isomorphous crystals of rhodochrosite and calcite (hexagonal system).

an investigator would say that they are two different substances. Analysis shows, however, that both calcite and aragonite consist of nearly pure calcium carbonate, $CaCO_3$. They are polymorphous crystalline forms of this substance, calcium carbonate.

The structures of the crystals of calcite and aragonite have been determined. It has been found that each of them consists of calcium ions and carbonate ions, but that the calcium ions and carbonate ions are arranged in a different way in calcite from that in aragonite.

Another phenomenon shown by crystals is *isomorphism*. Isomorphism is a strong resemblance in form of the crystals of two or more different substances. For example, the mineral rhodochrosite, which is manganous carbonate, $MnCO_3$, forms crystals which very closely resemble those of calcite, $CaCO_3$, except for difference in color (rhodochrosite is rose-pink in color, and calcite is colorless). The resemblance of the crystals is indicated in Figure 6-4. The rhombohedral angle (the angle between two edges, at the bottom or top of one of the rhombic faces) is measured on the crystals as 102°50′ for rhodochrosite and 101°55′ for calcite.

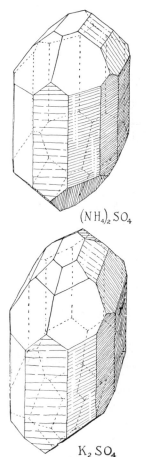

$(NH_4)_2SO_4$

K_2SO_4

FIG. 6-5

Isomorphous crystals of ammonium sulfate and potassium sulfate (orthorhombic system).

Another example of isomorphism is provided by crystals of ammonium sulfate, $(NH_4)_2SO_4$, and potassium sulfate, K_2SO_4, shown in Figure 6-5.

The phenomenon of isomorphism was discovered in 1819 by Eilhardt Mitscherlich, who noticed the close similarity between crystals of the substances $Na_2HPO_4 \cdot 12H_2O$ and $Na_2HAsO_4 \cdot 12H_2O$ (disodium hydrogen phosphate decahydrate, and the corresponding arsenate). Isomorphism is due to close similarity in the way the crystals are built of atoms, ions, or molecules. Isomorphous crystals usually have similar formulas, and corresponding atoms or ions usually are nearly equal in size.

Isomorphous substances usually crystallize together from a mixed solution in a solvent to form a solid solution (crystalline solution). In a solid solution the different atoms or ions are arranged at random in the positions occupied by one kind of ion alone in a pure substance. For example, solid solutions of chrome alum, $KCr(SO_4)_2 \cdot 12H_2O$, and alum, $KAl(SO_4)_2 \cdot 12H_2O$, may be prepared as single crystals varying in color from deep violet to colorless, with decrease in the fraction of chrome alum present.

The phenomenon of isomorphism was of value in the original determination of the correct atomic weights of the elements (Chap. 14).

Exercises

6-1.   Illustrate dependence of properties on atomic number by discussing three properties of lithium, beryllium, boron, and carbon.

6-2.   How is the decrease in electric conductivity of metals with increasing temperature explained by the electron theory of metals? How is the increase of electric conductivity of metalloids with increasing temperature explained by the electron theory?

6-3.   Discuss briefly the properties and uses of the alkali metals.

6-4.   Give the names and formulas of four compounds of sodium.

6-5.   Discuss the composition and action of baking powder.

6-6.   What are calcite, marble, limestone, aragonite, quicklime, slaked lime, mortar, gypsum, plaster of Paris?

6-7.   Write the equation for the conversion of colemanite, $Ca_2B_6O_{11} \cdot 5H_2O$, into borax, $Na_2B_4O_7 \cdot 10H_2O$, by treatment with sodium carbonate.

6-8.   Boric acid can be obtained from borax by treatment with sulfuric acid. The boric acid is not very soluble, and it crystallizes out as thin, pearly-white plates as the solution is cooled. Write the equation for this reaction.

6-9.   List the principal uses of aluminum and some of its compounds.

6-10.   What are the principal differences in properties of diamond and graphite?

6-11. Write the equation for the reaction of neutralization of ammonium hydroxide and hydrochloric acid, HCl.

6-12. Write the equations for the reactions of formation of hydrogen fluoride by treatment of fluorite with sulfuric acid, and the etching of glass by hydrofluoric acid.

Chapter 7

Weight Relations in Chemical Reactions

In every branch of chemistry it is necessary to make calculations about the weights of substances involved in chemical reactions: these are called *stoichiometric calculations* (from the Greek *stoicheion*, elementary constituent, and *metrein*, to measure).

These calculations can always be carried out by considering the atoms that are involved in the chemical reaction, and using their atomic weights. You must analyze each stoichiometric problem that you meet; do not memorize rules for solving these problems. When you have such a problem to solve, think about it until you are sure that you understand it; in particular, consider the behavior of the atoms involved. Then formulate a ratio of atomic weights to be used as a factor to get the answer, or formulate an equation containing the unknown quantity, and solve it. It is often helpful to solve a problem in steps, as is done in Example 4 below.

7–1. *The Quantitative Meaning of Chemical Symbols and Formulas*

A symbol such as Cu is used to indicate the element copper, either in the elementary substance or in compounds. It also means a definite amount of copper—one atom, or one atomic weight (63.54) in any weight units (such as 63.54 g or 63.54 lbs.). In particular, it is often used to mean one **gram-atom** of copper, 63.54 g—that is, the amount of copper that contains Avogadro's number of copper atoms.

Similarly, a formula such as $CuSO_4 \cdot 5H_2O$ represents the compound copper sulfate pentahydrate, which contains the four elements whose symbols are involved in the atomic ratios indicated by the formula. These ratios are 1Cu : 1S : 9O : 10H. The formula means also one formula weight (in arbitrary weight units) of the substance. In particular, the formula is often used to mean one **gram formula weight**, 249.69 g, and hence to mean 1 gram-atom of copper, plus 1 gram-atom of sulfur, 9 gram-atoms of oxygen, and 10 gram-atoms of hydrogen.

The *molecular weight* of a substance is the average weight* in atomic-weight units of a molecule of the substance. If the molecular formula of the substance is known the molecular weight can be calculated by adding the atomic weights of the atoms given in the formula of the substance. Inasmuch as the true molecular formula of a substance may not be known, it is often convenient to use the *formula weight*, the sum of the atomic weights of the atoms in an assumed formula for a substance, which need not be the correct molecular formula. A *gram formula weight* is then the amount of the substance with weight equal to the formula weight in grams, as indicated above for copper sulfate pentahydrate.

A **mole** (or *gram molecular weight*) of any substance is the amount of the substance with weight equal to the molecular weight in grams. When it is known that the formula written for a substance is its correct molecular formula the molecular weight and the formula weight are, of course, the same, and the mole equals the gram formula weight.

Often the state of aggregation of a substance is represented by appended letters; $Cu(c)$ and $Cu(s)$ refer to crystalline copper (*s* standing for solid), $Cu(l)$ to liquid copper, and $Cu(g)$ to gaseous copper. Sometimes a substance is indicated as solid or crystalline by a line drawn under its formula (both $\underline{AgCl}$ and $AgCl(c)$ mean crystalline silver chloride). A substance in solution in water is sometimes represented by its formula followed by *aq*.

7–2. *Examples of Stoichiometric Calculations*

There are no principles involved in stoichiometric calculations which should be new to the student of chemistry—the applications of arithmetic and algebra closely resemble those to the problems of physics or of everyday life. The only difficulty which he might have is that of getting accustomed to dealing with such small objects as atoms and mole-

---

* The expression "average weight" is used here because of the presence of different isotopes for most of the elements.

cules, and of recognizing the significance of a certain large number (Avogadro's number) of these atoms and molecules.

The sort of argument usually carried out in working stoichiometric problems is best indicated by the detailed solution of some examples.

In general, chemical problems may be solved by using a slide rule for the numerical work. This gives about three reliable figures in the answer, which is often all that is justified by the accuracy of the data. Sometimes the data are more reliable, and logarithms or longhand calculation must be used to obtain the answer with the accuracy called for.

Example 1.   How much copper is present in one pound of copper sulfate pentahydrate?

   Solution.   The formula of copper sulfate pentahydrate has been found by chemists of earlier generations to be $CuSO_4 \cdot 5H_2O$. Of the 21 atoms in a "molecule" of this substance (or, better, in a formula of the substance), only one is a copper atom. The formula weight of the substance is the weight (in atomic-weight units) of all 21 atoms:

1 Cu	63.54
1 S	32.07
4 O	64.00
10 H	10.08
5 O	80.00
	———
	249.69

Of this weight only 63.54 units is copper. Hence copper comprises the fraction $\dfrac{63.54}{249.69}$ of the substance, which is 0.254, or 25.4%.

   One pound of copper sulfate pentahydrate hence contains **0.254 lb.** of copper.

Example 2.   How much iron can be obtained by the reduction of five tons of hematite, Fe_2O_3?

   Solution.   We assume that all of the iron atoms in ferric oxide (hematite) can be converted into elementary iron by reduction. We may write the corresponding equation:

$$Fe_2O_3 + \text{reducing agent} \longrightarrow 2Fe + \text{product}$$

   The formula weight of Fe_2O_3 is 159.70. The weight of the product is twice the atomic weight of iron, $2 \times 55.85 = 111.70$. The ratio of the **weight of iron** to the weight of hematite is accordingly $\frac{111.70}{159.70}$. The **weight of iron**, in tons, that can be produced from five tons of hematite is accordingly $\frac{111.70}{159.70} \times 5 = $ **3.50 tons.**

Example 3. An oxide of europium contains 86.4% europium. What is its simplest formula?

    Solution. The relative amounts of europium and oxygen in the compound are 86.4 and 13.6. Dividing these by the respective atomic weights (Eu, 152.0; O, 16), we obtain 0.568 for Eu and 0.850 for O as the relative numbers of atoms. Setting the ratio $\frac{0.568}{0.850}$ on the slide rule, we see that it is very close to 2/3, being 2/2.994. Hence the simplest formula is Eu_2O_3.

    We say that this is the simplest formula in order not to rule out the possibility that the substance contains more complex molecules, such as Eu_4O_6, in which case it would be proper to indicate in the formula the correct numbers of atoms per molecule, if they were known.

Example 4. A substance, "mycomycin," similar to penicillin and streptomycin, is produced by the bacterium *Norcardia acidophilus*. Crystals of the active substance were obtained from the broth in which the bacteria had been growing. The crystals were found to contain only carbon, hydrogen, and oxygen. In order to find out its chemical formula, a sample of the substance weighing 0.1141 g was heated in a stream of oxygen until it had been completely burned. The oxygen containing the products of combustion was then passed through a weighed tube containing calcium chloride, which absorbed the water vapor, but not the oxygen or carbon dioxide. It then went through another weighed tube containing a mixture of sodium hydroxide and calcium oxide, which absorbed the carbon dioxide. When the first tube was weighed, after the combustion had been completed, it was found to have increased in weight by 0.0519 g, this being accordingly the weight of water produced by the combustion of the sample. The second tube was found to have increased in weight by 0.3295 g. What is the simplest formula of the substance?

    Solution. It is convenient to solve this problem in steps. Let us first find out how many moles of water were produced. The number of moles of water produced is found by dividing 0.0519 by 18.02

the molecular weight of water; it is 0.00288. Each mole of water vapor contains two gram-atoms of hydrogen; hence the number of gram-atoms of hydrogen in the original sample is twice this number, or 0.00576.

Similarly, the number of moles of carbon dioxide in the products of combustion is obtained by dividing the weight of carbon dioxide, 0.3295 g, by the molecular weight of the substance, 44.01. It is 0.00749, which is also the number of gram-atoms of carbon in the sample of substance, because each molecule of carbon dioxide contains one atom of carbon.

The amount of oxygen in the original substance is found by subtracting from the weight of the sample the weight of carbon plus the weight of hydrogen. The weight of carbon is the number of gram-atoms of carbon, 0.00749, multiplied by the atomic weight, 12.01; hence it is 0.0899 g. The weight of hydrogen is the number of gram-atoms of hydrogen, 0.00576, multiplied by the atomic weight, 1.008; it is 0.0058 g. The weight of carbon plus the weight of hydrogen is accordingly 0.0957 g. If we subtract this from the weight of the sample, 0.1141 g, we obtain 0.0184 g as the weight of oxygen in the sample. The number of gram-atoms of oxygen is found by dividing this number by the atomic weight of oxygen, 16; it is 0.00115.

The sample thus was found to contain 0.00749 gram-atom of carbon, 0.00576 gram-atom of hydrogen, and 0.00115 gram-atom of oxygen. If we divide all of the numbers by the smallest one, we obtain the ratios 6.51 : 5.01 : 1. It is evident that the simplest integral ratios are obtained by multiplying these numbers by 2, which gives 13 : 10 : 2. These are the relative numbers of carbon atoms, hydrogen atoms, and oxygen atoms in the compound.

The analysis of the compound accordingly leads to the formula $C_{13}H_{10}O_2$.

If the chemist investigating this antibiotic substance is interested in attempting to synthesize it, he must next find the way in which the 13 carbon atoms, 10 hydrogen atoms, and 2 oxygen atoms are linked together in the molecule (that is, he must determine the structural formula of the molecule). The ways of determining the structural formulas of compounds containing carbon are a part of the branch of chemistry called organic chemistry. The chemist might then synthesize other substances related to the natural substance in structure, and test their physiological properties. Many valuable drugs have been found in this way.

7–3. *Historical Remarks: The Laws of Constant Proportions, Simple Multiple Proportions, and Combining Weights*

Three laws of stoichiometry may now be considered: the *law of constant proportions*, the *law of simple multiple proportions*, and the *law of combining weights*. These were originally empirical laws, based upon experiment. At the time when the laws were formulated it was seen that the atomic theory provides a simple explanation of them, and although the laws do not require that the atomic theory be true, most chemists accepted the theory as providing the simplest explanation of chemical weight relations.

Now, when there is no question as to the reality of atoms, and when their mode of combination in molecules and crystals is well understood, the three laws of stoichiometry are seen to be simple consequences of the existence and properties of atoms.

The Law of Constant Proportions. *Different samples of a substance contain elements in the same proportions.*

The properties of atoms are such that they tend to combine to form molecules or crystals in which atoms of different kinds are present in numbers which are in the ratios of small integers. With constant atomic weights, a substance consisting of such molecules or crystals would have constant composition.

In practice, constancy of composition is used as an important test of purity of substances. Other tests of purity often used are constancy of melting point, boiling point, density, and other physical properties on application of methods of purification such as fractional crystallization (the crystallization of a fraction of a substance, leaving the remaining fraction in solution) and fractional distillation.

The discovery of isotopes has caused the ideas about constancy of composition to be revised in an obvious way; only if the distribution of isotopes were uniform would substances show constant composition by weight. It has been found by experiment that for most elements the natural distribution of isotopes is uniform to within experimental error, which is often as small as one part in 100,000 in weight composition or one part in 1,000 in ratio of isotopes. An exception is lead; the amount of lead in purified lead compounds made from certain minerals varies over a range of about 1%, because of the predominance of either a light isotope (Pb^{206}) or a heavy isotope (Pb^{208}). The natural variations in the relative abundance of the isotope of sulfur, also, are sufficiently large to correspond to a range in the atomic weight from 32.063 to 32.069.

Daltonides and Berthollides. The law of constant proportions was enunciated by the French chemist Joseph Louis Proust (1754–1826) in 1799, and it was given strong support by John Dalton, because of its close relation to the atomic theory. The law was vigorously attacked by Claude Louis Berthollet (1748–1822), who contended that the composition of a compound depended on the way in which it was prepared. Proust defended the law by pointing out that some of the materials described by Berthollet as exceptions were mixtures (of different lead oxides, of mercurous salts and mercuric salts, etc.) or solutions.

Recently it has become customary to accept as substances not only those materials that, when purified, show constant composition, but also those that may have a small range of variability in composition. The substances with constant composition are called *daltonides*. They include molecular substances in general, such as water (H_2O), benzene (C_6H_6), organic compounds without exception. Salts in general are daltonides; the compound of sodium and chlorine, with composition represented by the formula Na^+Cl^-, contains equal numbers of sodium ions and chloride ions.

On the other hand, many compounds of metals with metals or of metals with metal-loids or with some non-metals show a range of composition—the composition depends on the condition of preparation. Compounds of this sort are called *berthollides*. An example is the compound that is obtained by heating iron and sulfur together in approximately equi-atomic ratios. When a small excess of iron is present during the preparation the composition of the phase corresponds approximately to the formula FeS. When, however, an excess of sulfur is present the composition of the FeS phase is approximately Fe_5S_6. Any composition between these limits can be achieved by varying the conditions of preparation of the substance.

Many intermetallic compounds are berthollides. An example is the phase γ brass, which has the ideal composition Cu_5Zn_8, corresponding to 62 weight-percent zinc. The composition varies, in fact, from 59 to 67 percent zinc. In the case of γ brass and many other berthollides the variability in composition is due to the replacement of atoms of one kind by atoms of the other kind in the crystal lattice; that is, there is a similarity between these compounds and the solid solutions described in Chapter 2.

The Law of Simple Multiple Proportions.   *When two elements combine to form more than one compound, the weights of one element which combine with the same weight of the other are in the ratios of small integers.*

This law is an obvious consequence of the simple integral atomic ratios in compounds. Thus water, H_2O, and hydrogen peroxide, H_2O_2, contain 8 g and 16 g, respectively, of oxygen combined with 1.008 g of hydrogen. Similarly, the oxides of nitrogen, N_2O, NO, N_2O_3, NO_2 (N_2O_4), and N_2O_5 contain nitrogen and oxygen in the ratio by weight of 14.008 g of nitrogen to 8, 16, 24, 32, and 40 g of oxygen, which are in the ratios 1 : 2 : 3 : 4 : 5.

The law of simple multiple proportions was originally stated by John Dalton, about the year 1803, largely on the basis of his speculations on the atomic structure of matter. Dalton assumed that compounds consist of molecules containing small numbers of atoms. This led him logically to the formulation of the law. The experimental basis for it at that time was very slight—most existent analyses gave ratios differing from integral ratios by 5 or 10%. Better analyses, reliable to 1%, were obtained in the period 1808–1812 by the Swedish chemist Berzelius.

The Law of Combining Weights.   *The weights of two elements (or simple multiples of these weights) which react with the same weight of a third element may also react with each other.*

The combining weights of the elements, to which the law refers, are the atomic weights or integral fractions of them; for some elements (hydrogen, sodium, chlorine, etc.) the combining weight is conventionally taken as equal to the atomic weight, and for other elements as equal to the atomic weight divided by a small integer. *Equivalent weights* of elements are the combining weights defined in this way. Thus the equivalent weights of hydrogen, oxygen, sodium, and chlorine are 1.0080, 8, 22.997, and 35.457, respectively; these weights of the elements combine to form the binary compounds H_2O, NaH, HCl, Na_2O, Cl_2O, and NaCl. In other known compounds, such as H_2O_2 and Na_2O_2, the elements have different equivalent weights.

The first work on combining weights was that of Cavendish, who in 1766 showed that the amounts of nitric acid and sulfuric acid which neutralize the same amount of potash (potassium carbonate) also react completely with the same amount of marble (calcium carbonate). Similar quantitative experiments with several acids and bases were carried out in 1791 by the German chemist J. B. Richter (1762–1807), and after Dalton's development of the atomic theory progress was rapid in the determination of equivalent weights.

Dalton had no way of determining the correct formulas of compounds, and he arbitrarily chose formulas as simple as possible, writing HO for water and HN for ammonia. His atomic weights for oxygen and nitrogen were thus the equivalent weights of these elements. Berzelius, using arguments which we shall mention later (Chap. 14), selected the correct multiples of the equivalent weights for nearly all the elements (his values for sodium, potassium, and silver were twice the modern values); but not all chemists accepted his assignments, and general agreement that water is H_2O and not HO was not reached until 1858. Because of this uncertainty of atomic weights some early chemists, including Davy, preferred to use only equivalent weights.

7–4. *Explanation and Reality*

In a preceding section it has been stated that the atomic theory provides a simple explanation of the laws of stoichiometry, and that there is now no question as to the reality of atoms. The thoughtful student may ask what the meanings of the words "explanation" and "reality" are, in these statements. These questions are not easy to answer; the great philosophers and scientists of past ages and of today have been deeply interested in them. The following discussion is far from exhaustive.

By the "explanation" of a phenomenon the scientist usually means the deduction of the phenomenon from general principles—that is, from laws or theories. For example, we may take as a phenomenon one of the laws of stoichiometry, say the law of multiple proportions, and as a general principle the atomic theory. From the discussion in the preceding sections we have seen that if we grant the atomic theory the law of multiple proportions follows necessarily, as a logical consequence. In short, we can deduce the law of multiple proportions from the atomic theory. And so we say that the atomic theory explains the law of multiple proportions. Again, let us take as a phenomenon the formation by the metal radium of a chloride containing 76% radium and 24% chlorine, and as a general principle the periodic law. The periodic law implies that every element has an atomic number and a (very nearly constant) atomic weight, both determinable by experiment. Experiment shows the atomic number of radium to be 88. This value places radium in group II of the periodic table. The periodic law then states that radium is almost certain to have a chloride with formula $RaCl_2$. Experiment further shows the atomic weights of radium and chlorine to be 226 and 35.5, respectively. These values lead to the observed percentage composition. Thus we explain the occurrence of a chloride of radium with the composition in question in terms of the periodic law.

A fascinating question which these examples may suggest is the following: Is it ever possible to explain the general principle used in a given explanation in terms of principles still more general? This is indeed frequently possible. An example is the explanation of the periodic law in terms of the electronic structure of the atoms, which was discovered about a quarter century ago, and of which we shall give an elementary account in Chapters 8, 9, and 10. Every discovery of this kind—every explanation of an explanation—marks an important advance in knowledge. By the same token, scientific explanation is not complete; it would be so only if a single general principle were to be found which would explain all known phenomena. The attainment of this goal seems extremely improbable so long as new phenomena continue to be sought for and found by observation and experiment, and we are at any rate very far from it at present.

What do we mean by the statement that atoms are real? Fortunately we can answer this without having to define reality in general—a question which is the subject matter of the branch of philosophy called metaphysics and has no place in science. By our statement we mean simply that atoms are things which have many of the properties of ordinary, visible, material objects. Both things, the atom and the ordinary material object, have their properties as the result of certain operations that we can carry out. As an ordinary material object let us consider a brick. The brick has a mass, which can be found by the operation of weighing the brick. It has a certain size and shape: by the operation of measurement we can find that the brick is two inches thick, and that a row of one hundred similar bricks would be two hundred inches long. It has a structure, which can be determined by a multitude of operations such as looking at it, cutting it into pieces, etc. In the same way, an atom has a mass, which can be found by suitable operations; the fact that these operations are, to a large extent, different from those used to determine the mass of the brick is beside the point. Furthermore, an atom has a definite size, which can be measured by spectroscopic methods or by X-ray diffraction. Finally, an atom has a structure, detailed information concerning which can be obtained from suitable experiments (that is, operations). This list of properties of a type which bricks and atoms have in common can be greatly extended, and it constitutes the essential content of our statement that atoms are real.

The reality of atoms thus defined must, however, not be taken to mean that atoms have all the properties of ordinary material objects, or vice versa. A perhaps trivial illustration of this is the fact that atoms are too small to be visible even under the highest-powered microscopes. But there are also very important respects in which atoms differ from ordinary material objects. Thus a quarter century ago it was discovered that a stream of atoms passing through a minute pinhole does not continue in a well-defined beam, as would be expected of ordinary material particles, but instead produces a set of diffraction rings, similar to those that would have been made by a beam of light. The production of the diffraction rings in this experiment shows that the atoms have another property, described by a wavelength—the moving atoms have *wave character*, as well as the character of ordinary particles. The laws of motion for atomic particles (electrons, protons, neutrons) are somewhat different from Newton's laws of motion. They are called the *laws of wave mechanics* or *quantum mechanics*. The difference between the quantum mechanical laws of motion and Newton's laws of motion becomes negligible as the mass of the particle becomes large.

The fact that atoms, electrons, nuclei, and other forms of matter have some properties that lead us to describe them as particles and other properties that we associate with waves is referred to as the *wave-particle duality* of matter. This wave-particle duality is hard to understand; but it is a fact—a part of the world in which we live. We shall discuss this question further in the following chapter.

7–5. The Determination of Atomic Weights by Chemical Methods

The chemical method of accurately determining atomic weights involves the determination of stoichiometric ratios. The procedure is illustrated by the examples given below and the problems at the end of the chapter.

In addition to this method, extensive use is made of the method of gas densities and, in recent years, of the mass-spectrographic method. The gas-density method is discussed in Chapter 14, and the mass-spectrographic method in the section following this one.

The modern values are due largely to Professor Theodore William Richards of Harvard University (1868–1928).

It has been found that few oxides can be prepared in sufficient purity to permit their direct use. On beginning his work Richards determined the ratio Ag : $AgNO_3$ by converting pure silver into silver nitrate. This ratio, 1 : 1.57479, and the value 14.008 for N, which was given by the gas-density method, led to 107.880 for Ag. He accepted this as the reference point for his other determinations. It has since been verified.

Let us carry out Richards' calculation:

We let x = the atomic weight of silver. We then have

$$\begin{array}{cc} x & x + 62.008 \\ \text{Ag} & : \text{AgNO}_3 \\ 1 & 1.57479 \end{array}$$

Hence

$$x = \frac{x + 62.008}{1.57479}$$

or, solving for x,

$$x = \frac{62.008}{0.57479} = \mathbf{107.880}$$

One method of checking the assumption of the value 14.008 for N is by determining the ratio Ag : NH_3. This was done[*] by determining the weight of ammonia required to neutralize a solution of hydrochloric acid or hydrobromic acid. The weight of silver which, on conversion into silver nitrate, just sufficed to precipitate all the halogen ion in the solution was then determined. The equations for the chemical reactions involved show that the ratio of this weight to that of the ammonia is the desired ratio Ag : NH_3; for eight experiments the average found is 6.33420. To use this ratio and that for Ag : $AgNO_3$ given above we proceed in the following way:

Let x = atomic weight of Ag, y = atomic weight of N.

$$\begin{array}{cc} x & x + y + 48 \\ \text{Ag} & : \text{AgNO}_3 \\ 1 & 1.57479 \end{array}$$

[*] G. P. Baxter and C. H. Greene, *J. Am. Chem. Soc.*, **53**, 604 (1931).

Hence
$$x = \frac{x + y + 48}{1.57479}$$

or
$$x = \frac{y + 48}{0.57479} \qquad\qquad (7\text{-}1)$$

We also have

$$x \quad y + 3 \times 1.0080$$
$$\text{Ag} : \text{NH}_3$$
$$6.33420 \quad 1$$

Hence
$$\frac{x}{6.33420} = y + 3.0240$$

or
$$x = 6.33420y + 6.33420 \times 3.0240. \qquad\qquad (7\text{-}2)$$

Eliminating x from 1 and 2, we obtain

$$6.33420y + 6.33420 \times 3.0240 = \frac{y + 48}{0.57479}$$

or

$$6.33420 \times 0.57479y - y = 48 - 6.33420 \times 3.0240 \times 0.57479$$

or

$$y = \textbf{14.0070,} \text{ the atomic weight of nitrogen}$$

Hence

$$x = \textbf{107.878,} \text{ the atomic weight of silver}$$

These values are only slightly smaller than the accepted values.

Values of the atomic weights of the halogens have been determined by the conversion of silver into silver halides. The halides have been found to be very useful in the determination of other atomic weights.

A survey of work done in this field is made annually by the Committee on Atomic Weights of the International Union of Chemistry. Its report is published in the *Journal of the American Chemical Society*, as well as in foreign journals.

7–6. *The Determination of Atomic Weights by Use of the Mass Spectrograph*

In 1907 Sir J. J. Thomson developed a method* of determining the *ratio of charge to mass* of an ionized atom (or ionized gas molecule) by

---

* J. J. Thomson, *Phil. Mag.*, **13**, 561 (1907); **20**, 752 (1910); **21**, 225 (1911); **24**, 209 (1912).

measuring the deflection of a beam of the ionized atoms in electric and magnetic fields. The apparatus is called a mass spectrograph. This physical apparatus has become useful in several ways in attacking chemical problems. Its principal uses have been for the discovery of isotopes and the determination of atomic weights. The importance of these uses justifies a brief discussion of the apparatus and the way it works.

Gaseous Ions.   The operation of a mass spectrograph depends upon the existence of *gaseous ions.*

Ions are atoms or molecules (complexes of atoms) which are not electrically neutral, but have a positive or negative electric charge. A positive charge occurs when the number of electrons present in the ion is less than the number required to neutralize the positive charge of the nucleus or nuclei—that is, is less than the atomic number of the atom, or the sum of the atomic numbers of the atoms in the molecule; and a negative charge occurs when the number of electrons is greater than the number required to neutralize the positive charge of the nucleus or nuclei.

Positive ions are called **cations,** and negative ions are called **anions.** These names are based upon the names of electrodes: cations are attracted toward the *cathode,* which is the negatively charged electrode; and anions are attracted toward the *anode.*

Let us consider, as an example, the element iodine, which was used as an example also in Chapter 2. Iodine gas at ordinary temperatures consists of diatomic molecules, I_2. As the temperature is raised some of these molecules respond to the greatly increased thermal agitation by being broken into separate atoms, I. This partial dissociation of the gas into atoms can also be achieved at room temperature by passing an electric discharge through the gas. A fast-moving electron (or ion) in the electric discharge may strike a molecule of iodine so vigorously as to cause it to split into atoms:

$$I_2 \longrightarrow 2I$$

In such a discharge ions of iodine also are formed. An iodine molecule may be struck such a blow as to cause the two nuclei to separate with unequal numbers of electrons; that is, the molecule is caused to dissociate into one anion, with an extra electron, and one cation, with an electron missing:

$$I_2 \longrightarrow I^- + I^+$$

A cation I^+ might suffer another collision which would cause it to lose another electron, converting it into a doubly charged cation:

$$I^+ \xrightarrow[\text{collision}]{} I^{++} + e^-$$

The symbol e^- is used for a free electron, and the obvious symbols I^-, I^+, I^{++} for ions, their electric charges being indicated by superscripts.

All atoms, even such stable atoms as those of the inert gases, can be made to form gaseous cations in an electric discharge through a gas at low pressure. Some atoms also form stable, singly charged gaseous anions. Molecules also form ions under these circumstances: an electric discharge through methane, CH_4, produces gaseous molecular ions such as CH_4^+, CH_3^+, CH_2^+, and CH^+ as well as atomic ions such as H^+ (H^{++}, of course, does not exist), C^+, C^{++}, C^{+++}.

The Principle of the Mass Spectrograph.   The principle of the mass spectrograph can be illustrated by the simple apparatus shown in Figure 7-1.

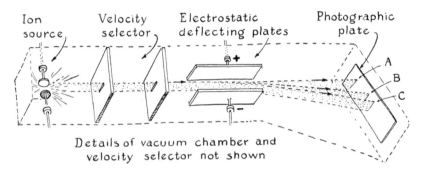

FIG. 7-1   *Diagram of a simple mass spectrograph.*

At the left is a chamber in which positive ions are formed by an electric discharge, and then accelerated toward the right by an electric potential. The ions passing through the first slit have different velocities; in the second part of the apparatus those with approximately a certain velocity are selected, and allowed to pass through the second slit, the ions with other velocities being stopped. [We shall not attempt to describe the construction of the velocity selector; the curious student may refer to W. R. Smythe, *Physical Review*, **28**, 1275 (1926).] The ions passing the second slit then move on between two metal plates, one with a positive electric charge and the other with a negative charge; the ions accordingly undergo an acceleration toward the negative plate, and are deflected from the straight-line path A that they would pursue if the plates were not charged.

The electrostatic force acting on an ion between these plates is proportional to $+ne$, its charge (n being the number of missing electrons), and its inertia is proportional to its mass M. The amount of deflection is hence determined by ne/M, the ratio of the charge of the ion to its mass.

Of two ions with the same charge, the lighter one will be deflected in this apparatus by the greater amount. The beam C might accord-

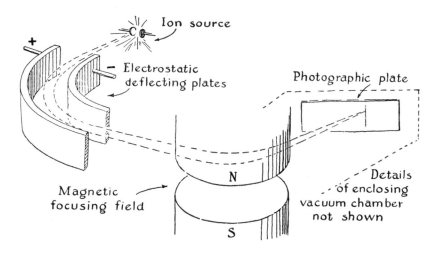

FIG. 7-2 *A focusing mass spectrograph, using both electrostatic and magnetic deflection of the beam of ions.*

ingly represent the ion C^+, with charge $+e$ and mass 12 atomic-weight units, and the beam B the heavier ion O^+, with the same charge and mass 16.

Of two ions with the same mass, the one with the greater charge will be deflected by the greater amount. Beams B and C might represent O^{++} and O^{+++}, respectively.

By measuring the deflection of the beams (as by measuring their traces on a photographic film) relative values of ne/M for different ions can be determined. Since e is constant, relative values of ne/M for different ions are also inverse relative values of M/n; therefore this method permits the direct experimental determination of the relative masses of atoms, and hence their atomic weights. By this method Thomson discovered the first non-radioactive isotopes, those of neon, in 1913.

The value of the integer n, the degree of ionization, can usually be fixed from knowledge of the substances present in the discharge tube; thus neon gives ions with $M/n = 20$ and 22 $(n = 1)$, 10 and 11 $(n = 2)$, etc.

Instead of the mass spectrograph described above, others of different design, using both an electric field and a magnetic field, are usually used. These instruments are designed so that they focus the beam of ions with given value of M/n into a sharp line on the photographic plate. An instrument of this sort,* using both an electric field, with curved plates, and a magnetic field, is sketched in Figure 7-2.

Thomson's apparatus did not permit very accurate results to be obtained. The method was increased in accuracy by F. W. Aston,† also working in the Cavendish Laboratory, and later by A. J. Dempster § of the University of Chicago. Modern types of mass spectrographs (Fig. 7-2) have an accuracy of about one part in 100,000 and a resolving power of 10,000 or more (that is, they are able to separate ion beams with values of ne/M differing by only one part in 10,000).

The great accuracy of modern mass spectrographs makes the mass-spectrographic method of determining atomic weights about as useful and important at present as the chemical method.

Mass-spectrographic comparisons with O^{16} are made in the following way. An ion source which produces ions both of oxygen and of the element to be investigated is used; the lines of oxygen and of the other element, in such states of ionization that their ne/M values are nearly the same, are then obtained; thus for S^{32}, S^{33}, and S^{34} the doubly ionized lines would lie near the line for singly ionized oxygen. Accurate relative measurements of these lines can then be made.

The Physicists' Atomic Weight Scale.   Atomic masses obtained with the mass spectrograph are reported relative to $O^{16} = 16.00000$. These atomic masses are called the *atomic weights on the physicists' scale*. Since ordinary oxygen contains 0.2% O^{18} and 0.04% O^{17}, these mass values must be corrected by division by a suitable divisor to give values on the chemists' atomic-weight scale, based on the average weight 16.00000 for ordinary oxygen; the value of this conversion divisor is 1.000272.

The Determination of Atomic Weights with the Mass Spectrograph.
The value of the atomic mass for a simple element (with only one iso-

---

* F. W. Aston, *Nature*, **137**, 357, 613 (1936).

† F. W. Aston, *Phil. Mag.*, **38**, 707 (1919); *Isotopes*, Longmans, 1924.

§ A. J. Dempster, *Phys. Rev.*, **11**, 316 (1918); **18**, 415 (1921); **21**, 209 (1923).

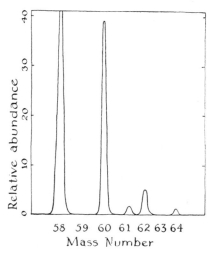

FIG. 7-3

Mass spectrogram of nickel, showing relative amounts of five isotopes.

tope) is its atomic weight. Thus for gold, consisting entirely of one isotope, Au^{197}, the mass-spectrographic mass (relative to O^{16}) is reported to be 197.039. Division by 1.000272 changes this to 196.985. The present value for the atomic weight of gold is 197.2; it is not unlikely that this will soon be revised to the mass-spectrographic value by the International Committee.

For an element consisting of several isotopes the chemical atomic weight is found by determining the masses of the different isotopes and also their relative amounts. The way that this is done is indicated in Figure 7-3, which shows the results of measurements on nickel. The composition of this element is found in this way to be Ni^{58}, 67.4%; Ni^{60}, 26.7%; Ni^{61}, 1.2%; Ni^{62}, 3.8%; and Ni^{64}, 0.88%. From these values and the isotopic masses the atomic weight is calculated to be 58.71 ± 0.02, in approximate agreement with the accepted value 58.69.

7–7. *The Determination of Atomic Weights by the X-Ray Method*

A new method of determining atomic weights, which may become of increased value in the future, is that of determining the molecular volume of a crystal by the evaluation of the dimensions of the unit parallelepiped by means of X-rays, and combining this with the density of the crystal to obtain a value of the molecular weight, from which the atomic weight of any element in the crystal can be found by use of known values for the other elements present. The use of this method for an elementary substance is illustrated in Exercise 7-24.

The X-ray method has been used* for the determination of the molecular weight of lithium fluoride, from which, by subtracting the atomic weight of lithium, the value

* C. A. Hutchinson and H. L. Johnson, "The Atomic Weight of Fluorine Calculated from Density and X-Ray Data," *J. Am. Chem. Soc.*, **69**, 1580 (1941).

18.9935 was obtained for the atomic weight of fluorine. This agrees very well with the accepted value 19.00.

A related use of X-rays is for the decision between two alternative chemical formulas for a substance. For example, the chemical analysis of ordinary crystalline ammonium paramolybdate ("ammonium molybdate") corresponds approximately to either of the formulas $(NH_4)_tH_7(MoO_4)_6$ and $(NH_4)_6H_8Mo_7O_{28}$, with formula weights 1,057 and 1,236, respectively. The volume of the unit cell is found by X-rays to be $2,865 \times 10^{-24}$ cm³, which gives, when multiplied by the measured density of the crystal, 2.871 g/cm³, and by Avogadro's number, 0.6024×10^{24}, the value 4,959 for the mass of the atoms in a mole of unit cells. This must be a multiple of the formula weight, since each unit cell contains an integral number of molecules. Of the two formula weights given above, the quotient of 4,959 by the first is 4.69, and that of 4,959 by the second is 4.01. The first quotient is not an integer; that is, an integral number of molecules with the first formula could not be present in the unit cell of the crystal, and the first formula is accordingly ruled out. On the other hand, the second quotient is equal to the integer 4, to within experimental error; hence the second formula is the correct one.*

Exercises

Note: Slide-rule accuracy is usually sufficient for chemical problems. This is not so for atomic-weight problems which contain data given to five or six significant figures; for these problems five-place or seven-place logarithms or some equivalent method of calculation must be used, and the atomic weights should be calculated to five or six significant figures.

7-1. What is the elementary composition of iron alum, $KFe(SO_4)_2 \cdot 12H_2O$; that is, what is the percentage of each element in it?

7-2. Calculate the elementary composition of sucrose, $C_{12}H_{22}O_{11}$.

7-3. A known fluoride of silver contains 91.9% Ag. What is its simplest formula? (Answer: Ag_2F.)

7-4. Two chlorides of a metal contain the metal to the extent of 50.91% and 46.37%, respectively. What are the possible values of the atomic weight of the metal? What is the metal? (Refer to the atomic-weight table.)

7-5. What is the composition by weight of the mixture of Hg_2I_2 and HgI_2 which is obtained by grinding together equal weights of mercury and iodine?

7-6. An oxychloride of vanadium is found on analysis to have the elementary composition V 60.17%, O 18.89%, Cl 20.94%. What is the simplest formula that can be assigned to it?

7-7. A sample of goat cheese weighing 0.1103 g was ignited, and the ash was dissolved in water and precipitated with silver nitrate, forming 0.00283 g of AgCl. Assuming the chloride in the cheese to be sodium chloride, calculate the percentage of sodium chloride in the cheese.

7-8. On combustion of a hydrocarbon (a substance containing only hydrogen and carbon) 0.02998 g gave 0.01587 g of H_2O and 0.10335 g of CO_2. What are possible formulas of the substance?

*J. H. Sturdivant, "The Formula of Ammonium Paramolybdate," *ibid.*, **59,** 630 (1937).

7-9. A compound of silicon, oxygen, and bromine was found on analysis to contain 10.20% Si and 86.85% Br. What is its simplest possible formula?

7-10. How much stannic chloride, $SnCl_4$, can be prepared from a ton of stannous fluoride, SnF_2, by the following reaction with chlorine?

$$2SnF_2 + 2Cl_2 \longrightarrow SnCl_4 + SnF_4$$

7-11. What is the percentage by weight of nitrogen in ammonium hexanitratocerate, $(NH_4)_2Ce(NO_3)_6$?

7-12. Kernite, $Na_2B_4O_7 \cdot 4H_2O$, can be shipped to its destination and there treated with water to form borax, $Na_2B_4O_7 \cdot 10H_2O$. What saving in freight costs results from doing this, instead of converting it to borax before shipping?

7-13. What is the percentage of oxygen in water, H_2O? in heavy water, D_2O (deuterium oxide)?

7-14. Potassium and cadmium form an intermetallic compound containing 2.61% potassium. What is its simplest formula?

7-15. Evaluate the atomic weight of iodine to five figures from the experimental ratio $AgI/AgCl = 1.638062$, assuming the accepted values for silver and chlorine.

7-16. In one experiment 1.44966 g of holmium chloride, $HoCl_3$, was precipitated with silver nitrate, forming 2.29770 g of silver chloride. Find the atomic weight of holmium.

7-17. In one experiment 2.25215 g of $POCl_3$ was dissolved in ammonium hydroxide solution and precipitated with silver nitrate, forming 6.31508 g of AgCl. Find the atomic weight of phosphorus.

7-18. By dissolving aluminum in hydrochloric acid, precipitating $Al(OH)_3$ with base, and heating the collected precipitate to convert it to the oxide, the ratio of aluminum to oxygen in the oxide was found to be 1.124015. Find the atomic weight of aluminum.

7-19. On complete combustion 6.06324 g of anthracene, $C_{14}H_{10}$, gave 20.96070 g of CO_2. Find the atomic weight of carbon, using 1.0080 for H.

7-20. $RaBr_2$ when heated in a stream of Cl_2 and HCl forms $RaCl_2$. From the ratio $RaBr_2/RaCl_2 = 1.299423$ find the atomic weight of radium.

7-21. Calculate (to five places) the atomic weight of iron on the chemists' scale from the following mass-spectrographic data:

Isotope	Fe^{54}	Fe^{56}	Fe^{57}	Fe^{58}
Atomic abundance	6.04%	91.57%	2.11%	0.28%
Mass (O^{16})	53.962	55.961	56.960	57.959

7-22. Calculate the atomic weight of titanium on the chemists' scale from the following mass-spectrographic data:

Isotope	Ti^{46}	Ti^{47}	Ti^{48}	Ti^{49}	Ti^{50}
Atomic abundance	7.95%	7.75%	73.45%	5.51%	5.34%
Mass ($O^{16} = 16$)	45.966	46.965	47.963	48.965	49.963

7-23. The isotopic ratios of oxygen, as determined by the mass spectrograph, are $O^{16}/O^{18} = 503 \pm 10$ and $O^{18}/O^{17} = 4.9 \pm 0.2$. Assuming the masses of the three isotopes to be in the ratios 16 : 17 : 18, calculate the conversion divisor from the mass-spectrographic atomic-weight scale ($O^{16} = 16.00000$) to the chemical atomic-weight scale ($O = 16.00000$). Note that this divisor can be obtained to six decimals with a slide-rule, by use of an appropriate method.

7-24. The edge of the unit cube of tungsten, containing two atoms, is found by X-rays to be 3.160×10^{-8} cm. The experimentally determined density is 19.35 g/cm³. Using 0.6024×10^{24} for Avogadro's number, calculate from the data the atomic weight of tungsten.

7-25. The amount 6.20 g of a compound containing only sulfur, hydrogen, and carbon is burned in chlorine. The products are HCl, 21.9 g; CCl₄, 30.8 g; SCl₂, 10.3 g. What is the simplest formula of the substance?

7-26. The isotopic composition of oxygen in the largest planet of Alpha Centauri is O^{16} 80%, O^{17} 20%, and that of calcium is Ca^{40} 50%, Ca^{44} 20%, Ca^{49} 30%. Calculate with slide-rule accuracy the chemical atomic weight of calcium on this planet, taking the physical atomic weights as exactly equal to the mass numbers.

7-27. An oxysulfide of phosphorus is found by experiment to contain 39.2% phosphorus, 40.4% oxygen, and 20.3% sulfur. An X-ray investigation of the substance shows that it consists of molecules, and that there are two molecules in a cubic unit of structure, with $a_0 = 9.00$ Å. The density of the substance is found by experiment to be 1.46 g/cm³. What is the simplest formula of the substance? What is its molecular formula?

7-28. The quantity 1.000 g of an oxide of uranium is treated with fluorine, to produce oxygen and 1.254 g of uranium hexafluoride, UF_6. What is the simplest formula of the substance?

7-29. The fermentation of sugar to ethyl alcohol in the manufacture of wine corresponds to the equation

$$C_6H_{12}O_6 \longrightarrow 2C_2H_5OH + 2CO_2$$

How much alcohol would be obtained by complete fermentation of 100 g of sugar?

7-30. When the mineral sphalerite is heated in air it is converted to zinc oxide by the reaction

$$2ZnS + 3O_2 \longrightarrow 2ZnO + 2SO_2$$

How much zinc oxide and how much sulfur dioxide would be produced from 100 kg of sphalerite?

Chapter 8

Quantum Theory and Molecular Structure

In the discussion of valence and the chemical bond in the two following chapters it will be necessary to refer to the quantum numbers that describe the electrons in atoms and molecules. Our present knowledge of molecular structure and understanding of chemistry in terms of electrons and nuclei have developed largely together with the quantum theory.

We shall now discuss some of the experiments upon which the quantum theory rests, and some of the arguments that were involved in its development. Knowledge of these aspects of physical science is essential to the proper appreciation of modern chemistry; and, moreover, the development of the quantum theory, aside from its significance to chemistry, constitutes one of the most interesting chapters in the intellectual history of man.

8–1. *The Birth of the Quantum Theory*

The quantum theory is a child of the twentieth century: it was announced, in its primitive form, in 1900, by its discoverer, Max Planck (1858–1947), a professor in the University of Berlin. He was led to the theory by the consideration of the nature of the radiation given out by a hot solid body.

In Chapter 3 we have discussed the wave properties of light. The wavelengths of light in the visible region, the infrared region, and the ultraviolet region have been determined by the use of a prism or a ruled grating, and the wavelengths of X-rays have been determined by diffraction from a crystal grating (see Figs. 3-20 to 3-26). The whole spectrum of light waves (electromagnetic waves) is shown in Figure 27-1, and the sequence of colors in the visible region is also shown, in the diagram next to the top one in this figure.

The visible spectrum is only a small part of the complete spectrum of electromagnetic waves. Ordinary X-rays have wavelengths approximately 1 Å. Even shorter wavelengths, 0.1, 0.01, 0.001 Å, are possessed by the gamma rays that are produced in radioactive decompositions and through the action of cosmic rays (Chap. 33). The ultraviolet region, not visible to the eye, consists of light somewhat shorter in wavelength than violet light, and the infrared consists of wavelengths somewhat longer than that of red light. Then there come the microwave regions, approximately 1 cm, and the longer radiowaves.

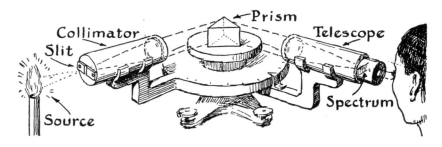

FIG. 8-1   *A simple spectroscope. The light from the source is refracted into a spectrum by use of a glass prism; it could instead be diffracted into a spectrum by use of a ruled grating, in place of the prism.*

When gases are heated or are excited by the passage of an electric spark the atoms and molecules in the gases emit light of definite wavelengths. The light that is emitted by an atom or molecule under these conditions is said to constitute its *emission spectrum*. The emission spectra of the alkali metals, mercury, and neon are shown in Figure 27-1. The emission spectra of elements, especially of the metals, can be used for identifying them, and *spectroscopic chemical analysis* is an important technique of analytical chemistry. The *spectroscope* is an instrument, using a ruled grating or a prism, for analyzing light into its constituent wavelengths, and determining their values. A simple spectroscope is shown in Figure 8-1. An instrument of this sort was used by the German chemist Robert Wilhelm Bunsen (1811–1899) to discover rubidium and cesium, in 1860. The instrument had been invented by the physicist Kirchhoff just the year before, and cesium was the first element to be discovered with its use.

It was found that the light that emerges through a hole from the hollow center of a hot body does not show characteristic emission lines, but has a smooth distribution of intensity with wavelength, characteristic of the temperature but independent of the nature of the hot body. This distribution is indicated, for three temperatures, in Figure 8-2. It is seen that at low temperatures, below 4,000° K, most of the energy is in the infrared region and only a small amount is in the visible region, between 4,000 Å and 8,000 Å. At 6,000° K the wavelength with the maximum amount of energy is about 5,000 Å, and a large fraction of the emitted energy is in the visible region. This is the temperature of the surface of the sun.

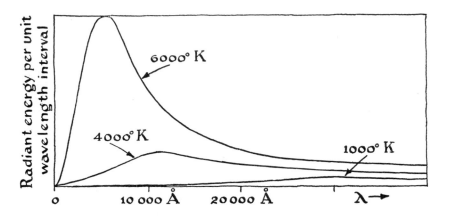

FIG. 8-2   *Curves showing the distribution of energy as a function of wavelength in the light in equilibrium with a hot body, at three different temperatures. Through the analysis of experimental curves of this sort Max Planck was led to the discovery of the quantum theory, in 1900.*

The theoretical physicists who were interested in the problem of the emission of light by hot bodies, during the years before 1900, found that they were unable to account for the curves shown in Figure 8-2 on the basis of the emission and absorption of light by vibrating molecules in the hot body, making use of the kinetic theory of molecular motion. Max Planck then discovered that a satisfactory theory could be formulated if the assumption were made that the hot body cannot emit or absorb light of a given wavelength in arbitrarily small amount, but must emit or absorb a certain quantum of energy of light of that wavelength. Although Planck's theory did not require that the light itself be considered as consisting of bundles of energy—*light quanta* or *photons*—it was soon pointed out by Einstein (in 1905) that other evidence supports this concept.

The amount of light energy of wavelength λ absorbed or emitted by a solid body in a single act was found by Planck to be proportional to the frequency ν (equal to c/λ):

$$E = h\nu \qquad (8\text{-}1)$$

In this equation E is the amount of energy of light with frequency ν emitted or absorbed in a single act, and h is the constant of proportionality. This constant h is a very important constant; it is one of the fundamental constants of nature, and the basis of the whole quantum theory. It is called **Planck's constant.** Its value is

$$h = \mathbf{6.6252 \times 10^{-27}\ erg\ sec} \qquad (8\text{-}2)$$

(The units of h, erg sec, have the dimensions of energy times time, as is required by Equation 8-1.)

We see that light of short wavelength consists of large bundles of energy and light of long wavelength of small bundles of energy. Some of the experiments in which these bundles of energy express their magnitudes will be discussed in the following section.

8–2. *The Photoelectric Effect and the Light Quantum*

In 1887 the German physicist Heinrich Hertz (1857–1894), who discovered radiowaves, observed that a spark passes between two metal electrodes at a lower voltage when ultraviolet light is shining on the electrodes than when they are not illuminated. It was then discovered by J. J. Thomson in 1898 that negative electric charges are emitted by a metal surface on which ultraviolet light impinges. A simple experiment to show this effect is represented in Figure 8-3. An electroscope is

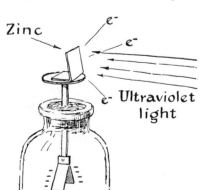

FIG. 8-3

A simple experiment showing the photoelectric effect. A negative charge is emitted by a zinc plate upon which ultraviolet light impinges.

negatively charged, and ultraviolet light is allowed to fall on the zinc plate in contact with it. The leaves of the electroscope fall, showing that the negative electric charge is being removed under the action of the ultraviolet light. If the electroscope has a large positive charge the leaves do not fall, showing that positive charges are not emitted under similar conditions. An uncharged electroscope becomes charged when the metal plate is illuminated with ultraviolet light, and the charge that remains on the leaves of the electroscope is a positive charge, showing that negative charges have left the metal.

J. J. Thomson was able to show that the negative electric charge that leaves the zinc plate under the influence of ultraviolet light consists of electrons. The emission of electrons by action of ultraviolet light or X-rays is called the *photoelectric effect*. The electrons that are given off by the metal plate are called *photoelectrons;* they are not different in character from other electrons.

A great deal was learned by the study of the photoelectric effect. It was soon found that visible light falling on a zinc plate does not cause the emission of photoelectrons, whereas ultraviolet light with a wavelength shorter than about 3,500 Å does cause their emission. The maximum wavelength that is effective is called the *photoelectric threshold*.

Substances differ in their photoelectric thresholds: the alkali metals are especially good photoelectric emitters, and their thresholds lie in the visible region; that for sodium is about 6,500 Å, so that visible light is effective with this metal except at the red end of the spectrum.

It was discovered that the photoelectrons are emitted with extra kinetic energy, depending upon the wavelength of the light. An apparatus somewhat like the photoelectric cell shown in Figure 8-4 can be used for this purpose. In this apparatus the photoelectrons that are emitted when the metal is illuminated are collected by a collecting electrode, and the number of them that strike the electrode can be found

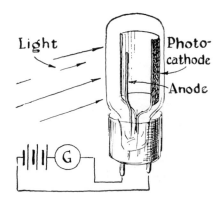

Light

Photo-cathode

Anode

FIG. 8-4

A photoelectric cell.

by measuring the current that flows along the wire to the electrode. A potential difference can be applied between the electrode and the emitting metal. If the collecting electrode is given a slight negative potential, which requires work to be done on the electrons to transfer them from the emitting metal to the collecting electrode, the flow of photoelectrons to the collecting electrode is stopped if the incident light has a wavelength close to the threshold, but it continues if the incident light has a wavelength much shorter than the threshold wavelength. By increasing the negative charge on the collecting electrode the potential difference can be made great enough to stop the flow of photoelectrons to the electrode.

These observations were explained by Einstein in 1905, by means of his theory of the photoelectric effect. He assumed that the light that impinges on the metal plate consists of *light quanta*, or *photons*, with energy $h\nu$, and that when the light is absorbed by the metal all of the energy of one photon is converted into energy of a photoelectron. However, the electron must use a certain amount of energy to escape from the metal. This may be represented by the symbol E_i (the energy of ionizing the metal). The remaining energy is kinetic energy of the photoelectron. The *Einstein photoelectric equation* is

$$h\nu = E_i + \tfrac{1}{2}mv^2 \tag{8-3}$$

This famous equation states that the energy of the light quantum, $h\nu$, is equal to the energy required to remove the electron from the metal, E_i, plus the kinetic energy imparted to the electron, $\tfrac{1}{2}mv^2$. The success of this equation in explaining the observations of the photoelectric effect was largely responsible for the acceptance of the idea of light quanta.

It is difficult to measure the velocity of the electrons directly. Instead, the energy quantity $\tfrac{1}{2}mv^2$ is measured by measuring the potential difference, V, which is necessary to keep the photoelectrons from striking the collecting electrode; the product of the potential difference V and the charge of the electron, e, is the amount of work done against the electrostatic field, and when V has just the value required to prevent the electrons from reaching the collecting plate there holds the relation

$$eV = \tfrac{1}{2}mv^2$$

Introducing this in the preceding equation, we obtain

$$eV = h\nu - E_i$$

or

$$V = \frac{h\nu}{e} - \frac{E_i}{e} \tag{8-4}$$

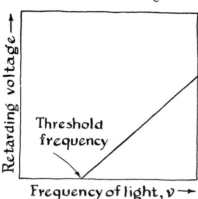

FIG. 8-5

Curve representing the result of experiments on the retarding voltage necessary to prevent the flow of photoelectrons to the anode, as a function of the frequency of light producing the photoelectrons. The threshold frequency is the frequency of light such that one quantum has just enough energy to remove an electron from the metal; a quantum of light with larger frequency is able to remove the electron from the metal and to give it some kinetic energy.

In Figure 8-5 this equation is plotted. The equation expresses a linear relation between the retarding voltage and the frequency of the light. The experimental observations lie on a line of just this sort. The intercept on the frequency axis, ν_0, corresponds to the photoelectric threshold for the metal. The slope of the curve is seen from Equation 8-4 to be equal to h/e—that is, to the ratio of Planck's constant, h, to the charge of the electron, e. R. A. Millikan in 1912 carried out careful measurements of the retarding voltage, in order to verify the Einstein equation. He used an apparatus similar to that shown in Figure 8-4, and his measurements led to a value of h/e which he could combine with his value of e to obtain a value for Planck's constant; this value for many years was the most accurate known.

The Photoelectric Cell. The photoelectric cell is used in talking motion pictures, television, automatic door-openers, and many other practical applications. The cell may be made by depositing a thin layer of an alkali metal on the inner surface of a small vacuum tube, as shown in Figure 8-4. The collecting electrode is positively charged, so that the photoelectrons are attracted to it. Illumination of the metal surface by any radiation with wavelength shorter than the photoelectric threshold causes the emission of photoelectrons, and a consequent flow of electric current through the circuit. The current may be registered on an ammeter. It is found that the magnitude of the current is proportional to the intensity of the light.

Example 1. How much energy is there in one quantum of light with wavelength 6,500 Å?

Solution. The amount of energy in a light quantum is $h\nu$, where h is Planck's constant and ν is the frequency of the light. The frequency of light of wavelength λ is c/λ; hence

$$\nu = \frac{3 \times 10^{10}}{6{,}500 \times 10^{-8}} = 4.62 \times 10^{14} \text{ cycles/sec}$$

Thus we obtain

energy of light quantum $= h\nu = 6.624 \times 10^{-27} \times 4.62 \times 10^{14} =$ $\mathbf{3.06 \times 10^{-12}}$ **erg**

Example 2. What retarding voltage would be required to stop the flow of photoelectrons produced by light of wavelength 6,500 Å from a sodium metal surface?

Solution. The photoelectric threshold of sodium metal is 6,500 Å. Accordingly, the photoelectrons that are produced have no kinetic energy: the amount of energy in the light quantum is just enough to remove the electron from the metal. Hence an extremely small retarding potential would stop the flow of photoelectrons under these conditions.

Example 3. What retarding potential would be required to stop the flow of photoelectrons in a photoelectric cell with sodium metal illuminated with light of wavelength 3,250 Å?

Solution. If, using the method of the solution of Example 1, we calculate the energy of a light quantum with wavelength 3,250 Å, we obtain the value 6.12×10^{-12} erg. This result can be obtained, in fact, with little calculation by noting that this wavelength is just half that of the photoelectric threshold, 6,500 Å; hence the frequency ν is twice as great, and the energy $h\nu$ is also twice as great (Example 1).

Of this total amount of energy in the light quantum, the amount 3.06×10^{-12} erg is used to remove the electron from the metal. The remaining amount, 3.06×10^{-12} erg, is kinetic energy of the photoelectron. The retarding potential that would slow the electron down to zero speed is such that its product with the charge of the electron is equal to this amount of energy:

$$eV = 3.06 \times 10^{-12} \text{ erg}$$

$$V = \frac{3.06 \times 10^{-12}}{4.80 \times 10^{-10}} = 6.38 \times 10^{-3} \text{ statvolt}$$

To convert statvolts into volts we multiply by 300 (1 statvolt = 300 volts); hence the retarding potential necessary to prevent the flow of photoelectrons in the sodium photoelectric cell illuminated with wavelength 3,250 Å is $300 \times 6.38 \times 10^{-3} =$ **1.91 volts.**

The Production of X-rays. The X-ray tube has been described in Chapters 3 and 4. In this tube there occurs the *inverse photoelectric effect*—

the production of a light quantum by slowing down a fast-moving electron.

In the X-ray tube electrons from the cathode are speeded up to high velocity by a potential difference V. Their kinetic energy then becomes equal to the energy quantity eV. When such a fast-moving electron strikes the anode it is quickly brought down to low velocity, perhaps to velocity zero. If it is brought to velocity zero the whole of its energy eV is converted into X-radiation (light), with energy $h\nu$ and corresponding frequency ν. The frequency of this radiation can hence be calculated from the photoelectric equation, $eV = h\nu$ (the ionization energy of the metal, E_i, can be neglected in this case, because it is a small energy quantity in comparison with the others). If the electron is not slowed down completely the frequency of the X-ray quantum that is emitted will be somewhat smaller than the limiting value.

Example 4.   An X-ray tube is operated at 50,000 volts. What is the short-wavelength limit of the X-rays that are produced?
  Solution.   The energy of an electron that strikes the anode in the X-ray tube is eV. The value of V, in electrostatic units, is $50,000/300 = 166.7$ statvolts. The value of eV is accordingly $4.80 \times 10^{-10} \times 166.7 = 8.01 \times 10^{-8}$ erg. This is equal to $h\nu$; hence for ν we have

$$\nu = \frac{8.01 \times 10^{-8}}{6.624 \times 10^{-27}} = 1.208 \times 10^{19} \text{ cycles/sec}$$

The wavelength λ is obtained by dividing the velocity of light by this quantity:

$$\lambda = \frac{c}{\nu} = \frac{3 \times 10^{10}}{1.208 \times 10^{19}} = 2.48 \times 10^{-9} \text{ cm} = \textbf{0.248 Å}$$

Hence the short-wavelength limit of an X-ray tube operated at 50,000 volts is calculated to be 0.248 Å.
  It is interesting to note that the preceding calculation can be simplified by combining all the steps into a single equation:

$$\text{short-wavelength limit (in Å)} = \frac{12,372}{\text{accelerating potential (in volts)}}$$

$$(8\text{-}5)$$

This equation states that a quantum of light in the near infrared, with wavelength 12,372 Å, has the same energy as an electron that has been accelerated by a potential difference of 1 volt. This energy quantity is sometimes called 1 *electron volt*, with abbreviation 1 ev.

The relations among the commonly used units of energy are summarized in Appendix I of this book.

Example 5. A beam of light with wavelength 6,500 Å and carrying the energy 1×10^5 ergs per second falls on a photoelectric cell, and is completely used in the production of photoelectrons. (This is about the energy of the light from the sun and sky on a bright day that strikes an area of 1 cm².) What is the magnitude of the photoelectric current that then flows in the circuit of which the photoelectric cell is a part?

Solution. The energy of one quantum of light with wavelength 6,500 Å is 3.06×10^{-12} erg. Hence there are $1 \times 10^5/3.06 \times 10^{-12} = 0.327 \times 10^{17}$ photons in the amount of light carrying 1×10^5 ergs of radiant energy, and this number of photons impinges on the metal of the photoelectric cell every second. The same number of photoelectrons would be produced. Multiplying by the charge of the electron, 4.80×10^{-10} statcoulomb, we obtain 1.57×10^7 statcoulombs as the amount of electric charge transferred from the sodium metal surface in the photoelectric cell to the collecting electrode each second. Dividing by 3×10^9, the number of statcoulombs in one coulomb, we obtain 5.22×10^{-3} as the number of coulombs transferred per second. One ampere is a flow of electricity at the rate of 1 coulomb per second; hence the current that is produced by the beam of light is 5.22×10^{-3} amp— that is, **5.22 milliamperes.**

8–3. *The Quantum Theory of Atomic Structure*

Most of our knowledge of the electronic structure of atoms has been obtained by the study of the light given out by atoms when they are excited by high temperature or by an electric arc or spark. The light that is emitted by atoms consists of lines of certain frequencies; it is described as the *line spectrum* of the atom.

The careful study of line spectra began about 1880. Early investigators made some progress in the interpretation of spectra, in recognizing regularities in the frequencies of the lines: the frequencies of the spectral lines of the hydrogen atom, for example, show an especially simple relationship with one another, which will be discussed below. The regularity is evident in the reproduction of a part of the spectrum of hydrogen in Figure 8-6. It was not until 1913, however, that the interpretation of the spectrum of hydrogen in terms of the electronic structure of the hydrogen atom was achieved. In this year Niels Bohr successfully applied the quantum theory to this problem, and laid the basis for the extraordinary advance in our understanding of the nature of matter that has been made during the past forty years.

The Quantum Theory of the Hydrogen Atom.   The hydrogen atom consists of an electron and a proton. The interaction of their electric charges, $-e$ and $+e$, respectively, corresponds to inverse-square attraction, in the same way that the gravitational interaction of the earth and the sun corresponds to inverse-square attraction. If Newton's laws of motion were applicable to the hydrogen atom we should accordingly expect that the electron, which is light compared with the nucleus,

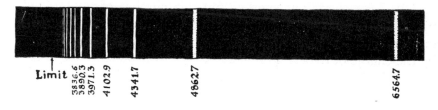

FIG. 8-6   *The Balmer series of spectral lines of atomic hydrogen. The line at the right, with the longest wavelength, is Hα. It corresponds to the transition from the state with* n = 3 *to the state with* n = 2.

would revolve about the nucleus in an elliptical orbit, in the same way that the earth revolves about the sun. The simplest orbit for the electron about the nucleus would be a circle, and Newton's laws of motion would permit the circle to be of any size, as determined by the energy of the system.

After the discovery of the electron and the proton this model was considered by physicists interested in atomic structure, and it became evident that the older theories of the motion of particles (Newton's laws of motion) and of electricity and magnetism could not apply to the atom. If the electron were revolving around the nucleus it should, according to electromagnetic theory, produce light, with the frequency of the light equal to the frequency of revolution of the electron in the atom. This emission of light by the moving electron is similar to the emission of radiowaves by the electrons that move back and forth in the antennae of a radio station. However, with the continued emission of energy, in the form of light, by the atom, the electron would move in a circle approaching more and more closely to the nucleus, and the frequency of its motion about the nucleus would become greater and greater. Accordingly, the older (classical) theories of motion and of electromagnetism would require that hydrogen atoms produce a spectrum of light of all wavelengths (a *continuous spectrum*). This is contrary to observation: the spectrum of hydrogen, produced in a discharge tube containing hydrogen atoms (formed by dissociation of hydrogen molecules), consists of lines, as shown in Figure 8-6. Moreover, it is known that the volume occupied by a hydrogen atom, in a solid or liquid substance, corresponds to a diameter of about 1 Å, whereas the older theory of the hydrogen atom contained no mechanism for preventing the electron from approaching more and more closely to the nucleus, and the atom from becoming far smaller than 1 Å in diameter.

A hint as to the way to solve this difficulty had been given to Bohr by Planck's quantum theory of emission of light by a hot body, and by Einstein's theory of the photoelectric effect and the light quantum. Both Planck and Einstein had assumed that light of frequency ν is not emitted or absorbed by matter in arbitrarily small amounts, but only in quanta of energy $h\nu$. If a hydrogen atom in which the electron is revolving about the nucleus in a large circular orbit emits a quantum of energy $h\nu$, the electron must then be in a much different (smaller) circular orbit, corresponding to an energy value of the atom $h\nu$ less than its initial energy. Bohr accordingly assumed that *the hydrogen atom can exist only in certain states*, which are called the *stationary states* of the atom. He assumed that one of these states, the *ground state* or *normal state*, represents the minimum energy possible for the atom; it is accordingly the most stable state of the atom. The other states, with an excess of energy relative to the ground state, are called the *excited states* of the atom. He further assumed, in agreement with the earlier work of Planck and Einstein, that when an atom changes from a state with energy E'' to a state with energy E' the difference in energy $E'' - E'$ is equal to the energy of the light quantum that is emitted. This equation,

$$h\nu = E'' - E' \tag{8-6}$$

is called the *Bohr frequency rule;* it tells what the frequency of the light is that is emitted when an atom changes from an excited state with energy E'' to a lower state with energy E'.

The same equation also applies to the absorption of light by atoms. The frequency of the light absorbed in the transition from a lower state to an upper state is equal to the difference in energy of the upper state and the lower state divided by Planck's constant. The equation also applies to the emission and absorption of light by molecules and more complex systems.

Example 6.   It is found that a tube containing hydrogen atoms in their normal state does not absorb any light in the visible region, but only in the far ultraviolet. The absorption line of longest wavelength has $\lambda = 1,216$ Å. What is the energy of the excited state of the hydrogen atom that is produced from the normal state by the absorption of a quantum of this light?

> **Solution.**   The frequency of the absorbed light is $\nu = c/\lambda = $ (2.998 $\times$ 10^{10} cm/sec)/(1.216 $\times$ 10^{-5} cm) = 2.467 $\times$ 10^{15} sec^{-1}. The energy of a light quantum is $h\nu$. This is just the energy of the excited state relative to the normal state of the hydrogen atom. Accordingly, the answer to our problem is
>
> energy of excited state relative to normal state = $h\nu$ = 6.624 $\times$ 10^{-27} erg sec $\times$ 2.467 $\times$ 10^{15} sec^{-1} = **1.634 $\times$ 10^{-11} erg**
>
> This can be converted into electron volts in the usual way (Example 4); the answer is **10.20 ev.** This result could be obtained simply by applying Equation 8-5; 12,372/1,216 Å = 10.20 ev.

Bohr also discovered a method of calculating the energy of the stationary states of the hydrogen atom, with use of Planck's constant. He found that the correct values of the energies of the stationary states were obtained if he assumed that the orbits of the electrons are circular, and that the angular momentum of the electron has for the normal state the value $h/2\pi$, for the first excited state the value $2h/2\pi$, for the next excited state the value $3h/2\pi$, and so on.

In general, the angular momentum of the electron in the circular orbit about the nucleus (the *Bohr orbit*) was represented by Bohr as having the value

$$\text{angular momentum} = \frac{nh}{2\pi}, \text{ with } n = 1, 2, 3 \cdots \qquad (8\text{-}7)$$

The number n introduced in this way in the Bohr theory is called the *principal quantum number* of the Bohr orbit.

The radius of the Bohr orbit is found to be equal to n^2a_0, in which

$$a_0 = h^2/4\pi^2me^2 = 0.530 \text{ Å}$$

In this equation m is the mass of the electron and e is the electronic charge. Thus the radius of the Bohr orbit for the normal state of the hydrogen atom is 0.530 Å, that for the first excited state is four times as great, that for the next excited state nine times as great, **and** so on, as illustrated in Figure 8-7.

The energy of the atom in the nth stationary state is given by the Bohr theory (as described in the following section) by the equation

$$E_n = -\frac{2\pi^2 me^4}{n^2 h^2} \tag{8-8}$$

Making use of the Bohr frequency rule, we obtain from this expression the following equation for the wavelength of the light emitted or ab-

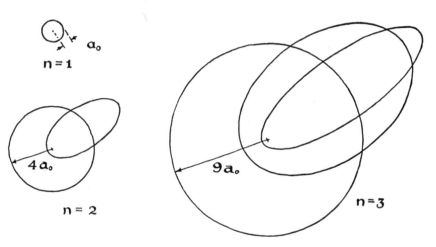

FIG. 8-7   *Bohr orbits for an electron in the hydrogen atom. These circular and elliptical orbits were involved in the Bohr theory. They do not provide a correct description of the motion of the electron in the hydrogen atom. According to the theory of quantum mechanics, which seems to be essentially correct, the electron moves about the nucleus in the hydrogen atom in roughly the way described by Bohr, but the motion in the normal state (n = 1) is not in a circle, but is radial (in and out, toward the nucleus and away from the nucleus). The average distance of the electron from the nucleus, according to quantum mechanics, is the same as the radius of the Bohr orbit.*

sorbed on transition between the n' stationary state and the n'' stationary state:

$$\frac{1}{\lambda} = \frac{2\pi^2 me^4}{ch^3} \left[\frac{1}{n'^2} - \frac{1}{n''^2} \right] \tag{8-9}$$

On introducing the numerical values of the mass of the electron, the charge of the electron, the velocity of light, and Planck's constant, we obtain

$$\frac{1}{\lambda} = 109{,}678 \left[\frac{1}{n'^2} - \frac{1}{n''^2} \right] \text{cm}^{-1} \tag{8-10}$$

This equation, with n'' and n' given various integral values, accounts for the line spectrum of hydrogen. There was great excitement in 1913 when Bohr developed this theory, because the theory permitted him to calculate the spectral lines of hydrogen completely from physical quantities that had been determined by the use of other experiments. The charge of the electron had been determined by Millikan's oil-drop method; the mass of the electron had been determined by experiments such as that of J. J. Thomson, described in Chapter 3; Planck's constant had been determined by Planck from the experimental measurements of the distribution of intensity with wavelengths in the light given out by a hot body, and more accurately by Millikan through his experiments on the photoelectric effect; and the velocity of light had been determined by Albert A. Michelson. Many investigators immediately began to extend the theory and to check it by further experiment.

The spectrum shown in Figure 8-6 does not contain the lines representing transitions to the normal state of hydrogen ($n' = 1$), but rather the lines representing transitions from the higher excited states to the first excited state ($n' = 2$) (Fig. 8-8). The equation for these lines is

$$\frac{1}{\lambda} = 109{,}678 \left[\frac{1}{4} - \frac{1}{n''^2} \right] \text{cm}^{-1}, \; n'' = 3, \, 4, \, 5, \, \dots$$

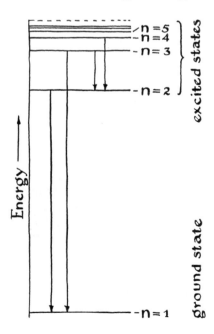

FIG. 8-8

Energy-level diagram for the hydrogen atom.

That is, the value of n' has been placed equal to 2, corresponding to the first excited state. This series of lines is called the *Balmer series* of spectral lines of hydrogen. The series involving as its lower state the state with $n = 3$, and that involving the state with $n = 4$, were also known at the time that Bohr carried out his work. The series with the ground state, $n = 1$, as the lower state for the transition had not, however, been recognized. Bohr predicted that this series would exist, and he calculated the wavelengths of the lines ($\lambda = 1{,}216$ Å, etc.). Experimental physicists immediately began the search for these lines, lying in the far ultraviolet region, which involved difficult experimental technique, and in 1915 Professor Theodore Lyman of Harvard University discovered the lines, which are called the Lyman series.

Bohr's Mathematical Theory of the Hydrogen Atom.   We may calculate the properties of the hydrogen atom in the way first carried out by Bohr. In Figure 8-9, representing the motion of the electron about the nucleus in the circular orbit, we see that the velocity of the electron, which at any instant is in a direction tangent to the circular orbit, changes as the electron proceeds around the circle. This requires that the electron be accelerated toward the nucleus. The amount of the acceleration is calculated from the geometry of the figure to be v^2/r, and hence the force required to produce it is mv^2/r. This force is the coulomb force of attraction, e^2/r^2. We thus have the equation

$$\frac{mv^2}{r} = \frac{e^2}{r^2}$$

or, multiplying by r,

$$mv^2 = \frac{e^2}{r} \tag{8-11}$$

Note that this equation gives a relation between the kinetic energy, which is $\frac{1}{2}mv^2$, and the potential energy, which is $\dfrac{-e^2}{r}$; namely, the kinetic energy is equal to ½ the potential energy, with the sign changed.

The angular momentum of the electron in its circular orbit is the linear momentum times the radius; that is, it is equal to mvr. Bohr made the assumption that the angular momentum must be equal to $nh/2\pi$:

FIG. 8-9

Diagram illustrating the calculation of centrifugal force to balance the centripetal force of electrostatic attraction, in the Bohr theory of the hydrogen atom.

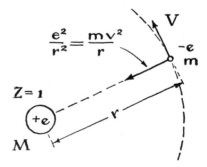

$$mvr = \frac{nh}{2\pi} \tag{8-12}$$

Multiplying Equation 8-11 by mr^2, we obtain

$$m^2v^2r^2 = e^2mr$$

The left side of this equation is just the square of the quantity on the left side of Equation 8-12; accordingly, it is equal to the square of the right side of this equation, which is $\frac{n^2h^2}{4\pi^2}$. Thus we obtain the equation

$$\frac{n^2h^2}{4\pi^2} = e^2mr$$

The equation for the radius of the orbit is given by solving this for r:

$$r = \frac{n^2h^2}{4\pi^2me^2} = n^2 \times 0.530 \text{ Å} \tag{8-13}$$

With use of Equation 8-12, we can solve for the velocity, obtaining

$$v = \frac{2\pi e^2}{nh} = \frac{2.18 \times 10^8}{n} \text{ cm/sec} \tag{8-14}$$

The total energy, which is the sum of the kinetic energy and the potential energy, is seen to be given by the expression quoted above (Equation 8-8).

8–4. *Excitation and Ionization Energies*

Interesting verification of Bohr's idea about stationary states of atoms and molecules was provided by some electron-impact experiments carried out by James Franck (born 1882) and Gustav Hertz (born 1887) during the years 1914 to 1920. They were able to show that when a fast-moving electron collides with an atom or molecule it bounces off with only small loss of kinetic energy, unless it has a high enough speed to be able to raise the atom or molecule from its normal electronic state to an excited electronic state, or even to ionize the atom or molecule, by knocking an electron out of it.

The apparatus that they used is indicated diagrammatically in Figure 8-10. Electrons are boiled out of the hot filament, and are accelerated toward the grid by the accelerating potential difference V_1. Many of these electrons pass through the perforations in the grid, and strike the collecting plate, which is held at a negative voltage relative to the grid. The electrons are able to move against the electrostatic field between the grid and the collecting plate because of the kinetic energy that they have gained while being accelerated from the filament to the grid. Even if there are some atoms or gas molecules in the space between the filament and the grid, the electrons may bounce off from them without much loss in energy.

If, however, the accelerating voltage V_1 is great enough so that the kinetic energy picked up by the electron exceeds the excitation energy of the atom or molecule with which the electron may collide, then the electron on impact with the atom or molecule may raise it from the normal state to the first excited state. The colliding electron will retain only the kinetic energy equal to its original kinetic energy minus the excitation energy of the atom or molecule with which it has collided. It may then not have enough residual kinetic energy to travel to the plate, against the opposing field, and the current registered by the galvanometer to the plate may show a decrease, as the accelerating voltage is increased.

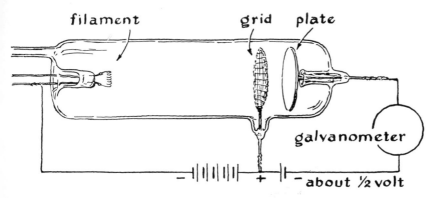

FIG. 8-10   *Apparatus for electron-impact experiments of the sort carried out by Franck and Hertz.*

With hydrogen atoms in the tube, for example, no change in the plate current would be registered on the galvanometer until the accelerating voltage reaches 10.2 v. At this accelerating voltage the electrons obtain from the field between the filament and the grid just enough energy to raise a normal hydrogen atom to the first excited state—that is, to change the quantum number from $n = 1$ to $n = 2$. There then occurs a decrease in the plate current. The voltage 10.2 v is called a *critical voltage* or *critical potential* for atomic hydrogen. Other critical potentials occur, corresponding to the other excited states, and a large one occurs at 13.60 v. This critical voltage, 13.60 v, corresponds to the energy, 13.60 ev, required to remove an electron completely from the hydrogen atom; that is, it corresponds to the energy required to convert a normal hydrogen atom into a proton plus an electron, far removed from it. The voltage 13.60 v is called the *ionization potential* of the hydrogen atom, and the amount of energy 13.60 ev is called the *ionization energy* of the hydrogen atom.

The first ionization energies of some atoms (the energy required to remove the first electron from the neutral atom) are given in Table 8-1, in both electron volts and kilocalories per mole. It is interesting to note that there is a correlation between the ionization energies and the chemical properties of the elements. The element with the smallest ionization energy, cesium, is the most metallic of all elements, and the other strongly metallic elements, the alkali metals, also have small ionization energies. The elements of the second group, the alkaline-earth metals, have somewhat larger ionization energies, and the ionization energies increase in value, although not regularly, to the halogens. The noble gases have very large ionization energies, which are, of course, associated with their chemical inertness.

We can, moreover, understand why for a given group in the periodic table the ionization energy decreases with increase in atomic number. The atoms become larger as the atomic number increases, and the electron that is removed on ionization, which is one of the outermost electrons of the atom, is not bound so tightly to the nucleus in a large atom as in a small atom.

TABLE 8-1   *Ionization Energies of Elements*

ELEMENT	IONIZATION ENERGY	
	in ev	in kcal/mole
Hydrogen	13.60	313.6
Helium	24.58	567
Lithium	5.39	124.3
Beryllium	9.32	214.9
Boron	8.30	191.4
Carbon	11.26	259.7
Nitrogen	14.54	335.3
Oxygen	13.61	314.0
Fluorine	17.42	402.0
Neon	21.56	497.2
Sodium	5.14	118.5
Potassium	4.34	100.1
Rubidium	4.16	95.9
Cesium	3.87	89.2

8–5. *The Pauli Exclusion Principle and the Spin of the Electron*

Several important additions to the theory of atomic structure were made in the years 1924 and 1925. These include the discovery of the spinning electron, the formulation of the Pauli exclusion principle, the discovery of the wave character of the electron, and the development of a new theory of quantum mechanics.

The lines in the Balmer series of hydrogen, shown in Figure 8-6, are not, in fact, single lines, but are split into pairs of lines that differ only slightly in wavelength. Similarly, many of the spectral lines of the alkali metals are doublets; an example is provided by the sodium D lines, which were mentioned in an earlier section as having the wavelengths 5,890 Å and 5,896 Å (see Fig. 27-1). The explanation of this splitting of energy levels into doublet levels was provided in 1925 by G. E. Uhlenbeck (born 1900) and S. Goudsmit (born 1902), who had discovered that the splitting could be accounted for quantitatively by assuming that the electron is spinning about its own axis. Because the electron is negatively charged, the spin about its axis confers on it a magnetic moment; that is, it is similar in nature to a small magnet, with a north-seeking pole and a south-seeking pole. The quantum theory requires that this small magnet, the electron spin, be oriented in a magnetic field in one of two ways, either parallel to the field or antiparallel (opposed) to the field. In the motion of the electron around the nucleus the orbit of the electron itself corresponds to an electric circuit, and produces a magnetic field, which interacts with the magnetic field of the electron spin in such a way as to change the energy of the system. The two orientations of the electron spin correspond then to two energy levels that lie close together.

In the same year, 1925, Wolfgang Pauli (born 1900) proposed a simple principle of great importance, which is called the *Pauli exclusion principle*. He stated that no two electrons can have exactly the same set of quantum numbers—that is, that no two electrons can be in exactly the same state. Thus in the helium atom two electrons might occupy the most stable orbit, the orbit with $n = 1$. According to the Pauli exclusion principle, however, they can do so only if their spins are opposed. Moreover, we see that lithium, the third element, cannot have three electrons in the orbit with $n = 1$, because the third electron would have to have its spin parallel to the spin of the first electron or the spin of the second electron, and this is ruled out by the exclusion principle. Accordingly, the lithium atom in its normal state must have two electrons in the orbit with $n = 1$, the most stable orbit, and one electron in a less stable orbit, with $n = 2$.

The great variety of chemical properties of the ninety-eight elements, and the periodicity that permitted the periodic system to be formulated, are the result of the property of nature that is expressed in the Pauli exclusion principle. If it were not for this principle—if successive electrons in any number could enter the most stable orbit in every atom, with $n = 1$—the chemical and physical properties of substances would change only uniformly with increase in the atomic number, and the world would not show the great variety in structure and composition that it does show.

8–6. *Electron Waves and Quantum Mechanics*

During the period of twelve years following the formulation by Bohr of the orbital theory of the atom great progress was made in interpreting the observed spectra and other experimental results, such as those obtained by the electron-impact method. Especially important was the discovery by Arnold Sommerfeld (1868–1951) that the quantum theory could be applied to elliptical orbits as well as circular orbits. Some quantized elliptical orbits are shown in Figure 8-7.

Many difficulties in interpreting observations in terms of the quantum theory arose, however, and these were not overcome until the years 1924 and 1925. During these years there occurred a great increase in our knowledge about the nature of matter. It was recognized that electrons and other forms of matter have properties similar to those of waves, as well as properties that we normally ascribe to particles.

The wave character of the electron was discovered by the French physicist Louis de Broglie (born 1892). While making a theoretical study of the quantum theory, to serve as his thesis for the doctor's degree from the University of Paris, he recognized that a striking analogy between the properties of electrons and the properties of light quanta could be recognized if a moving electron were to be assigned a wavelength. This wavelength is now called the *de Broglie wavelength of the electron*.

The equation for the wavelength of the electron is

$$\lambda = \frac{h}{mv} \tag{8-15}$$

In this equation λ is the wavelength of the electron, h is Planck's constant, m is the mass of the electron, and v is the velocity of the electron. It is seen that according to this equation a stationary electron has infinite wavelength, and that the wavelength decreases with increase in the velocity of the electron.

Example 7.   What is the wavelength of an electron with 13.6 ev of kinetic energy?

Solution.   One volt is 1/300 statvolt. The energy of a 13.6-ev electron is accordingly

$$E = 13.6 \times 4.80 \times 10^{-10}/300 = 0.218 \times 10^{-10} \text{ erg}$$

This is equal to $\frac{1}{2}mv^2$, the kinetic energy of an electron moving with velocity v; accordingly,

$$mv^2 = 0.436 \times 10^{-10} \text{ erg}$$

Multiplying both sides of this equation by m, we obtain

$$m^2v^2 = 0.436 \times 10^{-10} \times m = 0.436 \times 10^{-10} \times 9.107 \times 10^{-28}$$
$$= 3.96 \times 10^{-38}$$

By taking the square root of each side of this equation we obtain

$$mv = 1.99 \times 10^{-19} \text{ g cm sec}^{-1}$$

By use of the de Broglie equation we can now obtain the value for the wavelength:

$$\lambda = \frac{h}{mv} = \frac{6.624 \times 10^{-27} \text{ g cm}^2 \text{ sec}^{-1}}{1.99 \times 10^{-19} \text{ g cm sec}^{-1}} = 3.33 \times 10^{-8} \text{ cm} = \textbf{3.33 Å}$$

Accordingly, we have found that the de Broglie wavelength of an electron that has been accelerated by a 13.6-v potential difference is 3.33 Å.

We can now calculate easily the wavelength of an electron with 100 times as much kinetic energy—that is, an electron that has been accelerated by a potential difference of 1,360 v. Since the energy is proportional to the square of the velocity, such an electron has a velocity ten times that of a 13.6-ev electron, and, according to the de Broglie equation, its wavelength is 1/10 as great. Thus the wavelength of a 1,360-ev electron is 0.333 Å.

The Analogy Between the Photon and the Electron.   One part of the argument carried out by de Broglie in his discovery of the wavelength of the electron can be easily presented. The energy of a photon with frequency ν is $h\nu$. The mass of the photon is related to the energy by the Einstein equation

$$mc^2 = h\nu$$

where m represents the mass of the photon. Dividing each side of this equation by c, we obtain

$$mc = \frac{h\nu}{c}$$

In this equation v/c can be replaced by $1/\lambda$, giving

$$mc = \frac{h}{\lambda}$$

or

$$\lambda = \frac{h}{mc}$$

De Broglie pointed out that the same equation might be applied to an electron, by using m for the mass of the electron instead of the mass of the photon, and replacing c, the velocity of the photon, by v, the velocity of the electron. In this way the de Broglie equation is obtained.

The Wavelength of the Electron and the Bohr Orbit. De Broglie pointed out that the wavelength of the electron as given by his equation has just the value to give reinforcement of electron waves in the successive circular Bohr orbits. An example is the circular Bohr orbit with total quantum number n equal to 5. The length of the orbit, 2π times the radius, is just equal to five times the de Broglie wavelength for an electron moving with the velocity given by Bohr's theory for the electron in this orbit. Thus the electron waves could be considered to reinforce one another as the electron moves about the nucleus in this orbit, whereas in slightly smaller or slightly larger orbits the waves would interfere.

The calculation verifying this statement has been made in Example 7 above. The kinetic energy of an electron in the first Bohr orbit, the normal state of the hydrogen atom, is 13.60 ev. In the solution of this example we have found the wavelength of the electron to be 3.33 Å. The radius of the first Bohr orbit is 0.530 Å. When this is multiplied by 2π, the value 3.33 Å is obtained. Hence in the first Bohr orbit there is, according to de Broglie's calculation, just one wavelength in the circumference of the orbit. According to the Bohr theory the velocity of the electron in the nth Bohr orbit is just $1/n$ times the velocity in the first Bohr orbit, and the wavelength is accordingly $n \times 3.33$ Å. The circumference of the Bohr orbit is, however, proportional to n^2 (Equation 8-13), being equal to $n^2 \times 3.33$ Å. This calculation hence shows, as de Broglie discovered, that there are n electron wavelengths in the circumference of the nth Bohr orbit.

The Direct Experimental Verification of the Wavelength of the Electron. The wave character of moving electrons was established beyond question by the work of the American physicist C. J. Davisson (born 1881) and the English physicist G. P. Thomson (born 1892). These investigators found that electrons that are scattered by crystals produce a diffraction pattern, similar to that produced by X-rays scattered by crystals, and, moreover, that the diffraction pattern, interpreted by the Bragg law, corresponds to the wavelength given by the de Broglie equation.

The penetrating power of electrons through matter is far less than that of X-rays with the same wavelength. It is accordingly necessary to reflect the beam of electrons from the surface of a crystal (as was done by Davisson and his collaborators, using a single crystal of nickel), or to shoot a stream of high-speed electrons through a very thin crystal or layer of crystalline powder (as was done by Thomson).

The structure of crystals can be investigated by the electron-diffraction method as well as by the X-ray–diffraction method. The electron-diffraction method has been especially useful in studying the structure of very thin films on the surface of a crystal. For example, it has been shown that when argon is adsorbed on a clean face of a nickel crystal the argon atoms occupy only one-quarter of the positions formed by triangles of nickel atoms (in the octahedral face of the cubic closest-packed crystal). The structure of very thin films of metal oxide that are formed on the surface of metals, and that protect them against further corrosion, has been studied by this method.

The electron-diffraction method is also very useful for determining the structure of gas molecules. The way in which the diffraction pattern is formed is illustrated by Figure 3-20, which corresponds to the scattering of waves by a diatomic molecule. The molecules in a gas have different orientations, and the diffraction pattern is accordingly somewhat blurred. It consists of a series of rings. Knowledge of the wavelength of the electrons and measurement of the diameters of these rings permit calculation of the interatomic distances in the molecules. Since the discovery of the electron-diffraction method the structures of several hundred molecules have been determined in this way.

8–7. *Quantum Mechanics and Atomic Structure*

A great improvement in quantum theory, involving also the wave character of the electron, was made in 1925. The improved theory, which is called *quantum mechanics*, or *wave mechanics*, was developed principally by the German physicist Werner Heisenberg (born 1901), the Austrian physicist Erwin Schrödinger (born 1887), and the English physicist Paul Adrien Maurice Dirac (born 1902). The theory of quantum mechanics seems to be in complete agreement with the experimental information about the structure of atoms and molecules, but some additions probably need to be made before the theory is applicable to the discussion of the structure of nuclei. Quantum mechanics cannot be discussed in a brief elementary way, and in this book we shall have to be content with the description of some of its results, especially with respect to the electronic structure of atoms and molecules.

Quantum mechanics does not describe the motion of electrons in the atom so precisely as was done by Bohr. The properties of the atom that can be measured are, however, correctly given by the quantum-mechanical equations. These properties include, for example, the average distance of the electron from the nucleus, in a particular quantum state, and also the average speed with which the electron moves. It is found that the average distance of the electron from the nucleus is the same as was calculated by Bohr, and the average speed (the root-mean-square speed) is also the same. The angular momentum, however, is different, and in particular the electron in the hydrogen atom in its normal state is not moving around the nucleus in an orbit with angular momentum $h/2\pi$, but is moving in toward and out from the nucleus, in an orbit with zero angular momentum.

The electrons moving about a nucleus are described in quantum mechanics by certain mathematical functions, called *wave functions*. The wave function for one electron is called an *orbital wave function*, and the electron is said to occupy an *orbital* (rather than an orbit). The use of a different name indicates that the motion of the electron according to quantum mechanics is somewhat different from the motion in a Bohr orbit. There is only one orbital with principal quantum number $n = 1$; this orbital is called the $1s$ orbital, and is said to constitute the K shell. For $n = 2$ there are four orbitals; one of them is an orbital of high eccentricity and no angular momentum, called the $2s$ orbital, and the other three are orbitals corresponding to a nearly circular orbit, the $2p$ orbitals. The three different $2p$ orbitals represent different orientations of the orbit in space. These four orbitals, one $2s$ orbital and three $2p$ orbitals, constitute the L shell. The M shell is constituted of one $3s$ orbital, three $3p$ orbitals, and five $3d$ orbitals.

The electronic structure of atoms, as described by distributing the electrons among these orbitals, will be discussed in Chapter 10.

8–8. *What Is Light? What Is an Electron?*

During recent years many people have asked the following questions: Does light *really* consist of waves, or of particles? Is the electron *really* a particle, or is it a wave?

These questions cannot be answered by one of the two alternatives. Light is the name that we have given to describe a part of nature. The name refers to all of the properties that light has, to all of the phenomena that are observed in a system containing light. Some of the properties of light resemble those of waves, and can be described in terms of a wavelength. Other properties of light resemble those of particles, and can be described in terms of a light quantum, having a certain amount of energy, $h\nu$, and a certain mass, $h\nu/c^2$. A beam of light is neither a sequence of waves nor a stream of particles; it is both.

In the same way, an electron is neither a particle nor a wave, in the ordinary sense. In many ways the behavior of electrons is similar to that expected of small particles, with mass m and electric charge $-e$. But electrons differ from ordinary particles, such as ball bearings, in that they also behave as though they had wave character, with wavelength given by the de Broglie equation. The electron, like the photon, has to be described as having the character both of a particle and of a wave.

After the first period of adjustment to these new ideas about the nature of light and of electrons, scientists became accustomed to them, and found that they could usually predict when, in a certain experiment, the behavior of a beam of light would be determined mainly by its wavelength, and when it would be determined by the energy and mass of the photon; that is, they would know when it was convenient to consider light as consisting of waves, and when to consider it as consisting of particles, the photons. Similarly, they learned when it was convenient to consider an electron as a particle, and when as a wave. In some experiments the wave character and the particle character both contribute significantly, and it is then necessary to carry out a careful theoretical treatment, using the equations of quantum mechanics, in order to predict how the light or the electron will behave.

You may ask two other questions: Do electrons exist? What do they look like?

The answer to the first question is that electrons do exist: "electron" is the name that scientists have used in discussing certain phenomena, such as the beam in the electric discharge tube studied by J. J. Thomson, the carrier of the unit electric charge on the oil drops in Millikan's apparatus, the part that is added to the neutral fluorine atom to convert it into a fluoride ion. The second question—what does the electron look like?—cannot be answered. No one knows how to look at an electron— it is too small to be seen by scattering ordinary visible light from it, and unless somebody discovers some better way of studying nature than is now known, this question will remain unanswered.

Exercises

8-1.   Discuss briefly Planck's constant and its relation to the photoelectric effect.

8-2.   When an uncharged metal plate is illuminated with ultraviolet light the plate becomes positively charged. Explain the phenomenon, in particular why the plate becomes positively charged rather than negatively charged.

8-3.   The amount of energy required to remove an electron from a sodium atom in sodium vapor (to ionize the sodium atom) is 5.14 ev. What is the longest wavelength of light that you would expect to be able to ionize sodium atoms, assuming that the energy of ionization must be provided by one quantum of the light?

8-4.   Ozone, O_3, is produced in the upper atmosphere by ultraviolet light from the sun. The first step in the production of the ozone is the dissociation of an oxygen molecule into two oxygen atoms; each of the oxygen atoms then combines with another oxygen molecule, to form a molecule of ozone. The amount of energy required to dissociate an oxygen molecule into oxygen atoms is 5.08 ev. Calculate the limits of the region of wavelengths of ultraviolet light that would be effective in producing ozone.

8-5.   The amount of energy required to remove an electron from the metal platinum is 4.43 ev. What is the longest wavelength of light that will produce photoelectrons from platinum?

8-6.   The photoelectric threshold for magnesium is 3,700 Å. What is the energy, in electron volts, of photoelectrons produced from magnesium by light of wavelength 3,000 Å? What is the velocity of these electrons, in cm/sec?

8-7.   Describe how Millikan used the photoelectric effect to determine the value of Planck's constant.

8-8.   An X-ray tube is operated at a voltage of 40,000 v. What is the shortest wavelength of X-rays present in the beam from the tube?

8-9.   What are the values of the quantum numbers for the initial states and the final state of the spectrum lines in the Balmer spectrum of hydrogen? Draw an energy-level diagram for the hydrogen atom, and indicate the transitions corresponding to the emission of the Balmer lines.

8-10.   What is the dependence of the size of the orbits, in the Bohr theory, on the principal quantum number, and on the atomic number of the atom (the charge of the nucleus)?

8-11.   Describe the electron-impact experiments carried out by Franck and Hertz in the period 1914 to 1920. What properties of atoms or molecules are measured by this experiment?

8-12.   The ionization energies of hydrogen, helium, and lithium are 13.60 ev, 24.58 ev, and 5.39 ev, respectively. Discuss the relation of these values to the chemical properties of the three elements.

8-13.   Describe the electronic structures of the normal hydrogen atom, helium atom, and lithium atom in terms of Bohr orbits, the spin of the electron, and the Pauli exclusion principle.

8-14. The de Broglie wavelength of the electron is equal to h/mv. Calculate the wave-length of an electron that has been accelerated through 40,000 volts of accelerating potential. (Electrons with this wavelength are used in the determination of the structure of gas molecules by the electron-diffraction method.)

8-15. Describe briefly an experiment in which light behaves like a wave; an experiment in which light behaves like a particle, the light quantum; an experiment in which electrons behave like waves; an experiment in which electrons behave like particles.

Chapter 9

Ions, Ionic Valence, and Electrolysis

9–1. *The Concept of Valence*

If there were no order in the way in which atoms of different elements combine to form the molecules and crystals of compounds it would be necessary for us to memorize one by one the formulas of thousands of substances. Fortunately there is a great deal of order in the formulas of substances, resulting from the fact that some elements have a definite combining power, or *valence* (from Latin *valentia*, vigor or capacity), which determines the number of other atoms with which an atom of the element can combine. Other elements, more complex in their behavior, may exhibit any one of two or more definite combining powers. The topics discussed in the following pages—the nature of valence, the valences of the elements and their relation to atomic structure, and the systematization of the valences and other properties of the elements by the periodic table—constitute a very important part of chemical science.

The General Concept.   There exist binary compounds (compounds of two elements) with many different formulas, corresponding to different atomic ratios; examples are $NaCl$, H_2O, NH_3, CH_4, PCl_5, SF_6, Al_2O_3, Si_3N_4, P_2O_5, P_3N_5, Mn_2O_7, OsF_8. Some elements are known the atoms of which usually do not combine with more than one atom of any other element. Hydrogen is an element of this sort; it forms compounds HCl, H_2S, etc., but not compounds with formula HX_2, HX_3, $\cdots$. An element of this sort is said to have "the valence one"—to be *univalent*. The valence of another element may be defined as the number of atoms of a univalent element with which one atom of the element combines. Thus one atom of oxygen combines with two atoms of hydrogen to form water, H_2O; hence oxygen is *bivalent* in this compound. Nitrogen in NH_3 is *tervalent*, and carbon in CH_4 is *quadrivalent*.*

Oxygen is bivalent in most of its compounds. Since oxygen combines with most of the elements, some of which form several different oxides, the common valences of the elements can be found by considering the formulas of their oxides. Thus sodium, with oxide Na_2O, is univalent; calcium (oxide CaO) is bivalent; aluminum (oxide Al_2O_3) is tervalent; phosphorus (common oxides P_2O_3 and P_2O_5) is tervalent and quinquevalent.

Often a distinction is made between *positive valence* and *negative valence*, the metals being assigned positive valences and the non-metals negative valences. A detailed discussion of this point is given later, in the sections on ionic valence and on the oxidation numbers of the elements.

Valence bonds between atoms in a molecule may be represented by lines connecting pairs of atoms:

$$O—H \qquad H—\overset{\displaystyle H}{\underset{}{N}}—H \qquad H—\overset{\displaystyle H}{\underset{\displaystyle H}{C}}—H \qquad O{=}C{=}O \qquad H—C{\equiv}N$$

A double line represents a *double bond*, and a triple line a *triple bond*. The number of valence bonds associated with each atom in these formulas is equal to the valence of the atom. Similarly, formulas such as H—H and N≡N can be written for elementary substances.

More Precise Concepts.   The concept of valence as discussed above is not rigorously defined, and many puzzling questions may present themselves. Thus elementary hydrogen may be considered to have either the valence zero, since it is not combined with any other element, or the valence one, since the molecule may be assigned the structural formula H—H. Similarly, carbon in the compound acetylene, C_2H_2, may be taken as univalent, since it is combined with an equal number of atoms of the univalent element hydrogen, or as quadrivalent, by writing for the molecule the valence-bond formula H—C≡C—H.

The effort to obtain a clear understanding of the nature of valence

* Since the word "valence" has a Latin root, the Latin prefixes are preferred, leading to the adjectives univalent, bivalent, tervalent, quadrivalent, quinquevalent, sexivalent, septivalent, octavalent. The adjectives monovalent, divalent, trivalent, tetravalent, etc., which have the same meanings, are also used.

and of chemical combination in general has led in recent years to the dissociation of the concept of valence into several new concepts—of *ionic valence, oxidation number, covalence, coordination number*—corresponding to different modes of interaction of the atoms. These new concepts are discussed in later sections. Some chemists have felt that the word "valence" might well be allowed to drop into disuse, in favor of these more precise terms. In practice, however, "valence" continues to be used as a general expression of the combining powers of the elements or as a synonym for one or another of the more precise terms.

9–2. *Ions and Ionic Valence*

The Existence of Stable Ions.   In the discussion of the mass spectrograph in Chapter 6 it was mentioned that atoms in a gas have the power to add an extra electron, forming a negative ion such as I^-, or to lose an electron, forming a positive ion such as I^+. This affinity for electrons or ability to lose electrons is so great for many elements as to cause their anions or cations to be very stable, and to be present in most of the compounds of these elements.

Of the various ions which the iodine atom can form, only the singly charged negative ion, I^-, is stable in the compounds of iodine. This ion, called the *iodide ion*, is present in the iodides of the stronger metals. The other halogens also form singly charged anions: the *fluoride ion* F^-, the *chloride ion* Cl^-, and the *bromide ion* Br^-.

Neutral atoms of the alkali metals have no affinity for additional electrons, but instead each of these atoms holds one of its electrons only loosely—so loosely that in the presence of a halogen, which can take up the electron, it loses an electron, forming a singly charged positive ion. These cations, which are present in nearly all of the compounds of the alkali metals, are called the *lithium ion* Li^+, the *sodium ion* Na^+, the *potassium ion* K^+, the *rubidium ion* Rb^+, and the *cesium ion* Cs^+.

The Structure of an Ionic Crystal.   When metallic sodium and gaseous chlorine react each sodium atom transfers an electron to a chlorine atom:

$$2Na + Cl_2 \longrightarrow 2Na^+ + 2Cl^-$$

There occurs a strong *electrostatic attraction* between each sodium ion and every chloride ion in its neighborhood. There also occurs repulsion between ions of like sign. In consequence of these forces, and the repulsive forces which occur between all ions or molecules when they get so close to one another that their electronic structures are in contact, the ions pile up together in a regular way, each sodium ion surrounding itself with six chloride ions as nearest neighbors, and keeping all other sodium ions somewhat farther away. The structure of the sodium chloride crystal is represented in Figure 4-4.

Many of the properties of crystalline sodium chloride are determined by the structure of the crystal—that is, by the stable way in which the sodium ions and chloride ions aggregate to form the crystal. The *density* of the crystal is determined by the equilibrium distance between the ions, and hence by the sizes of the ions. The ability of the crystals to form *cubes* as they grow, with plane faces at right angles to one another, and their *cubic cleavage* (the ability to be cleaved along cube faces when struck a blow), are both determined by the cubic symmetry of the ionic arrangement.* The *hardness* of the crystals and their *high melting point* are due to the strong electrostatic attraction between the oppositely charged ions.

The Ionic Bond: Ionic Valence.   The strong electrostatic forces acting between anions and cations are called *ionic bonds*. The magnitude of the electric charge (in units *e*) on an ion is called its *ionic valence*. Thus sodium has ionic valence +1 in sodium chloride and is said to be *unipositive*, and chlorine has ionic valence −1 and is said to be *uninegative*.

Any specimen of matter of macroscopic size—that is, big enough to be seen by the eye—must be essentially electrically neutral.† Hence a crystal of sodium chloride must contain substantially as many Na^+ ions as Cl^- ions, and its formula must be Na^+Cl^-. The composition of the crystal and the formula of the compound are thus determined by the ionic valences of the constituent elements: these ionic valences must add up to zero.

Ionic Valence and the Periodic Table.   It is a striking fact that *every alkali ion and every halide ion contains the same number of electrons as one of the noble gases*. The stability of these ions and the lack of chemical reactivity of the noble gases can thus be attributed to the same cause—the *ex-*

---

* The habit (mode of face development) of a crystal depends on the conditions of crystallization; for example, salt crystallizes from water solution as cubes and from a solution containing urea as octahedra. The cleavage is independent of the shape—both kinds of salt crystals show cubic cleavage. These crystals with different face development are, of course, the same substance, just as large cubes and small cubes of salt are the same substance.

† It might have an excess of either positive or negative ions, and thus be charged positively or negatively, but the amount of charge (measured in units *e*) is always small compared with the number of atoms.

traordinary stability of configurations of 2, 10, 18, 36, 54, and 86 electrons about an atomic nucleus.

The alkali metals (in group I of the periodic table) are unipositive because their atoms contain one more electron than a noble-gas atom, and this electron is easily lost. The halogens, in group VII of the periodic table, are uninegative because each of their atoms contains one less electron than a noble-gas atom, and readily gains an electron.

Similarly, atoms of the elements of group II of the periodic table can by losing two electrons produce ions (Be^{++}, Mg^{++}, Ca^{++}, Sr^{++}, Ba^{++}) with the noble-gas structures. These elements are hence bipositive in valence. The elements of group III are terpositive, those of group VI are binegative, etc.

The formulas of binary salts, such as $Mg^{++}(F^-)_2$, $Ca^{++}O^{--}$, $Ba^{++}S^{--}$, $(Al^{+++})_2 (O^{--})_3$, etc., can thus be written from knowledge of the positions of the elements in the periodic table.

Ionic compounds are formed between the strong metals, in groups I, II, and III, and the strong non-metals, in the upper right-hand corner of the periodic system. In addition, ionic compounds are formed containing the *cations* of the strong metals and the *anions of acids*, especially of the oxygen acids. The principal oxygen acids and their ions are given in Table 9-1.

TABLE 9-1   *The Names and Formulas of the Principal Oxygen-Containing Acids and Their Anions*

carbonic acid	H_2CO_3	carbonate ion	CO_3^{--}
silicic acid	H_4SiO_4	silicate ion	SiO_4^{----}
nitric acid	HNO_3	nitrate ion	NO_3^{-}
phosphoric acid	H_3PO_4	phosphate ion	PO_4^{---}
sulfuric acid	H_2SO_4	sulfate ion	SO_4^{--}
sulfurous acid	H_2SO_3	sulfite ion	SO_3^{--}
perchloric acid	$HClO_4$	perchlorate ion	ClO_4^{-}
chloric acid	$HClO_3$	chlorate ion	ClO_3^{-}

It is seen that many of the formulas given in Chapters 5 and 6 could be predicted: the fluoride of sodium must be Na^+F^- and that of calcium $Ca^{++}(F^-)_2$ (fluorite); their carbonates must be $(Na^+)_2(CO_3)^{--}$ and $Ca^{++}(CO_3)^{--}$ (and we can also write $Na^+H^+(CO_3)^{--}$ for sodium hydrogen carbonate and $Ca^{++}(H^+CO_3^{--})_2$ for calcium hydrogen carbonate); their normal phosphates must be $(Na^+)_3(PO_4)^{---}$ and $(Ca^{++})_3(PO_4^{---})_2$. Crystals of all of these salts consist of cations and complex anions piled together in a regular array.

Ions Without Noble-Gas Structure.   In addition to the ions with the electronic structure of a noble gas, there are many ions, all cations, with other structures that are stable in aqueous solutions. These ions are formed by the metals in the long periods of the periodic table: thus chromium, manganese, iron, cobalt, and nickel all form bipositive ions and terpositive ions. These ions have different stability: chromic ion, Cr^{+++}, is more easily formed than chromous ion, Cr^{++}; manganous ion, Mn^{++}, is more stable than manganic ion, Mn^{+++}; iron readily forms both ferrous ion, Fe^{++}, and ferric ion, Fe^{+++}; the cobaltous ion, Co^{++}, and the nickelous ion, Ni^{++}, are more stable than the corresponding terpositive ions. Copper has as its stable ion the cupric ion Cu^{++}, and zinc forms the ion Zn^{++}. The rare-earth metals all form ionic compounds containing the terpositive ions, such as $EuCl_3 \cdot 9H_2O$, and some of them form bipositive or quadripositive ions also.

9–3. *The Electrolytic Decomposition of Molten Salts*

The discovery of ions resulted from the experimental investigations of the interaction of an electric current with chemical substances. These investigations were begun early in the nineteenth century, and were carried on effectively by Sir Humphry Davy and J. J. Berzelius, and especially by Michael Faraday, in the period around 1830.

The Electrolysis of Molten Sodium Chloride.   Molten sodium chloride, like other molten salts, conducts an electric current. During the process of conducting the current a chemical reaction occurs: the salt is decomposed. If two electrodes (carbon rods) are dipped into a crucible containing molten sodium chloride and an electric potential (from a battery or generator) is applied, metallic sodium is produced at the negative electrode—the cathode—and gaseous chlorine at the positive electrode—the anode. Such electric decomposition of a substance is called *electrolysis*.

The Mechanism of Ionic Conduction.   The explanation of the phenomenon is the following. Molten sodium chloride, like the crystalline substance, consists of equal numbers of sodium ions and chloride ions. These ions are very stable, and neither gain nor lose electrons easily. Whereas the ions in the crystal are firmly held in place by their neighbors, those in the molten salt move about with considerable freedom.

An electric generator or battery forces electrons into the cathode and pumps them away from the anode—electrons move freely in a metal or a semi-metallic conductor such as graphite. But electrons cannot ordinarily get into a substance such as salt; the crystalline substance is an insulator, and the electric conductivity shown by the liquid is not electronic conductivity (metallic conductivity), but is conductivity of a different kind, called *ionic conductivity* or *electrolytic conductivity*. This results from the motion of the ions in the liquid; the cations, Na^+, are attracted by the negatively charged cathode and move toward it, and the anions, Cl^-, are attracted by the anode and move toward it (Fig. 9-1).

The Electrode Reactions. The preceding statement describes the mechanism of the conduction of the current through the liquid. We must now consider the way in which the current passes between the electrodes and the liquid; that is, we consider the *electrode reactions*. The process which occurs at the cathode is this: sodium ions, attracted to the cathode, combine with electrons carried by the cathode to form sodium atoms—that is, to form sodium metal. The *cathode reaction* is

$$Na^+ + e^- \longrightarrow Na \qquad (9\text{-}1)$$

the symbol e^- representing an electron (in this case coming from the cathode). Similarly, at the anode chloride ions give up their extra electrons to the anode, and become chlorine atoms, which are combined as the molecules of chlorine gas. The *anode reaction* is

$$2Cl^- \longrightarrow Cl_2 + 2e^- \qquad (9\text{-}2)$$

The Over-All Reaction. The whole process of conduction in this system thus occurs in the following steps:
1. An electron is pumped into the cathode.
2. The electron jumps out of the cathode onto an adjacent sodium ion, converting it into an atom of sodium metal.
3. The charge of the electron is conducted across the liquid by the motion of the ions.
4. A chloride ion gives its extra electron to the anode, and becomes half of a molecule of chlorine gas.
5. The electron moves out of the anode toward the generator or battery.

The student should note that there is nothing mysterious about this complex phenomenon, once it is separated into its parts and the individual processes are analyzed. If the phenomenon seems mysterious, he should study it further, and ask, if necessary, for its clarification.

The over-all reaction for the electrolytic decomposition is the sum

Anode   Cathode

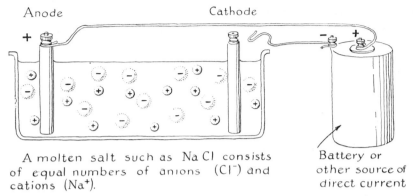

A molten salt such as Na Cl consists
of equal numbers of anions (Cl⁻) and
cations (Na⁺).

Battery or
other source of
direct current

When the circuit is closed electrons flow as through a tube.

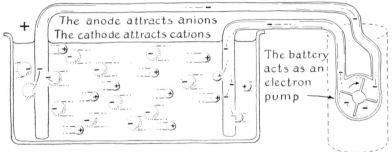

The anode attracts anions
The cathode attracts cations

The battery
acts as an
electron
pump

Anions give up their extra
electrons to the anode and
become neutral atoms.

Cations receive electrons
from the cathode and also
become neutral atoms.

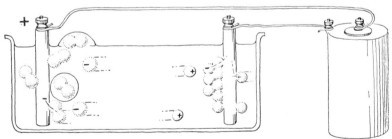

Neutral atoms of chlorine
unite to form bubbles
of chlorine gas (Cl₂).

Neutral sodium atoms
form a layer of
metallic sodium

FIG. 9-1 *Electrolysis of molten sodium chloride.*

of the two electrode reactions. Since two electrons are shown on their way around the circuit in Equation 2, we must double Equation 1:

$$2Na^+ + 2e^- \longrightarrow 2Na$$
$$2Cl^- \longrightarrow Cl_2 + 2e^-$$
$$\overline{2Na^+ + 2Cl^- \underset{\text{electr.}}{\longrightarrow} 2Na + Cl_2} \tag{9-3}$$

or

$$2NaCl \underset{\text{electr.}}{\longrightarrow} 2Na + Cl_2 \tag{9-4}$$

Equations 3 and 4 are equivalent; both represent the decomposition of sodium chloride into its elementary constituents. The abbreviation "electr." (for electrolysis) is written beneath the arrow to indicate that the reaction occurs on the passage of an electric current.

9–4. *The Electrolytic Dissociation of Substances in Solution*

Water itself has a very low electric conductivity. There are no free electrons (metallic electrons) in the substance to give it electronic or metallic conductivity, and there are not enough ions (such as the sodium ions and chloride ions in molten sodium chloride) to give it appreciable ionic conductivity.

Many aqueous solutions, especially those of organic substances (sugar, glycerol, alcohol), are also poor conductors of electricity. But many other aqueous solutions conduct an electric current very well. These include solutions of most acids (hydrochloric acid, acetic acid, etc.), bases (sodium hydroxide, calcium hydroxide, etc.), and salts (sodium chloride, potassium tartrate, etc.).

The explanation of the large electric conductivity of these solutions was given in 1887 by the Swedish chemist Svante Arrhenius (1859–1927), who suggested that part or all of the solute is present in the form of separate ions, carrying positive and negative charges, rather than in the form of molecules. This postulate is now generally accepted; the support for it is so strong that we speak of it now as more than a theory—as a fact.

Strong Electrolytes and Weak Electrolytes. The ordinary mineral acids (hydrochloric, nitric, sulfuric), inorganic bases, and many salts give strongly conducting aqueous solutions. These substances are called *strong electrolytes:* they are almost completely ionized (dissociated) in solution. Other substances—ammonium hydroxide (NH_4OH), acetic acid, mercuric chloride—have in solutions of the same concentrations much smaller conductivity than do strong electrolytes; these substances are called *weak electrolytes*.

The properties of weak electrolytes result from the presence in their solutions of undissociated solute molecules as well as ions—that is, from the formation of a smaller number of separate ions in the solution than would be expected from the amount of substance present. Thus a solution of mercuric chloride, $HgCl_2$, contains the solute molecular species*

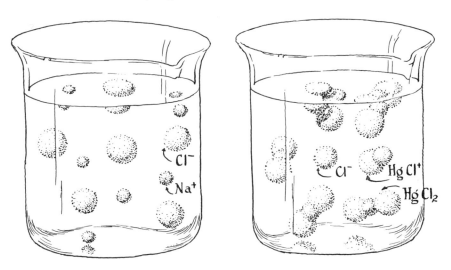

FIG. 9-2   *A solution of a completely dissociated salt (at the left) and of a partially dissociated salt (at the right).*

Hg^{++}, Cl^-, $HgCl^+$, and $HgCl_2$, all in appreciable concentrations, corresponding to the equilibrium

$$HgCl_2 \rightleftharpoons HgCl^+ + Cl^- \rightleftharpoons Hg^{++} + 2Cl^-$$

The difference between a solution of a strong electrolyte and a solution of a weak electrolyte is illustrated in Figure 9-2.

Writing Equations for Ionic Reactions.   In writing an equation for a chemical reaction between strong electrolytes in solution, ions should be written as reactants and products; thus the precipitation of silver chloride on addition of a solution of hydrochloric acid to a solution of silver nitrate would be written

$$Ag^+ + Cl^- \longrightarrow AgCl \downarrow$$

* It is customary to use the term "molecular species" to refer to ions as well as neutral molecules.

and not

$$AgNO_3 + HCl \longrightarrow AgCl + HNO_3$$

The ionic equation represents the actual reaction, the combination of silver ion and chloride ion to form the product silver chloride. It is true that nitrate ion was present in solution with the silver ion, and hydrogen ion was present with the chloride ion; but these ions remain in essentially their original state after the reaction has occurred, and there is hence usually no reason to indicate them in the equation.

The same equation,

$$Ag^+ + Cl^- \longrightarrow AgCl \downarrow$$

is, moreover, applicable also to the precipitation of, say, silver perchlorate solution (containing Ag^+ and ClO_4^-) by sodium chloride solution (containing Na^+ and Cl^-).

A good rule to follow is to *write the chemical equation to correspond as closely as possible to the actual reaction, showing the molecules or ions which actually react and are formed.*

In accordance with this rule, either the ions or the molecules may be shown for reactions involving weak electrolytes. If a substance is not ionized at all, its molecules should be shown in the equation.

9–5. *The Importance of Water as an Electrolytic Solvent*

Salts are insoluble in most solvents. Gasoline, benzene, carbon disulfide, carbon tetrachloride, alcohol, ether—these substances are "good sol-

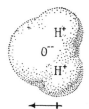

Dipole moment

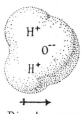

Dipole moment

1 Å

FIG. 9-3

Two water molecules with their electric dipole moment vectors oriented in opposite directions.

vents" for grease, rubber, organic materials generally; but they do not dissolve salts. (There are rare exceptions: thus silver perchlorate, $AgClO_4$, is soluble in benzene.)

The reasons why water is so effective in dissolving salts are that *it has a very high dielectric constant* and that *its molecules tend to combine with ions*, to form hydrated ions. Both of these properties are due to the *large electric dipole moment* of the water molecule.

The water molecule has a considerable amount of ionic character; it can be thought of as an oxygen ion O^{--} with two hydrogen ions H^+ attached near its surface. These hydrogen ions are 0.95 Å from the oxygen nucleus, and on the same side, the angle H—O—H being 105°. Hence there is a separation of positive charge and negative charge within the molecule, causing the center of the positive charge in the molecule to be to one side of the center of the negative charge. Such a combination of separated positive and negative charges is called an electric dipole moment (Fig. 9-3).

The Effect of the High Dielectric Constant.   In an electric field, as between the electrostatically charged plates of a condenser, the water molecules tend to orient themselves, pointing their positive ends toward

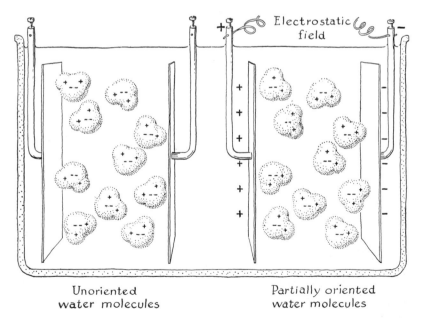

Unoriented
water molecules

Partially oriented
water molecules

FIG. 9-4   *Orientation of polar molecules in an electrostatic field, producing the effect of a high dielectric constant.*

the negative plate and their negative ends toward the positive plate (Fig. 9-4). This partially neutralizes the applied field, an effect described by saying that the medium (water) has a dielectric constant greater than unity.

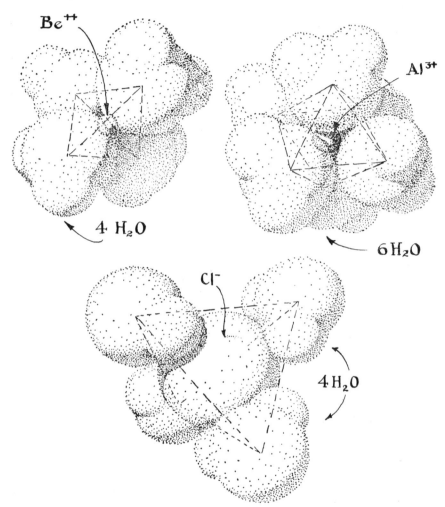

FIG. 9-5 *Diagrams showing the structure of hydrated ions.*

The dielectric constant of liquid water at room temperature is 80. This means that two opposite electric charges in water attract each other with a force only 1/80 as strong as in air (or a vacuum). It is clear that the ions of a crystal of sodium chloride placed in water could dissociate away from the crystal far more easily than if the crystal were in air, since the electrostatic force bringing an ion back to the surface of the crystal from the aqueous solution is only $1/80$ as strong as from air; and hence it is not surprising that thermal agitation at room temperature is great enough to overcome this relatively weak attraction, and to cause large numbers of the ions to dissociate into the aqueous medium, producing a concentrated salt solution.

The Hydration of Ions. A related effect which stabilizes the dissolved ions is the formation of hydrates of the ions. Each negative ion attracts the positive ends of the adjacent water molecules, and tends to hold several water molecules attached to itself. The positive ions, which are usually smaller than the anions, show this effect still more strongly; each cation attracts the negative ends of the water molecules, and binds several molecules tightly about itself, forming a hydrate which may have considerable stability, especially for the bipositive and terpositive cations.

The number of water molecules attached to a cation (called its *co-ordination number*) is determined by the size of the cation. A small cation, such as Be^{++}, forms the tetrahydrate* $Be(OH_2)_4^{++}$. A somewhat larger one, such as Mg^{++} or Al^{+++} or Ni^{++}, forms a hexahydrate, $Mg(OH_2)_6^{++}$ or $Al(OH_2)_6^{+++}$ or $Ni(OH_2)_6^{++}$. K^+, Rb^+, and the larger cations form higher hydrates: the rare-earth ions, for example, form the complexes $La(OH_2)_9^{+++}$, etc. (Fig. 9-5).

The forces between cations and water molecules are so strong that the ions often retain a layer of water molecules in crystals (water of hydration). This effect is more pronounced for bipositive and terpositive ions than for unipositive ions. The tetrahedral complex $Be(H_2O)_4^{++}$ occurs in various salts, including $BeCO_3 \cdot 4H_2O$, $BeCl_2 \cdot 4H_2O$, $BeSO_4 \cdot 4H_2O$, and $BeSeO_4 \cdot 4H_2O$, and is no doubt present also in solution. Larger ions, including Mg^{++}, Al^{+++}, Fe^{++}, Fe^{+++}, Ni^{++}, etc., attach six water molecules at the corners of a circumscribed octahedron. These are present in salts such as the following as well as in solution:

$MgCl_2 \cdot 6H_2O$	$AlCl_3 \cdot 6H_2O$
$NH_4MgPO_4 \cdot 6H_2O$	$Al(ClO_3)_3 \cdot 6H_2O$
$Mg(ClO_3)_2 \cdot 6H_2O$	$KAl(SO_4)_2 \cdot 12H_2O$
$Mg(ClO_4)_2 \cdot 6H_2O$	$Fe(NH_4)_2(SO_4)_2 \cdot 6H_2O$
$MgSiF_6 \cdot 6H_2O$	$FeSiF_6 \cdot 6H_2O$
$NiCl_2 \cdot 6H_2O$	$Fe(NO_3)_2 \cdot 6H_2O$
$NiSnCl_6 \cdot 6H_2O$	$FeCl_3 \cdot 6H_2O$
$Ni(NO_3)_2 \cdot 6H_2O$	$Fe(NO_3)_3 \cdot 6H_2O$ or $9H_2O$
$NiSO_4 \cdot 6H_2O$ or $7H_2O$	$KFe(SO_4)_2 \cdot 12H_2O$

* In these formulas water is written OH_2, instead of H_2O, to indicate that the oxygen atom of the water molecule is near the metal ion, the hydrogen atoms being on the outside. Usually the formulas are written $Be(H_2O)_4^{++}$, etc.

In a crystal such as $FeSO_4 \cdot 7H_2O$ six of the water molecules are attached to the iron ion, in the complex $Fe(H_2O)_6^{++}$, and the seventh occupies another position, being packed near a sulfate ion. In the alums (such as $KAlSO_4 \cdot 12H_2O$) six of the twelve water molecules are attached to the aluminum ion and the other six are near the alkali ion.

Crystals also exist in which some or all of the water molecules have been removed from the cations; for example, magnesium sulfate forms the three crystalline phases $MgSO_4 \cdot 7H_2O$, $MgSO_4 \cdot H_2O$, and $MgSO_4$.

A further discussion of complex ions is given in a later chapter (Chap. 23).

Other Electrolytic Solvents.   Some liquids other than water can serve as ionizing solvents, dissolving electrolytes to give conducting solutions. These liquids include liquid ammonia, hydrogen peroxide, and hydrogen fluoride. All of these liquids, like water, have very large dielectric constants—the reason that ionic solutions are formed by them is that there is strong interaction between the electric charges of the ions and the solvent molecules which stabilizes the ionic solutions. Liquids with low dielectric constants, such as benzene and carbon disulfide, do not act as ionizing solvents.

Liquids with large dielectric constants are sometimes called *dipolar liquids* (or simply *polar liquids*). It is interesting to note that these dipolar liquids are good solvents for ionic crystals (containing electric "poles," or charges), and that non-polar liquids (benzene, etc.) are good solvents for non-polar substances.

9–6. *The Electrolysis of an Aqueous Salt Solution*

When a current of electricity passes through an aqueous electrolytic solution there occur phenomena analogous to those described in the preceding section for molten salt. The five steps are the following:

1. Electrons are pumped into the cathode.
2. Electrons jump from the cathode to adjacent ions or molecules, producing the cathode reaction.
3. The current is conducted across the liquid by the motion of the dissolved ions.
4. Electrons jump from ions or molecules in the solution to the anode, producing the anode reaction.
5. The electrons move out of the anode toward the generator or battery.

Let us consider a dilute solution of sodium chloride (Fig. 9-6). The

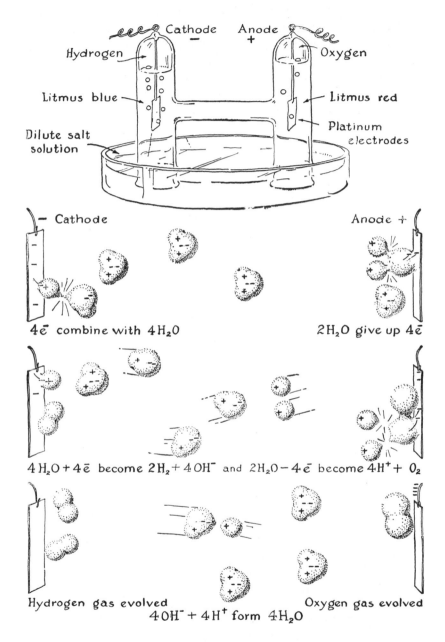

FIG. 9-6   *Electrolysis of dilute aqueous salt solution.*

process of conduction through this solution (step 3) is closely similar to that for molten sodium chloride; here it is the dissolved sodium ions that move toward the cathode and the dissolved chloride ions that move toward the anode.

But the electrode reactions for dilute salt solution are entirely different from those for molten salt. Electrolysis of dilute salt solution produces hydrogen at the cathode and oxygen at the anode.

The *cathode reaction* is

$$2e^- + 2H_2O \longrightarrow H_2 \uparrow + 2OH^- \tag{9-5}$$

Two electrons from the cathode react with two water molecules to produce a molecule of hydrogen and two hydroxide ions. The molecular hydrogen bubbles off as hydrogen gas (after the solution near the cathode has become saturated with hydrogen), and the hydroxide ions stay in the solution.

The *anode reaction* is

$$2H_2O \longrightarrow O_2 \uparrow + 4H^+ + 4e^- \tag{9-6}$$

Four electrons enter the anode from two water molecules, which de-compose to form an oxygen molecule and four hydrogen ions.

(These electrode reactions, like other chemical reactions, may occur in steps; the description given in the preceding sentence of the course of the anode reaction is not to be interpreted as giving the necessary sequence of events.)

The over-all reaction is obtained by multiplying Equation 5 by two and adding Equation 6: it is

$$6H_2O \underset{\text{electr.}}{\longrightarrow} \underset{\text{cathode}}{2H_2 \uparrow} + \underset{\text{anode}}{O_2 \uparrow} + \underset{\text{anode}}{4H^+} + \underset{\text{cathode}}{4OH^-} \tag{9-7}$$

In the course of time the ions H^+ produced near the anode and OH^- produced near the cathode may diffuse together and combine to form water:

$$H^+ + OH^- \longrightarrow H_2O$$

If this occurs completely, the over-all electrolysis reaction is

$$2H_2O \underset{\text{electr.}}{\longrightarrow} \underset{\text{cathode}}{2H_2 \uparrow} + \underset{\text{anode}}{O_2 \uparrow} \tag{9-8}$$

In discussing the electrode reactions we have made no mention or use of the fact that the electrolyte is sodium chloride. In fact, *the electrode reactions are the same for most dilute aqueous electrolytic solutions*, and even for pure water as well. When electrodes are placed in pure water and a potential is applied the electrode reactions 5 and 6 begin to take place. Very soon, however, a large enough concentration of hydroxide ions is built up near the cathode and of hydrogen ions near the anode to produce a back electric potential that tends to stop the reactions. Even in pure water there are a few ions (hydrogen ion, H^+, and hydroxide ion, OH^-); these slowly move to the electrodes, and neutralize the ions (OH^- and H^+, respectively) formed by the electrode reactions. It is the smallness of the current which the few ions present in pure water can carry through the region between the electrodes that causes the electrolysis of pure water to proceed only very slowly.

Equations 5 and 6 above represent water molecules undergoing decomposition at the electrodes. These are probably the usual molecular reactions in neutral solutions. However, in acidic solutions, in which there is a high concentration of hydrogen ions, the cathode reaction may well be simply

$$2H^+ + 2e^- \longrightarrow H_2 \uparrow$$

and in basic solutions, in which there is a high concentration of hydroxide ions, the anode reaction may be

$$4OH^- \longrightarrow O_2 \uparrow + 2H_2O + 4e^-$$

The ions in an electrolytic solution can carry a larger current between the electrodes than in pure water. In a sodium chloride solution undergoing electrolysis sodium ions move to the cathode region, where their positive electric charges compensate the negative charges of the hydroxide ions that have been formed by the cathode reaction. Similarly, the chloride ions that move toward the anode compensate electrically the hydrogen ions that have been formed by the anode reaction.

The production of hydroxide ion at the cathode and of hydrogen ion at the anode during the electrolysis can be demonstrated by means of litmus or a similar indicator.

The electrolysis of dilute aqueous solutions of other electrolytes is closely similar to that of sodium chloride, producing hydrogen and oxygen gases at the electrodes. Concentrated electrolytic solutions may behave differently; concentrated brine (sodium chloride solution) on electrolysis produces chlorine at the anode, as well as oxygen.

Exercises

9-1. Assuming hydrogen to be univalent and oxygen bivalent, select the elements which, in any of the following compounds, are (a) univalent; (b) bivalent; (c) tervalent; (d) quadrivalent; (e) quinquevalent; (f) sexivalent:

SO_2, SO_3, NaH, Na_2O, HCl, HF, Cl_2O, PH_3, NH_3, NO, N_2O_3, NO_2, N_2O_5, H_2S, Al_2O_3, SiO_2, P_2O_3, P_2O_5, Mn_2O_7, Cr_2O_3, CrO_3, FeO, Fe_2O_3, MgO, CaO, TiO_2, V_2O_5, NiO, Cu_2O, CuO, As_2O_3, As_2O_5, SnO, SnO_2.

9-2. Assuming that their atoms can lose enough electrons to reach the neon configuration, show the corresponding positive ions for the elements from sodium to
sulfur, inclusive, and write the formulas of the corresponding oxides of these
elements. Do the same for the elements from potassium to chromium, assuming
that their atoms reach the argon configuration.

9-3. Assign ionic valences to the elements in the following compounds:

LiF	Na_2O	HCl	$CoCl_2$
$MgCl_2$	CaO	Cr_2O_3	AgF
Al_2O_3	KBr	$FeCl_2$	$CdCl_2$
NaH	Sc_2O_3	$FeCl_3$	$CaCl_2$
BF_3	TiO_2	ZnF_2	BaO
SiF_4	Mn_2O_7	Na_2S	$RaCl_2$

Underline the ions which do not have a noble-gas structure.

9-4. Assign ionic valences to the central atoms of the eight acids in Table 9-1. Which
of these correspond to noble-gas structures for the ions of these atoms, and which
do not?

9-5. What is the relation between the atomic numbers of the noble gases and the
squares of small integers? (Consider the differences between atomic numbers of
successive noble gases.)

9-6. What would be the charge on an iron ion that had the electronic structure of
the preceding noble gas? Why do the transition elements tend to form ions (such
as Mn^{++}, Fe^{++}, Fe^{+++}) with smaller charges than correspond to a noble-gas
structure?

9-7. What forces hold a sodium chloride crystal together?

9-8. Magnesium oxide and sodium fluoride have the same crystal structure (the
sodium chloride structure, shown in Fig. 4-4). Magnesium oxide has hardness 6
on the Mohs scale, and sodium fluoride has hardness 3. Can you explain why
the two substances differ so much in hardness? Can you also explain why the
melting point of magnesium oxide (2,800° C) is very much higher than that of
sodium fluoride (992°)? Note that the ions in the two substances have the same
electronic structure.

9-9. How is electric current carried along a metallic wire? from an inert cathode
into fused sodium chloride? through fused sodium chloride? from fused sodium
chloride into an inert anode?

9-10. Why does molten sodium chloride conduct a current much better than does
solid sodium chloride?

9-11. What substance would be formed at each electrode on electrolysis of molten
lithium hydride, Li^+H^-, with inert electrodes?

9-12. Why does an aqueous solution containing 1 gfw of hydrochloric acid per liter
conduct the electric current much better than a similar solution of acetic acid?

9-13. Outline the complete mechanism of conduction of electricity between inert electrodes in a dilute sodium chloride solution.

9-14. Write equations for the anode reaction, the cathode reaction, and the over-all reaction for electrolysis of the following systems, with inert electrodes:
(a) Fused potassium bromide
(b) Fused sodium oxide
(c) Dilute aqueous solution of sodium hydroxide
(d) Dilute aqueous solution of hydrochloric acid
(e) Concentrated solution of hydrochloric acid
(f) Fused silver bromide, Ag^+Br^-
(g) Dilute solution of silver nitrate (silver deposits on cathode)
(h) Fused zinc chloride, $ZnCl_2$

9-15. Can you suggest an explanation for the fact that mercuric chloride, $HgCl_2$, is much more soluble in benzene than is magnesium chloride?

9-16. Can you explain why sodium chloride crystallizes from solution as unhydrated NaCl, beryllium chloride as $BeCl_2 \cdot 4H_2O$, and magnesium chloride as $MgCl_2 \cdot 6H_2O$?

Chapter 10

Covalence and Electronic Structure

10–1. *The Shared-Electron-Pair Bond; Covalence*

In the preceding chapter we have discussed chemical compounds which contain *ions*, and which owe their stability to the tendency of certain atoms to lose electrons and of others to gain them. When these ionic substances are melted or are dissolved in water the ions become able to move about independently, and the molten substance or solution is a conductor of electricity.

There are many other substances, however, that do not have these properties. These non-ionic substances are so numerous that it is not necessary to search for examples—nearly every substance except the salts is in this class. Thus molten sulfur, like solid sulfur, is an electric insulator, as are liquid air (liquid oxygen, liquid nitrogen), bromine, gasoline, carbon tetrachloride, and many other liquid substances. Gases, too, are insulators, and do not contain ions, unless they have been ionized by an electric discharge or in some similar way.

These non-ionic substances consist of *molecules* made of atoms that are bonded tightly together. Thus the pale straw-colored liquid that is obtained by melting sulfur contains S_8 molecules, each built of eight sulfur atoms; liquid air contains the stable diatomic molecules O_2 and N_2, bromine the molecules Br_2, carbon tetrachloride the molecules CCl_4, and so on.

The atoms in these molecules are held tightly together by a very important sort of bond, the *shared-electron-pair bond* or *covalent bond*. This bond is so important, so nearly universally present in substances, that

Professor Gilbert Newton Lewis of the University of California (1875–1946), who discovered its electronic structure, called it *the* chemical bond. It is the bond that is represented by a dash in the valence-bond for-

$$\begin{array}{c} Cl \\ | \\ mulas, such\ as\ Br—Br\ and\ Cl—C—Cl, which\ have\ been\ so\ written\ by \\ | \\ Cl \end{array}$$

mulas, such as Br—Br and Cl—C—Cl, which have been so written by

chemists for nearly a hundred years.*

The Hydrogen Molecule.   The simplest example of a covalent molecule is the hydrogen molecule, H_2. For this molecule the electronic structure H : H is written, indicating that the two electrons are shared between the two atoms, forming the bond between them. This structure corresponds to the valence-bond structure H—H.

The meaning of this structure is that the two electrons are held jointly by the two nuclei, and constitute a firm attachment between them. The nature of the electronic structure is indicated in Figure 4-5, which shows the electron distribution in two separated hydrogen atoms and in the hydrogen molecule.

The bond between the two nuclei is a very strong one. It holds the nuclei at the average distance 0.74 Å apart—they oscillate with an amplitude of a few hundredths of an Ångström at room temperature, and with a somewhat larger amplitude at higher temperatures. A large amount of energy is required to break the bond, 103.4 kilocalories per mole, and this amount of energy is evolved when molecular hydrogen is formed from hydrogen atoms:

$$2H \longrightarrow H_2 + 103.4\ kcal/mole$$

We have seen in the consideration of ionic valence that there is a very strong tendency for atoms of the stronger metals and non-metals to achieve the electron number of an inert gas by losing or gaining one or more electrons. It was pointed out by G. N. Lewis that the same tendency is operative in the formation of molecules containing covalent bonds, and that the electrons in the bond are to be counted for each of the bonded atoms.

Thus the hydrogen atom, with one electron, can achieve the helium structure by taking up one electron, to form the hydride anion, $H:^-$, present in lithium hydride, Li^+H^-, and other metallic hydrides (Na^+H^-, $Ca^{++}(H^-)_2$, etc.). It can also achieve the helium structure by sharing

* Structures of this sort should not, however, be written for truly ionic substances, such as sodium chloride; this substance is represented better by Na^+Cl^- than by Na—Cl.

an electron pair with another hydrogen atom, each of the two atoms contributing one of the electrons, and the shared pair being counted first for one atom and then for the other:

10–2. *The Electronic Structure of Atoms*

After the development of the Bohr theory of the hydrogen atom, in 1913, there occurred rapid progress in the determination of the electronic structure of atoms containing many electrons. This progress resulted from the study of many physical phenomena, especially the line spectra of the atoms. By 1925 detailed knowledge had been obtained of the electronic structure of all the atoms. This knowledge is required for the understanding of valence and molecular structure.

The Electronic Structure of the Noble Gases; Electron Shells. A heavy atom contains some electrons which stay very close to the nucleus, some which move about at a larger average distance from the nucleus, and so on. These electrons are said to be in concentric electron shells about the nucleus.

The **helium atom** contains two electrons, each of which carries out motion about the nucleus similar to that of the one electron in the hydrogen atom. These two electrons are said to occupy an electron shell, the *K shell*. No more than two electrons can be put in this shell. *All heavier atoms have two K electrons close to the nucleus.*

The **neon atom** consists of two *K* electrons close to the nucleus and an *outer shell* of eight *L electrons*. **Argon** has, in addition to the *K* shell and the *L* shell, another shell of eight electrons, the *M shell*.

Both neon and argon are hence related to the preceding noble gas by an increase of the nuclear charge by 8 and the addition of a new outer shell of 8 electrons. This relation does not hold, however, for the noble gases heavier than the first three. **Krypton** has, it is true, a new outer shell of 8 electrons, the *N shell*, but also the next inner shell, the *M* shell, has *expanded* from 8 to 18 electrons. At **xenon** there is added a new outer shell of 8 electrons, the *O shell*, and again the next inner shell (the *N* shell) has expanded from 8 to 18.

Thus each of the two short periods in the periodic table involves the addition of a new outer shell of 8 electrons; and each of the two long periods involves the addition of a new outer shell of 8 electrons and also the insertion of 10 additional electrons into the next inner shell.

The very long period, completed at **radon,** involves the addition of a new outer shell of 8 electrons, the *P shell*, the insertion of 10 additional electrons into the next inner shell (the *O* shell), and also the insertion of 14 additional electrons into the following inner shell (the *N* shell).

The successive shells *K*, *L*, *M*, *N*, *O*, *P* are also represented by the numbers 1, 2, 3, 4, 5, 6, respectively, which are the values of the *principal quantum number.*

The electronic structures of the noble gases may be summarized as in Table 10-1.

TABLE 10-1   *Electron Shells of the Noble Gases*

	K	*L*	*M*	*N*	*O*	*P*
He 2	2					
Ne 10	2	8				
A 18	2	8	8			
Kr 36	2	8	18	8		
Xe 54	2	8	18	18	8	
Rn 86	2	8	18	32	18	8

The numbers 2, 8, 18, and 32, which are the maximum numbers of electrons that can occupy the successive shells *K*, *L*, *M*, and *N*, are seen to be equal to $2n^2$, with $n = 1, 2, 3,$ and 4, respectively.

Subshells of Electrons.   A given shell may be occupied by any number of electrons up to its maximum capacity. The configurations with 2, 8, 18, and 32 in a shell are, however, especially stable; thus the *N* shell contains 8 electrons in krypton, 18 in xenon, and 32 in radon. The stability of these numbers of electrons results from the fact that each

TABLE 10-2   *Subshells of Electrons*

$$
\begin{array}{ll}
M\ \text{shell:} &
\left.\begin{array}{l}
3s - 2 \\
3p - 6
\end{array}\right\}8 \\
& 3d - 10
\end{array}\Bigg\}18
$$

$$
\begin{array}{ll}
N\ \text{shell:} &
\left.\begin{array}{l}
4s - 2 \\
4p - 6
\end{array}\right\}8 \\
& 4d - 10 \\
& 4f - 14
\end{array}\Bigg\}18\ \Bigg\}32
$$

shell (except the K shell) consists of two or more subshells, with varying stability. The L shell contains a $2s$ subshell of 2 electrons and a $2p$ subshell of 6 electrons; for other shells the subshells are as in Table 10-2. The letters s, p, d, f used for successive subshells derive from an unsystematic nomenclature introduced by spectroscopists before the theory of atomic structure and atomic spectra had been developed.

These noble-gas electronic structures, corresponding to 2, 10, 18, 36, 54, or 86 electrons arranged in a particular way about an atomic nucleus, have very great stability. This is shown by the fact that the *ionization energy* is greater for the noble-gas atoms than for atoms of other elements, this being the energy required to remove an electron from the atom—that is, the energy absorbed during the reaction

$$X \longrightarrow X^+ + e^-$$

Similarly, the *electron affinity*, the energy liberated on picking up an additional electron, according to the reaction

$$X + e^- \longrightarrow X^-$$

is zero for the noble gases, which do not have the power of adding another electron.

The Sizes of Atoms and Ions.   The additional outer shells of atoms do not increase their size greatly. As the atomic number increases, the

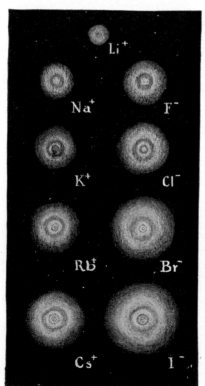

FIG. 10-1

The electron distribution in alkali ions and halide ions.

corresponding shells decrease in size (Fig. 10-1), permitting the new outer shell to be only a little larger than that for the preceding inert gas.

Although the outer electrons in an atom or ion are not rigorously restricted to a certain distance from the nucleus, *atomic radii* or *ionic radii* can be assigned to the atoms and ions, which indicate approximately the size of the atom. The noble gases, alkali ions, and halide ions have the radii given in Table 10-3.

TABLE 10-3   *Radii of Halide Ions, Noble-Gas Atoms, and Alkali Ions*

	He, 0.8 Å	Li^+, 0.60 Å
F^-, 1.36 Å	Ne, 1.1	Na^+, 0.95
Cl^-, 1.81	A, 1.5	K^+, 1.33
Br^-, 1.95	Kr, 1.7	Rb^+, 1.48
I^-, 2.16	Xe, 1.9	Cs^+, 1.69

The radius of a cation is smaller than that of the corresponding inert gas, because of the increase in atomic number (charge on the nucleus), and that of the corresponding anion is larger (compare Na^+, Ne, F^-).

Many of the properties of substances can be explained in terms of the sizes of atoms and ions. An example is given in the discussion of the formulas of the oxygen acids, Chapter 21.

The Structure of Other Atoms.   Each of the elements from lithium to neon, in the first short period of the periodic system, has an inner *K* shell of 2 electrons and an outer *L* shell containing from 1 electron to 8 electrons.

The *electron-dot* symbols of these atoms are

$$\dot{Li} \quad \dot{Be}\cdot \quad \dot{B}\cdot \quad \cdot\dot{C}\cdot \quad :\dot{N}\cdot \quad :\ddot{O}\cdot \quad :\ddot{F}\cdot \quad :\ddot{Ne}:$$

Note that the inner electrons (for these atoms the two *K* electrons) are not shown; the symbol Li, for example, here represents the lithium nucleus plus the two *K* electrons.

There are four orbitals in the *L* shell, each of which can be unoccupied, or can be occupied by one electron or by two electrons. Two electrons in an orbital constitute an *electron pair* (the Pauli exclusion principle requires that their spins be in opposite directions). Thus carbon is shown with four unpaired electrons in its *L* shell; it has just one electron for each of the four orbitals. Neon, however, with eight *L* electrons, can fit them into the four L orbitals only as four electron pairs. The completed noble-gas outer shell of four electron pairs is called an *octet* of electrons.

The atoms in the second short period may be represented similarly:

$$\text{Na} \quad \text{Mg·} \quad \text{Al·} \quad \text{·Si·} \quad \text{:P·} \quad \text{:S·} \quad \text{:Cl·} \quad \text{:A:}$$

The orbitals which constitute a noble-gas outer shell are an s orbital and three p orbitals. The first long period, containing eighteen elements, involves also a subshell of five $3d$ orbitals, in addition to the $4s$ orbital and the three $4p$ orbitals. It is usually considered that ten of the elements of this period (say from Sc to Zn, inclusive) correspond to the introduction of five electron pairs into the $3d$ subshell. These ten elements are sometimes called the *iron transition elements*.

It is not customary always to show all of the electrons outside of the argon shell for these elements. These electrons are shown for the first few elements:

$$\text{K·} \quad \text{Ca·} \quad \text{Sc·} \quad \text{·Ti·} \quad \text{·V·}$$

However, usually the five electron pairs in the $3d$ orbitals are omitted in the symbols of the last few elements of the period; that is, only the electrons of the N shell are represented:

$$\text{Zn·} \quad \text{Ga·} \quad \text{·Ge·} \quad \text{:As·} \quad \text{:Se·} \quad \text{:Br·} \quad \text{:Kr:}$$

There is no accepted usage for the elements in the middle of the period.

The elements of the second long period are similarly represented:

$$\text{Rb·} \quad \text{Sr·} \quad \text{Y·} \quad \text{·Zr·}$$

and

$$\text{Cd·} \quad \text{In·} \quad \text{·Sn·} \quad \text{:Sb·} \quad \text{:Te·} \quad \text{:I·} \quad \text{:Xe:}$$

The very long period begins with the three elements cesium, barium, and lanthanum:

$$\text{Cs·} \quad \text{Ba·} \quad \text{La·}$$

It is customary to ascribe the next fourteen elements, the *rare-earth metals*, to the introduction successively of fourteen electrons into the seven $4f$

orbitals. The remaining elements are similar to those shown directly above them in the periodic table, and are similarly represented.

An Energy-Level Diagram.   A diagram representing roughly the energy values of all electrons in all the atoms is given in Figure 10-2. Each orbital is represented by a square. The diagonal line indicates that there is room in each orbital for two electrons, one with positive orientation of its spin (arrow directed up) and one with negative orientation (arrow directed down). The energy of an electron in an orbital is indicated by the vertical coordinate in the diagram, the most stable orbital (with smallest energy) being the 1*s* orbital, at the bottom of the diagram. An energy scale is not shown, because the energy of an orbital depends on the charge of the nucleus (the atomic number of the atom) as well as on the quantum numbers of the orbital, and a different scale would be needed for each element.

The electrons are shown as being introduced in sequence, the first and the second in the 1*s* orbital, the next two in the 2*s* orbital, the next six in the three 2*p* orbitals, and so on. The sequence is indicated by arrows. The symbol and atomic number of each element are shown adjacent to the outermost electron (least firmly bound electron) in the neutral atom.

The distribution of electrons among the orbitals is called the *electron configuration* of the atom. It is represented by the symbols of the orbitals with the number of electrons in each orbital as a superscript. For example, the electron configuration of helium is $1s^2$, and that of iron is $1s^2\ 2s^2\ 2p^6\ 3s^2\ 3p^6\ 3d^6\ 4s^2$.

There may be several states of an atom corresponding to the same configuration. Thus oxygen, with the configuration $1s^2\ 2s^2\ 2p^4$, may have two unpaired 2*p* electrons, as shown in Figure 10-2, or may have no unpaired electrons:

2*p* 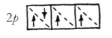   2*p*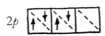

Two unpaired electrons   *No unpaired electrons*

For the heavier atoms the sets of states corresponding to two or more different configurations may have nearly the same energies, and there is some arbitrariness in deciding what electron configuration should be given in a table or diagram such as Figure 10-2. The configurations shown in Figure 10-2 are those of the lowest state of the free (gaseous) atom or of a state very close to the lowest state.

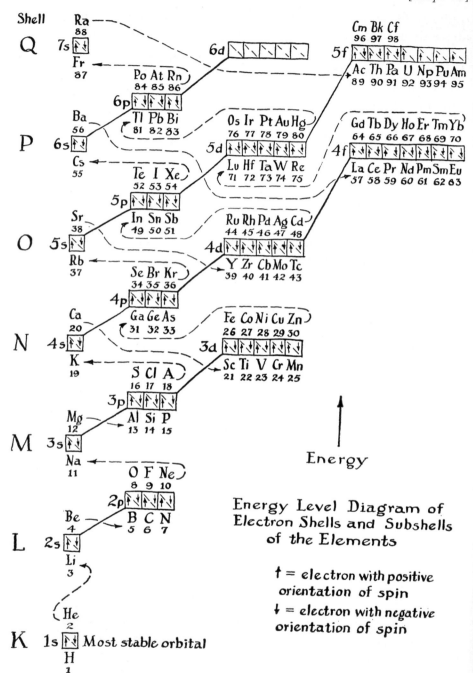

Energy

Energy Level Diagram of
Electron Shells and Subshells
of the Elements

↑ = electron with positive
orientation of spin

↓ = electron with negative
orientation of spin

FIG. 10-2

Example 1.   What is the electron configuration of the ferric ion, Fe^{+++}?
Does this ion contain any unpaired electrons?

    Solution.   From Figure 10-2 we see that the neutral iron atom has
the electron configuration $1s^2\ 2s^2\ 2p^6\ 3s^2\ 3p^6\ 3d^6\ 4s^2$. The three most
loosely bound electrons are to be removed from the atom to give
the ferric ion Fe^{+++}. The figure shows the $4s$ orbital and the $3d$
orbital to have essentially the same energy; hence the three most
loosely bound electrons might be three $3d$ electrons, or two $3d$ electrons and one $4s$ electron, or one $3d$ electron and two $4s$ electrons.
The electron configuration of Fe^{+++} might then be any one of the
following three:

    A. $1s^2\ 2s^2\ 2p^6\ 3s^2\ 3p^6\ 3d^3\ 4s^2$

    B. $1s^2\ 2s^2\ 2p^6\ 3s^2\ 3p^6\ 3d^4\ 4s$

    C. $1s^2\ 2s^2\ 2p^6\ 3s^2\ 3p^6\ 3d^5$

    This is as far as the solution of the problem can be taken without
additional information.*

10–3. *Covalent Molecules of Elements*

The general rule for the formation of covalent bonds is the following:
*Stable molecules or complex ions involving covalent bonds have structures such that
each atom achieves a noble-gas electronic configuration or some other stable configuration, the shared electrons being counted for each of the bonded atoms.* This
rule may be illustrated first by its application to the molecules and crystals of the non-metallic elements.

The Halogen Molecules.   A halogen atom, such as fluorine, $: \overset{\cdot\cdot}{\underset{\cdot\cdot}{F}} \cdot\,$,
lacks one electron of having a completed noble-gas octet. It can achieve
the noble-gas structure by forming a single covalent bond with another
halogen atom:

$$: \overset{\cdot\cdot}{\underset{\cdot\cdot}{F}} : \overset{\cdot\cdot}{\underset{\cdot\cdot}{F}} : \quad \text{or} \quad : \overset{\cdot\cdot}{\underset{\cdot\cdot}{F}} - \overset{\cdot\cdot}{\underset{\cdot\cdot}{F}} : \qquad : \overset{\cdot\cdot}{\underset{\cdot\cdot}{Cl}} : \overset{\cdot\cdot}{\underset{\cdot\cdot}{Cl}} : \quad \text{or} \quad : \overset{\cdot\cdot}{\underset{\cdot\cdot}{Cl}} - \overset{\cdot\cdot}{\underset{\cdot\cdot}{Cl}} :$$

$$: \overset{\cdot\cdot}{\underset{\cdot\cdot}{Br}} : \overset{\cdot\cdot}{\underset{\cdot\cdot}{Br}} : \quad \text{or} \quad : \overset{\cdot\cdot}{\underset{\cdot\cdot}{Br}} - \overset{\cdot\cdot}{\underset{\cdot\cdot}{Br}} : \qquad : \overset{\cdot\cdot}{\underset{\cdot\cdot}{I}} : \overset{\cdot\cdot}{\underset{\cdot\cdot}{I}} : \quad \text{or} \quad : \overset{\cdot\cdot}{\underset{\cdot\cdot}{I}} - \overset{\cdot\cdot}{\underset{\cdot\cdot}{I}} :$$

---

* It is, in fact, known from the magnetic properties of solutions of ferric salts that the ferric
ion contains five unpaired electrons. Configuration A permits only three unpaired electrons,
and hence is eliminated by the magnetic data. Both B and C permit five unpaired electrons
to be present, and it is hard to decide between them. Usually C is taken as the configuration
of the ferric ion.

This bond holds the atoms together in diatomic molecules, which are present in the elementary halogens in all states of aggregation—crystal, liquid, and gas.

The Elements of the Sixth Group.   An atom of a sixth-group element, such as sulfur, lacks two electrons of having a completed octet. It can complete its octet by forming single covalent bonds with two other atoms. These bonds may hold the molecule together either in a ring, such as an S_8 ring,

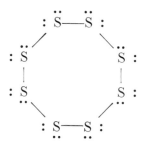

or in a very long chain, with the two end atoms having an abnormal structure,

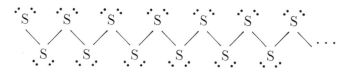

Sulfur itself occurs in both these forms. Ordinary sulfur (orthorhombic sulfur, monoclinic sulfur, the pale straw-colored liquid obtained by melting crystalline sulfur without overheating, and sulfur vapor) consists of staggered rings S_8, with the configuration shown in Figure 10-3. When molten sulfur is heated to a temperature considerably above its melting point it becomes deep-red in color and extremely viscous, so that it will not pour out of the test tube when the tube is inverted. This change in properties is the result of the formation of very large molecules, containing hundreds of atoms in a long chain—the S_8 rings break open, and then combine together into a "high polymer." * The deep-red color is due to the abnormal atoms at the ends of the chains, and the great viscosity is due to the interference with molecular motion caused by entanglement of the chains with one another.

When the viscous liquid is rapidly cooled it forms a plastic, rubbery

---

* A *polymer* is a molecule made by combination of two or more identical smaller molecules. A *high* polymer is made by combination of many identical smaller molecules.

"supercooled liquid." When this rubbery material is stretched the long chains align themselves parallel to the stretching direction, and the sulfur crystallizes as *fibrous sulfur*.

Selenium crystallizes as red crystals containing Se_8 molecules, and as semi-metallic gray crystals containing long staggered chains, stretching from one end of the crystal to the other. *Tellurium* crystals also contain long chains.

Ordinary oxygen contains diatomic molecules with an unusual electronic structure. We might expect these molecules to contain a *double*

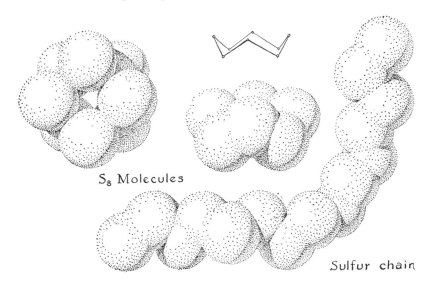

S₈ Molecules

Sulfur chain

FIG. 10-3   *The S₈ ring, and a long chain of sulfur atoms.*

bond—that is, to share two electron pairs between the two atoms, and thus to complete the octet for each atom:

$$: \overset{\cdot\cdot}{O} : : \overset{\cdot\cdot}{O} : \quad \text{or} \quad : \overset{\cdot\cdot}{O} = \overset{\cdot\cdot}{O} : $$

Instead, only one shared pair is formed, leaving two unpaired electrons:

$$: \overset{\cdot}{\underset{\cdot\cdot}{O}} : \overset{\cdot\cdot}{\underset{\cdot}{O}} : \quad \text{or} \quad : \overset{\cdot}{\underset{\cdot\cdot}{O}} - \overset{\cdot\cdot}{\underset{\cdot}{O}} : $$

These two unpaired electrons are responsible for the paramagnetism of oxygen.*

* The force of attraction between the oxygen atoms is much greater than that expected for a single covalent bond. This shows that the unpaired electrons are really involved in bond formation, of a special sort. The oxygen molecule may be said to contain a single covalent bond plus two *three-electron bonds*, and its structure may be written as $: O \vdots O :$

Ozone, the triatomic form of oxygen, has the electronic structure

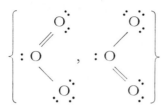

Here one of the end atoms of the molecule resembles a fluorine atom in that it completes its octet by sharing only one electron pair. It may be considered to be the negative ion, $: \ddot{\text{O}} \cdot ^{-}$, which forms one covalent bond. The central oxygen atom resembles a nitrogen atom, and may be considered to be the positive ion $: \dot{\text{O}} \cdot ^{+}$, which forms three covalent bonds (one double bond and one single bond). The angle between these bonds has been found to be 120° (Fig. 5-6).

Two structures for ozone are shown above, in braces. This indicates that the two end oxygen atoms are not different, but are equivalent. The molecule has a structure represented by the superposition of the two structures shown; that is, each bond is a *hybrid* of a single covalent bond and a double covalent bond (see Sec. 10-5, on resonance).

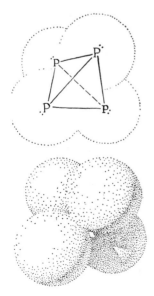

FIG. 10-4

The P₄ molecule.

Nitrogen and Its Congeners.   The nitrogen atom, lacking three electrons of a completed octet, may achieve the octet by forming three covalent bonds. It does this in elementary nitrogen by forming a *triple bond*
in the molecule N_2. Three electron pairs are shared by the two nitrogen
atoms:

$$: N ::: N :   \text{or}   : N \equiv N :$$

This bond is extremely strong, and the N_2 molecule is a very stable
molecule.

Phosphorus gas at very high temperatures consists of similar P_2 molecules, $: P \equiv P :$. At lower temperatures the molecule P_4 is stable. This
molecule has the tetrahedral structure shown in Figure 10-4 (see also

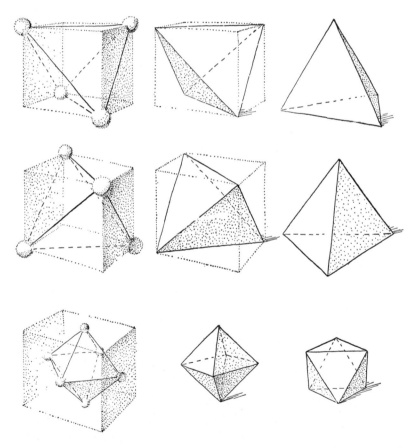

FIG. 10-5 *Drawing showing the relation of the tetrahedron and the
octahedron to the cube. These polyhedra are important in molecular structure.*

Fig. 10-5). Each phosphorus atom forms covalent bonds with three others. This molecule exists in phosphorus vapor, in solutions, and in solid white phosphorus. In other forms of the element (red phosphorus, black phosphorus) the atoms are bonded into larger aggregates.

Arsenic and *antimony* also form tetrahedral molecules, As_4 and Sb_4, and, at higher temperatures, diatomic molecules, As_2 and Sb_2, in the vapor phase. Crystals of these elementary substances and of bismuth, however, contain high polymers—layers of atoms in which each atom is bonded to three neighbors by single covalent bonds.

Carbon and Its Congeners.   Carbon, with four electrons missing from a completed octet, can form four covalent bonds. In *diamond* each atom

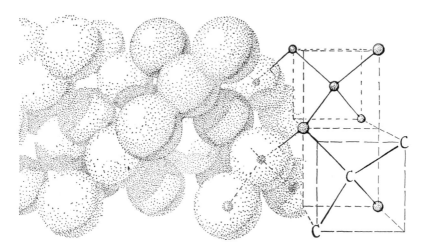

FIG. 10-6   *The structure of diamond.*

is bonded strongly to four neighboring atoms which are held about it at the corners of a regular tetrahedron (Fig. 10-6). These covalent bonds bind all of the atoms in the diamond crystal together into a single giant molecule, and since the C—C bonds are very strong the crystal is very hard. This structure helps to explain why diamond is the hardest substance known.

Graphite consists of layers of atoms, with the structure shown in Figure 10-7. Each atom has three near neighbors. It is bonded to two of them by single covalent bonds, and to the third by a double bond. This completes the octet for each atom. The double bonds are not fixed in position, but move around so as to give each bond some double-bond character. The covalent bonds tie the atoms very tightly together into layers; however, the layers are piled rather loosely on one another, and can be separated easily, which causes graphite to be a soft substance, which is even used as a lubricant.

Silicon, germanium, and gray *tin* also crystallize with the diamond structure. Ordinary tin (white tin) and lead have metallic structures (see Chap. 24).

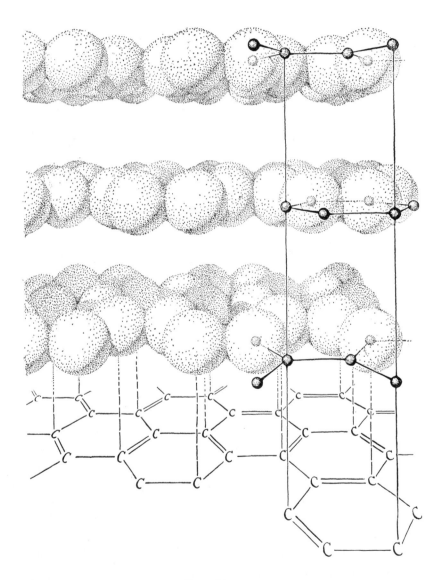

FIG. 10-7   *The structure of graphite.*

The Tetrahedral Atom.   The tetrahedral arrangement of four carbon atoms around each carbon atom in diamond is not the result of chance, but is instead the expression of an important property of the octet: *The four electron pairs of an octet, whether shared or unshared, tend to arrange themselves in space at the corners of a regular tetrahedron.* The angle between two single bonds formed by an atom thus tends to be near the tetrahedral angle, 109°28′. This explains why the S_8 ring and the S_∞ chain * are staggered; the sulfur bond angle is about 106°.

A double bond between two atoms may be represented by two tetrahedra sharing two corners—that is, sharing an edge (Fig. 10-8). The

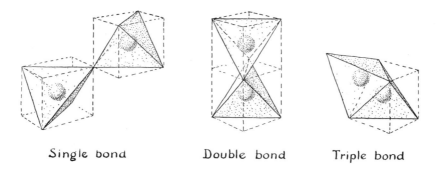

Single bond   Double bond   Triple bond

FIG. 10-8   *Tetrahedral atoms forming single, double, and triple bonds.*

four single bonds which the two can also form, if they are carbon atoms, then lie in the same plane. The ideal angle between a single bond and a double bond is 125°16′.

A triple bond between two atoms may similarly be represented by two tetrahedra sharing a face (Fig. 10-8).

10–4. *Hybrid Bond Orbitals*

The configuration $1s^2 2s^2 2p^2$ shown in Figure 10-2 for carbon represents the isolated carbon atom in its normal state, but is not the most interesting configuration to chemists. *To form a covalent bond an atom needs an orbital occupied by a single (unpaired) electron;* the two electrons, of two atoms joined by a bond, are paired together. The normal carbon atom has only two unpaired electrons, and hence could form only two covalent bonds.

In most of its compounds carbon forms four covalent bonds. The

---

* A very long chain of sulfur atoms is sometimes written S_x or S_∞. The symbol ∞ here means a very large number, rather than the mathematical "infinity."

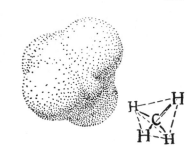

FIG. 10-9

The structure of the methane molecule.

electron configuration of the carbon atom in the quadrivalent state is $1s^2\ 2s\ 2p^3$. One electron has been raised (promoted) from the $2s$ orbital to the less stable $2p$ orbital. The atom can then form four covalent bonds, instead of two. The energy for promoting the electron is the energy of the two extra bonds that the atom can form.

Sometimes the electron configuration of the quadrivalent carbon atom

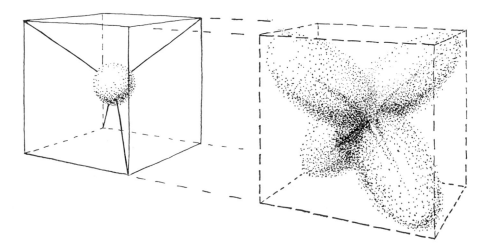

FIG. 10-10   *Diagram illustrating (left) the 1s orbital in the K shell of the carbon atom, and (right) the four tetrahedral orbitals of the L shell.*

is written $1s^2\ 2s\ 2p\ 2p\ 2p$, to show that all four valence electrons occupy different orbitals.

It might be thought that the carbon atom with this configuration would form one bond of one kind with its $2s$ electron and three bonds of another kind with its three $2p$ electrons. In fact, however, the four bonds that it forms are exactly equivalent; the methane molecule, CH_4, for example, has regular tetrahedral symmetry, with the nuclei of the four hydrogen atoms exactly the same distance from the nucleus of the carbon atom (Fig. 10-9). The explanation of this fact is that the 2*s* orbital and the three 2*p* orbitals can be *hybridized* (combined) to form four orbitals that are exactly equivalent to one another. These four orbitals are directed toward the four corners of a regular tetrahedron; they are called *tetrahedral bond orbitals*. They are better suited to forming bonds than are the 2*s* and 2*p* orbitals themselves, which are especially appropriate to describing isolated atoms.

The four tetrahedral bond orbitals of a quadricovalent atom are represented in Figure 10-10.

10–5. *Resonance*

In Section 10–3 it was mentioned that ozone has the structure

and that graphite has the structure indicated in Figure 10-7, but with the double bonds not fixed in place. The reason for these statements is that it is known from experiment that the two oxygen-oxygen bonds in ozone are not different, but are equivalent, and that the carbon-carbon bonds in graphite are also all equivalent. Equivalence of the bonds can be explained by the assumption of a *hybrid structure*. Each of the bonds in ozone is a hybrid between a single bond and a double bond, and its properties are intermediate.

It is customary to say that the double bond *resonates* between the two positions in ozone. The *resonance of molecules between two or more electronic structures* is an important concept. Often it is found difficult to assign to a molecule a single electronic structure of the valence-bond type that represents its properties satisfactorily. Often, also, two or more electronic structures seem to be about equally good. In these cases it is usually wise to say that the actual molecule resonates among the structures, and to indicate the molecule by writing the various resonating structures together in braces. These various structures do not correspond to different kinds of molecules; there is only one kind of molecule present, with an electronic structure which is a hybrid structure of two or more valence-bond structures.

10–6. *The Structure of Compound Substances*

The electronic structures of molecules of compound substances may usually be formulated by applying the methods used in the preceding sections. Thus methane, CH_4, can be assigned the tetrahedral covalent structure

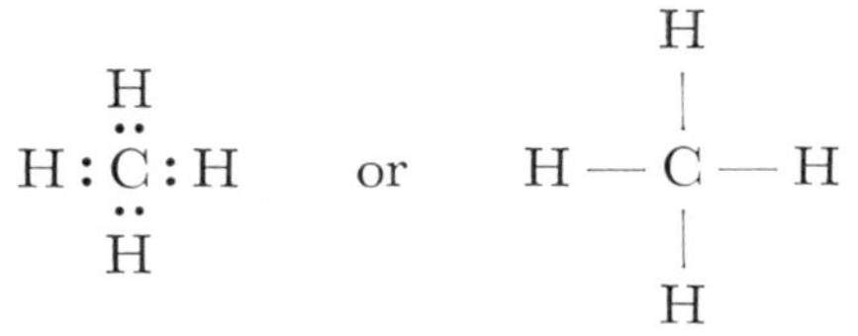

$$\begin{array}{ccc}
 & & H \\
H & & | \\
H : C : H & \text{or} & H - C - H \\
H & & | \\
 & & H
\end{array}$$

and chloroform, $CHCl_3$, the similar structure

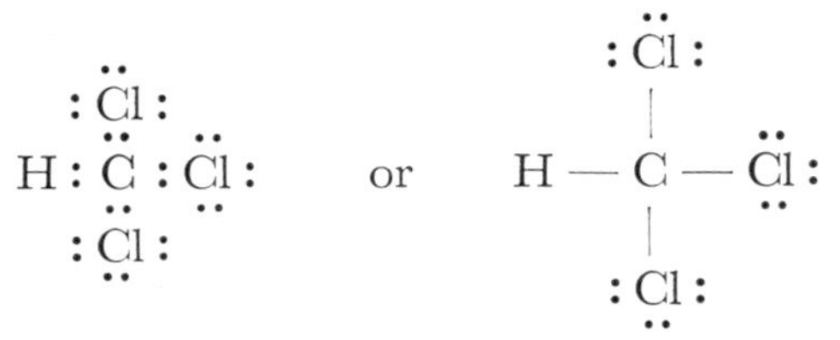

$$\begin{array}{ccc}
 & & : \overset{..}{Cl} : \\
: \overset{..}{Cl} : & & | \\
H : C : \overset{..}{Cl} : & \text{or} & H - C - \overset{..}{Cl} : \\
: \overset{..}{Cl} : & & | \\
 & & : \overset{..}{Cl} :
\end{array}$$

By sharing electrons each hydrogen atom achieves the helium structure, each carbon atom achieves the neon structure, and each chlorine atom achieves the argon structure.

The structures of these molecules are represented in the plane of the paper, but it must not be forgotten that the octet atoms are tetrahedral. When the spatial configuration is important a representation of the three-dimensional structure should be drawn (as for P_4, Fig. 10-4).

Other electronic structures of molecules containing covalent bonds may be readily written, by keeping in mind the importance of completing the octet of atoms of non-metallic elements. Note the use of square brackets around complex ions, and curved braces around resonating structures:

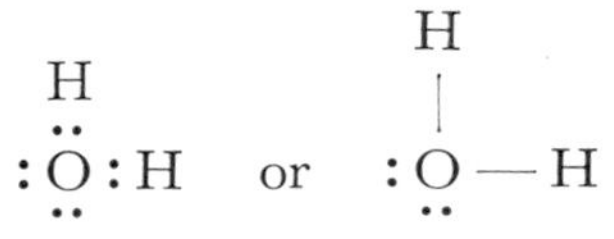

$$\begin{array}{ccc}
 & & H \\
H & & | \\
: \overset{..}{O} : H & \text{or} & : O - H \quad \text{water}
\end{array}$$

$$\left[: \overset{..}{O} - H \right]^{-} \qquad \text{hydroxide ion, present in basic solutions}$$

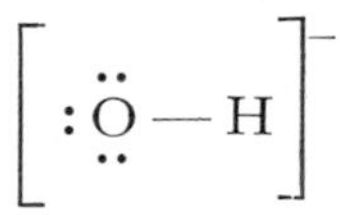

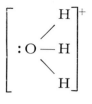

hydronium ion, present in acidic solutions

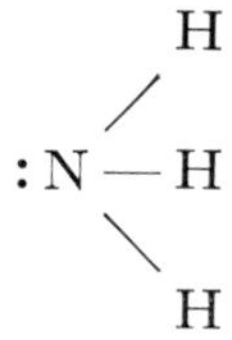

ammonia

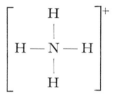

ammonium ion

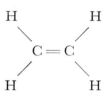

ethylene (all atoms in the same plane)

$$H - C \equiv C - H$$

acetylene (linear molecule)

$$H - C \equiv N :$$

hydrogen cyanide (linear molecule)

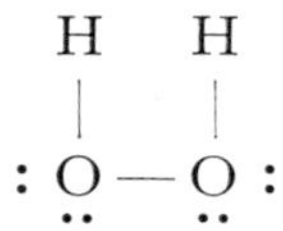

hydrogen peroxide

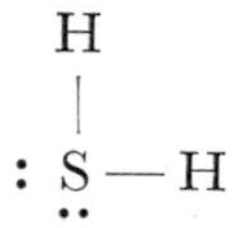

$$\overset{H}{\underset{}{\overset{|}{:} \overset{..}{S} - H}}$$

hydrogen sulfide

$$\overset{..}{:}\overset{\overset{..}{Cl}:}{\underset{}{\overset{|}{:} \overset{..}{S} - \overset{..}{Cl} :}}$$

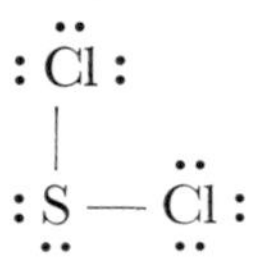

sulfur dichloride

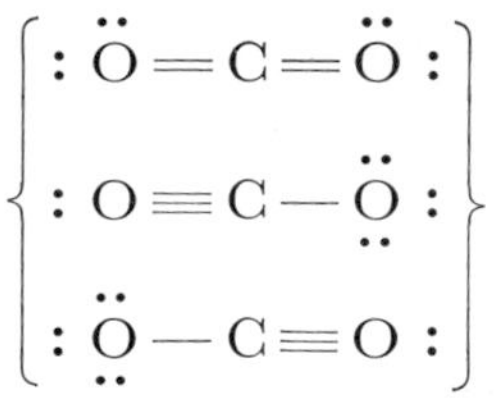

$$
\left\{
\begin{array}{l}
: \overset{..}{O} = C = \overset{..}{O} : \\[2ex]
: O \equiv C - \overset{..}{\underset{..}{O}} : \\[2ex]
: \overset{..}{\underset{..}{O}} - C \equiv O :
\end{array}
\right\}
$$
  carbon dioxide (linear molecule)

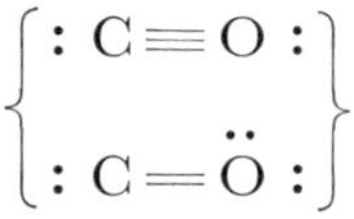

$$
\left\{
\begin{array}{l}
: C \equiv O : \\[2ex]
: C = \overset{..}{O} :
\end{array}
\right\}
$$
  carbon monoxide

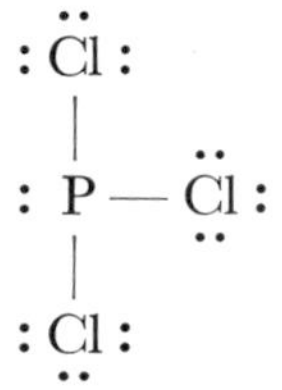

$$
\begin{array}{c}
: \overset{..}{\underset{..}{Cl}} : \\
| \\
: P - \overset{..}{\underset{..}{Cl}} : \\
| \\
: \underset{..}{Cl} :
\end{array}
$$
  phosphorus trichloride

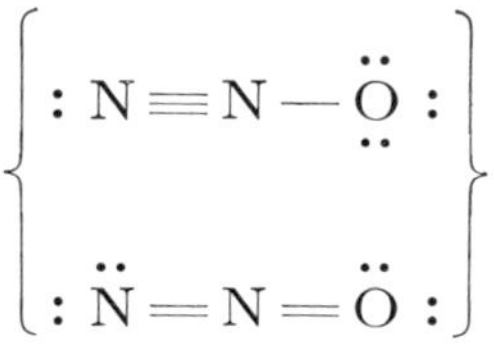

$$
\left\{
\begin{array}{l}
: N \equiv N - \overset{..}{\underset{..}{O}} : \\[2ex]
: \overset{..}{\underset{..}{N}} = N = \overset{..}{\underset{..}{O}} :
\end{array}
\right\}
$$
  nitrous oxide (linear molecule)

10–7. *The Partial Ionic Character of Covalent Bonds*

The decision often must be made whether to consider a molecule to contain an ionic bond or to contain a covalent bond. There is no doubt about the salt of a strong metal and a strong non-metal; an ionic structure is to be written for it. Thus for lithium chloride we write

$$
\text{Li}^+ \text{Cl}^- \qquad \text{or} \qquad \text{Li}^+ : \overset{..}{\underset{..}{Cl}} : {}^-
$$

Similarly, there is no doubt about nitrogen trichloride, NCl_3. This is an oily molecular substance, a compound of two non-metals, with the covalent structure

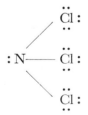

Between LiCl and NCl_3 there are the compounds $BeCl_2$, BCl_3, and CCl_4. Where does the change from an ionic structure to a covalent structure occur? Should BCl_3 be written

$$B^{+++}(Cl^-)_3 \quad \text{or} \quad :\!\ddot{C}l\!-\!B\!\!\begin{array}{c}\diagup\!\ddot{C}l: \\ \diagdown\!\ddot{C}l: \end{array} \quad \text{or} \quad :\!\ddot{C}l\!=\!B\!\!\begin{array}{c}\diagup\!\ddot{C}l: \\ \diagdown\!\ddot{C}l: \end{array} \quad ?$$

The answer to this question is provided by the theory of resonance. The transition from an ionic bond to a normal covalent bond does not occur sharply, but gradually. The structure of the boron trichloride molecule is best represented as the resonance hybrid of all the structures given above.

Often only the covalent structure is shown, and the chemist bears in mind that the covalent bonds have a certain amount of ionic character. These bonds are called *covalent bonds with partial ionic character*.

For example, the hydrogen chloride molecule may be assigned the resonating structure

$$\left\{ H^+ : \ddot{\underset{\cdot\cdot}{C}}l :^-, \quad H : \ddot{\underset{\cdot\cdot}{C}}l : \right\}$$

This is usually represented by the simple structure

$$H - \ddot{\underset{\cdot\cdot}{C}}l :$$

It is then borne in mind that the hydrogen-chlorine bond has a certain amount (about 20%) of ionic character, which gives the hydrogen end of the molecule a small positive charge and the chlorine end a small negative charge.

The Electronegativity Scale of the Elements.   It has been found possible to assign to the elements numbers representing their power of attraction for the electrons in a covalent bond, by means of which the amount of partial ionic character may be estimated. This power of attraction for the electrons in a covalent bond is called the electronegativity of the element. In Figure 10-11 the elements other than the transition elements (which all have electronegativity values close to 1.6) and the rare-earth metals (which have values close to 1.3) are shown on an electronegativity scale. The way in which this scale was set up is described in Chapter 31.

The scale extends from cesium, 0.7, to fluorine, 4.0. Fluorine is the most electronegative element by far, with oxygen in second place and nitrogen and chlorine in third place. Hydrogen and the characteristic metalloids are in the center of the scale, with electronegativity values close to 2. The metals have values of about 1.8 or less.

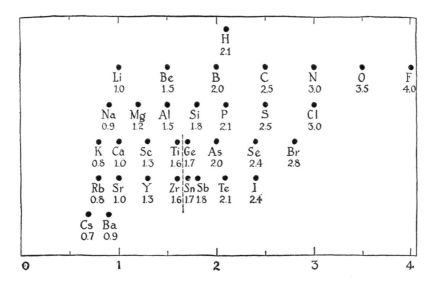

FIG. 10-11   *The electronegativity scale. The dashed line indicates approximate values for the transition metals.*

The farther away two elements are from one another on the scale (horizontally in Fig. 10-11), the greater is the amount of ionic character of a bond between them. When the separation on the scale is 1.9 the bond has about 50% ionic character. If the separation is greater than

TABLE 10-4   *Partial Ionic Character of Bonds and Electronegativity Difference of Atoms*

$x_A - x_B$	PARTIAL IONIC CHARACTER	$x_A - x_B$	PARTIAL IONIC CHARACTER
0.0	0%	1.4	32%
.2	1	1.6	40
.4	3	1.8	47
.6	7	2.0	54
.8	12	2.2	61
1.0	18	2.4	68
1.2	25	2.6	74

this, it would seem appropriate to write an ionic structure for the substance, and if it is less, to write a covalent structure. No rigid adherence to such a rule is called for, however.

The approximate relation between the amount of ionic character of a single bond between two atoms A and B and their electronegativity difference $x_A - x_B$ is given in Table 10-4.

An important use of the electronegativity scale is to indicate roughly the stability or strength of a bond. *The greater the separation of two elements on the electronegativity scale, the greater is the strength of the bond between them.* In general, great bond strength leads to the evolution of a large amount of energy as the bond is formed (see Chap. 31). This may be illustrated by the heats of formation of the hydrogen halides:

$$H_2 + F_2 \longrightarrow 2HF + 128 \text{ kcal}$$
$$H_2 + Cl_2 \longrightarrow 2HCl + 44 \text{ kcal}$$
$$H_2 + Br_2(g) \longrightarrow 2HBr + 25 \text{ kcal}$$
$$H_2 + I_2(g) \longrightarrow 2HI + 3 \text{ kcal}$$

Reactions between elements with nearly the same electronegativity usually are accompanied by small heat evolution or absorption.

10-8. *The Electroneutrality Principle*

A simple principle useful in the discussion of the electronic structure of molecules is the electroneutrality principle, which states that in stable compounds each atom is nearly electrically neutral. This principle is made reasonable by the fact that a great amount of energy is needed to remove a second or a third or a fourth electron from an atom. The successive ionization energies of aluminum, for example, are the following:

$$5.98 \text{ ev} + Al \longrightarrow Al^+ + e^-$$
$$18.82 \text{ ev} + Al^+ \longrightarrow Al^{++} + e^-$$
$$28.44 \text{ ev} + Al^{++} \longrightarrow Al^{+++} + e^-$$
$$119.96 \text{ ev} + Al^{+++} \longrightarrow Al^{++++} + e^-$$

The first ionization energy, 5.98 ev, is of the order of magnitude of the heat of chemical reactions involving one atom of aluminum or some other metal; for example, the heat of oxidation of Al to $\frac{1}{2}Al_2O_3$ (the heat liberated when aluminum is oxidized) is 190 kcal/mole, which is 8.24 ev per atom of aluminum. It is accordingly not unreasonable that the forces involved in the interactions between aluminum atoms and oxygen atoms might remove one electron from an aluminum atom (transferring it to an oxygen atom). The second ionization energy, 18.82 ev, is very much larger, however; it is nearly as large as the first ionization energy, 21.56 ev, of the noble gas neon, which holds its electrons so tightly that it does not form chemical bonds with any atoms, and accordingly it seems unlikely that in chemical reactions an aluminum atom would lose a second electron, and still more unlikely that it would lose a third electron.

Nevertheless, a solution of an aluminum salt is shown by its electric conductivity to contain tripositive aluminum ions, Al^{+++}. The explanation of the apparent contradiction is that the solution does not contain electrically charged atoms Al^{+++}, but instead contains the complexes $[Al(OH_2)_6]^{+++}$. Each of these complexes consists of an aluminum atom bonded to six oxygen atoms, of six water molecules, which lie at the corners of an octahedron about it. Its structural formula is

$$
\left[
\begin{array}{c}
\quad\quad \text{H} \quad\quad\quad \text{H} \\
\quad\quad | \quad\quad\quad\quad | \\
\text{H}\!-\!\text{O} \quad\quad \text{O}\!-\!\text{H} \\
\text{H}\diagdown \quad \diagdown \quad\diagup \quad \diagup\text{H} \\
\quad \text{O}\!-\!\!-\!\text{Al}\!-\!\!-\!\text{O} \\
\text{H}\diagup \quad \diagup \quad \diagdown \quad \diagdown\text{H} \\
\text{H}\!-\!\text{O} \quad\quad \text{O}\!-\!\text{H} \\
\quad\quad | \quad\quad\quad\quad | \\
\quad\quad \text{H} \quad\quad\quad \text{H}
\end{array}
\right]^{+++}
$$

If each of the bonds from aluminum to oxygen were a normal covalent bond, the aluminum atom would have six valence electrons, in addition to the ten electrons of its inner shells, and its electric charge would be -3. However, the electronegativity of aluminum is 1.5, and that of oxygen is 3.5, and their difference, 2.0, corresponds to 54% ionic character (Table 10-4). Each of the six bonds is hence 46% covalent, and contributes 0.46 valence electron to the aluminum atom. The total for six bonds is 2.76, which with the ten inner electrons gives 12.76, and leads, on subtraction from the nuclear charge $+13$, to a resultant charge $+0.24$ on the aluminum atom. Each oxygen atom is given the charge $+0.46$; however, the oxygen-hydrogen bonds (electronegativity difference 1.4) have 32% ionic character (Table 10-4), which leaves the oxygen atoms with charge -0.18 and places the charge $+0.32$ on each hydrogen atom.

This calculation (which is only a rough one, because the principles of molecular structure have not yet been completely worked out) shows how the presence of the electric charge $+3$ on the hydrated aluminum ion is compatible with the electroneutrality principle: the charge $+3$ is not on the aluminum atom, but is distributed over the aluminum atom and the twelve hydrogen atoms in such a way that each atom carries only a small charge.

Many applications may be made of the electroneutrality principle; we shall mention only one here. The hydrides of the group V elements, NH_3, PH_3, AsH_3, SbH_3, and BiH_3, differ in that only the first combines with hydrogen ion to form a stable complex ion.* The bonds in the ammonia molecule have 15% ionic character, giving the charge distribution $N^{-0.45}(H^{+0.15})_3$. Adding a proton leads to $[N^{+0.40}(H^{+0.15})_4]^+$, which is satisfactory. Phosphorus, however, has exactly the same electronegativity as hydrogen, and hence PH_3 has the charge distribution $P^0(H^0)_3$, which corresponds to stability, and PH_4^+ has the charge distribution $[P^{+1}(H^0)_4]^+$, which, because of the large charge on the phosphorus atom, corresponds to instability. The other hydrides contain central atoms still more electropositive than hydrogen, and hence their complex cations MH_4^+ would also be unstable. The electroneutrality principle in this way explains the non-existence of series of compounds of the congeners of nitrogen analogous to the ammonium salts.

* Although the phosphonium ion is not stable in aqueous solution, a few phosphonium compounds have been made, such as phosphonium iodide, PH_4I. This crystalline substance, the most stable of the phosphonium compounds, is presumably stabilized by the formation of partial covalent bonds between hydrogen and iodine.

10–9. *Deviations from the Octet Rule*

Sometimes heavy atoms form so many covalent bonds as to surround themselves with more than four electron pairs. Examples are

phosphorus pentachloride, PCl_5

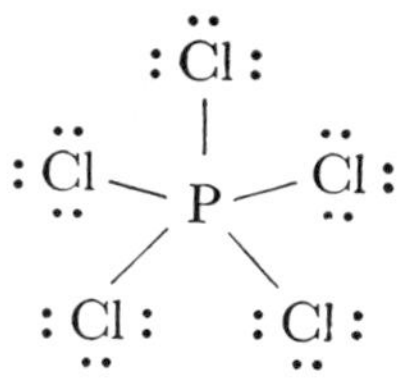

sulfur hexafluoride, SF_6

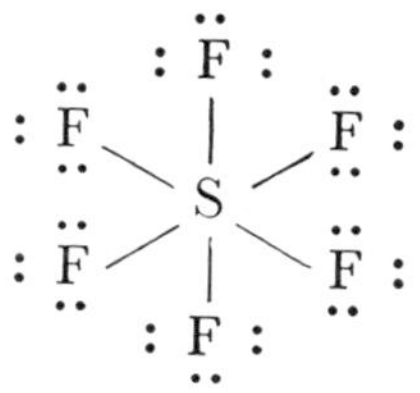

iodine trichloride, ICl_3

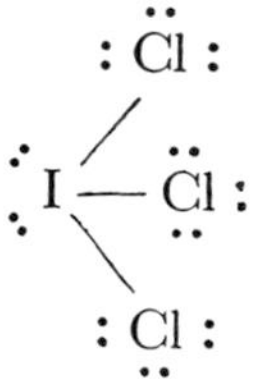

iodine pentafluoride, IF_5

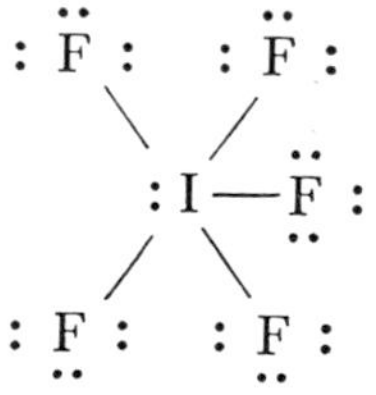

iodine heptafluoride, IF_7

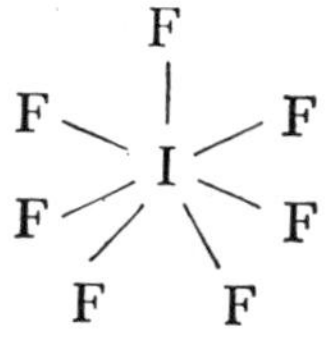

triiodide ion, I_3-

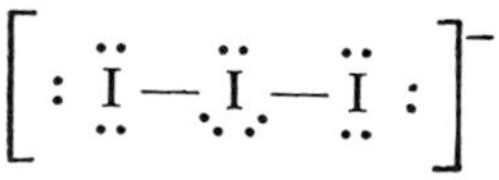

In some cases these represent only apparent, and not real, deviations from the octet rule. In PCl_5, for example, there may be four covalent bonds and one ionic bond resonating among the five positions:

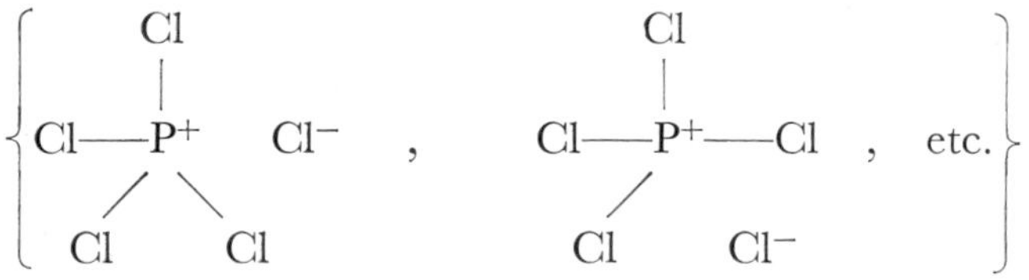

$$
\left\{
\begin{array}{c}
\text{Cl} \\
| \\
\text{Cl—P}^+ \quad \text{Cl}^- \\
\diagup \quad \diagdown \\
\text{Cl} \qquad \text{Cl}
\end{array}
\quad , \quad
\begin{array}{c}
\text{Cl} \\
| \\
\text{Cl—P}^+\text{—Cl} \\
\diagup \\
\text{Cl} \qquad \text{Cl}^-
\end{array}
\quad , \quad \text{etc.}
\right\}
$$

These five structures, together with the structure with five covalent bonds, provide a satisfactory hybrid electronic structure for the molecule.

The Oxygen Acids.   It is customary to write the following structures for the simpler oxygen acids:*

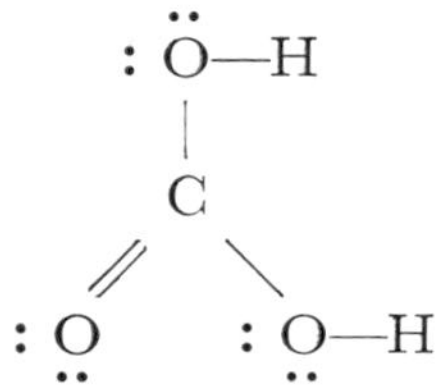

$$
\begin{array}{c}
\ddot{\,:\,}\ddot{\text{O}}\text{—H} \\
| \\
\text{C} \\
\diagup\!\!\diagup \qquad \diagdown \\
:\text{O} \qquad :\ddot{\text{O}}\text{—H}
\end{array}
\qquad \text{carbonic acid}
$$

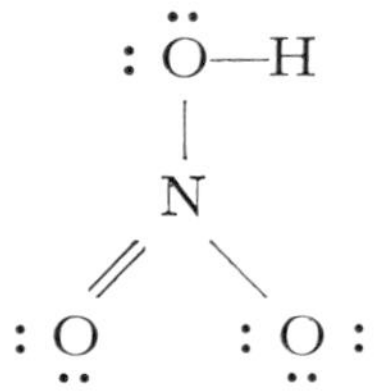

$$
\begin{array}{c}
:\ddot{\text{O}}\text{—H} \\
| \\
\text{N} \\
\diagup\!\!\diagup \qquad \diagdown \\
:\text{O} \qquad :\ddot{\text{O}}:
\end{array}
\qquad \text{nitric acid}
$$

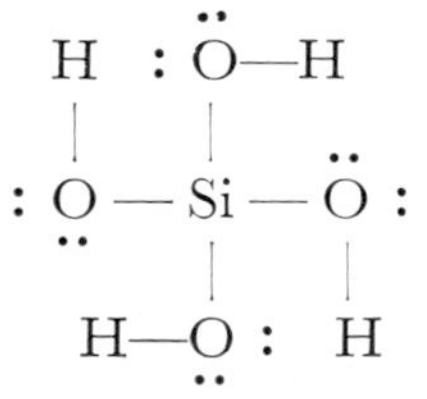

$$
\begin{array}{c}
\text{H} \quad :\ddot{\text{O}}\text{—H} \\
| \qquad | \\
:\ddot{\text{O}}\text{— Si —}\ddot{\text{O}}: \\
| \qquad | \\
\text{H—}\ddot{\text{O}}: \quad \text{H}
\end{array}
\qquad \text{silicic acid}
$$

---

* It is good practice to write electronic structures (and valence-bond structures) in such a way as to reproduce the actual structure of the molecule as closely as can be conveniently done. The valence-bond angle for oxygen is about 110°; hence we write $:\ddot{\text{O}}$ — H rather than

$$
\begin{array}{c}
:\ddot{\text{O}} \\
| \\
\text{S}
\end{array}
$$

$$\text{S} - \ddot{\text{O}} - \text{H}.$$

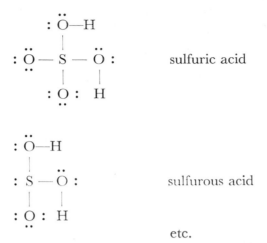

sulfuric acid

sulfurous acid

etc.

Structures of this sort for sulfuric acid and related substances were first written by Gilbert Newton Lewis; they are sometimes called *Lewis structures*. In these structures the atoms all satisfy the octet rule. Some of the structures violate the electroneutrality principle, however. Thus for sulfuric acid the Lewis structure places the charge $+2$ on the sulfur atom, and the partial ionic character of the S—O bonds would increase this positive charge. The observed values of interatomic distances in sulfuric acid and related substances indicate strongly that double bonds are formed between the central atom and the oxygen atoms, with the sulfur atom exceeding the octet; for sulfuric acid the most satisfactory single electronic structure is

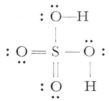

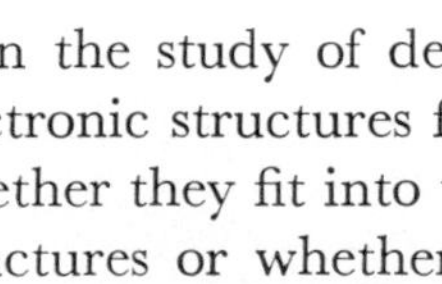

In the study of descriptive chemistry it is a good practice to write electronic structures for all the new substances encountered, and to see whether they fit into the simple scheme with all atoms having noble-gas structures or whether they constitute exceptions. It is possible in this way to make considerable progress toward the systematization of the facts of chemistry and the understanding of chemical phenomena.

10–10. *The Development of the Electronic Theory of Valence*

During the first decade of the nineteenth century many investigators made use of the electric battery newly discovered by Volta to carry out studies of the phenomenon of electrolysis of solutions and fused salts. It was observed that in the electrolysis of water hydrogen is liberated at the cathode and oxygen at the anode, and that in the electrolysis of fused salts and bases metals are liberated at the cathode and non-metals (oxygen, chlorine) at the anode. On the basis of these results Berzelius in 1811 developed his *dualistic theory* of chemical combination. This involved the idea that in a salt the base and acid have positive and negative charges, respectively, and that on electrolysis they are drawn to the oppositely charged electrodes and liberated by neutralization of their charges. The theory is seen to have foreshadowed closely the present theory of ionic valence.

With the development of organic chemistry during the latter part of the century the dualistic theory fell largely into disuse because of the impossibility of applying it satisfactorily to the compounds of carbon, which in the main contain covalent bonds. The theory of the valence bond was then developed. It was in 1852 that the statement was first made (by Edward Frankland in England) that atoms have a definite combining power, which determines the formulas of compounds. A few years later (1858) Archibald S. Couper* introduced the idea of the valence bond and drew the first structural formulas, and during the same year August Kekulé in Germany showed that carbon is quadrivalent and that the carbon atoms are bonded to one another to form chains in organic compounds, such as 2,2,4-trimethylpentane (iso-octane):

The idea that the four valence bonds of the carbon atom are directed toward the corners of a regular tetrahedron was advanced in 1874 by the Dutch chemist J. H. van't Hoff (1852–1911) and independently by the French chemist J. A. Le Bel (1847–1930) to explain the existence of right-handed and left-handed forms of some organic compounds, which shows itself in the face development of crystals (enantiomorphism) and in the power of solutions to rotate the plane of polarization of a transmitted beam of polarized light either to the right or to the left (optical activity). This phenomenon had been discovered during an investigation of tartaric acid by Louis Pasteur (1822–1895) in 1848.

Soon after the discovery of the electron by Sir J. J. Thomson efforts were made to develop a more detailed structural theory of valence. The general ideas of electron transfer and of electron sharing were developed at this time, but detailed electronic structures could not be assigned with confidence because of lack of knowledge of the number of electrons in an atom and lack of information about atomic structures in general. The determination of the atomic numbers of the elements by Moseley and the development of the quantum theory of the atom by Bohr, both in 1913, provided the basis for further progress. A most important contribution was made in 1916 by Gilbert Newton Lewis, who pointed out the significance of completed shells of two and eight

---

* An interesting account of the search made by Professor Crum Brown of Edinburgh for information about the life of Couper is given in *J. Chem. Ed.*, **11**, 331 (1934).

electrons and identified the covalent bond with a pair of electrons shared by two atoms and counting as part of the outer shell of each.

After the discovery of the theory of quantum mechanics in 1925 a detailed quantitative theory of the covalent bond was developed. In recent years great progress has been made in understanding valence and chemical combination through the experimental investigations of the structure of molecules and crystals and through theoretical studies. The theory of resonance was developed around 1930.

Exercises

10-1. Make a drawing of each of the noble gases, He, Ne, A, Kr, Xe, and Rn, showing by dots the proper numbers of electrons in the successive electron shells.

10-2. Satisfy yourself that you understand the way in which the periodic system is built up, by using the table of electron shells for the noble gases (Table 10-1) to deduce the electronic structures of N (atomic number 7), Al (13), K (19), Ni (28), Cu (29), Ba (56), Bi (83), Ra (88). Show these electronic structures in a table like that given in the text for the noble gases.

10-3. The new synthetic elements neptunium (93), plutonium (94), americium (95), and curium (96) are all reported to form terpositive ions, as does actinium (89). In what shells and subshells might the extra electrons that Np^{+++}, Pu^{+++}, Am^{+++}, and Cm^{+++} have in excess over those in Ac^{+++} be contained?

10-4. The following values of ionic radii represent the relative sizes of the ions: F^-, 1.36 Å; Na^+, 0.95 Å; Cl^-, 1.81 Å; K^+, 1.33 Å. Why do the sizes of these ions vary in this way?

10-5. Assuming that the following compounds are ionic, give the electron-dot formula for each ion, and put in parentheses the symbol of the noble gas with the same structure, or the total number of electrons if the structure is not a noble-gas structure:

HF   NaCl CaH_2 Al_2O_3 K_3FeF_6 $Al_2SiO_4F_2$
LiBr $KMgF_3$ MgO TiO_2 Na_2S $Be_3Al_2Si_6O_{18}$

10-6. Write electronic structures for the following polyatomic ions, indicating all electrons in the outer shell; assume that the various atoms of the ion are held together by covalent bonds:

O_2^{--} (peroxide ion)
S_3^{--} (trisulfide ion)
NO_2^+ (nitronium ion)
BH_4^- (borohydride ion)
NH_4^+ (ammonium ion)
$N(CH_3)_4^+$ (tetramethyl ammonium ion)

For each of these ions, what corresponding neutral molecule has the same electronic structure? (Example: HS^- has the same electronic structure as HCl.)

10-7. Write electronic structures for the molecules NH_3 and BF_3. These molecules combine to form the addition compound H_3NBF_3. What is the electronic structure of this compound? What similarity is there in the electronic rearrangements in the following chemical reactions?

$$NH_3 + H^+ \longrightarrow NH_4^+$$
$$NH_3 + BF_3 \longrightarrow H_3NBF_3$$

10-8. Assuming covalent bonds, write electronic structures for the molecules or ions ClF, BrF$_3$, Ag(NH$_3$)$_2^+$, HCN, Ag(CN)$_2^-$, SiCl$_4$, BCl$_3$, HgCl$_2$. In which of these cases are there atoms with electron configurations that are not noble-gas configurations?

10-9. Can you suggest some methods for distinguishing between substances which contain bonds that are almost purely ionic and substances in which the bonds are largely covalent?

10-10. Write the electronic structures of silicon hydride (SiH$_4$, silicane), phosphine (PH$_3$), hydrogen sulfide (H$_2$S), and hydrogen chloride (HCl). Refer to the electronegativity scale and suggest a reason for revising the position of hydrogen in the formula of ammonia, NH$_3$.

10-11. Why is there no hydride of aluminum with formula AlH$_5$? Suggest an electronic structure for sodium borohydride, NaBH$_4$, and for sodium aluminohydride, NaAlH$_4$. Write the equations for the chemical reactions you would expect these substances to undergo with water.

10-12. Write all the resonating electronic structures you can think of for NO$_3^-$, NO$_2^-$, CO, SCO (carbon oxysulfide), N$_3^-$ (azide ion).

10-13. How does the difference in the electronic structures of diamond and graphite manifest itself in the physical properties of these substances?

10-14. From the electronegativity scale, which of the following substances would you expect to be especially stable and which especially unstable?

Calcium fluoride, CaF$_2$ Carbon tetraiodide, CI$_4$
Aluminum oxide, Al$_2$O$_3$ Sodium iodide, NaI
Phosphine, PH$_3$ Chlorine fluoride, ClF
Titanium dioxide, TiO$_2$ Titanium tetrafluoride, TiF$_4$
Nitrogen trichloride, NCl$_3$ Hydrogen iodide, HI
Selenium diiodide, SeI$_2$ Cesium fluoride, CsF

Chapter 11

Oxidation-Reduction Reactions

There are many different kinds of chemical reactions. Sometimes it is possible to classify a chemical reaction by use of suitable words. The reaction of hydrogen and oxygen with one another to form water may be described as the *combination* of these elements to form the compound, or their *direct union*. The reaction of mercuric oxide when it is heated to form mercury and oxygen may be called the *decomposition* of this substance. Chlorine reacts with a compound such as methane, CH_4, in the sunlight or in the presence of catalysts to produce hydrogen chloride and methyl chloride, CH_3Cl:

$$CH_4 + Cl_2 \longrightarrow CH_3Cl + HCl$$

This reaction is usually described as the *substitution* of chlorine for hydrogen in methane. The substitution reaction will continue, if enough chlorine is present, until all of the hydrogen in the molecule has been replaced by chlorine:

$$CH_3Cl + Cl_2 \longrightarrow CH_2Cl_2 + HCl$$
$$CH_2Cl_2 + Cl_2 \longrightarrow CHCl_3 + HCl$$
$$CHCl_3 + Cl_2 \longrightarrow CCl_4 + HCl$$

(CH_2Cl_2 is the compound methylene chloride, $CHCl_3$ is chloroform, and CCl_4 is carbon tetrachloride; these substances are useful solvents.)

Although different kinds of chemical reactions are thus easily recognized, it has not been found very useful in general to attempt to classify reactions in a rigorous way. Nevertheless, there is one very important class of chemical reactions that deserves special study. These reactions are *oxidation-reduction reactions*, to which we now turn our attention.

11–1. *Oxidation and Reduction*

The Generalized Usage of the Word "Oxidation."   When charcoal burns in air it forms the gases carbon monoxide and carbon dioxide:

$$2C + O_2 \longrightarrow 2CO$$
$$2CO + O_2 \longrightarrow 2CO_2$$

When hydrogen burns in air it forms water:

$$2H_2 + O_2 \longrightarrow 2H_2O$$

Iron, when red hot, burns in oxygen to form iron oxide, and it also reacts slowly with air ("rusts") under ordinary conditions:

$$4Fe + 3O_2 \longrightarrow 2Fe_2O_3$$

This process of combining with oxygen was named *oxidation* many years ago.

It was then recognized by chemists that combination with a non-metallic element other than oxygen closely resembles combination with oxygen. Carbon burns in fluorine more vigorously than in oxygen:

$$C + 2F_2 \longrightarrow CF_4$$

Hydrogen burns in fluorine and in chlorine:

$$H_2 + F_2 \longrightarrow 2HF$$
$$H_2 + Cl_2 \longrightarrow 2HCl$$

Iron burns in fluorine, and when heated combines readily with chlorine and also with sulfur:

$$2Fe + 3F_2 \longrightarrow 2FeF_3$$
$$2Fe + 3Cl_2 \longrightarrow 2FeCl_3$$
$$Fe + S \longrightarrow FeS$$

Because of the similarity of these reactions, they have come to be described as involving a generalized sort of oxidation.

Oxidation and Electron Transfer.   In accordance with this usage, we say that metallic sodium is oxidized to sodium ion when it burns in chlorine:

$$2Na + Cl_2 \longrightarrow 2Na^+Cl^-$$

Here we have written sodium chloride as Na^+Cl^- to show that it consists of ions. The *oxidation of the metallic sodium is the process of removing an electron from each sodium atom:*

$$Na \longrightarrow Na^+ + e^-$$

Reduction. The reverse process to that of oxidation is called reduction. (The word comes from the usage "The ore [such as Fe_2O_3] is reduced to the metal.") The reduction of sodium ion to metallic sodium is not an easy process. It was first achieved by Davy, by electrolysis (Chap. 9).

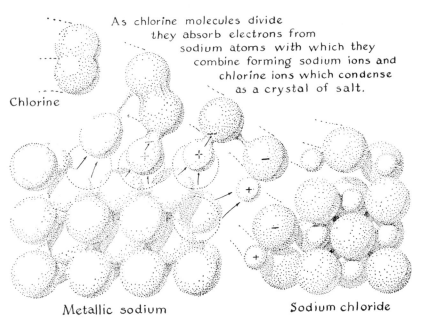

As chlorine molecules divide they absorb electrons from sodium atoms with which they combine forming sodium ions and chlorine ions which condense as a crystal of salt.

Chlorine

Metallic sodium   Sodium chloride

FIG. 11-1   *The reaction of sodium and chlorine to form sodium chloride.*

In the electrolysis of molten sodium chloride (Chap. 9) there occurs at the cathode the reaction

$$Na^+ + e^- \longrightarrow Na$$

This reaction is the reduction of sodium ion to metallic sodium by the addition of an electron from the cathode. The reaction is an example of *cathodic reduction.*

The Electronic Definitions of Oxidation and Reduction.   From these examples we see the justification for the modern usage of the words "oxidation" and "reduction": **Oxidation is the removal of electrons from an atom or group of atoms. Reduction is the addition of electrons to an atom or group of atoms.**

Professor E. C. Franklin of Stanford University made use of the terms *de-electronation* in place of "oxidation" and *electronation* in place of "reduction." It is useful to remember the following statements: **Oxidation is de-electronation. Reduction is electronation.**

When molten sodium chloride is decomposed by electrolysis, free chlorine is formed at the anode; the liberated electrons move into the anode:

$$2Cl^- \longrightarrow Cl_2 + 2e^-$$

This is an example of *anodic oxidation*.

The reactions which involve the liberation or capture of electrons at electrodes are called electrode reactions or electron reactions.

Oxidation and reduction reactions can take place either at electrodes, which supply electrons and take up electrons, or by direct contact of atoms or molecules, with direct transfer of electrons. Thus, when sodium burns in chlorine the sodium atoms transfer their electrons directly to the chlorine atoms, at the time that a molecule of chlorine strikes the surface of the metal (Fig. 11-1):

$$2Na \longrightarrow 2Na^+ + 2e^-$$
$$Cl_2 + 2e^- \longrightarrow 2Cl^-$$
$$\overline{2Na + Cl_2 \longrightarrow 2Na^+Cl^-}$$

A similar transfer of electrons takes place when iron burns in fluorine:

$$2Fe \longrightarrow 2Fe^{+++} + 6e^-$$
$$3F_2 + 6e^- \longrightarrow 6F^-$$
$$\overline{2Fe + 3F_2 \longrightarrow 2Fe^{+++}(F^-)_3}$$

The Simultaneous Occurrence of Oxidation and Reduction.   Oxidation or reduction of a substance could be carried out without simultaneous reduction or oxidation of another substance if one had at hand a very large electric condenser from which to remove electrons or in which to store them. Ordinarily such an electron reservoir is not available; even the very largest electric condenser charged to its maximum potential holds so few electrons that only a very small amount of chemical reaction can be produced by it. *There accordingly occur equivalent processes of oxidation and reduction in every oxidation-reduction reaction.*

Oxidizing Agents and Reducing Agents. An atom, molecule, or ion which takes up electrons is called an *oxidizing agent*, and one which liberates electrons is called a *reducing agent*.

For example, in the reaction

$$2Fe + 3F_2 \longrightarrow 2Fe^{+++}(F^-)_3$$

iron is the reducing agent and fluorine is the oxidizing agent.

We note that *every electron reaction involves an oxidizing agent and a reducing agent, which are closely related to one another.* Thus the reaction

$$Na \longrightarrow Na^+ + e^-$$

as written represents the oxidation (de-electronation) of metallic sodium, which is the reducing agent. But this reaction can be made to go the other way, in an electrolytic cell:

$$Na^+ + e^- \longrightarrow Na$$

Here the oxidizing agent Na^+ is being reduced by the cathode. Metallic sodium and sodium ion are called an *oxidation-reduction pair* or oxidation-reduction couple, and their interconversion by an electron reaction can be expressed by one equation, with a double arrow:

$$Na \rightleftarrows Na^+ + e^-$$

The direction in which this reaction actually proceeds in any system depends upon the nature of the system.

An example of the reversal of an electron reaction involving an oxidation-reduction pair is the following. The electrode equation for the bromine–bromide-ion pair is

$$Br_2 + 2e^- \rightleftarrows 2Br^-$$

Here bromine is the oxidizing agent and bromide ion is the reducing agent. Bromine is a strong enough oxidizing agent to liberate iodine from iodide ion:

$$Br_2 + 2e^- \longrightarrow 2Br^-$$
$$2I^- \longrightarrow I_2 + 2e^-$$
$$\overline{Br_2 + 2I^- \longrightarrow 2Br^- + I_2}$$

However, chlorine is a still stronger oxidizing agent (that is, it has a stronger affinity for electrons—greater electronegativity), and it is able to liberate bromine from bromide ion:

$$Cl_2 + 2e^- \longrightarrow 2Cl^-$$
$$2Br^- \longrightarrow Br_2 + 2e^-$$
$$\overline{Cl_2 + 2Br^- \longrightarrow 2Cl^- + Br_2}$$

Thus in these two oxidation-reduction reactions the bromine–bromide-ion electron reaction proceeds first in one direction and then in the other.

The conditions determining the direction in which an electron reaction proceeds are discussed later in this chapter and also in Chapter 32. The oxidation-reduction pairs can be arranged in a series, with increasing strength of the oxidizing agent and decreasing strength of the reducing agent. Reactions then tend to proceed in such direction that the stronger oxidizing agent oxidizes the stronger reducing agent, corresponding to the weaker oxidizing agent.

Thus as oxidizing agents the halogens lie in the order

$$F_2 > Cl_2 > Br_2 > I_2$$

and as reducing agents their ions lie in the reverse order:

$$I^- > Br^- > Cl^- > F^-$$

The non-metallic elements are strong oxidizing agents, and the metals are strong reducing agents.

11–2. *Oxidation Numbers of Atoms*

In the foregoing discussion of oxidation-reduction reactions the examples discussed have involved the interconversion of atoms and ions. It is convenient to extend the idea of electron transfer in such a way as to permit it to be applied to all substances. This is done by introducing the concept of *oxidation number*.

The oxidation number of an atom is a number which represents the electric charge that the atom would have if the electrons in a compound were assigned to the atoms in a certain way. The assignment of electrons is somewhat arbitrary, but the procedure is useful because it permits a simple statement to be made about the valences of the elements in a compound without considering its electronic structure in detail, and because it can be made the basis of a simple method of balancing equations for oxidation-reduction reactions.

An oxidation number may be assigned to each atom in a substance by the application of simple rules. These rules are, however, not completely unambiguous; although their application is usually a straightforward procedure, it sometimes requires considerable chemical insight and knowledge of molecular structure. The rules are given in the following sentences:

1. *The oxidation number of a monatomic ion in an ionic substance is equal to its electric charge.*
2. *The oxidation number of atoms in an elementary substance is zero.*
3. *In a covalent compound of known structure, the oxidation number of each atom is the charge remaining on the atom when each shared electron pair is assigned completely to the more electronegative of the two atoms sharing it. A pair shared by two atoms of the same element is split between them.*
4. *The oxidation number of an element in a compound of uncertain structure may be calculated from a reasonable assignment of oxidation numbers to the other elements in the compound.*

The application of the first three rules is illustrated by the following examples; the number by each atom is its oxidation number.

$Na^{+1} Cl^{-1}$ $\qquad$ $Mg^{+2}(Cl^{-1})_2$ $\qquad$ $(Al^{+3})_2 (O^{-2})_3$

H_2^0 $\qquad\qquad\qquad$ O_2^0 $\qquad\qquad$ C^0 (diamond or graphite)

H^{+1} (hydrogen ion) $\qquad\qquad\qquad$ $N^{-3}(H^{+1})_3$

$: \overset{..}{\underset{..}{O}} : ^{-2} H^{+1}$ (hydroxide ion)

$: \overset{+1}{\overset{..}{\underset{..}{Cl}}} : \overset{-1}{\overset{..}{\underset{..}{F}}} :$ $\qquad\qquad$ $I^{+3} (Cl^{-1})_3$ $\qquad\qquad$ $I^{+5}(F^{-1})_5$

$I^{+7}(F^{-1})_7$ $\qquad\qquad$ $C^{-4}(H^{+1})_4$ $\qquad\qquad$ $Os^{+8}(F^{-1})_8$

$C^{+4}(O^{-2})_2$ $\qquad\qquad$ $C^{+2}O^{-2}$ $\qquad\qquad$ $K^{+1}Mn^{+7}(O^{-2})_4$

Fluorine, the most electronegative element, has the oxidation number -1 in all of its compounds with other elements. Often the other halogens also have this oxidation number; exceptions are compounds with more electronegative halogens [$Cl^{+1} F^{-1}$, $I^{+3} (Cl^{-1})_3$, etc.] or oxygen ($Cl_2^{+1} O^{-2}$).

Oxygen is second only to fluorine in electronegativity, and in compounds it usually has oxidation number -2; examples are $Ca^{+2} O^{-2}$, $(Fe^{+3})_2 (O^{-2})_3$, $Ti^{+4} (O^{-2})_2$, $C^{+4} (O^{-2})_2$, $(Mn^{+7})_2 (O^{-2})_7$, $(K^{+1})_2 Cr^{+6} (O^{-2})_4$. Exceptions are $O^{+2}(F^{-1})_2$ and the peroxides, which are discussed in the section following the next one.

Hydrogen when bonded to a non-metal has oxidation number $+1$, as in $(H^{+1})_2\,O^{-2}$, $(H^{+1})_2\,S^{-2}$, $N^{-3}(H^{+1})_3$, $(P^{-2})_2(H^{+1})_4$. In compounds with metals, such as $Li^{+1}H^{-1}$, $Ca^{+2}(H^{-1})_2$, etc., its oxidation number is -1, corresponding to the electronic structure $H:^{-1}$ for a negative hydrogen ion with completed K shell (helium structure). On electrolysis of a fused alkali hydride, hydrogen is liberated at the anode according to the reaction

$$2H^- \longrightarrow H_2 \uparrow + 2e^-$$

11–3. *How to Balance Equations for Oxidation-Reduction Reactions*

The first step in writing the equation for an oxidation-reduction reaction is the same as for any other chemical reaction: *make sure that you know what the reactants are and what the products are.* The chemist finds what the reactants and products are by studying the reaction as it occurs in the laboratory or in nature, or by reading in journals or books to find out what other chemists have discovered about the reaction. Sometimes, of course, a knowledge of chemical theory permits a safe prediction about the nature of the reaction to be made.

The next step is to balance the equation for the reaction. In balancing the equation for an oxidation-reduction reaction it is usually wise to write the electron reactions separately (as they would occur in an electrolytic cell) and then to add them so as to cancel out the electrons. For example, ferric ion, Fe^{+++}, oxidizes stannous ion, Sn^{++}, to stannic ion, Sn^{++++} (that is, from the bipositive to the quadripositive state). The two electron reactions are

$$Fe^{+++} + e^- \longrightarrow Fe^{++}$$

and

$$Sn^{++} \longrightarrow Sn^{++++} + 2e^-$$

(Note that there is conservation of electric charge as well as conservation of atoms in each reaction.) Before adding these equations the first must be multiplied by 2, to use up the two electrons given by the second:

$$2Fe^{+++} + 2e^- \longrightarrow 2Fe^{++}$$
$$\underline{Sn^{++} \longrightarrow Sn^{++++} + 2e^-}$$
$$2Fe^{+++} + Sn^{++} \longrightarrow 2Fe^{++} + Sn^{++++}$$

The process of balancing a more complicated equation is illustrated by the following example.

Example. The oxidizing agent permanganate ion, MnO_4^-, on reduction in acid solution forms manganous ion, Mn^{++}. Ferrous ion, Fe^{++}, can accomplish this reduction. Write the equation for the reaction between permanganate ion and ferrous ion in acid solution.

Solution. The oxidation number of manganese in permanganate ion is $+7$, $[Mn^{+7}(O^{-2})_4]^-$. That of manganous ion is $+2$. Hence five electrons are involved in the reduction of permanganate ion. The electron reaction is

$$[Mn^{+7}(O^{-2})_4]^- + 5e^- + \text{other reactants} \longrightarrow Mn^{++} + \text{other products} \qquad (11\text{-}1a)$$

In reactions in aqueous solution water, hydrogen ion, and hydroxide ion may come into action as reactants or products. For example, in an acid solution hydrogen ion may be either a reactant or a product, and water may also be either a reactant or a product in the same reaction. In acid solutions hydroxide ion exists only in extremely low concentration, and would hardly be expected to enter into the reaction. Hence water and hydrogen ion may enter into the reaction now under consideration.

Reaction 1a is not balanced electrically; there are six negative charges on the left side and two positive charges on the right side. The only other ion which can enter into the reaction is hydrogen ion, and the number needed to give conservation of electric charge is 8. Thus we obtain

$$MnO_4^- + 5e^- + 8H^+ \longrightarrow Mn^{++} + \text{other products} \qquad (11\text{-}1b)$$

Oxygen and hydrogen occur here on the left side and not the right side of the reaction; conservation of atoms is satisfied if $4H_2O$ is written in as the "other products":

$$MnO_4^- + 5e^- + 8H^+ \longrightarrow Mn^{++} + 4H_2O \qquad (11\text{-}1)$$

We check this equation on three points—*proper change in oxidation number* (5 electrons used, with change of -5 in oxidation number of manganese, from Mn^{+7} to Mn^{+2}), *conservation of electric charge* (from $-1 -5 +8$ to $+2$), and *conservation of atoms*—and convince ourselves that it is correct.

The electron reaction for the oxidation of ferrous ion is now written:

$$Fe^{++} \longrightarrow Fe^{+++} + e^- \qquad (11\text{-}2)$$

This equation checks on all three points.

The equation for the oxidation-reduction reaction is obtained by combining the two electron reactions in such a way that the electrons liberated in one are used up in the other. We see that this is achieved by multiplying Equation 2 by 5 and adding it to Equation 1:

$$\begin{array}{l} 5Fe^{++} \longrightarrow 5Fe^{+++} + 5e^- \\ \underline{MnO_4^- + 5e^- + 8H^+ \longrightarrow Mn^{++} + 4H_2O} \\ MnO_4^- + 5Fe^{++} + 8H^+ \longrightarrow Mn^{++} + 5Fe^{+++} + 4H_2O \end{array} \qquad (11\text{-}3)$$

It is good practice to check this final equation also on all three points, to be sure that no mistake has been made:

1. *Change in oxidation number:* Mn^{+7} to Mn^{++}, change -5; $5Fe^{++}$ to $5Fe^{+++}$, change $+5$.

2. *Conservation of electric charge:* left side, $-1 +10 +8 = +17$; right side, $+2 +15 = +17$.

3. *Conservation of atoms:* left side, 1Mn, 4O, 5Fe, 8H; right side, 1Mn, 5Fe, 4O, 8H.

It is not always necessary to carry through this entire procedure. Sometimes an equation is so simple that it can be written at once and verified by inspection. An example is the reduction of silver ion, Ag^+, by metallic zinc:

$$\underline{Zn} + 2Ag^+ \longrightarrow 2Ag \downarrow + Zn^{++}$$

Sometimes, too, the conditions determine the reaction, as when a single substance decomposes. Thus ammonium nitrite decomposes to give water and nitrogen:

$$NH_4NO_2 \longrightarrow N_2 + 2H_2O$$

Here N^{+3} (of NO_2^-) oxidizes N^{-3} (of NH_4^+), both going to N^0 (of N_2).

11–4. *Stoichiometric Calculations*

Calculations of weight relations in oxidation-reduction reactions are made in the same way as for other reactions. Care must be taken to check the relative numbers of atoms, ions, or molecules which react or are formed, and to use the proper atomic and molecular weights.

Example 1.   How much metallic iron, converted to ferrous ion, would be required to reduce the permanganate ion in 10 g of $KMnO_4$, in acid solution?

Answer.   Equation 3 shows that 5 atoms of iron, converted into ferrous ion, would, in acid solution, reduce the permanganate ion in 1 formula of $KMnO_4$. We write

5Fe   equivalent to $1KMnO_4$
5 × 55.85   158.03

Here the proper multiples of atomic and molecular weights are written below the formulas. The ratio of iron to potassium permanganate is $\dfrac{5 \times 55.85}{158.03}$, and the amount of iron is obtained by multiplying this ratio by 10 g, the amount of potassium permanganate:

$$\frac{5 \times 55.85 \times 10 \text{ g}}{158.03} = 17.67 \text{ g}$$

Oxidation Equivalents and Reduction Equivalents.   The *oxidizing capacity* or *reducing capacity* of an oxidizing agent or reducing agent is equal to the number of electrons involved in its reduction or oxidation. An oxidation-reduction equation is balanced when the amounts of oxidizing agent and reducing agent indicated as reacting have the same capacities.

An *oxidation equivalent* or *reduction equivalent* of a substance is the amount which takes up or gives up one electron (one mole of electrons). Thus the gram equivalent weight (equivalent weight expressed in grams) of potassium permanganate as an oxidizing agent in acid solution (see Equation 1) is one-fifth of the gram formula weight, whereas the gram equivalent weight of ferrous ion as a reducing agent is just the gram atomic weight.

Equivalent weights of oxidizing agents and reducing agents react exactly with one another, since they involve the taking up or giving up of the same number of electrons.

Normal Solutions of Oxidizing and Reducing Agents. *A solution of an oxidizing agent or reducing agent containing 1 gram equivalent weight per liter of solution is called a 1 normal (1 N) solution.* In general the *normality* of the solution is the number of gram equivalent weights of the oxidizing or reducing agent present per liter.

It is seen from the definition that equal volumes of an oxidizing solution and a reducing solution of the same normality react exactly with each other.

Example 2.   What is the normality, for use as an oxidizing agent in acid solution, of a permanganate solution made by dissolving one-tenth of a gram formula weight of $KMnO_4$ ($1/10 \times 158.03$ g) in water and diluting to a volume of 1 l?

> **Answer.**   The reduction of permanganate ion in acid solution involves 5 electrons (Equation 1). Hence 1 gram molecular weight is 5 equivalents. The solution is accordingly 0.5 N.
>
> It is necessary to take care that the conditions of the use of a reagent are known in stating its normality. Thus permanganate ion is sometimes used as an oxidizing agent in neutral or basic solution, in which it is reduced by only three steps, to manganese dioxide, MnO_2, in which manganese has oxidation number 4. The above solution would have normality 0.3 for this use.

11–5. *The Electromotive-Force Series of the Elements*

It is found that if a piece of one metal is put into a solution containing ions of another metallic element the first metal may dissolve, with the deposition of the second metal from its ions. Thus a strip of zinc placed in a solution of a copper salt causes a layer of metallic copper to deposit on the zinc, as the zinc goes into solution:

$$Zn \longrightarrow Zn^{++} + 2e^-$$
$$Cu^{++} + 2e^- \longrightarrow Cu \downarrow$$
$$\overline{Zn + Cu^{++} \longrightarrow Zn^{++} + Cu \downarrow}$$

On the other hand, a strip of copper placed in a solution of a zinc salt does not cause metallic zinc to deposit.*

TABLE 11-1   *The Electromotive-Force Series of the Elements*

		$E°$			$E°$
1.	$Cs = Cs^+ + e^-$..........	3.08	18.	$Co = Co^{++} + 2e^-$.......	0.28
2.	$Li = Li^+ + e^-$..........	3.02	19.	$Ni = Ni^{++} + 2e^-$........	.25
3.	$Rb = Rb^+ + e^-$..........	2.99	20.	$Sn = Sn^{++} + 2e^-$........	.14
4.	$K = K^+ + e^-$..........	2.92	21.	$Pb = Pb^{++} + 2e^-$........	.13
5.	$Ba = Ba^{++} + 2e^-$........	2.90	22.	$H_2 = 2H^+ + 2e^-$.........	0.00
6.	$Sr = Sr^{++} + 2e^-$........	2.89	23.	$Cu = Cu^{++} + 2e^-$........	−0.34
7.	$Ca = Ca^{++} + 2e^-$.......	2.87	24.	$2I^- = I_2 + 2e^-$..........	−0.53
8.	$Na = Na^+ + e^-$.........	2.71	25.	$Ag = Ag^+ + e^-$..........	−0.80
9.	$La = La^{+++} + 3e^-$........	2.37	26.	$Pd = Pd^{++} + 2e^-$........	−0.83
10.	$Mg = Mg^{++} + 2e^-$.......	2.34	27.	$Hg = Hg^{++} + 2e^-$........	−0.85
11.	$Be = Be^{++} + 2e^-$........	1.70	28.	$2Br^- = Br_2(l) + 2e^-$......	−1.06
12.	$Al = Al^{+++} + 3e^-$........	1.67	29.	$Pt = Pt^{++} + 2e^-$..........	−1.2
13.	$Mn = Mn^{++} + 2e^-$......	1.05	30.	$2H_2O = O_2 + 2H^+ + 4e^-$..	−1.23
14.	$Zn = Zn^{++} + 2e^-$........	0.76	31.	$2Cl^- = Cl_2 + 2e^-$........	−1.36
15.	$Cr = Cr^{+++} + 3e^-$........	.71	32.	$Au = Au^+ + e^-$..........	−1.68
16.	$Fe = Fe^{++} + 2e^-$........	.44	33.	$2F^- = F_2 + 2e^-$.........	−2.85
17.	$Cd = Cd^{++} + 2e^-$........	.40			

* It is not strictly correct to say that zinc can replace copper in solution and that copper cannot replace zinc. If a piece of metallic copper is placed in a solution containing zinc ion in appreciable concentration (1 mole per liter, say) and no cupric ion at all, the reaction

$$Cu + Zn^{++} \rightarrow Cu^{++} + Zn \downarrow$$

will occur to a very small extent, stopping when a certain very small concentration of copper ion has been produced. If metallic zinc is added to a 1-molar solution of cupric ion the reaction

$$Zn + Cu^{++} \rightarrow Zn^{++} + Cu \downarrow$$

the reverse of the preceding reaction, will take place almost to completion, stopping when the concentration of copper ion has become very small. The principles of thermodynamics require that the ratio of concentrations of the two ions Cu^{++} and Zn^{++} in equilibrium with solid copper and solid zinc be the same whether the equilibrium is approached from the Cu, Zn^{++} side or the Zn, Cu^{++} side. The statement "zinc replaces copper from solution" means that at equilibrium the ratio of cupric-ion concentration to zinc-ion concentration is small. This matter will be discussed in greater detail in Chapter 32.

By experiments of this sort, the metallic elements can be arranged in a table showing their ability to reduce ions of other metals. This table is given as Table 11-1. The metal with the greatest reducing power is at the head of the list. It is able to reduce the ions of *all* the other metals.

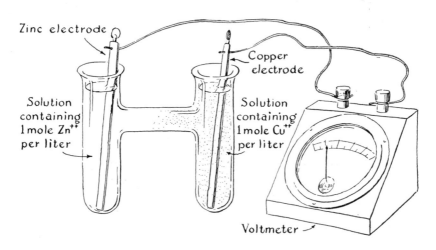

Zinc electrode

Copper electrode

Solution containing 1 mole Zn^{++} per liter

Solution containing 1 mole Cu^{++} per liter

Voltmeter

FIG. 11-2 *A cell involving the* Zn, Zn^{++} *electrode and the* Cu, Cu^{++} *electrode.*

This series is called the *electromotive-force series* because the tendency of one metal to reduce ions of another can be measured by setting up an *electric cell* and measuring the voltage which it produces. ("Electromotive force" is here a synonym for "voltage.") It is conventional to

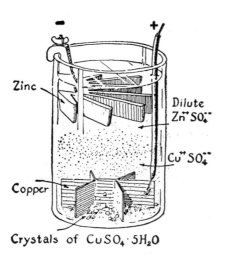

Zinc

Dilute $Zn^{++}SO_4^{--}$

$Cu^{++}SO_4^{--}$

Copper

Crystals of $CuSO_4 \cdot 5H_2O$

FIG. 11-3

The gravity cell.

have each metal ion present at a carefully specified concentration (approximately 1 mole per liter—see Chapter 32). Thus the cell shown in Figure 11-2 would be used to measure the voltage between the electrodes at which occur the electrode reactions

$$\underline{Zn} \longrightarrow Zn^{++} + 2e^-$$

and

$$Cu^{++} + 2e^- \longrightarrow Cu \downarrow$$

This cell produces a voltage of about 1.1 volts, the difference of the values of $E°$ shown in the table. (The cell is used to some extent in practice; it is called the gravity cell when made as shown in Fig. 11-3.)

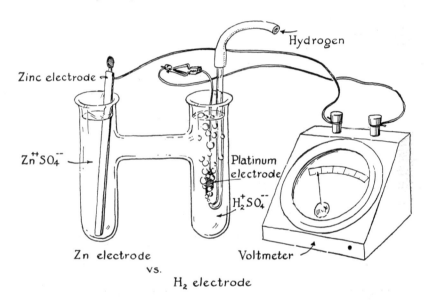

FIG. 11-4   *A cell involving the zinc electrode and the hydrogen electrode.*

The standard reference point in the E.M.F. series is the *hydrogen electrode*, which consists of gaseous hydrogen at 1 atm bubbling over a platinum electrode in an acidic solution (Fig. 11-4). Similar electrodes can be made for some other non-metallic elements, and a few of these elements are included in the table.

The table can be extended to include also many other oxidation-reduction pairs. An extended table is given in Chapter 32, in which its use is discussed.

11–6. *An Example: The Reactions of Hydrogen Peroxide*

Preparation, Properties, and Structure of Hydrogen Peroxide.
When sodium is burned in oxygen it forms the compound Na_2O_2, called
sodium peroxide:

$$2Na + O_2 \longrightarrow Na_2O_2$$

When barium oxide, $Ba^{++}O^{--}$, is heated to a dull red heat in a stream
of air it adds oxygen to form a similar compound, BaO_2, *barium peroxide:*

$$2BaO + O_2 \longrightarrow 2BaO_2$$

Each of these salts contains the *peroxide ion*, O_2^{--}. This ion has the
electronic structure

$$\left[: \overset{\cdot\cdot}{\underset{\cdot\cdot}{O}} - \overset{\cdot\cdot}{\underset{\cdot\cdot}{O}} : \right]^{--}$$

There is a single covalent bond between the two oxygen atoms. The
oxidation number of oxygen in the peroxide ion and in peroxides is -1.
These substances represent an intermediate oxidation state between free
oxygen (O^0 in O_2) and oxides (O^{--}).

The electrolysis of a peroxide solution leads to the liberation of one
mole of oxygen at the anode by twice Avogadro's number of electrons,
the anode reaction being

$$O_2^{--} \longrightarrow O_2 + 2e^-$$

Care must be taken to distinguish between *peroxides*, which contain
two oxygen atoms with a single covalent bond between them, and

dioxides. Thus BaO_2 is a peroxide, containing Ba^{++} and $\left[: \overset{\cdot\cdot}{\underset{\cdot\cdot}{O}} - \overset{\cdot\cdot}{\underset{\cdot\cdot}{O}} : \right]^{--}$,

and TiO_2 is a dioxide, containing Ti^{+4} and two oxygen ions, $\left[: \overset{\cdot\cdot}{\underset{\cdot\cdot}{O}} : \right]^{--}$.

Hydrogen peroxide, H_2O_2, is made by treating sodium peroxide or barium
peroxide with sulfuric acid or phosphoric acid, and distilling:

$$Na_2O_2 + H_2SO_4 \longrightarrow Na_2SO_4 + H_2O_2$$
$$BaO_2 + H_2SO_4 \longrightarrow BaSO_4 + H_2O_2$$

Pure hydrogen peroxide is a colorless, syrupy liquid, with density
1.47 g/cm^3, melting point $-1.7°$ C, and boiling point $151°$ C. It is a very

strong oxidizing agent, which spontaneously oxidizes organic substances. Its uses are in the main determined by its oxidizing power.

Commercial hydrogen peroxide is an aqueous solution, sometimes containing a small amount of a stabilizer, such as phosphate ion, to decrease its rate of decomposition to water and oxygen by the reaction

$$2H_2O_2 \longrightarrow 2H_2O + O_2$$

Drug-store hydrogen peroxide is a 3% solution (containing 3 g of H_2O_2 per 100 g), for medical use as an antiseptic, or a 6% solution, for bleaching hair. A 30% solution and, in recent years, an 85% solution are used in chemical industries.

The structure of the hydrogen peroxide molecule* is

$$\begin{array}{cc} \text{H} & \text{H} \\ | & | \\ :\text{O} - \text{O}: \\ \cdot\cdot & \cdot\cdot \end{array}$$

Hydrogen Peroxide as an Oxidizing Agent.   When hydrogen peroxide serves as an oxidizing agent each oxygen atom changes its oxidation number from -1 to -2. In acidic solution, for example, the electron reaction is

$$H_2O_2 + 2H^+ + 2e^- \longrightarrow 2H_2O$$

The over-all reaction for the oxidation of ferrous ion is

$$H_2O_2 + 2H^+ + 2Fe^{++} \longrightarrow 2H_2O + 2Fe^{+++}$$

The uses of the substance as a bleaching agent may be illustrated by its conversion of lead sulfide, a black substance, to lead sulfate, which is white:

$$PbS + 4H_2O_2 \longrightarrow PbSO_4 + 4H_2O$$

Here the sulfur atom is oxidized from S^{-2} to S^{+6}, as eight oxygen atoms are reduced from -1 to -2. This reaction occurs when oil paintings which have been discolored by the formation of lead sulfide from the white lead (a hydroxide-carbonate of lead) in the paint are treated with a hydrogen-peroxide wash.

* Each bond angle H   in this molecule is about 110°. The molecule is not coplanar, but is twisted through about 90°; from the end it has the appearance H   H.

Hydrogen Peroxide as a Reducing Agent.   Hydrogen peroxide can also serve as a reducing agent, with increase in oxidation number of oxygen from -1 to 0, and the liberation of molecular oxygen.

This activity is shown, for example, by the decolorizing of acidic permanganate solution by hydrogen peroxide. The electron reactions are

$$H_2O_2 \longrightarrow O_2 + 2H^+ + 2e^-$$
$$MnO_4^- + 5e^- + 8H^+ \longrightarrow Mn^{++} + 4H_2O$$

or, with the proper factors to balance the electrons,

$$5H_2O_2 \longrightarrow 5O_2 + 10H^+ + 10e^-$$
$$\underline{2MnO_4^- + 10e^- + 16H^+ \longrightarrow 2Mn^{++} + 8H_2O}$$
$$2MnO_4^- + 5H_2O_2 + 6H^+ \longrightarrow 2Mn^{++} + 5O_2 \uparrow + 8H_2O$$

Hydrogen peroxide also reduces permanganate ion in basic solution, forming a precipitate of MnO_2, manganese dioxide:

$$H_2O_2 + 2OH^- \longrightarrow O_2 + 2H_2O + 2e^-$$
$$MnO_4^- + 3e^- + 2H_2O \longrightarrow MnO_2 \downarrow + 4OH^-$$

or

$$3H_2O_2 + 6OH^- \longrightarrow 3O_2 + 6H_2O + 6e^-$$
$$\underline{2MnO_4^- + 6e^- + 4H_2O \longrightarrow 2MnO_2 \downarrow + 8OH^-}$$
$$2MnO_4^- + 3H_2O_2 \longrightarrow 2MnO_2 \downarrow + 3O_2 \uparrow + 2H_2O + 2OH^-$$

The Auto-Oxidation of Hydrogen Peroxide.   When hydrogen peroxide decomposes, by the reaction

$$2H_2O_2 \longrightarrow 2H_2O + O_2$$

it is carrying on an *auto-oxidation-reduction process* (usually called *auto-oxidation*), in which the substance acts simultaneously as an oxidizing agent and as a reducing agent; half of the oxygen atoms are reduced to O^{-2}, and the other half are oxidized to O^0.

It is interesting that this process occurs only extremely slowly in pure hydrogen peroxide and its pure aqueous solutions. It is accelerated by catalysts, such as dust particles and active spots on ordinary solid surfaces. The stabilizers which are added to hydrogen peroxide inactivate these catalysts.

The most effective catalysts for the decomposition of hydrogen peroxides are certain complex organic substances, with molecular weights of 100,000 or more, which occur in the cells of plants and animals. These substances, which are called *catalases* (a special kind of *enzyme*), have the specific job in the organism of causing the decomposition of peroxides.

The Peroxy Acids.   Acids containing a peroxide group are called *peroxy acids*. Examples are

peroxysulfuric acid, H_2SO_5

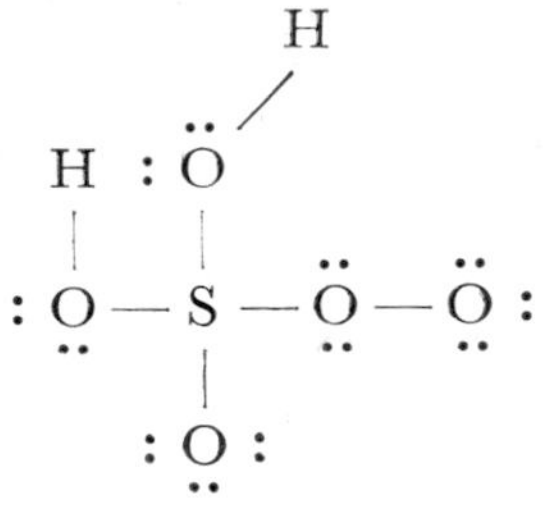

$$\begin{array}{c} \overset{\displaystyle H}{\diagup} \\ H : \overset{\displaystyle \cdot\cdot}{O} \\ | \\ : \overset{\displaystyle \cdot\cdot}{O} - S - \overset{\displaystyle \cdot\cdot}{\underset{\displaystyle \cdot\cdot}{O}} - \overset{\displaystyle \cdot\cdot}{\underset{\displaystyle \cdot\cdot}{O}} : \\ | \\ : \overset{}{\underset{\displaystyle \cdot\cdot}{O}} : \end{array}$$

peroxydisulfuric acid, $H_2S_2O_8$

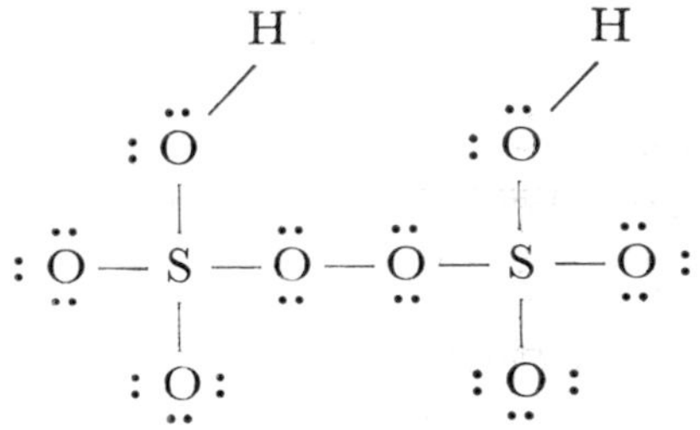

$$: \overset{\cdot\cdot}{\underset{\cdot\cdot}{O}} - S - \overset{\cdot\cdot}{\underset{\cdot\cdot}{O}} - \overset{\cdot\cdot}{\underset{\cdot\cdot}{O}} - S - \overset{\cdot\cdot}{\underset{\cdot\cdot}{O}} :$$

When moderately concentrated (50%) sulfuric acid is electrolyzed hydrogen is formed at the cathode and peroxydisulfuric acid at the anode:

Cathode reaction: $2H^+ + 2e^- \longrightarrow H_2 \uparrow$
Anode reaction: $2H_2SO_4 \longrightarrow H_2S_2O_8 + 2H^+ + 2e^-$

This solution when heated forms peroxysulfuric acid:

$$H_2S_2O_8 + H_2O \longrightarrow H_2SO_5 + H_2SO_4$$

and when heated to higher temperature it forms hydrogen peroxide, which can be separated by distillation:

$$H_2SO_5 + H_2O \longrightarrow H_2O_2 + H_2SO_4$$

This method is used commercially for making 30% hydrogen peroxide.

The peroxy acids and their salts are strong oxidizing agents. Note that perchloric acid, $HClO_4$, is not a peroxy acid.

The Superoxides.   Another exceptional class of substances is the *superoxides*, which contain the ion $[O_2]^-$, in which oxygen has the oxidation number $-\frac{1}{2}$. The superoxide ion is intermediate in oxidation state between peroxide ion, $[O_2]^{--}$, and molecular oxygen, O_2. Its electronic structure is

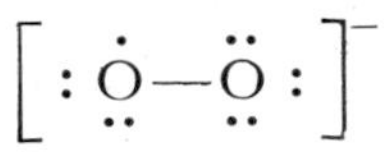

$$\left[: \overset{\cdot}{\underset{\cdot\cdot}{O}} - \overset{\cdot\cdot}{\underset{\cdot\cdot}{O}} : \right]^- \qquad \text{or} \qquad \left[: \overset{\cdot\cdot\cdot}{\underset{\cdot\cdot}{O}} \overset{}{O} : \right]^-$$

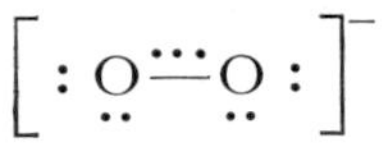

Potassium superoxide, KO_2, is a paramagnetic yellow crystalline substance formed when potassium is burned in oxygen. It is a convenient source of gaseous oxygen; three-fourths of its oxygen is liberated (by auto-oxidation-reduction) when the salt is exposed to water or carbon dioxide:

$$4KO_2 + 2H_2O \longrightarrow 4KOH + 3O_2$$
$$4KO_2 + 2CO_2 \longrightarrow 2K_2CO_3 + 3O_2$$

Rubidium and cesium also form superoxides.

Exercises

11-1.   Give three examples of oxidation-reduction reactions in everyday life. In each case designate the oxidizing agent and the reducing agent.

11-2.   Define an oxidation-reduction pair, and write an electron equation in illustration.

11-3.   Assign oxidation numbers to elements in the following compounds:

Cuprous oxide, Cu_2O Bleaching powder, $CaClOCl$
Cupric oxide, CuO Sodium hydride, NaH
Barium peroxide, BaO_2 Ammonia, NH_3
Potassium superoxide, KO_2 Nitric acid, HNO_3
Potassium chloroplatinate, K_2PtCl_6 Lead sulfide, PbS
Potassium chloroplatinite, K_2PtCl_4 Pyrite, FeS_2
Phosphorus, P_4 Copper iron sulfide, $CuFeS_2$
Permanganate ion, MnO_4^- Calomel, Hg_2Cl_2
Peroxysulfate ion, SO_5^{--} Silver subfluoride, Ag_2F
Potassium chromate, K_2CrO_4 Potassium dichromate, $K_2Cr_2O_7$
Potassium chlorochromate, $KCrO_3Cl$ Aurous chloride, $AuCl$
Borax, $Na_2B_4O_7 \cdot 10H_2O$ Auric chloride, $AuCl_3$
Silica, SiO_2 Nitrous acid, HNO_2
Nitrous oxide, N_2O Ammonium nitrite, NH_4NO_2

11-4.   What is the oxidation number of carbon in CH_4, C_2H_6 (ethane), C_2H_4 (ethylene), C_2H_2 (acetylene), C (diamond)? How many covalent bonds does each carbon atom form in these substances?

11-5.   Complete and balance the following equations:

$$MnO_2 + HCl \longrightarrow MnCl_2 + Cl_2$$
$$Cl_2 + I^- \longrightarrow I_2 + Cl^-$$
$$F_2 + H_2O \longrightarrow F^- + O_2$$
$$Sn + I_2 \longrightarrow SnI_4$$
$$P_4 + OH^- \longrightarrow H_2PO_2^- + PH_3$$
$$KClO_3 \longrightarrow KClO_4 + KCl$$
$$S_2O_3^{--} + I_2 \longrightarrow S_4O_6^{--} + I^-$$
$$Fe^{++} + Cr_2O_7^{--} \longrightarrow Fe^{+++} + Cr^{+++} \text{ (in acid solution)}$$
$$ClO_2 + OH^- \longrightarrow ClO_2^- + ClO_3^-$$
$$Co(NH_3)_6^{++} + H^+ \longrightarrow Co(NH_3)_6^{+++} + H_2$$
$$ClO_4^- + Sn^{++} \longrightarrow Cl^- + Sn^{++++}$$

$$IO_3^- + Cl_2 \longrightarrow IO_4^- + Cl^-$$
$$S_2O_8^{--} + Ce^{+++} \longrightarrow SO_4^{--} + Ce^{++++}$$
$$Cr_2O_7^{--} + C_2H_6 + H^+ \longrightarrow CO_2 + H_2O + Cr^{+++}$$

11-6. Write equations for the electrochemical production of
(a) perchlorate ion, ClO_4^-, from chlorate ion, ClO_3^-
(b) permanganate ion, MnO_4^-, from manganate ion, MnO_4^{--}
(c) magnesium from molten magnesium chloride
(d) ferric ion from ferrous ion
(e) dichromate ion, $Cr_2O_7^{--}$, from chromic ion, Cr^{+++}
State in each case whether the reaction occurs at the anode or at the cathode.

11-7. Calculate the amount of ferrous ammonium sulfate, $(NH_4)_2Fe(SO_4)_2 \cdot 6H_2O$, required to make 1 l of 0.1 N solution, for use as a reducing agent.

11-8. It was found that 29.00 ml of a solution of potassium permanganate was required to oxidize 25.00 ml of 0.1 N ferrous solution, in the presence of acid. What is the normality of the permanganate solution? How many grams of $KMnO_4$ does it contain per liter? How many ml of 0.1 N stannous-ion solution would 29.00 ml of this permanganate solution oxidize?

11-9. A sample of commercial hydrogen peroxide weighing 5.00 g was found to require 78.3 ml of 0.1030 N permanganate solution for oxidation in the presence of acid. What was the strength of the hydrogen-peroxide solution, in weight percentage?

11-10. A sample of iron ore weighing 0.2792 g was dissolved, and the iron was converted into ferrous ion in solution in dilute sulfuric acid. The sample required 23.20 ml of 0.0971 N permanganate solution for its oxidation. What was the percentage of iron in the ore?

11-11. What weight of 3.00% hydrogen-peroxide solution would be required to oxidize 1.00 g of lead sulfide, PbS, to lead sulfate, $PbSO_4$?

11-12. What weight of magnesium would be required to reduce 50 lbs. of ferric oxide to metallic iron?

11-13. Would you expect zinc to reduce cadmium ion? iron to reduce mercuric ion? lead to reduce zinc ion? potassium to reduce magnesium ion? manganese to reduce hydrogen ion?

11-14. Which metal ions would you expect gold to reduce? Suggest a reason for calling gold and platinum noble metals.

11-15. What would you expect to happen if a large piece of lead were put in a beaker containing stannous ion (Sn^{++})? Note the values of the electromotive force in Table 11-1.

11-16. What would happen if chlorine gas were bubbled into a solution containing fluoride ion and bromide ion? if fluorine were bubbled into a solution containing both chloride ion and bromide ion?

Chapter 12

The Chemistry
of the Halogens

The noble gases are immediately followed in the periodic table by the alkali metals, which are the elements with the most pronounced metallic properties (the elements of group I), and are immediately preceded by the elements which differ the most from the metals. These non-metallic elements, in group VII of the periodic table, are the halogens—fluorine, chlorine, bromine, and iodine.*

Most of the compounds of the alkali metals, discussed in Chapter 6, represent the oxidation number +1, those of the alkaline-earth metals the oxidation number +2, and those of aluminum and its congeners the oxidation number +3. Differences in properties of the compounds can be attributed largely to the differences in size of the atoms (or ions) of these metals. The chemistry of the halogens is much more complex than that of these metals. Compounds of the halogens other than fluorine exist representing most of the oxidation numbers throughout the range from −1 to +7, and these compounds take part in many important oxidation-reduction reactions. The chemistry of the compounds of the halogens can be systematized and clarified by correlation with the electronic theory of valence, and their structure and reactions serve well to illustrate the principles discussed in the preceding chapters.

12–1. *The Halogens*

Some of the physical properties of the halogens are given in Table 12-1, and of the hydrogen halides in Table 12-2.

* Element 85, *astatine*, is also a halogen, but little is known about its properties.

TABLE 12-1   *Properties of the Halogens*

	SYMBOL	ATOMIC NUMBER	ATOMIC WEIGHT	COLOR AND FORM	MELTING POINT	BOILING POINT	RADIUS OF ANION, X⁻
Fluorine	F	9	19.00	Pale-yellow gas	−223° C	−187° C	1.36 Å
Chlorine	Cl	17	35.457	Greenish-yellow gas	−101.6°	−34.6°	1.81
Bromine	Br	35	79.916	Reddish-brown liquid	−7.3°	58.7°	1.95
Iodine	I	53	126.91	Grayish-black, lustrous solid	113.5°	184°	2.16

Chlorine (from Greek *chloros*, green), the most common of the halogens, is a greenish-yellow gas, with a sharp, irritating odor. It was first made by K. W. Scheele in 1774, by the action of manganese dioxide on hydrochloric acid. It is now manufactured on a large scale by the electrolysis of a strong solution of sodium chloride (see Chap. 13).

Chlorine is a very reactive substance, but less reactive than fluorine. It combines with most elements, to form chlorides, at room temperature or on gentle warming. Hydrogen burns in chlorine, after being ignited, to form hydrogen chloride. Iron burns in chlorine, producing ferric chloride ($FeCl_3$), a brown solid, and other metals react similarly with it. Chlorine is a strong oxidizing agent, and because of this property it is effective in killing bacteria. It is used extensively to sterilize drinking water and the water in swimming pools, and is also used in many ways throughout the chemical industry.

Hydrogen chloride, HCl, is a colorless gas with an unpleasant sharp odor. It can be made by heating sodium chloride with sulfuric acid. The gas dissolves readily in water, with the production of a large amount

TABLE 12-2   *Properties of the Hydrogen Halides*

	FORMULA	MELTING POINT	BOILING POINT
Hydrogen fluoride	HF	−92.3° C	19.4° C
Hydrogen chloride	HCl	−112°	−84°
Hydrogen bromide	HBr	−88.5°	−67°
Hydrogen iodide	HI	−50.8°	−35.3°

of heat. The solution is called **hydrochloric acid.** It is a strong acid—it dissolves zinc and other active metals, with the evolution of hydrogen, and combines with bases (such as sodium hydroxide) to form salts. The salts formed by hydrochloric acid are called *chlorides.*

Bromine (from Greek *bromos*, stench) occurs (as bromide ion) in small quantities in sea water and in natural salt deposits. The free element is an easily volatile, dark reddish-brown liquid with a strong, disagreeable odor and an irritating effect on the eyes and throat. It produces painful sores when spilled on the skin. It can be made by treating a bromide with a strong oxidizing agent, such as chlorine.

Hydrogen bromide, HBr, is a colorless gas. Its solution in water, **hydrobromic acid,** is a strong acid. The principal bromides are sodium bromide, NaBr, and potassium bromide, KBr, which are used in medicine, and silver bromide, AgBr, which, like silver chloride, AgCl, and silver iodide, AgI, is used in making photographic emulsions (see Photography, Sec. 27–6).

Iodine (from Greek *iodes*, violet) occurs (as iodide ion) in very small quantities in sea water, and, as sodium iodate, $NaIO_3$, in deposits of Chile saltpeter. It is made commercially from the saltpeter, and also from kelp, which concentrates it from the sea water. The free element is an almost black crystalline solid with a slightly metallic luster. On gentle warming it gives a beautiful blue-violet vapor. Its solutions in chloroform, carbon tetrachloride, and carbon disulfide are also blue-violet in color, indicating that the molecules I_2 in these solutions closely resemble the gas molecules. The solutions of iodine in water containing potassium iodide and in alcohol (tincture of iodine) are brown; this change in color suggests that the iodine molecules have undergone chemical reaction in the solutions. The complex tri-iodide ion I_3^- is present in the first solution, and a compound with alcohol in the second.

Hydrogen iodide, HI, is a colorless gas, whose solution in water, called **hydriodic acid,** is a strong acid.

Iodine is used as an antiseptic, in photography (silver iodide), and in the chemical industry. A hormone,* *thyroxine*, which is produced by the thyroid gland, contains iodine (its formula is $C_{10}H_{11}O_4NI_4$); and a suitable supply of iodine in the food or drinking water is necessary for health.

---

* Hormones are chemical substances which travel through the blood from one organ or tissue to another, and by catalytic action or in a similar way act as regulators of physiological activity. Some of the hormones, including thyroxine, are relatively simple chemical substances with known structure; but many of them are very complex protein molecules, containing thousands of atoms per molecule (see Chap. 29).

12–2. *The Oxidation States of the Halogens*

The compounds of the halogens discussed in the preceding section and in Chapter 5 (compounds of fluorine) represent the oxidation state -1, which is the oxidation state corresponding to the position of the halogens in the periodic table, just preceding the noble gases. This oxidation state is the only one shown by compounds of fluorine. The other halogens, however, form oxygen compounds in which several other oxidation states are represented, as summarized in the following diagram:

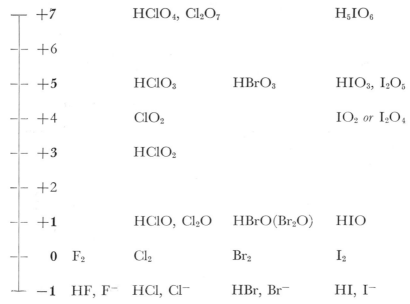

$+7$		$HClO_4$, Cl_2O_7		H_5IO_6
$+6$				
$+5$		$HClO_3$	$HBrO_3$	HIO_3, I_2O_5
$+4$		ClO_2		IO_2 *or* I_2O_4
$+3$		$HClO_2$		
$+2$				
$+1$		$HClO$, Cl_2O	$HBrO(Br_2O)$	HIO
0	F_2	Cl_2	Br_2	I_2
-1	HF, F^-	HCl, Cl^-	HBr, Br^-	HI, I^-

The range of oxidation states extends from -1, corresponding to the achievement for each halogen atom of the structure of the adjacent noble gas, to $+7$, corresponding for chlorine to the inner noble-gas structure (neon) and for iodine to the eighteen-electron-shell structure.

The effect of decreasing electronegativity in the sequence fluorine, chlorine, bromine, iodine is strikingly illustrated by the ability of a lighter halogen, as the element, to oxidize a heavier halide ion, whereas the heavier halogen, as element, reduces the oxygen compounds of a lighter halogen:

$$Cl_2 + 2I^- \longrightarrow 2Cl^- + I_2$$
$$I_2 + 2ClO_3^- \longrightarrow 2IO_3^- + Cl_2$$

Each of these reactions goes in the direction which decreases the oxidation number of the lighter halogen and increases that of the heavier halogen.

Except for some halogen oxides (discussed below), the compounds of the halogens all correspond to odd oxidation numbers. This regularity is the result of the stability of electronic structures involving pairs of electrons (shared or unshared), which leads to even oxidation states for elements in even groups of the periodic system, and to odd oxidation states for elements in odd groups.

12–3. *The Oxygen Acids and Oxides of Chlorine*

The oxygen acids of chlorine and their anions have the following formulas and names:

$HClO_4$, perchloric acid ClO_4^-, perchlorate ion
$HClO_3$, chloric acid ClO_3^-, chlorate ion
$HClO_2$, chlorous acid ClO_2^-, chlorite ion
$HClO$, hypochlorous acid ClO^-, hypochlorite ion

The electronic structures of the four anions are shown in Figure 12-1.

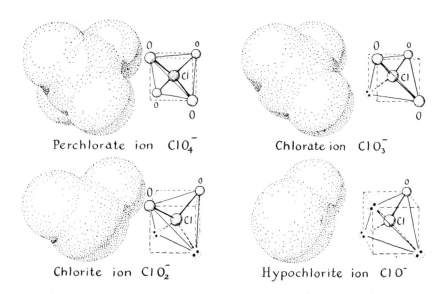

Perchlorate ion ClO_4^- Chlorate ion ClO_3^-

Chlorite ion ClO_2^- Hypochlorite ion ClO^-

FIG. 12-1 *The structure of ions of the four oxygen acids of chlorine.*

Hypochlorous acid, $HClO$, and most hypochlorites are known only in aqueous solution. A mixture of chloride ion and hypochlorite ion is formed by reaction of chlorine with an alkaline solution:

$$Cl_2 + 2OH^- \longrightarrow Cl^- + ClO^- + H_2O$$

A solution of sodium hypochlorite made in this way or by electrolysis of sodium chloride solution is a popular household sterilizing and bleaching agent. The hypochlorite ion is an active oxidizing agent, and its oxidizing power is the basis of its sterilizing and bleaching action.

Bleaching powder is a compound obtained by passing chlorine over calcium oxide:

$$CaO + Cl_2 \longrightarrow CaCl(ClO)$$

The formula $CaCl(ClO)$, which approximates the composition of commercial bleaching powder, indicates it to be a calcium chloride-hypochlorite, containing the two anions Cl^- and ClO^-.

Hypochlorous acid itself is a weak acid, and the solution obtained by adding another acid, such as sulfuric acid, to a solution of a hypochlorite contains molecules $HClO$, and very few hypochlorite ions ClO^-. On careful distillation of such a solution the hypochlorous acid can be separated from the salt.

Chlorine monoxide, Cl_2O, is a yellow gas obtained by gently heating hypochlorous acid in a partially evacuated system (that is, under reduced pressure):

$$2HClO \longrightarrow H_2O + Cl_2O \uparrow$$

or by passing chlorine over mercuric oxide:

$$2Cl_2 + HgO \longrightarrow HgCl_2 + Cl_2O \uparrow$$

The gas condenses to a liquid at about 4° C. It is the *anhydride* of hypochlorous acid; that is, it reacts with water to give hypochlorous acid.

The electronic structure of chlorine monoxide is $: \overset{\cdot\cdot}{\underset{}{O}} \overset{}{\underset{}{-}} \overset{\cdot\cdot}{\underset{\cdot\cdot}{Cl}} :$ $\left|\begin{array}{c} : \overset{\cdot\cdot}{Cl} : \\ | \end{array}\right.$, in which chlorine and

oxygen exercise their normal covalences of 1 and 2, respectively.

Chloric acid, $HClO_3$, is an unstable acid which, like its salts, is a strong oxidizing agent. The most important salt of chloric acid is **potassium chlorate,** $KClO_3$, which is made by passing an excess of chlorine through a hot solution of potassium hydroxide, or by heating a solution containing hypochlorite ion and potassium ion:

$$3ClO^- \longrightarrow ClO_3^- + 2Cl^-$$

The potassium chlorate can be separated from potassium chloride by crystallization, its solubility at low temperatures being much less than that of the chloride (5 g and 31 g, respectively, per 100 g of water at

10° C). A cheaper way of making potassium chlorate is to electrolyze a solution of potassium chloride, using inert electrodes and keeping the solution mixed.

Potassium chlorate is a white substance, which is used as the oxidizing agent in matches and fireworks.

A solution of the similar salt **sodium chlorate,** $NaClO_3$, is used as a weed-killer. Potassium chlorate would be as good as sodium chlorate; however, sodium salts are cheaper than potassium salts, and for this reason they are often used when only the anion is important. Sometimes the sodium salts have unsatisfactory properties, such as deliquescence (attraction of water from the air, to form a solution), which make the potassium salt preferable, even though more expensive.

The chlorates form sensitive explosive mixtures when mixed with reducing agents, and great care must be taken in handling them.

Chlorine dioxide, ClO_2, is the only compound of quadripositive chlorine. It is a reddish-yellow gas, which is very explosive, decomposing readily to chlorine and oxygen. The violence of this reaction makes it very dangerous to add sulfuric acid or any other strong acid to a chlorate or any dry mixture containing a chlorate. Chlorine dioxide can be made by carefully adding sulfuric acid to potassium chlorate. It would be expected that this mixture would react to produce chloric acid, and then, because of the dehydrating power of sulfuric acid, to produce the anhydride of chloric acid:

$$2KClO_3 + H_2SO_4 \longrightarrow K_2SO_4 + 2HClO_3$$
$$2HClO_3 \longrightarrow H_2O + Cl_2O_5$$

However, chlorine pentoxide, Cl_2O_5, is very unstable—its existence has never been verified. If it is formed at all, it decomposes at once to give chlorine dioxide and oxygen:

$$2Cl_2O_5 \longrightarrow 4ClO_2 + O_2$$

The over-all reaction may be written as

$$4KClO_3 + 2H_2SO_4 \longrightarrow 2K_2SO_4 + 4ClO_2 \uparrow + O_2 \uparrow + 2H_2O$$

Chlorine dioxide is an **odd molecule**—that is, a molecule containing an odd number of electrons. It was pointed out by G. N. Lewis in 1916 that odd molecules (other than those containing transition elements) are rare, and that they are usually colored and are always paramagnetic. Every electronic structure that can be written for chlorine dioxide contains one unpaired electron. This unpaired electron presumably resonates among the three atoms, the electronic structure of the molecule being a resonance hybrid:

When chlorine dioxide is dissolved in an alkaline solution, chlorate and chlorite ion are formed:

$$2ClO_2 + 2OH^- \longrightarrow ClO_3^- + ClO_2^- + H_2O$$

On acidification, chloric acid and **chlorous acid**, $HClO_2$, are produced. Chlorous acid and its salts are very unstable.

Potassium perchlorate, $KClO_4$, is made by heating potassium chlorate to its melting point:

$$4KClO_3 \longrightarrow 3KClO_4 + KCl$$

At this temperature very little decomposition with evolution of oxygen occurs. It may also be made by long-continued electrolysis of a solution of potassium chloride, potassium hypochlorite, or potassium chlorate.

Potassium perchlorate and other perchlorates are oxidizing agents, somewhat less vigorous and less dangerous than the chlorates. Potassium perchlorate is used in explosives, and anhydrous magnesium perchlorate, $Mg(ClO_4)_2$, and barium perchlorate, $Ba(ClO_4)_2$, are used as drying agents (desiccants). Nearly all the perchlorates are soluble in water. Potassium perchlorate is exceptional for its low solubility, 0.75 g per 100 g at 0° C.

Perchloric acid, $HClO_4 \cdot H_2O$, is a colorless liquid made by distilling, under reduced pressure, a solution of a perchlorate to which sulfuric acid has been added. The perchloric acid distills as the monohydrate, and on cooling it forms crystals of the monohydrate. These crystals are isomorphous with ammonium perchlorate, NH_4ClO_4, and the substance presumably is hydronium perchlorate, $(H_3O)^+(ClO_4)^-$.

The anhydride of perchloric acid, chlorine heptoxide, Cl_2O_7, is a violently explosive oily liquid made by dehydration of perchloric acid by phosphorus pentoxide.

12–4. *The Oxygen Acids of Bromine*

Bromine forms only two stable oxygen acids—hypobromous acid and bromic acid— and their salts:

HBrO, hypobromous acid	KBrO, potassium hypobromite
HBrO₃, bromic acid	KBrO₃, potassium bromate

Their preparation and properties are similar to those of the corresponding compounds of chlorine.

No effort to prepare perbromic acid or perbromates has succeeded. The bromite ion, BrO_2^-, has been reported to exist in solution.

Two very unstable oxides of bromine, Br_2O and Br_3O_3, have been described.

12–5. *The Oxygen Acids and Oxides of Iodine*

Iodine reacts with hydroxide ion to form the **hypoiodite ion,** IO^-, and iodide ion:

$$I_2 + 2OH^- \longrightarrow IO^- + I^- + H_2O$$

On warming the solution, it reacts further to form iodate ion, IO_3^-:

$$3IO^- \longrightarrow IO_3^- + 2I^-$$

The salts of iodic acid and hypoiodous acid may be made in this way. **Iodic acid** itself, HIO_3, is usually made by oxidizing iodine with concentrated nitric acid:

$$I_2 + 10HNO_3 \longrightarrow 2HIO_3 + 10NO_2 + 4H_2O$$

Periodic acid has the normal formula H_5IO_6, with an octahedral structure (Fig. 12-2). This composition results from the large size of the iodine atom, which permits it to coordinate six oxygen atoms about itself. Two series of periodates exist: $K_2H_3IO_6$, Ag_5IO_6, etc., and KIO_4, $NaIO_4$, etc. Sodium periodate, $NaIO_4$, occurs in small amounts in Chile saltpeter. A solution of sodium periodate usually crystallizes as $Na_2H_3IO_6$.

It is to be noted that the two forms of periodic acid, H_5IO_6 and HIO_4 (unstable, but forming stable salts), represent the same oxidation state of iodine, and differ only in their coordination number. The equilibrium between the two forms is a hydration reaction:

$$HIO_4 + 2H_2O \rightleftarrows H_5IO_6$$

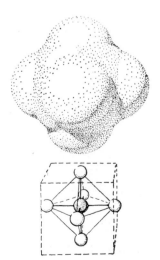

FIG. 12-2

The periodate ion, $IO_6{}^{5-}$.

Iodine pentoxide, I_2O_5, is obtained as a white powder by gently heating either iodic acid or periodic acid:

$$2HIO_3 \longrightarrow I_2O_5 + H_2O \uparrow$$
$$2H_5IO_6 \longrightarrow I_2O_5 + 5H_2O \uparrow + O_2 \uparrow$$

A lower oxide, IO_2 or I_2O_4, can also be made.

12–6. *Compounds of Halogens with Non-Metals and Metalloids*

The halogens form covalent compounds with most of the non-metallic elements (including each other) and metalloids. These compounds are usually molecular substances, with the relatively low melting points and boiling points characteristic of substances with small forces of intermolecular attraction. Examples of normal covalent chlorides are the following:

	CCl_4	NCl_3	Cl_2O	ClF
m.p. (° C).	$-23°$	$-40°$	$-20°$	$-154°$
b.p. (° C).	$77°$	$70°$	$4°$	$-100°$

	$SiCl_4$	PCl_3	SCl_2	Cl_2
m.p. (° C).	$-70°$	$-112°$	$-78°$	$-102°$
b.p. (° C).	$60°$	$74°$	$59°$	$-34°$

	$GeCl_4$	$AsCl_3$
m.p. (° C).	$-50°$	$-18°$
b.p. (° C).	$83°$	$130°$

	$SnCl_4$	$SbCl_3$	$TeCl_2$	ICl
m.p. (° C).	$-33°$	$73°$	$209°$	$27°$
b.p. (° C).	$114°$	$223°$	$327°$	$97°$

In addition, many compounds such as PCl_5, ClF_3, SCl_4, etc., exist, to which a normal covalent structure with noble-gas configuration for the central atom cannot be assigned.

Many of these substances react readily with water, to form a hydride of one element and a hydroxide of the other:

$$ClF + H_2O \longrightarrow HClO + HF$$
$$PCl_3 + 3H_2O \longrightarrow P(OH)_3 + 3HCl$$

In general, in a reaction of this sort, called *hydrolysis*, the more electronegative element combines with hydrogen, and the less electronegative element combines with the hydroxyl group. This rule is seen to be followed in the above examples.

Exercises

12-1. What chemical reaction do you expect to take place when a solution of bleaching powder is acidified? Can this be used as a method of preparing pure hypochlorous acid?

12-2. What chemical reaction takes place at each electrode in the electrolytic preparation of sodium hypochlorite from sodium chloride? Would a well-stirred solution become more acidic or more basic during the course of this electrolysis?

12-3. How do the electronegativities of the halogens affect the relative stabilities of the various oxidation levels of these elements?

12-4. What is the chemical reaction for the hydrolysis of Cl_2O? Is there any oxidation or reduction in this chemical reaction?

12-5. Under what conditions is $KClO_3$ decomposed to give O_2 and KCl and under what conditions does it react to form $KClO_4$ and KCl?

12-6. Write chemical reactions for the preparation of all of the oxides of chlorine.

12-7. What is the composition of the perchloric acid obtained by distilling a solution of a metal perchlorate in sulfuric acid? What is the state of this material at room temperature? In what ways does this substance resemble a salt?

12-8. Complete and balance the chemical reaction

$$I_2 + HNO_3 \longrightarrow$$

12-9. Can you suggest an explanation of the fact that periodic acid, H_5IO_6, has a different formula from perchloric acid, $HClO_4$?

12-10. What is the oxidation number of chlorine in each of the compounds ClF, ICl, PCl_3, NCl_3, $HClO$, $HClO_2$, $HClO_3$, $HClO_4$?

Chapter 13

The Laws of Electrolysis; Electrochemical Processes

A discussion of the chemical reactions which occur at electrodes has been given in Chapter 9. Many electrochemical processes are important in science and industry; some of these processes are described below. This description is preceded by a treatment of the relations between the weight of chemical substances produced or destroyed in electrode reactions and the quantity of electricity which passes through the electrochemical cell.

13–1. *Faraday's Laws of Electrolysis*

In 1832 and 1833 Michael Faraday reported his discovery by experiment of the fundamental laws of electrolysis. These are

1. *The weight of a substance produced by a cathode or anode reaction in electrolysis is directly proportional to the quantity of electricity passed through the cell.*
2. *The weights of different substances produced by the same quantity of electricity are proportional to the equivalent weights of the substances.*

These laws are now known to be the result of the fact that electricity is composed of individual particles, the electrons. Quantity of electricity can be expressed as number of electrons; the number of molecules of a substance produced by an electrode reaction is related in a simple way to the number of electrons involved; hence the weight of substance produced is proportional to the quantity of electricity, in a way which involves the molecular weight or chemical equivalent weight of the substance (equivalent weight was discussed in Chap. 11).

The amounts of substances produced by a given quantity of current can be calculated from knowledge of the electrode reactions. *The magnitude of the charge of one mole of electrons* (Avogadro's number of electrons) *is 96,500 coulombs of electricity* (1 coulomb = 1 ampere second). This is called a **faraday.**

1 faraday = 96,500 coulombs

Note that the electric charge of the electron (Chap. 3) is -1.602×10^{-19} coulomb, as determined by the X-ray method, the Millikan oil-drop experiment, and other methods. Avogadro's number is 0.6024×10^{24}. The product of these is $-96,500$ coulombs of electricity (more precisely, $-96,493.1$). It is customary to define the faraday as this quantity of positive electricity. **The quantitative treatment of electrochemical reactions is made in the same way as the calculation of weight relations in ordinary chemical reactions, with use of the faraday to represent one mole of electrons.**

Example 1. For how long a time would a current of 10 amperes have to be passed through a cell containing fused sodium chloride to produce 23 g of metallic sodium at the cathode? How much chlorine would be produced at the anode?

Solution. The cathode reaction is

$$Na^+ + e^- \longrightarrow Na$$

Hence 1 mole of electrons passing through the cell would produce 1 mole of sodium atoms. One mole of electrons is 1 faraday, and 1 mole of sodium atoms is a gram-atom of sodium, 23.00 g. Hence the amount of electricity required is 96,500 coulombs. One coulomb is 1 ampere second. Hence 96,500 coulombs of electricity passes through the cell if 10 amperes flows for 9,650 seconds. The answer is thus **9,650 sec.,** or 160 min. 50 sec.

The anode reaction is

$$2Cl^- \longrightarrow Cl_2 + 2e^-$$

To produce 1 mole of molecular chlorine, Cl_2, 2 faradays must pass through the cell. One faraday will produce 1/2 mole of Cl_2, or 1 gram-atom of chlorine, which is **35.46 g.** Note that two moles of electrons are required to produce one mole of molecular chlorine.

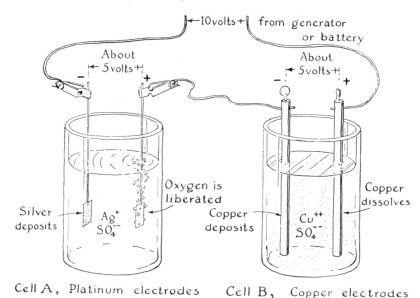

FIG. 13-1   *Two electrolytic cells in series.*

Example 2.   Two cells are set up in series, and a current is passed through them. Cell A contains an aqueous solution of silver sulfate, and has platinum electrodes (which are unreactive). Cell B contains a copper sulfate solution, and has copper electrodes. The current is passed through until 1.6 g of oxygen has been liberated at the anode of cell A. What has occurred at the other electrodes? (See Fig. 13-1.)

Solution.   At the anode of cell A the reaction is

$$2H_2O \longrightarrow O_2\uparrow + 4H^+ + 4e^-$$

Hence 4 faradays of electricity liberates 32 g of oxygen, and 0.2 faraday liberates 1.6 g.

At the cathode of cell A the reaction is

$$Ag^+ + e^- \longrightarrow Ag\downarrow$$

One gram-atom of silver, 107.880 g, would be deposited by 1 faraday, and the passage of 0.2 faraday through the cell would hence deposit **21.576 g** of silver on the platinum cathode.

At the cathode in cell B the reaction is

$$Cu^{++} + 2e^- \longrightarrow Cu\downarrow$$

One gram-atom of copper, 63.57 g, would hence be deposited on the cathode by 2 faradays of electricity, and **6.357 g** by 0.2 faraday.

The same amount of copper, **6.357 g,** would be dissolved from the anode of cell B, since the same number of electrons flows through the anode as through the cathode. The anode reaction is

$$\underline{Cu \longrightarrow Cu^{++} + 2e^-}$$

Note that the total voltage difference supplied by the generator or battery (shown as 10 volts) is divided between the two cells in series. The division need not be equal, as indicated, but is determined by the properties of the two cells.

The Cost of Electrochemical Processes.   Faraday's laws do not tell us enough to determine the cost of the electric energy required to carry out an electrochemical process. Calculations such as those given above determine the *quantity of electricity* required to produce a given amount of substance electrolytically, but not the *electrical pressure* (the voltage) at which it must be supplied. The principles determining the voltage which a cell provides or needs for its operation are more complicated; they are described briefly in Chapter 32.

In any commercial process, a considerable fraction of the required voltage is that needed to overcome the electrical resistance of the electrolyte in the cell. The corresponding energy is converted into heat, and sometimes serves to keep the electrolyte molten.

If the operating voltage of a cell is known, and the cost of electric power, per watt-second (ampere-volt-second), or, usually, per kilowatt-hour (kwh), is known, a calculation of cost can be made.

13–2. *Electrolytic Production of Elements*

Many metals and some non-metals are made by electrolytic methods. Hydrogen and oxygen are produced by the electrolysis of water containing an electrolyte. The alkali metals, alkaline-earth metals, magnesium, aluminum, and many other metals are manufactured either entirely or for special uses by electrochemical reduction of their compounds. Some of the processes used are described below.

The Manufacture of Sodium and Chlorine.   Many electrochemical processes depend for their success on ingenious devices for securing the purity of the products. As illustration we may consider a cell used for making metallic sodium and elementary chlorine from sodium chloride. The molten sodium chloride (usually with some sodium carbonate added to reduce its melting point) is in a vessel containing a carbon anode and an iron cathode, separated by an iron screen which leads to pipes, as indicated in Figure 13-2. The gaseous chlorine is led off through one pipe, and the molten sodium, which is lighter than the electrolyte, rises and is drawn off into a storage tank.

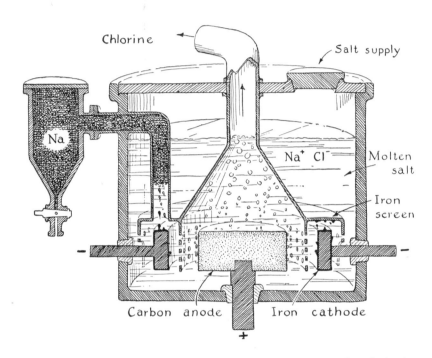

FIG. 13-2   *A cell used for making sodium and chlorine by electrolysis of fused sodium chloride.*

The Manufacture of Aluminum.   All commercial aluminum is made electrolytically, by a process discovered in 1886 by a young American, Charles M. Hall (1863–1914), and independently, in the same year, by a young Frenchman, P. L. T. Héroult (1863–1914).* A carbon-lined iron box, which serves as cathode, contains the electrolyte, which is the molten mineral *cryolite*, Na_3AlF_6 (or a mixture of AlF_3, NaF, and sometimes CaF_2), in which aluminum oxide, Al_2O_3, is dissolved (Fig. 13-3). The aluminum oxide is obtained from the ore *bauxite* by a process of purification. The anodes in the cell are made of carbon. The passage

* Note the surprising parallelism in the lives of these two men.

of the current provides heat enough to keep the electrolyte molten, at about 1,000° C. The aluminum metal sinks to the bottom, and is tapped off:

$$Al^{+++} + 3e^- \longrightarrow Al \downarrow$$

Carbon dioxide is produced at the anodes, according to the equation

$$2O^{--} + C \longrightarrow CO_2 \uparrow + 4e^-$$

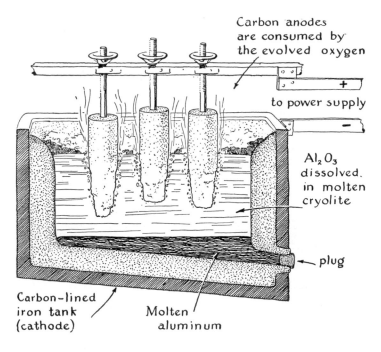

FIG. 13-3   *The electrolytic production of aluminum.*

The cells operate at about 5 volts potential difference between the electrodes.

Bauxite is a mixture of aluminum minerals [AlO(OH), Al(OH)$_3$], which contains some iron oxide. It is purified by treatment with sodium hydroxide solution, which dissolves hydrated aluminum oxide (as aluminate ion), but does not dissolve iron oxide:

$$\underline{Al(OH)_3 + OH^-} \longrightarrow Al(OH)_4^-$$
$$\text{aluminate ion}$$

The solution is filtered, and then acidified with carbon dioxide, reversing the above reaction. The precipitated aluminum hydroxide is then dehydrated by ignition (heating to a high temperature), and the purified aluminum oxide is ready for addition to the electrolyte.

The world's production of aluminum by this process is of the order of two million tons per year.

13–3. *The Electrolytic Refining of Metals*

Several metals, won from their ores by either chemical or electrochemical processes, are further purified (refined) by electrolytic methods.

Metallic **copper** is sometimes obtained by leaching a copper ore with sulfuric acid and then depositing the metal by electrolysis of the copper

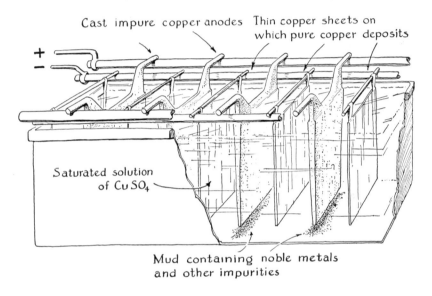

FIG. 13-4   *The electrolytic refining of copper.*

sulfate solution. Most copper ores, however, are converted into crude copper by chemical reduction. This crude copper is cast into anode plates about ¾ in. thick, and is then refined electrolytically.

The process of electrolytic refining of copper is a simple one (see Fig. 13-4). The anodes of crude copper alternate with cathodes of thin sheets of pure copper coated with graphite, which makes it possible to strip off the deposit. The electrolyte is copper sulfate. As the current passes through, the crude copper dissolves from the anodes and a purer copper deposits on the cathodes. Metals below copper in the E.M.F. series (Chap. 10), such as gold, silver, and platinum, remain undissolved, and fall to the bottom of the tank as a sludge, from which they can be recovered. More active metals, such as iron, remain in the solution.

Aluminum is sometimes subjected to electrolytic refining by the Hoopes process. The electrolytic cell (Fig. 13-5) contains three superimposed liquid layers. The top layer, A, which serves as the cathode, is pure molten aluminum, and the bottom layer, C, is impure aluminum in which copper and silicon have been dissolved to increase its density. The middle layer, B, is a fused salt mixture with intermediate density;

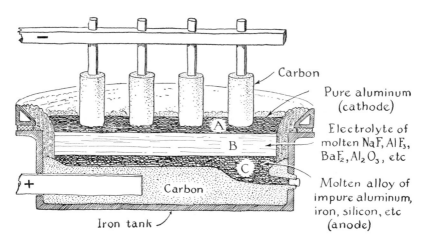

Carbon

Pure aluminum (cathode)

Electrolyte of molten NaF, AlF$_3$, BaF$_2$, Al$_2$O$_3$, etc

Carbon

Molten alloy of impure aluminum, iron, silicon, etc (anode)

Iron tank

FIG. 13-5   *The electrolytic refining of aluminum.*

it contains NaF, AlF$_3$, BaF$_2$, and Al$_2$O$_3$. During electrolysis aluminum from C passes into B as aluminum ions, and is reconverted to aluminum metal at A. The other metals in C do not pass into the electrolyte.

13–4. *Other Electrolytic Processes*

Many electrolytic processes have been mentioned in preceding chapters, such as the oxidation of chloride ion to hypochlorite ion, chlorate ion, and perchlorate ion, of manganate ion to permanganate ion, and of sulfuric acid to peroxysulfuric acid.

An interesting electrolytic process which may serve as a further example is the Castner-Kellner process for making chlorine and sodium hydroxide. If concentrated brine is electrolyzed, chlorine is formed at the anode and hydroxide ion at the cathode:

$$2Cl^- \longrightarrow Cl_2 + 2e^-$$
$$2H_2O + 2e^- \longrightarrow H_2 + 2OH^-$$

If brine is electrolyzed as just described, using graphite electrodes, the alkali produced is present in solution together with some undecomposed salt, from which it must be separated by crystallization. This troublesome step is avoided in the Castner-Kellner process. This process involves use of a slate tank divided into three compartments by slate partitions not quite touching the floor of the tank (Fig. 13-6). A layer of mercury covers the floor. Dilute sodium hydroxide solution is put in the central compartment, and brine in the end compartments. The brine is electrolyzed between graphite anodes and the mercury, which serves as a

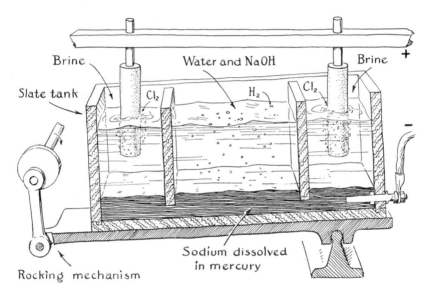

FIG. 13-6   *The Castner-Kellner process for making chlorine and sodium hydroxide.*

cathode. The anode reaction is that given above, producing chlorine. The cathode reaction is

$$e^- + Na^+ \longrightarrow Na(amalgam)$$

["Na(amalgam)" means a solution of sodium in mercury; the alloys of mercury with other metals are called amalgams.] During the electrolysis the cell is rocked, causing the amalgam to flow back and forth.

The amalgam reacts with the water in the central compartment:

$$2Na(amalgam) + 2H_2O \longrightarrow H_2 \uparrow + 2NaOH(aq)$$

In this way a pure solution of sodium hydroxide is produced. It is in practice found convenient to introduce iron electrodes in the central compartment, and to assist this reaction to occur by use of an applied electric potential, with the amalgam as anode and the iron electrode as cathode. The electrode reactions are the following:

Anode reaction: $Na(amalgam) \longrightarrow Na^+ + e^-$
Cathode reaction: $2H_2O + 2e^- \longrightarrow H_2 \uparrow + 2OH^-$

The factors which determine the nature of the electrode reactions in a case such as those just mentioned (where both the salt concentration and the electrode material are seen to be significant) will be discussed in detail in a later chapter (Chap. 32), dealing with oxidation-reduction potentials. At present we may say that of the possible electrode reactions the one that can occur most easily, according to the principles of chemical equilibrium and reaction rate, will be the one which usually occurs. This is usually the reaction that forms the most stable products. Thus in the case of dilute salt solution a possible cathode reaction is

$$Na^+ + e^- \longrightarrow Na$$

forming sodium metal. But we know that sodium metal decomposes water to liberate hydrogen:

$$2Na + 2H_2O \longrightarrow 2Na^+ + 2OH^- + H_2$$

Thus sodium metal is not the product of the cathode reaction, and indeed there is no need to bring sodium ion and sodium metal into the reaction at all. On the other hand, dilute sodium amalgam does not react with concentrated brine, to liberate hydrogen; hence the cathode reaction in the Castner-Kellner process produces this amalgam rather than hydrogen.

13–5. *Primary Cells and Storage Cells*

The production of an electric current through chemical reaction is achieved in *primary cells* and *storage cells*. Primary cells are cells in which an oxidation-reduction reaction can be carried out in such a way that its driving force (release of free energy) produces an electric potential. This is achieved by having the oxidizing agent and reducing agent separated; the oxidizing agent then removes electrons from one electrode and the reducing agent gives electrons to another electrode, the flow of current through the cell itself being carried by ions. Storage cells are similar cells, which, however, can be returned to their original state after current has been drawn from them (can be *charged*) by applying an impressed electric potential between the electrodes, and reversing the oxidation-reduction reaction.

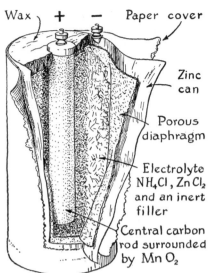

Wax   **+**   **–**   Paper cover

Zinc can

Porous diaphragm

Electrolyte NH_4Cl, $ZnCl_2$ and an inert filler

Central carbon rod surrounded by MnO_2

FIG. 13-7

The dry cell.

One primary cell, the gravity cell, has been described in Chapter 11. This cell is called a *wet cell*, because it contains a liquid electrolyte. A very useful cell is the common *dry cell*, shown in Figure 13-7. This cell consists of a zinc cylinder which contains as electrolyte a paste of ammonium chloride (NH_4Cl), a little zinc chloride, water, and diatomaceous earth or other filler. The central electrode, which is the positive pole, is a carbon rod surrounded by manganese dioxide. The electrode reactions are

$$Zn \longrightarrow Zn^{++} + 2e^-$$
$$2NH_4^+ + 2MnO_2 + 2e^- \longrightarrow 2MnO(OH) + 2NH_3$$

(The zinc ion combines to some extent with ammonia to form the zinc-ammonia complex ion, $[Zn(NH_3)_4]^{++}$.) This cell produces a potential of about 1.48 v.

The most common storage cell is that in the *lead storage battery* (Fig. 13-8). The electrolyte is a mixture of water and sulfuric acid with density about 1.290 g/cm^3 in the charged cell (38% H_2SO_4 by weight). The plates are lattices made of a lead alloy, the pores of one plate being filled with spongy lead, and those of the other with lead dioxide, PbO_2. The reactions which take place as the cell is being discharged are

$$\underline{Pb} + SO_4^{--} \longrightarrow \underline{PbSO_4} + 2e^-$$
$$\underline{PbO_2} + SO_4^{--} + 4H^+ + 2e^- \longrightarrow \underline{PbSO_4} + 2H_2O$$

Each reaction produces the insoluble substance $PbSO_4$, lead sulfate,

Capped hole for testing and
replenishing electrolyte of
H_2SO_4 and distilled water

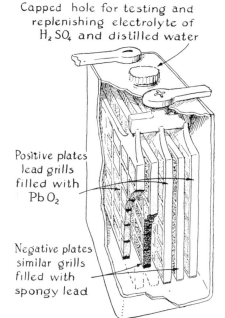

Positive plates
lead grills
filled with
PbO_2

Negative plates
similar grills
filled with
spongy lead

FIG. 13-8

The lead storage cell.

which adheres to the plates. As the cell is discharged sulfuric acid is removed from the electrolyte, which decreases in density. The cell can be charged again by applying an electric potential across the terminals, and reversing the above electrode reactions. The charged cell produces an electromotive force of slightly over 2 volts.

It is interesting that the same element changes its oxidation state in the two plates of this cell: the oxidizing agent is PbO_2 ($Pb^{+4} \longrightarrow Pb^{+2}$), and the reducing agent is Pb ($Pb^0 \longrightarrow Pb^{+2}$).

13–6. *Electrolytic Rectifiers*

Some electrolytic systems have the power of permitting an electric current to pass through them in only one direction, provided that the impressed voltage is not too great. An example of such a system is the *aluminum rectifier*, Figure 13-9. One electrode, made of ferrosilicon, permits the current to flow either way. The aluminum electrode, however, permits electrons to flow into the solution, but not to flow from the solution into the electrode, even with an applied potential of several hundred volts.

The explanation of this behavior is that when the applied potential tends to pull electrons from the aluminum electrode and out through

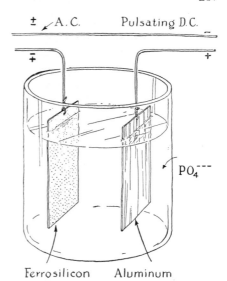

A.C. Pulsating D.C.

PO_4^{---}

FIG. 13-9

The aluminum electrolytic rectifier.

Ferrosilicon   Aluminum

the terminal some aluminum atoms at the surface of the electrode are converted into ions:

$$Al \longrightarrow Al^{+++} + 3e^-$$

The electrolyte may be a phosphate solution, containing phosphate ions, PO_4^{---}. These ions may unite with the aluminum ions, forming a very thin film of aluminum phosphate, $AlPO_4$, over the surface of the electrode, and insulating it so effectively as to keep any current from flowing. When the applied potential is reversed, and electrons are forced into the aluminum electrode, the film disappears:

$$AlPO_4 + 3e^- \longrightarrow Al \downarrow + PO_4^{---}$$

The current is then able to flow in the corresponding direction.

A related phenomenon is the passage of a current in one direction only through a contact between a metallic wire and a semi-conducting crystal, such as silicon, germanium, selenium, and galena (lead sulfide, PbS). The rectification by these systems also presumably is the result of the formation of a non-conducting film when the current begins to flow in one direction, and its destruction when the applied potential is reversed.

Exercises

13-1. Sodium metal is made commercially by the electrolysis of fused sodium hydroxide, NaOH. (a) Write the anode and cathode reactions and the over-all reaction. (b) Calculate the weight of sodium formed per hour in a cell through which 1,000 amperes is flowing.

13-2. A current is passed between a copper electrode and a silver electrode in 1 l of electrolyte which originally contained 1 gfw of $AgNO_3$. How much copper has dissolved after 0.1000 g of silver has been deposited on the silver electrode?

13-3. Solid silver iodide at temperatures even considerably below its melting point is a good ionic conductor. Two silver electrodes, each weighing 10.0000 g, are placed in contact with the two ends of a cylinder of silver iodide weighing 20 g, and a direct current of 2 amp is passed through the system for 1 hour. What should be the final weights of anode, cathode, and electrolyte?

13-4. (a) How much electricity is needed to produce one pound of aluminum by electrolysis of Al_2O_3 dissolved in cryolite? (This is the commercial process of winning the metal.) (b) If a potential difference of 5 volts is used, and the electricity costs 0.1 cent per kilowatt-hour, what is the power cost per pound of aluminum? The market price of aluminum is ordinarily about 20 cents per pound.

13-5. In a cell with anode and cathode compartments connected by a narrow tube each compartment holds 1 l of electrolytic solution. 9,650 coulombs of electricity is passed through the cell, producing hydrogen and oxygen. Initially each cell contained 1 gfw of $MgSO_4$. Discuss the electrode reactions and describe the final contents of each compartment.

13-6. How many grams of $NaClO_3$ are produced per hour by the electrolysis of an alkaline solution of NaCl in a cell through which a current of 10 amperes is passing?

13-7. The international ampere is defined as that current which, under specified conditions, deposits 0.001118 g of silver per second. From this and the atomic weight of silver, 107.880, calculate the value of the faraday.

13-8. In one of the most reliable determinations of the value of the faraday which have been made, Vinal and Bates* found that 4.82844 g of iodine was liberated at an anode in potassium iodide solution by 3,671.82 coulombs of electricity. Evaluate the faraday from this, using 126.92 for the atomic weight of iodine.

13-9. At what rate, in grams per hour, would chlorine be produced in a Castner-Kellner cell by a current of 10,000 amp?

13-10. Why does the electrolytic refining of copper purify it from gold? from iron?

13-11. What difference is there in the electrolysis of a dilute sodium chloride solution with platinum electrodes and with mercury electrodes?

13-12. In which direction does an aluminum rectifier pass a current? Why?

13-13. Calculate the life of a dry cell in ampere-hours per gram of MnO_2, assuming that the other reactants are present in excess.

* G. W. Vinal and S. J. Bates, *Bulletin of the Bureau of Standards*, **10**, 425 (1914).

Chapter 14

The Properties
of Gases

14–1. *The Nature of the Gas Laws*

Gases differ remarkably from liquids and solids in that the volume of a sample of gas depends in a striking way on the temperature of the gas and the applied pressure. The volume of a sample of liquid water, say 1 kg of water, remains essentially the same when the temperature and pressure are changed somewhat. Increasing the pressure from 1 atm to 2 atm causes the volume of a sample of liquid water to decrease by less than 0.01%, and increasing the temperature from 0° C to 100° C causes the volume to increase by only 2%. On the other hand, the volume of a sample of air is cut in half when the pressure is increased from 1 atm to 2 atm, and it increases by 36.6% when the temperature is changed from 0° C to 100° C.

We can understand why these interesting phenomena attracted the attention of scientists during the early years of development of modern chemistry through the application of quantitative experimental methods of investigation of nature, and why many physicists and chemists during the past century have devoted themselves to the problem of developing a sound theory to explain the behavior of gases.

In addition to our desire to understand this part of the physical world, there is another reason, a practical one, for studying the gas laws. This reason is concerned with the *measurement of gases*. The most convenient way to determine the amount of material in a sample of a solid is to weigh it on a balance. This can also be done conveniently for liquids; or we may measure the volume of a sample of a liquid, and, if we want to know its weight, multiply the volume by its density, as found by a previous experiment. The method of weighing is usually not conveniently used for gases, because their densities are very small; volume measurements can be made much more accurately and easily. But the volume of a sample of gas depends greatly on both the pressure and the temperature, and to calculate the weight of gas in a measured volume the law of this dependence must be known. It is partly for this reason that study of the pressure-volume-temperature properties of gases is a part of chemistry.

Another important reason for studying the gas laws is that the *density* of a dilute gas is related in a simple way to its *molecular weight*, whereas there is no similar simple relation for liquids and solids. This relation for gases (*Avogadro's law*) was of great value in the original decision as to the correct atomic weights of the elements, and it is still of great practical significance, permitting the direct calculation of the approximate density of a gas of known molecular composition, or the experimental determination of the effective (average) molecular weight of a gas of unknown molecular composition by the measurement of its density. These uses are discussed in detail in the following sections.

It has been found by experiment that **all ordinary gases behave in nearly the same way.** The nature of this behavior is described by the *perfect-gas laws* (often referred to briefly as the *gas laws*).

It is found experimentally that, within the reliability of the gas laws (better than 1% under ordinary conditions), the volume of a sample of any gas is determined by only three quantities: the *pressure* of the gas, the *temperature* of the gas, and the *number of molecules* in the sample of the gas. The law describing the dependence of the volume of the gas on the pressure is called *Boyle's law;* that describing the dependence of the volume on the temperature is called the *law of Charles and Gay-Lussac;* and that describing the dependence of the volume on the number of molecules in the sample of gas is called *Avogadro's law.*

In the following sections of this chapter these three laws are formulated and applied in the solution of some problems. It is also shown that they can be combined into a single equation, which is called the *perfect-gas equation.*

14–2. *The Dependence of Gas Volume on Pressure: Boyle's Law*

Experiments on the volume of a gas as a function of the pressure have shown that, **for nearly all gases, the volume of a sample of gas at**

constant temperature is inversely proportional to the pressure; that is, the product of pressure and volume under these conditions is constant:

$$pV = \text{constant} \quad \text{(temperature constant, moles of gas}$$
$$\text{constant)} \qquad \qquad \text{(14-1)}$$

This equation expresses Boyle's law. The law was inferred from experimental data by the English natural scientist Robert Boyle in 1662.

The limitation that the number of moles of the gas be constant is made in order to account for the exceptional behavior of certain gases. Whereas all of the common gases, such as oxygen, hydrogen, nitrogen, carbon monoxide, carbon dioxide, etc., behave in the way described by Boyle's law, there are some gases that do not. One of these is the gas *nitrogen dioxide*, NO_2, the molecules of which can combine to form double molecules, of *dinitrogen tetroxide*, N_2O_4. A sample of this gas under ordinary conditions contains some molecules NO_2 and some molecules N_2O_4. When the pressure on the sample of the gas is changed the number of molecules of each of these kinds changes, causing the volume to depend on the pressure in a complicated way, rather than in the simple way described by Boyle's law. This effect will be discussed in Chapter 20.

The practical use of Boyle's law may be illustrated by some examples.

Example 1.   The air in an automobile tire, with volume 1 cubic foot, is under 30 lbs. per sq. in. pressure. How much air would come out of the tire if the valve were opened?

Solution.   By "under 30 lbs. per sq. in. pressure" it is usually meant in common speech that the pressure is 30 lbs. per sq. in. greater than atmospheric. (Such a pressure difference is called "gauge pressure.") Since 1 atm = 14.7 lbs. per sq. in., the total pressure is 44.7 lbs. per sq. in. To the precision of the measurement by an ordinary gauge this is just 3 atm.

From Boyle's law we see that if the pressure on a sample of gas were to change from 3 atm to 1 atm, becoming only 1/3 as great, the volume would have to increase by the factor 3. Hence, if the pressure on 1 cu. ft. of air were decreased from 3 atm to 1 atm the air would expand to 3 cu. ft. (the temperature being assumed to stay constant). Of this total volume, 1 cu. ft. would stay in the tire, so that **2 cu. ft.** of air (at 1 atm pressure) would come out of the tire.

In working this problem we have assumed that the tire does not change in volume when the pressure is released, as well as that there is no significant change in temperature during the expansion of air.

Example 2.   What is the weight of oxygen that can be put in an oxygen tank with volume 2 cu. ft. under pressure of 1,500 lbs. per sq. in.? The density of oxygen at 1 atm pressure and room temperature (18° C) is 1.34 g/l.

> **Solution.**   Let us convert the volume of the tank to liters and the pressure to atmospheres. The number of liters in 1 cu. ft. can be found by remembering that 2.54 cm = 1 inch. The number of cm^3 in 1 cu. ft. is accordingly $(12 \times 2.54)^3 = 30.48^3 = 28,316\ cm^3$. Hence 1 cu. ft. = 28.32 l, and 2 cu. ft., the volume of the tank, is 56.6 l. The pressure on the tank in atmospheres is 1,500/14.7 = 102 atm. By application of Boyle's law we see that a volume of 56.6 l of gas at 102 atm will become much larger, by the factor 102, when the pressure is decreased to 1 atm; the volume at 1 atm is accordingly
>
> $$102 \times 56.6 = 5,773\ l$$
>
> The weight of this volume of oxygen in grams is the product of the volume by the density, 1.34 g/l, which is 7,730 g or, dividing by 454, the number of grams in a pound, 17.0 lbs. The weight of oxygen that the tank will hold under this pressure is accordingly **17.0 lbs.**

Correction for the Vapor Pressure of Water.   When a sample of gas is collected over water the pressure of the gas is due in part to the water vapor in it. The pressure due to the water vapor in the gas in equilibrium with liquid water is equal to the vapor pressure of water. Values of the vapor pressure at different temperatures are given in Appendix II.

The way in which a correction for the vapor pressure of water can be made is illustrated in the following example.

Example 3.   An experiment is made to find out how much oxygen is liberated from a given amount of potassium chlorate, $KClO_3$. The quantity 2.00 g of this salt is weighed out, mixed with some manganese dioxide, to serve as catalyst, and introduced into a hard-glass test tube, which is provided with a cork and delivery tube leading to a bottle filled with water and inverted in a pneumatic trough. The test tube is heated, and the heating is continued until the evolution of gas ceases. A glass plate is then slipped under the mouth of the bottle, the bottle is inverted, and the volume of gas in it is determined to be 596 ml by finding what volume of water is required to displace the gas, just filling the bottle. The temperature of the water in the pneumatic trough was tested with a thermometer and found to be 18° C. The barometric pressure was observed on a barometer to be 748.3 mm Hg. It was noted that as the test tube cooled, with the end of its delivery tube under water, some water was sucked into the delivery tube; the volume of this water was measured and found to be 5 ml. What was the weight of oxygen liberated? How does this compare with the theoretical yield?

Solution. The atmospheric pressure, 748.3 mm Hg, is balanced in part by the pressure of the oxygen collected in the bottle, and in part by the pressure of the water vapor dissolved by the oxygen as it bubbles through the water. By reference to Appendix II we see that the vapor pressure of water at 18° C is 15.5 mm Hg. Accordingly, the pressure due to the oxygen in the bottle is less than 748.3 mm by this amount, and is equal to $748.3 - 15.5 = 732.8$ mm Hg.

Let us now find what volume the liberated oxygen would occupy at standard pressure, 760 mm Hg. A small correction must first be made to the measured volume. When the test tube was first heated, the air in it was expanded because of the increased temperature, and some of this air bubbled into the bottle. Then, at the end of the experiment, the test tube was allowed to cool, and it was found that 5 ml of water was sucked into the delivery tube. Accordingly 5 ml of gas that should not be counted was transferred to the bottle, and the volume of the liberated oxygen should hence be taken as $596 - 5 = 591$ ml.

The volume at the smaller pressure 732.8 mm Hg thus is 591 ml. We know that gases become smaller in volume when they are compressed; the volume at the higher pressure, 760 mm, will be less than 591, and we see that the volume 591 must be multiplied by the fraction $\dfrac{732.8}{760}$:

$$\text{volume of oxygen at 760 mm Hg} = 591 \times \frac{732.8}{760} = 570 \text{ ml}$$

In the preceding example the density of oxygen at 1 atm pressure and 18° C was given as 1.34 g/l. The weight of 570 ml of oxygen under these conditions is easily calculated; this is the answer to the first question in our example:

weight of oxygen liberated $= \dfrac{570}{1,000} \times 1.34 = \mathbf{0.764\ g}$

Note how simple the means are by which the weight of liberated oxygen was found, to 1-mg accuracy; only rough volume measurements (to 1 ml) needed to be made.

To answer the second question let us calculate the theoretical yield of oxygen from 2.00 g of potassium chlorate. The equation for the decomposition of potassium chlorate is

$$KClO_3 \longrightarrow KCl + \tfrac{3}{2}O_2 \uparrow$$

(Note that it is sometimes convenient to represent a fractional number of molecules in an equation.) We see that 1 gram-formula weight of $KClO_3$, 122.5 g, should liberate 3 gram-atoms of oxygen, 48.0 g. Hence the amount of oxygen that should be liberated from 2.00 g of potassium chlorate is $\dfrac{48.0}{122.5} \times 2.00 = 0.786$ g.

The observed amount of oxygen liberated is seen to be less than the theoretical amount by 0.022 g, or **2.8%**.

In applying Boyle's law in the solution of a problem you should always check your calculations by deciding whether the change in pressure given in the problem should cause the volume to increase or to decrease, and then verifying that your answer agrees with your decision on this point.

14–3. *Dependence of Gas Volume on Temperature: the Law of Charles and Gay-Lussac*

After the discovery of Boyle's law, it was more than one hundred years before the dependence of the volume of a gas on the temperature was investigated. Then in 1787 the French physicist Jacques Alexandre Charles (1746–1823) reported that different gases expand by the same fractional amount for the same rise in temperature. John Dalton in England continued these studies in 1801, and in 1802 Joseph Louis Gay-Lussac (1778–1850) extended the work, and determined the amount of expansion per degree centigrade. He found that all gases expand by 1/273 of their volume at 0° C for each degree centigrade that they are heated above this temperature. Thus a sample of gas with volume 273 ml at 0° C has the volume 274 ml at 1° C and the same pressure, 275 ml at 2° C, 373 ml at 100° C, etc.

We now state the law of the dependence of the volume of a gas on temperature, the **law of Charles and Gay-Lussac,** in the following way: **If the pressure and the number of moles of a sample of gas remain constant, the volume of the sample of gas is proportional to the absolute temperature:**

$$V = \text{constant} \times T \quad \text{(pressure constant, number of moles}$$
$$\text{constant)} \qquad (14\text{-}2)$$

You will note that the dependence of volume on the absolute temperature is a direct proportionality, whereas the volume is inversely proportional to the pressure. The nature of these two relations is illustrated in Figure 14-1.

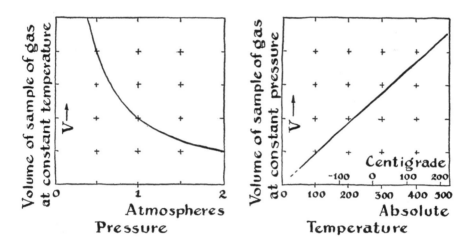

FIG. 14-1 *Curves showing, at the left, the dependence of the volume of a sample of gas at constant temperature and containing a constant number of molecules on the pressure, and, at the right, the dependence of the volume of a sample of gas at constant pressure and containing a constant number of molecules on the temperature.*

The use of the law of Charles and Gay-Lussac in working problems is illustrated by the examples given below.

Standard Conditions. It is customary to refer the volumes of gases to 0° C and a pressure of 1 atm. This temperature and pressure are called **standard conditions.** A sample of gas is said to be *reduced to standard conditions* when its volume is calculated at this temperature and pressure.

Example 4. One gram of methane has a volume of 1,513 ml at 25° C and 1 atm. What is its volume at standard conditions?

Solution.   Our problem is to find the volume of a sample of gas at 0° C which has the volume 1,513 ml at 25° C; or, changing to the absolute temperature scale, to find the volume of a sample of gas at 273° K which has volume 1,513 ml at 298° K.

Cooling a gas causes its volume to decrease. Accordingly, we know that we must multiply the volume at the higher temperature by 273/298, rather than by the reciprocal of this fraction. Thus we have

volume of gas at standard conditions $= \dfrac{273}{298} \times 1{,}513 =$ **1,386 ml.**

Example 5.   The first balloons that were made were filled with hot air. What would be the lifting power of a balloon with volume 10,000 cu. ft. filled with air heated to 200° C? The density of air at room temperature (18° C) and 1 atm is 1.21 g/l.

Solution.   Let us first find the volume of the balloon in liters. We calculated in an earlier example that 1 cu. ft. contains 28.3 l; hence the balloon has a volume of about 283,000 l. The weight displaced by this balloon in the atmosphere is 283,000 × 1.21 = 342,000 g, or, dividing by 454, the number of grams in a pound, 764 lbs.

Let us now calculate the weight of hot air in the balloon. The temperature of the hot air is 200 + 273 = 473° K. The room temperature is 291° K. If the hot air in the balloon were to be cooled to room temperature, it would shrink to the volume 291/473 of its original volume. The weight of this amount of air is accordingly this fraction of the weight of the air required to fill the balloon at room temperature, which we have just calculated to be 764 lbs.:

weight of hot air in balloon $= 764 \times \dfrac{291}{473} = 470$ lbs.

The lifting power of the hot-air balloon is thus found to be 764 − 470 = **294 lbs.**

Correction of the Volume of a Gas for Change in Both Pressure and Temperature.   Boyle's law and the law of Charles and Gay-Lussac can be applied in a straightforward manner to calculate the change in volume of a sample of gas from one pressure and temperature to another pressure and temperature, as is illustrated by the following example:

Example 6.   A sample of gas has volume 1,200 ml at 100° C and 800 mm pressure. Reduce to standard conditions.

Solution.   We may solve this problem by multiplying the original volume by a ratio of pressures to correct for the change in pressure, and by a ratio of temperatures to correct for the change in temperature. We must decide for each ratio whether the correction is greater or less than one.

In this case the sample is initially at a greater pressure than 1 atm (760 mm), and hence it will expand when the pressure is reduced to 1 atm. Accordingly, the pressure factor must be 800/760, and not 760/800. Also the sample will contract (decrease in volume) when it is cooled, and hence the temperature factor must be 273/373, and not 373/273. Therefore we write

$$V = 1,200 \times \frac{800}{760} \times \frac{273}{373} = \textbf{925 ml.}$$

This method is to be used in solving any pressure-volume-temperature problem for a sample of gas, provided that the number of molecules in the sample remains constant.

The Absolute Temperature Scale.   The idea of the absolute zero of temperature was developed as a result of the discovery of the law of Charles and Gay-Lussac; the absolute zero would be the temperature at which an ideal gas would have zero volume at any finite pressure. For some years (until 1848) the absolute temperature scale was defined in terms of a gas thermometer; the absolute temperature was taken as proportional to the volume of a sample of gas at constant pressure. Since, however, no real gas approaches a perfect gas closely enough at practically useful pressures to permit an accurate gas thermometer to be constructed, an absolute temperature scale based on the laws of thermodynamics was formulated by Lord Kelvin. This is the absolute temperature scale which is now accepted, and which was discussed in Chapter 2. The hydrogen gas thermometer agrees very closely with the thermodynamic scale except at very low temperatures, and is widely used in practice.

By the usual methods of reaching low temperatures (the compression and expansion of gases) every gas has been liquefied. Helium, the gas with the lowest boiling point, boils at 4.2° K. By boiling liquid helium under low pressure a temperature of about 0.82° K was reached in 1923 by Heike Kamerlingh Onnes, the great Dutch investigator of low temperatures, working in Leiden, Holland. This seemed to be close to the limit that could be achieved in the effort to reach extremely low temperatures; but in 1927 a young American physical chemist, William F.

Giauque of the University of California, suggested and put into practice a novel method of reaching extremely low temperatures. This consists in the demagnetization of a paramagnetic substance previously cooled with liquid helium; in this way temperatures of about 0.001° K have been reached. The laws of thermodynamics indicate that it is impossible by any real mechanism to reach the absolute zero of temperature.

14–4. *Avogadro's Law*

In 1805 Gay-Lussac began a series of experiments to find the volume percentage of oxygen in air. In the course of this work he made a very important discovery. The experiments were carried out by mixing a certain volume of hydrogen with air and exploding the mixture, and then testing the remaining gas to see whether oxygen or hydrogen had been present in excess. He was surprised to find a very simple relation: 1,000 ml of oxygen required just 2,000 ml of hydrogen, to form water. Continuing the study of the volumes of gases that react with one another, he found that 1,000 ml of hydrogen chloride combines exactly with 1,000 ml of ammonia, and that 1,000 ml of carbon monoxide combines with 500 ml of oxygen to form 1,000 ml of carbon dioxide. On the basis of these observations he formulated the **law of combining volumes:** *the volumes of gases which react with one another or are produced in a chemical reaction are in the ratios of small integers.*

Such a simple empirical law as this called for a simple theoretical interpretation, and in 1811 Amedeo Avogadro, professor of physics at the University of Turin, Italy, proposed a hypothesis to explain the law. Avogadro's hypothesis was that **equal numbers of molecules are contained in equal volumes of all gases under the same conditions.** This hypothesis has been thoroughly verified to within the accuracy of approximation of real gases to ideal behavior, and it is now called a law—**Avogadro's law.** *

During the last century Avogadro's law provided the most satisfactory and the only reliable way of determining which multiples of the equivalent weights of the elements should be accepted as their atomic weights; the arguments involved are discussed in the following sections. But the value of this law remained unrecognized by chemists from 1811 until 1858. In this year Stanislao Cannizzaro (1826–1910), an Italian chemist working in Geneva, showed how to apply the law systematically, and immediately the uncertainty regarding the correct atomic weights of the elements and the correct

* Dalton had considered and rejected the hypothesis that equal volumes of gases contain equal numbers of atoms; the idea that elementary substances might exist as polyatomic molecules (H_2, O_2) did not occur to him.

formulas of compounds disappeared. Before 1858 many chemists used the formula HO for water and accepted 8 as the atomic weight of oxygen; since that year H_2O has been accepted as the formula for water by everyone.*

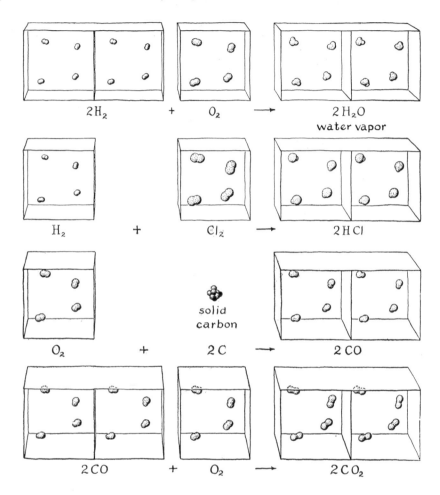

FIG. 14-2 *The relative volumes of gases involved in chemical reactions.*

Avogadro's Law and the Law of Combining Volumes. Avogadro's law requires that the volumes of gaseous reactants and products (under the same conditions) be approximately in the ratios of small integers; the numbers of molecules of reactants and products in a chemical reaction are in integral ratios, and the same ratios represent the relative gas

---

* The failure of chemists to accept Avogadro's law during the period from 1811 to 1858 seems to have been due to a feeling that molecules were too "theoretical" to deserve serious consideration.

volumes. Some simple diagrams illustrating this for several reactions are given in Figure 14-2. Each square in these diagrams represents the volume occupied by four gas molecules.

14–5. *The Use of Avogadro's Law in the Determination of the Correct Atomic Weights of Elements*

The way in which Avogadro's law was applied by Cannizzaro in 1858 for the selection of the correct approximate atomic weights of elements was essentially the following. Let us accept, as is justified by Avogadro's law, as the molecular weight of a substance the weight in grams of 22.4 liters of the gaseous substance reduced to standard conditions. (Any other volume could be used—this would correspond to the selection of a different base for the atomic weight scale.) *Then it is probable that of a large number of compounds of a particular element at least one compound will have only one atom of the element per molecule; the weight of the element in the standard gas volume of this compound is its atomic weight.*

TABLE 14-1

	WEIGHT OF GAS, IN GRAMS	WEIGHT OF CONTAINED HYDROGEN, IN GRAMS
Hydrogen (H_2)	2	2
Methane (CH_4)	16	4
Ethane (C_2H_6)	30	6
Water (H_2O)	18	2
Hydrogen sulfide (H_2S)	34	2
Hydrogen cyanide (HCN)	27	1
Hydrogen chloride (HCl)	36	1
Ammonia (NH_3)	17	3
Pyridine (C_5H_5N)	79	5

For gaseous compounds of hydrogen the weight per standard volume and the weight of the contained hydrogen per standard volume are shown in Table 14-1. In these and all other compounds of hydrogen the minimum weight of hydrogen in the standard gas volume is found to be 1 g, and the weight is always an integral multiple of the minimum weight; hence 1 can be accepted as the atomic weight of hydrogen. The elementary substance hydrogen then is seen to consist of diatomic molecules H_2, and water is seen to have the formula H_2O_x, with x still to be determined.

For oxygen compounds a similar table of experimental data can be set up (Table 14-2). From the comparison of oxygen and water in this table it can be concluded rigorously that the oxygen molecule contains two atoms or a multiple of two atoms; we see that the standard volume of oxygen contains twice as much oxygen (32 g) as is contained by the standard volume of water vapor (16 g of oxygen). The data for the other compounds provide no evidence that the atomic weight of oxygen is less than 16; hence this value may be adopted. Water thus is given the formula H_2O.

TABLE 14-2

	WEIGHT OF GAS, IN GRAMS	WEIGHT OF CONTAINED OXYGEN, IN GRAMS
Oxygen (O_2)	32	32
Water (H_2O)	18	16
Carbon monoxide (CO)	28	16
Carbon dioxide (CO_2)	44	32
Nitrous oxide (N_2O)	44	16
Nitric oxide (NO)	30	16
Sulfur dioxide (SO_2)	64	32
Sulfur trioxide (SO_3)	80	48

Note that this application of Avogadro's law provided rigorously only a maximum value of the atomic weight of an element. The possibility was not eliminated that the true atomic weight was a sub-multiple of this value.

14–6. *Other Methods of Determining Correct Atomic Weights*

1. At the present time there is one completely reliable method of determining which multiple of the equivalent weight of an element is its atomic weight. This method is to determine the atomic number of the element from its X-ray spectrum. The atomic weight is then twice its atomic number (for light elements) or a little more (up to 25% more for heavy elements). This reliable method was not available at the time of discovery of most of the elements.

2. The modern theory of gases requires that the molar heat capacity* of gases at constant pressure be approximately 5 cal per degree for monatomic gases, 7 cal per degree for diatomic gases (and linear polyatomic gases, such as carbon dioxide), and 8 cal per degree for other polyatomic gases. The heat capacity is the amount of energy required to raise the temperature of a substance by one degree; the molar heat capacity refers to one mole of substance. This method was used in 1876 to show that mercury

* See Chapter 31 for a discussion of heat capacity.

vapor consists of monatomic molecules, and hence that its atomic weight is equal to its molecular weight as determined by the gas-density method (see a later section in this chapter). It was also applied to the noble gases (which are monatomic) on their discovery.

3. It was pointed out in 1819 by Dulong and Petit in France that for the heavier solid elementary substances (with atomic weights above 35) the product of the heat capacity per gram and the atomic weight is approximately constant, with value about 6.2 cal per degree. This is called the *rule of Dulong and Petit*. The rule can be used to get a rough value of the atomic weight of a solid element by dividing 6.2 by the measured heat capacity of the solid elementary substance in cal/g. For example, the heat capacity of bismuth is 0.0294 cal/g. By dividing this into 6.2 we obtain 211 as the rough value of the atomic weight of bismuth given by the rule of Dulong and Petit; the actual atomic weight of bismuth is 209.

4. In the same year (1819) the German chemist Eilhardt Mitscherlich (1794–1863) discovered the phenomenon of *isomorphism* (the existence of different crystalline substances with essentially the same crystal form, and capable of forming crystalline solutions with one another; see Sec. 6-8), and suggested his *rule of isomorphism*, which states that isomorphous crystals have similar chemical formulas. This rule and the rule of Dulong and Petit were of great use in fixing atomic weights. An interesting application of the rule of isomorphism was made by the English chemist Henry E. Roscoe in determining the correct atomic weight of vanadium. Berzelius had attributed the atomic weight 68.5 to vanadium in 1831. In 1867 Roscoe noticed that the corresponding formula for the mineral vanadinite was not analogous to the formulas of other minerals isomorphous with it:

Apatite	$Ca_5(PO_4)_3F$
Pyromorphite	$Pb_5(PO_4)_3Cl$
Mimetite	$Pb_5(AsO_4)_3Cl$
Vanadinite	$Pb_5(VO_3)_3Cl$ (wrong)

The formula for vanadinite analogous to the other formulas is $Pb_5(VO_4)_3Cl$. On reinvestigating the compounds of vanadium Roscoe found that this latter formula is indeed the correct one, and that Berzelius had accepted the oxide VO, vanadium monoxide, as the elementary substance. The atomic weight of vanadium now accepted is 50.95.

5. The method of chemical analogy—based on the assumption that substances with similar chemical properties usually have similar formulas—was of considerable use in the early period.

14–7. The Complete Perfect-Gas Equation

Boyle's law, the law of Charles and Gay-Lussac, and Avogadro's law can be combined into a single equation:

$$pV = nRT \qquad (14\text{-}3)$$

In this equation p is the pressure acting on a given sample of gas, V is the volume occupied by the sample of gas, n is the number of moles of gas in the sample (that is, the total number of molecules divided by

Avogadro's number), R is a quantity called the *gas constant*, and T is the absolute temperature.

The gas constant R has a value depending on the units in which it is measured (that is, the units used for p, V, n, and T). If p is measured in atmospheres, V in liters, n in moles, and T in degrees Kelvin, the value of R is **0.0820 liter atmosphere per mole degree.**

If the number of moles in a sample of gas, n, remains constant and the temperature T remains constant, the perfect-gas equation simplifies to

$$pV = \text{constant}$$

The value of the constant in this equation is nRT. This equation is seen to be just the equation expressing Boyle's law.

Similarly, if the pressure p is constant and the number of moles in the sample of gas is constant, the perfect-gas equation simplifies to

$$V = \left(\frac{nR}{p}\right)T = \text{constant} \times T$$

This is the expression of the law of Charles and Gay-Lussac.

The perfect-gas equation can also be written in the form

$$n = \frac{pV}{RT}$$

This equation states that the number of moles of any gas is equal to a product of quantities independent of the nature of the gas, but depending only on the pressure, volume, and temperature; accordingly, equal volumes of all gases under the same condition are stated by this equation to contain the same number of moles (molecules). This equation accordingly expresses Avogadro's law.

The value of the gas constant R is found experimentally by determining the volume occupied by 1 mole of a perfect gas at standard conditions. One mole of oxygen weighs exactly 32 g, and the density of oxygen gas at standard conditions is found by experiment to be 1.429 g/l. The quotient $32/1.429 = 22.4$ l is accordingly the volume occupied by 1 mole of gas (Avogadro's number of gas molecules) at standard conditions.

The volume 22.4 liters is the volume of one mole of gas at standard conditions (0° C, 1 atm).

More accurate determinations, involving the measurement of the density of oxygen at low pressure, where it approaches a perfect gas more closely, have led to the value **22.4140 l** for the molar gas volume.

The volume occupied by one mole of gas at standard conditions is seen from the perfect-gas equation to be just the product of R and the temperature $0°$ C on the absolute scale. The value of R can hence be found by dividing 22.4 by 273:

$$R = \frac{22.4}{273} = 0.0820 \text{ liter atm/mole deg}$$

The Partial Pressures of Components of a Gas Mixture. It is found by experiment (Dalton, 1801) that when two samples of gas at the same pressure are mixed there is no change in volume. If the two samples of gas were originally present in containers of the same size, at a pressure of 1 atm, each container after the mixing was completed would contain a mixture of gas molecules, half of them of one kind and half of the other. It is reasonable to assume that each gas in this mixture exerts the pressure of 1/2 atm, as it would if the other gas were not present. Dalton's **law of partial pressures** states that *in a gas mixture the molecules of gas of each kind exert the same pressure as they would if present alone*, and that *the total pressure is the sum of the partial pressures exerted by the different gases in the mixture.*

We have made use of the law of partial pressures in an earlier section, in correcting the total pressure of a gas containing water vapor by subtracting the partial pressure (vapor pressure) of the water vapor (Example 3).

14–8. *Calculations Based on the Perfect-Gas Equation*

Some of the ways in which the perfect-gas equation can be used in the solution of chemical problems are discussed in the following paragraphs.

The Calculation of the Density of a Gas or the Weight of a Sample of Gas from Its Molecular Formula. If the molecular formula of a gaseous substance is known, an approximate value of its density can be calculated. This calculation can also be carried out for a mixture of known composition of gases of known molecular formulas. The method to be used is illustrated in the following example:

Example 7. What is the density of carbon dioxide at standard conditions?

  Solution. The molecular weight of carbon dioxide, CO_2, is 44. The volume occupied by 1 mole, 44 g, of carbon dioxide at standard conditions is 22.4 l. The density is the weight per unit volume; that is,

$$\text{density of carbon dioxide} = \frac{44}{22.4} = \textbf{1.96 g/l}$$

Example 8.   What is the approximate value of the density of air at 25° C?

  Solution.   Air is a mixture of oxygen and nitrogen, being mainly (about 80%) nitrogen. The molecular weight of oxygen is 32, and that of nitrogen is 28; we see that the average molecular weight of the mixture is approximately 29. The weight of 1 l of air at standard conditions is accordingly 29/22.4 = 1.29 g/l.

  When air is heated from 0° C (273° K) to 25° C (298° K) it increases in volume, and accordingly decreases in density. The fraction by which the density at 0° C must be multiplied to obtain the density at 25° C is seen to be 273/298; hence

$$\text{density of air at 25° C} = \frac{273}{298} \times 1.29 = \textbf{1.17 g/l}$$

The Determination of the Molecular Weight of a Gas.   In the investigation of a new substance, such as a physiologically active substance isolated from a plant, one of the first things that a chemist does is to determine its molecular weight. If the substance can be vaporized without decomposing it, the density of its vapor provides a value of the molecular weight, and this method is usually used for volatile substances. The methods of molecular-weight determination used for substances that cannot be vaporized are described in Chapter 16.

  The density of a substance which is a gas under ordinary conditions is usually determined by the simple method of weighing a flask of known volume filled with the gas under known pressure, and then weighing the flask after it has been evacuated with a vacuum pump. In ordinary work the second weighing may be replaced by a weighing of the flask filled with air, oxygen, or other gas of known density. The volume of the flask is determined by weighing it filled with water.

  Various refinements of technique are needed for accurate work. It is customary to counterbalance the flask by a similar sealed flask placed on the other pan of the balance. In very accurate work a correction must be made for the contraction of the evacuated flask resulting from the outside pressure. In ordinary work flasks with volumes of one or two liters are used, weighed on a balance with an accuracy of 0.1 mg. In determining the molecular weight of radon in 1911 the English chemists Ramsay and Gray had available only about 0.1 mm³ of the gas, weighing about 0.001 mg; the weight of this sample was determined to within 0.2% by use of a very sensitive microbalance.

Example 9: Determination of the Molecular Weight of a Substance by the Hofmann Method.

A chemist isolated a substance in the form of a yellow oil. He found on analysis that the oil contained only hydrogen and sulfur, and the amount of water obtained when a sample of the substance was burned showed that it consisted of about 3% hydrogen and 97% sulfur. To determine the molecular weight he prepared a very small glass bulb, weighed the glass bulb, filled it with the oil, and weighed it again; the difference in the two weighings, which is the weight of the oil, was 0.0302 g. He then introduced the filled bulb into the space above the mercury column in a tube, as shown in Figure 2-22. The level of the mercury dropped to 118 mm below its original level, after the oil had been completely vaporized. The temperature of the tube was 30° C. The volume of the gas phase above the mercury at the end of the experiment was 73.2 ml. Find the molecular weight and formula of the substance.

Solution. The vapor of the substance is stated to occupy the volume 73.2 ml at temperature 30° C and pressure 118 mm Hg. Its volume corrected to standard conditions is seen to be

$$73.2 \times \frac{273}{303} \times \frac{118}{760} = 10.24 \text{ ml}$$

One mole of gas at standard conditions occupies 22.4 l; hence the number of moles in the sample of the substance is $10.24/22,400 = 0.000457$. The weight of this fraction of a mole is stated to be 0.0302 g; hence the weight of one mole is this weight divided by the number of moles:

$$\text{molecular weight of substance} = \frac{0.0302}{0.000457} = \mathbf{66.0}$$

The substance was found by analysis to contain 3% hydrogen and 97% sulfur. If we had 100 g of the oil, it would contain 3 g of hydrogen, which is 3 gram-atoms, and 97 g of sulfur, which is also 3 gram-atoms (the atomic weight of sulfur is 32). Hence the molecule contains equal numbers of hydrogen atoms and sulfur atoms. If its formula were HS, its molecular weight would be the sum of the atomic weights of hydrogen and sulfur, 33. It is evident from the observed molecular weight that the formula is $\mathbf{H_2S_2}$, the molecular weight of which is 66.15.

Atomic-Weight Determinations by the Gas-Density Method. If a sufficiently careful measurement of the density of a gas is made, under conditions such that the gas obeys the perfect-gas law, a good value for the molecular weight of the gas can be obtained, which can be used to find the atomic weight of one of the elements in the gas. The way to determine this ideal value of the density of a gas is to determine the density of the gas at smaller and smaller pressures, and to extrapolate to zero pressure—all gases approach the perfect-gas law in their behavior as the pressure becomes very low.

For example, it has been found that the observed densities of sulfur dioxide at very low pressures correspond to an ideal density of 2.85796 g/l at standard conditions. The product of this value of the density and the precise value of the molar volume, 22.4140 l per mole, is **64.058,** which is the gas-density value of the molecular weight of sulfur dioxide. The sulfur dioxide molecule contains two oxygen atoms, which weigh exactly 32 g, and one sulfur atom. The weight of the sulfur atom, in atomic weight units, is hence seen to be **32.058,** from these measurements; this agrees well with the accepted value of the atomic weight of sulfur, 32.066.

The gas-density method has provided many of the best values of modern atomic weights.

14–9. *The Kinetic Theory of Gases*

During the nineteenth century the concepts that atoms and molecules are in continual motion and that the temperature of a body is a measure of the intensity of this motion were developed. The idea that the behavior of gases could be accounted for by considering the motion of the gas molecules had occurred to several people (Daniel Bernoulli in 1738, J. P. Joule in 1851, A. Kronig in 1856), and in the years following 1858 this idea was developed into a detailed kinetic theory of gases by Clausius, Maxwell, Boltzmann, and many later investigators. The subject is discussed in courses in physics and physical chemistry, and it forms an important part of the branch of theoretical science called statistical mechanics.

In a gas at temperature T the molecules are moving about, different molecules having at a given time different speeds v and different kinetic energies of translational motion $\frac{1}{2}mv^2$ (m being the mass of a molecule). It has been found that the average kinetic energy per molecule, $\frac{1}{2}m[v^2]_{\text{average}}$, is the same for all gases at the same temperature, and that its value increases with the temperature, being directly proportional to T.

The average (root-mean-square*) velocity of hydrogen molecules at 0° C is 1.84×10^5 cm/sec—over a mile per second. At higher temperatures the average velocity is greater; it reaches twice as great a value, 3.68×10^5 cm/sec, for hydrogen molecules at 820° C, corresponding to an increase by 4 in the absolute temperature.

---

* The root-mean-square average of a quantity is the square root of the average value of the square of the quantity.

Since the average kinetic energy is equal for different molecules, the average value of the square of the velocity is seen to be inversely proportional to the mass of the molecule, and hence the average velocity (root-mean-square average) is inversely proportional to the square root of the molecular weight. The molecular weight of oxygen is just 16 times that of hydrogen; accordingly, molecules of oxygen move with a speed just one quarter as great as molecules of hydrogen at the same temperature. The average speed of oxygen molecules at $0°$ C is 0.46×10^5 cm/sec.

The explanation of Boyle's law given by the kinetic theory is simple. A molecule on striking the wall of the container of the gas rebounds, and contributes momentum to the wall; in this way the collisions of the molecules of the gas with the wall produce the gas pressure which balances the external pressure applied to the gas. If the volume is decreased by 50%, each of the molecules strikes the walls twice as often, and hence the pressure is doubled. The explanation of the law of Charles and Gay-Lussac is equally simple. If the absolute temperature is doubled, the speed of the molecules is increased by the factor $\sqrt{2}$. This causes the molecules to make $\sqrt{2}$ times as many collisions as before, and each collision is increased in force by $\sqrt{2}$, so that the pressure itself is doubled by doubling the absolute temperature. Avogadro's law is also explained by the fact that the average kinetic energy is the same at a given temperature for all gases.

The Effusion and Diffusion of Gases; the Mean Free Paths of Molecules. There is an interesting dependence of the rate of effusion of a gas through a small hole on the molecular weight of the gas. The speeds of motion of different molecules are inversely proportional to the square roots of their molecular weights. If a small hole is made in the wall of a gas container, the gas molecules will pass through the hole into an evacuated

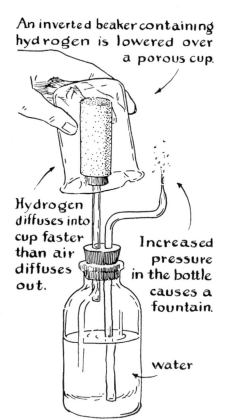

An inverted beaker containing hydrogen is lowered over a porous cup.

Hydrogen diffuses into cup faster than air diffuses out.

Increased pressure in the bottle causes a fountain.

water

FIG. 14-3

Experiment illustrating the greater rate of effusion of hydrogen than of air.

region outside at a rate determined by the speed at which they are moving (these speeds determine the probability that a molecule will strike the hole). Accordingly, the kinetic theory requires that the rate of *effusion* of a gas through a small hole be inversely proportional to the square root of its molecular weight. This law was discovered experimentally before the development of the kinetic theory—it was observed that hydrogen effuses through a porous plate four times as rapidly as oxygen.

An interesting experiment can be carried out which illustrates this effect. If a porous cup filled with air is attached to a bottle of water provided with a fine nozzle, as shown in Figure 14-3, and an inverted beaker filled with hydrogen is lowered over the porous cup, water will be vigorously forced out of the nozzle. The explanation of this phenomenon is that the rate of effusion of hydrogen from the outside through the pores of the porous cup to the inside of the cup is nearly four times as great as the rate of effusion of air (oxygen and nitrogen) from the inside of the cup to the outside. Hence more gas will enter the cup than leave the cup, and the pressure inside the system will become correspondingly greater, causing the water to be forced out of the nozzle.

In the foregoing discussions we have ignored the appreciable sizes of gas molecules, which cause the molecules to collide often with one another. In an ordinary gas, such as air at standard conditions, a molecule moves only about 500 Å, on the average, between collisions; that is, its *mean free path* under these conditions is only about two hundred times its own diameter.

The value of the mean free path is significant for phenomena which depend on molecular collisions, such as the viscosity and the thermal conductivity of gases. Another such phenomenon is the *diffusion* of one gas through another or through itself (such as of radioactive molecules of a gas through the non-radioactive gas). In the early days of kinetic theory it was pointed out by skeptics that it takes minutes or hours for a gas to diffuse from one side of a quiet room to the other, even though the molecules are attributed velocities of about a mile per second. The explanation of the slow diffusion rate is that a molecule diffusing through a gas is not able to move directly from one point to another a long distance away, but instead is forced by collisions with other molecules to follow a tortuous path, making only slow progress in its resultant motion. Only when diffusing into a high vacuum can the gas diffuse with the speed of molecular motion.

14–10. *Deviations of Real Gases from Ideal Behavior*

Real gases differ in their behavior from that represented by the perfect-gas equation for two reasons. First, the molecules have finite size, so that each molecule prevents others from making use of a part of the volume of the gas container. This causes the volume of a gas to be larger than that calculated for ideal behavior. Second, the molecules even when some distance apart do not move independently of one another, but attract one another slightly. This tends to cause the volume of a gas to be smaller than the calculated volume.

The amounts of the deviation for some gases are shown in Figure 14-4. It is seen that for hydrogen at 0° C the deviation is positive at all pressures—it is due essentially to the volume of the molecules, the effect of their attraction at this high temperature (relative to the boiling point, $-252.8°$ C) being extremely small.

At pressures below 120 atmospheres nitrogen (at $0°$ C) shows negative deviations from ideal behavior, intermolecular attraction having a greater effect than the finite size of the molecules.

The deviation of hydrogen and nitrogen at $0°$ C from ideal behavior is seen to be less than 10% at pressures less than 300 atmospheres. Oxygen, helium, and other gases with low boiling points also show small

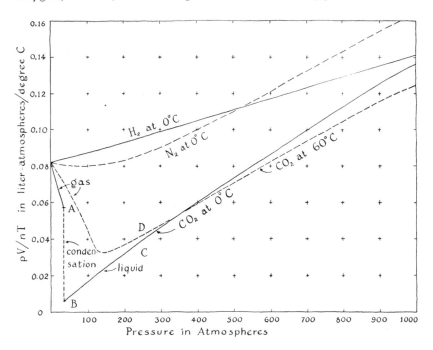

FIG. 14-4   *The value of the product* pV/nT *for some gases, showing deviation from the perfect-gas law at high pressures.*

deviations from the perfect-gas law. For these gases the perfect-gas law holds to within 1% at room temperature or higher temperatures and at pressures below 10 atm.

Larger deviations are shown by gases with higher boiling points—in general, the deviations from ideal behavior become large as the gas approaches condensation. It is seen from the figure that for carbon dioxide at $60°$ C the volume of the gas is only about 30% as great at 120 atm pressure as the volume calculated by the perfect-gas equation.

If the temperature is low, the deviations are shown in a pronounced way by the condensation of the gas to a liquid (see the curve for carbon dioxide at 0° C). After carbon dioxide has been compressed to about 40 atmospheres at 0° C, the effect of the attraction of the molecules for one another becomes so great that they cling together, forming a liquid, the system then consisting of two phases, the gaseous phase and the liquid phase. On further compression the volume decreases without change in pressure (region A of the figure) until all of the gas is condensed (point B). From point B on the volume of the liquid decreases much less rapidly with increase in pressure than would that of a gas, because the molecules of the liquid are effectively in contact; hence the curve rises (region C).

An extraordinary phenomenon, the **continuity of the liquid and gaseous states,** was discovered about eighty years ago by Thomas Andrews (1813–1885). He found that above a temperature characteristic of the gas, called the **critical temperature,** the transition from the gaseous state to the liquid state occurs without discontinuity on increasing the pressure. The critical temperature of carbon dioxide is 31.1° C. Above this temperature (at 60° C, for example, corresponding to the curve shown in the figure), the properties of the substance change continuously, showing no signs that the gas has condensed to a liquid. Nevertheless, when the pressure becomes greater than about 200 atm the substance behaves like carbon dioxide liquid, rather than like a gas (region D of Figure 14-4). It is, indeed, possible to change from the

TABLE 14-3   *Critical Constants of Some Substances*

GAS	CRITICAL TEMPERATURE	CRITICAL PRESSURE	CRITICAL DENSITY
Helium	−267.9° C	2.26 atm	0.0693 g/cm³
Hydrogen	−239.9°	12.8	.031
Nitrogen	−147.1°	33.5	.31
Carbon monoxide	−139°	35	.31
Argon	−122°	48	.53
Oxygen	−118.8°	49.7	.43
Methane	−82.5°	45.8	.16
Carbon dioxide	31.1°	73.0	.46
Ethane	32.1°	48.8	.21
Nitrous oxide	36.5°	71.7	.45
Ammonia	132.4°	111.5	.24
Chlorine	144.0°	76.1	.57
Sulfur dioxide	157.2°	77.7	.52
Water	374.2°	218.4	.33

gas at 0° C and 1 atm pressure to the liquid at 0° C and 50 atm either by the ordinary process of condensing the gas to the liquid, passing through the two-phase stage, or, without condensation or any discontinuity, by heating to 60°, increasing the pressure to about 200 atm, cooling to 0°, and then reducing the pressure to 50 atm. The liquid could then be made to boil, simply by reducing the pressure and keeping the temperature at 0° C; and then, by repeating the cycle, it could be brought back to 0° C and 50 atm pressure without condensation, and be made to boil again.

Values of the critical temperature, critical pressure, and critical density of some substances are given in Table 14-3.

The possibility of continuous transition from the gaseous to the liquid state is understandable in view of the mutual characteristic of randomness of structure of these phases, as discussed in Chapter 2. It is, on the other hand, difficult to imagine the possibility of a gradual transition from a disordered state (liquid) to a completely ordered state (crystal); and correspondingly it has not been found possible to crystallize substances or to melt crystals without passing through a discontinuity at the melting point—there is no critical temperature for melting a crystal. A continuous transition from a solid state to a liquid state does occur for some substances (silica, various silicates and borates, etc.), but the solid states are not crystalline. In these *non-crystalline solids* the molecules are randomly arranged, as in a liquid, and are frozen in place, held by surrounding molecules. A substance of this nature is called a *supercooled liquid* or *glass;* it is a liquid with such high viscosity that it can no longer change its shape.

Exercises

14-1.   The volume of a sample of gas is 124.8 ml at 250° C. What is its volume at 125° C under the same pressure?

14-2.   Calculate the volume occupied at 20° C and 1 atm pressure by the gas evolved from 1 cm^3 of solid carbon dioxide (density 1.53 g/cm^3).

14-3.   The density of helium at 0° C and 1 atm is 0.1785 g/l. Calculate its density at 100° C and 200 atm.

14-4.   A vessel is filled with hydrogen at a pressure of 1 atm at 25° C. What pressure is there in the vessel at 21° K? What is the density of the gas at the beginning and at the end of this experiment?

14-5.   What is the volume in cubic feet at standard conditions of one ounce-molecular-weight of a gas? *

* It is interesting in this connection that the master craftsmen of Lübeck defined the ounce as one one-thousandth of the weight of one cubic foot of ice-cold water.

14-6. The density of hydrogen cyanide at standard conditions is 1.29 g/l. Calculate the apparent molecular weight of hydrogen cyanide vapor.

14-7. What is the weight in ounces of 22.4 cu. ft. of carbon dioxide at standard conditions?

14-8. The volume of an ordinary hand-operated bicycle pump is about 0.01 cu. ft., and the volume of a bicycle tire is about 0.06 cu. ft. At what point in the stroke of the pump does air start to enter a tire which is at a gauge pressure of 47 lbs. per sq. in.? Does the pressure in the tire change more per stroke when the tire is at gauge pressure of 50 lbs. per sq. in. than at 20 lbs. per sq. in.?

14-9. At 3,000° K, hydrogen gas at a total pressure of 1 atm is 9.03% dissociated into hydrogen atoms. What is the density of the gas? What would the density of the gas at 1 atm and 3,000° K be if the diatomic molecules did not dissociate into atoms?

14-10. At 2,500° K and 1 atm pressure the observed density of CO_2 gas is 0.1991 g/l. What is the average molecular weight of the molecules in the gas? Assuming that the molecular weight is decreased because the carbon dioxide has partially decomposed into carbon monoxide and oxygen, calculate what fraction of the CO_2 molecules have decomposed in this way.

14-11. The heat capacity of an element (a metalloid) is 0.0483 calories per gram. Calculate a rough value of the atomic weight of the element. The hydride of this element is found to contain 1.555% hydrogen. What are possible values of the exact atomic weight of the element? From the two experimental data, determine the exact atomic weight.

14-12. A gas was observed to have a density of 5.37 g/l at 25° C. What is the molecular weight of the gas? Its heat capacity was found on measurement to be 0.039 cal/g. How many atoms are there in the molecule of the gas? Can you identify this gas?

14-13. The density of ethylene at very low pressure corresponds to the ideal density 1.251223 g/l at standard conditions. The formula of ethylene is C_2H_4. Calculate from this information a precise value of the molecular weight of ethylene. Assuming the atomic weight of hydrogen to be 1.0080, calculate the atomic weight of carbon.

14-14. The density of phosphorus trioxide, with elementary composition P_2O_3, was found to be 2.35 g/l at 800° C and 1 atm. What is the correct formula of the vapor?

14-15. What is the atomic weight of an element which has the two following properties? (a) 1 g of the element combines with 0.3425 g of chlorine. (b) The heat capacity of the solid element at 20° C is 0.031 cal/g.

14-16. Would deuterium (atomic weight 2.0147) effuse through a porous plate more rapidly or less rapidly than hydrogen? Calculate the relative rates of effusion of the two molecules. What would be the relative rate of effusion of a molecule made of one light hydrogen atom and one deuterium atom?

14-17. A piece of metal weighing 1.038 g was treated with acid, and was found to liberate 229 ml of hydrogen, measured over water. The temperature was 18° C, and the barometric pressure was 745.5 mm. What are possible values of the atomic weight of the element? The heat capacity of the solid element was found to be 0.0552 cal/g. Which of the possible values of the atomic weight is the correct one?

14-18.　Why is diffusion normally such a slow process, despite the rapid movement of gas molecules? Under what conditions does diffusion take place with the speed of molecular motion?

14-19.　An organic compound was analyzed by combustion, and it was found that a sample weighing 0.200 g produced 0.389 g of carbon dioxide and 0.277 g of water. Another sample, weighing 0.150 g, was found on combustion to produce 37.3 ml of nitrogen at standard conditions. What is the empirical formula of the compound?

14-20.　A sample of gas weighing 0.1100 g was found to occupy 24.16 ml of volume at 25° C and 740.3 mm. Calculate the molecular weight of the substance.

14-21.　A sample of gas with volume 191 ml at 20° C and 743 mm was found to weigh 0.132 g. What is the molecular weight of the gas? What do you think the gas is?

14-22.　(a) What volume of oxygen would be required for the complete combustion of 200 ml of acetylene, C_2H_2, and what volume of CO_2 would be produced? (b) Sulfur dioxide, SO_2, and hydrogen sulfide, H_2S, can be made to react to form free sulfur and water. What volume of sulfur dioxide would react in this way with 25 ml of hydrogen sulfide?

14-23.　Calculate the volume of sulfur dioxide, at standard conditions, that would be formed by the complete combustion of 8.00 g of sulfur.

14-24.　A sample of a certain hydrocarbon was found to contain 7.75% hydrogen and 92.25% carbon. The density of the vaporized hydrocarbon at 100° C and 1 atm was found to be 2.47 times as great as that of oxygen under the same conditions. What is the molecular weight of the hydrocarbon, and what is its formula?

14-25.　A sample of gas collected over water at 25° C was found to have volume 543.0 ml, the atmospheric pressure being 730 mm Hg. What is the volume of the dry gas at standard conditions?

Chapter 15

Water

Water is one of the most important of all chemical substances. It is a major constituent of living matter and of the environment in which we live. Its physical properties are strikingly different from those of other substances, in ways that determine the nature of the physical and biological world.

15–1. *The Composition of Water*

Water was thought by the ancients to be an element. Henry Cavendish in 1781 showed that water is formed when hydrogen is burned in air, and Lavoisier first recognized that water is a compound of the two elements hydrogen and oxygen.

The formula of water is H_2O. The relative weights of hydrogen and oxygen in the substance have been very carefully determined as 2.016 : 16.000. This determination has been made both by weighing the amounts of hydrogen and oxygen liberated from water by electrolysis and by determining the weights of hydrogen and oxygen which combine to form water.

Purification of Water by Distillation. Ordinary water is impure; it usually contains dissolved salts and dissolved gases, and sometimes organic matter. For chemical work water is purified by distillation. Pure tin vessels and pipes are often used for storing and transporting distilled water. Glass vessels are not satisfactory, because the alkaline constituents of glass slowly dissolve in water. Distilling apparatus and vessels made of fused silica are used in making very pure water.

The impurity which is hardest to keep out of distilled water is carbon dioxide, which dissolves readily from the air.

Removal of Ionic Impurities from Water. Ionic impurities can be effectively and cheaply removed from water by an interesting process which involves the use of *giant molecules*—molecular structures which are so big as to constitute visible particles. A crystal of diamond is an example of such a giant molecule (Chap. 10). Some complex inorganic crystals, such as the minerals called *zeolites*, are of this nature. These minerals are used to "soften" hard water. Hard water is water containing calcium ion, magnesium ion, and ferric ion, which are undesirable because they form a precipitate with ordinary soap. The zeolite is able to remove these ions from the water, replacing them by sodium ion.

A zeolite is an aluminosilicate, with formula such as $Na_2Al_2Si_4O_{12}$. It consists of a rigid framework formed by the aluminum, silicon, and oxygen atoms, honeycombed by corridors in which sodium ions are located. These ions have some freedom of motion, and when hard water flows over zeolite grains some of the sodium ions run out of the corridors into the solution and are replaced by ions of calcium, iron, or magnesium. In this way the hardness of the water is removed. After most of the sodium ion has been replaced, the zeolite is regenerated by allowing it to stand in contact with a saturated brine; the reaction is then reversed, Na^+ replacing Ca^{++}, Fe^{+++}, and Mg^{++} in the corridors of the zeolite.

The reactions which occur may be written with symbols. If Z^- is used to represent a small portion of the zeolite framework, carrying one negative charge, the replacement of calcium ion in the water by sodium ion may be written

$$\underline{2Na^+Z^-} + Ca^{++} \longrightarrow \underline{Ca^{++}(Z^-)_2} + 2Na^+$$

When concentrated salt solution (brine) is run through the zeolite the reverse reaction occurs:

$$2Na^+ + \underline{Ca^{++}(Z^-)_2} \longrightarrow \underline{2Na^+Z^-} + Ca^{++}$$

The reason why giant molecules—the aluminosilicate framework—are important here is that these molecules, which look like large grains of sand, are not carried along in the water, but remain in the water-softening tank. Small molecules may also be used, but not so conveniently. Thus sodium carbonate can be used to soften hard water; it causes the calcium ion to precipitate as calcium carbonate:

$$Ca^{++} + (Na^+)_2(CO_3)^{--} \longrightarrow CaCO_3 \downarrow + 2Na^+$$

It is then necessary, however, to filter the precipitate, or to allow it to settle.

Both the positive ions and the negative ions can be removed from water by a similar method, illustrated in Figure 15-1. The first tank, A, contains grains which consist of giant organic molecules in the form of a porous framework to which acidic groups are attached. These groups are represented in the figure as carboxyl groups, —COOH:

$$
R-C\begin{array}{c} \ddot{\,}\ddot{O}-H \\ \\ \\ \ddot{O}\,\ddot{\,} \end{array}
$$

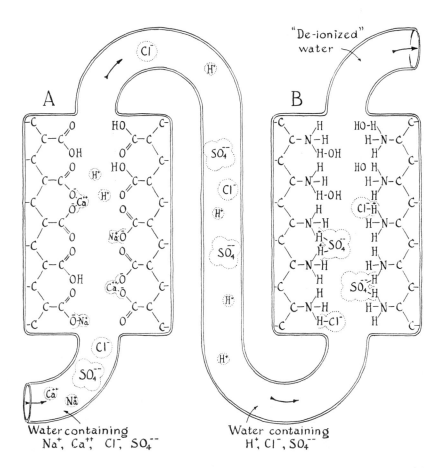

FIG. 15-1   *The removal of ions from water by use of giant molecules with attached acidic and basic groups.*

The reactions which occur when a solution containing salts passes through tank A may be written as

$$RCOOH + Na^+ \longrightarrow (RCOO)^- Na^+ + H^+$$

$$2RCOOH + Ca^{++} \longrightarrow (RCOO)^-_2 Ca^{++} + 2H^+$$

That is, sodium ions and calcium ions are removed from the solution by the acidic framework, and hydrogen ions are added to the solution. The solution is changed from a salt solution (Na^+, Cl^-, etc.) to an acid solution (H^+, Cl^-, etc.).

This acid solution then runs through tank B, which contains grains of giant organic molecules with basic groups attached. These groups are shown in Figure 15-1 as *substituted ammonium hydroxide* groups, $(RNH_3)^+(OH)^-$:

$$\left[\begin{array}{c} H \\ | \\ R - N - H \\ | \\ H \end{array} \right]^+ \qquad \left[: \overset{..}{\underset{..}{O}} - H \right]^-$$

The hydroxide ion of these groups combines with the hydrogen ion in the water:

$$OH^- + H^+ \longrightarrow H_2O$$

The negative ions then remain, held by the ammonium ions of the framework. The reactions are

$$(RNH_3)^+(OH)^- + Cl^- + H^+ \longrightarrow (RNH_3)^+ Cl^- + H_2O$$

$$2(RNH)_3{}^+(OH)^- + SO_4{}^{--} + 2H^+ \longrightarrow (RNH_3)^+{}_2(SO_4)^{--} + 2H_2O$$

The water which passes out of the second tank contains practically no ions, and may be used in the laboratory and in industrial processes in place of distilled water.

The giant molecules in tank A may be regenerated after use by passing a moderately concentrated solution of sulfuric acid through the tank, to restore the acid groups:

$$2(RCOO)^- Na^+ + H_2SO_4 \longrightarrow 2RCOOH + 2Na^+ + SO_4{}^{--}$$

Those in tank B may be regenerated by use of a moderately concentrated solution of sodium hydroxide:

$$(RNH_3)^+ Cl^- + OH^- \longrightarrow (RNH_3)^+ OH^- + Cl^-$$

15–2. *The Principle of Le Châtelier*

The reactions that occur in the softening of water by a zeolite and the regeneration of the zeolite provide a good example of an important general principle, **the principle of Le Châtelier.** This principle, which is named after the French chemist Henry Louis Le Châtelier (1850–1936), may be expressed in the following way: **If the conditions of a system, initially at equilibrium, are changed the equilibrium will shift in such a direction as to tend to restore the original conditions.**

Let us recall the reaction that occurs when a hard water, containing calcium ions, is brought into contact with a sodium zeolite; this reaction is

$$2Na^+Z^- + Ca^{++} \longrightarrow Ca^{++}(Z^-)_2 + 2Na^+$$

After a large amount of hard water has been run through the zeolite no further replacement of calcium ions by sodium ions occurs; a *steady state* has been reached. The reason for the existence of the steady state is that there is also the possibility of the reverse reaction:

$$2Na^+ + Ca^{++}(Z^-)_2 \longrightarrow 2Na^+Z^- + Ca^{++}$$

Even a very few sodium ions in the water might react with the calcium zeolite to cause this reaction to take place. The steady state occurs when the concentrations of calcium ion and sodium ion in the water and bound into the zeolite are such that the rate at which calcium ion is replacing sodium ion is just equal to the rate at which sodium ion is replacing calcium ion; this equilibrium of the two rates can be expressed by a single equation, with a double arrow:

$$2Na^+Z^- + Ca^{++} \rightleftarrows Ca^{++}(Z^-)_2 + 2Na^+$$

If, now, conditions are changed by the addition of a large quantity of sodium ion, in high concentration (the addition of a concentrated salt solution), the equilibrium shifts in the way stated by Le Châtelier's principle—namely, in the direction that reduces the concentration of sodium ion in the solution. This is the direction to the left: the sodium zeolite is thus regenerated.

The quantitative study of chemical equilibrium and the rate of chemical reactions will be taken up in Chapters 19 and 20. It is often possible to reach a useful qualitative conclusion about a chemical system, however, simply by applying Le Châtelier's principle. The example that we are discussing shows that a chemical reaction may be made to proceed

first in one direction and then in the opposite direction by changing
the concentration of one or more of the reacting substances.

15–3. *The Ionic Dissociation of Water*

An acidic solution contains hydrogen ions, H^+ (actually hydronium ions,
H_3O^+). A basic solution contains hydroxide ions, OH^-. A number of
years ago chemists asked, and answered, the question, "Are these ions
present in pure neutral water?" The answer is that they are present,
in equal but very small concentrations.

**Pure water contains hydrogen ions in concentration 1×10^{-7} mole
per liter, and hydroxide ions in the same concentration.** These
ions are formed by the dissociation of water:

$$H_2O \rightleftharpoons H^+ + OH^-$$

When a small amount of acid is added to pure water the concentration of hydrogen ion is increased. The concentration of hydroxide
ion then decreases, *but not to zero.* Acidic solutions contain hydrogen ion
in large concentration and hydroxide ion in very small concentration.
The equation connecting these concentrations is discussed in Chapters
20 and 21.

15–4. *The Physical Properties of Water*

Water is a clear, transparent liquid, colorless in thin layers. Thick
layers of water have a bluish-green color.

The physical properties of water are used to define many physical
constants and units. The freezing point of water (saturated with air at
1 atm pressure) is taken as $0°$ C, and the boiling point of water at 1 atm
is taken as $100°$ C. The unit of mass in the metric system is chosen so that
1 cm³ of water at $4°$ C (the temperature of its maximum density) weighs
1.00000 gram. A similar relation holds in the English system: 1 cu. ft.
of water weighs approximately 1,000 ounces.

Most substances diminish in volume, and hence increase in density,
with decrease in temperature. Water has the very unusual property of
having a temperature at which its density is a maximum. This temperature is $4°$ C. With further cooling below this temperature the volume
of a sample of water increases somewhat (Fig. 15-2).

A related phenomenon is the increase in volume which water undergoes on freezing. These properties are discussed in detail in the last section of this chapter.

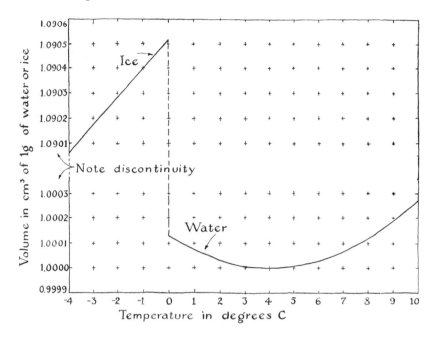

FIG. 15-2 *Dependence of the volume of ice and water on temperature.*

15–5. *The Melting Points and Boiling Points of Substances*

All molecules exert a weak attraction upon one another. This attraction, the *electronic van der Waals attraction*, is the result of the mutual interaction of the electrons and nuclei of the molecules; it has its origin in the electrostatic attraction of the nuclei of one molecule for the electrons of another, which is largely but not completely compensated by the repulsion of electrons by electrons and of nuclei by nuclei. The van der Waals attraction is significant only when the molecules are very close together—almost in contact with one another. For monatomic molecules, such as those of a noble gas, the force of attraction is inversely proportional to the seventh power of the distance between the centers of the molecules, and hence is less than 1% as great when the molecules are 10 Å apart as when they are 5 Å apart. At small distances (about 4 Å for argon, for example) the force of attraction is balanced by a force of repulsion due to interpenetration of the outer electron shells of the molecules (Fig. 15-3).

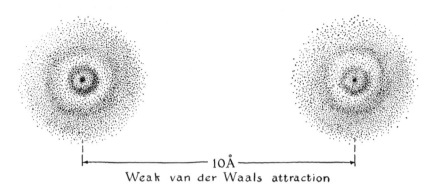

|← ————————— 10Å ————————— →|
Weak van der Waals attraction

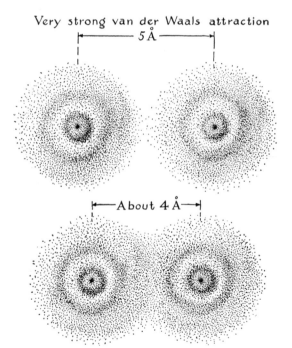

Very strong van der Waals attraction
|← ——— 5Å ——— →|

|←——About 4 Å——→|

Van der Waals attraction just
balanced by repulsive forces due to
interpenetration of outer electron shells

FIG. 15-3   *Diagram illustrating van der Waals attraction and repulsion*
in relation to electron distribution of monatomic molecules of argon.

It is these intermolecular forces of electronic van der Waals attraction that cause substances such as the noble gases, the halogens, etc., to condense to liquids and to freeze into solids at sufficiently low temperatures. The boiling point is a measure of the amount of molecular agitation necessary to overcome the forces of van der Waals attraction, and hence is an indication of the magnitude of these forces. In general *the electronic van der Waals attraction between molecules increases with increase in the number of electrons per molecule*—that is, roughly also with the molecular

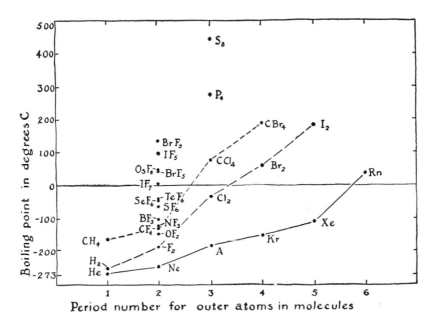

FIG. 15-4   *Diagram showing increase in boiling point with increase in molecular complexity.*

weight. *Heavy molecules (molecules containing many electrons) attract one another more strongly than light molecules; hence normal molecular substances with large molecular weight have high boiling points, and those with small molecular weight have low boiling points.*

This generalization is indicated in Figure 15-4, in which the boiling points of some molecular substances are shown. The steady increase in boiling point for sequences such as He, Ne, A, Kr, Xe, Rn and H_2, F_2, Cl_2, Br_2, I_2 is striking. The similar effect of increase in the number of atoms (with nearly the same atomic number) in the molecule is shown by the following sequences:

	A	Cl₂	P₄	S₈

$$\begin{array}{cccc} \text{A} & \text{Cl}_2 & \text{P}_4 & \text{S}_8 \end{array}$$

b.p.: $-185.7°$ $-34.6°$ $280°$ $444.6°$ C

$$\begin{array}{cccccc} \text{Ne} & \text{F}_2 & \text{CF}_4 & \text{SF}_6 & \text{IF}_7 & \text{OsF}_8 \end{array}$$

b.p.: $-245.9°$ $-187°$ $-128.1°$ $-62°$ $4.5°$ $47.5°$ C

The Effect of Molecular Dipoles on Boiling Point. The molecules which have been discussed above have simple structures, such that the center of positive electric charge coincides with the center of negative electric charge. In carbon tetrafluoride, for example, the four very electronegative fluorine atoms assume some negative charge, by attracting the bonding electron pairs more strongly than does the carbon atom, but their tetrahedral arrangement around the carbon atom causes their center of charge to coincide with the carbon atom. On the other hand, in nitrogen trifluoride, NF_3, the three fluorine atoms lie to one side of the nitrogen atom, and the partial ionic character of the N—F bonds hence causes the molecule to have a permanent electric dipole moment.* The interaction of the electric dipole moments of two molecules in relative position such that the positive end of one molecule is near the negative end of another gives rise to an attractive force in addition to the usual electronic van der Waals attraction, and so causes an increase in boiling point. This is seen in the following sequence:

$$\begin{array}{cccc} \text{CF}_4 & \text{NF}_3 & \text{OF}_2 & \text{F}_2 \end{array}$$

b.p.: $-128.1°$ $-129°$ $-144.8°$ $-187°$ C

Carbon tetrafluoride and fluorine have no dipole moments. The boiling points of nitrogen trifluoride and oxygen fluoride are seen to be about $19°$ and $22°$, respectively, greater than values predicted by interpolation; these increases in boiling point are due to the electric dipole moments of the molecules—that of nitrogen trifluoride is greater than that of oxygen fluoride because nitrogen and fluorine differ more in electronegativity than do oxygen and fluorine.

Bond Type and Atomic Arrangement. It has sometimes been thought that an abrupt change in melting point or boiling point in a series of related compounds could be accepted as proof of a change in type of bond. The fluorides of the elements of the second period, for example, have the following melting points and boiling points:

	NaF	MgF₂	AlF₃	SiF₄	PF₅	SF₆
m.p.:	980°	1,400°	1,040°	$-77°$	$-83°$	$-55°$ C
b.p.:	very high.........			$-96°$	$-75°$	$-64°$ C

*The magnitude of the electric dipole moment of two charges $+e$ and $-e$ a distance d apart is defined as de.

The great change between aluminum trifluoride and silicon tetrafluoride is not due to any great change in bond type—the bonds are in all cases intermediate in character between extreme ionic bonds M^+F^- and normal covalent bonds $M : \overset{..}{\underset{..}{F}} :$ —but rather to a change in atomic arrangement. The three easily volatile substances exist as discrete molecules SiF_4, PF_5, and SF_6 (with no dipole moments) in the liquid and crystalline states as well as the gaseous state (Fig. 15-5), and the thermal agitation necessary for fusion or vaporization is only that needed to overcome the weak intermolecular forces, and is essentially independent of the strength or nature of the interatomic bonds within a molecule. On the other hand, the other three substances in the crystalline state are giant molecules, with strong bonds between neighboring ions holding the whole crystal together (NaF, sodium chloride arrangement, Fig. 4-4; MgF_2,

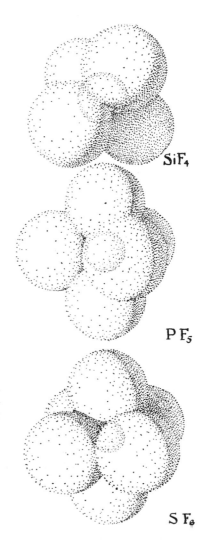

FIG. 15-5

Molecules of silicon tetrafluoride, phosphorus pentafluoride, and sulfur hexafluoride, three volatile substances.

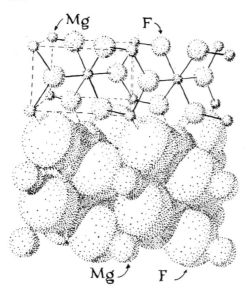

The structure of magnesium fluoride; this substance has high melting point and boiling point.

Fig. 15-6). To melt such a crystal some of these strong bonds must be broken, and to boil the liquid more must be broken; hence the melting point and boiling point are high.

The extreme case is that in which the entire crystal is held together by very strong covalent bonds; this occurs for diamond, with melting point 3,500° and boiling point 4,200° C.

The Dependence of Melting Point on Molecular Symmetry. The foregoing discussion has indicated that the melting points and boiling points of substances are determined by several factors. One of these is the **symmetry** of the molecules, which has a pronounced effect on the melting point, but not on the boiling point: the greater the symmetry of the molecule, the higher the melting point of the substance. This effect is shown by many organic compounds, and it is strikingly evident for the series of tetrahedral molecules CF_4, CF_3Cl, CF_2Cl_2, $CFCl_3$, CCl_4 (Fig. 15-7). The boiling points of these substances are very nearly a linear function of the number of chlorine atoms in

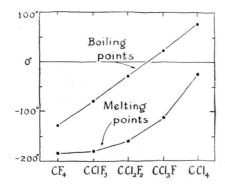

FIG. 15-7

The effect of molecular symmetry on melting point.

the molecule, but the melting points show a pronounced deviation from linearity. This can be explained in the following way. In the gaseous state and the liquid state, which have structures characterized by randomness of molecular arrangement, the molecules with different symmetry are equivalent to one another. In the crystal, however, there is a striking difference: a molecule of CF_2Cl_2 can fit into its place in the crystal in only two ways (differing in rotation of the molecule through 180° around the indicated axis), whereas a molecule of CF_3Cl can fit into its place in a crystal of this substance in three ways (differing by rotation through 120° around an axis through the carbon and chlorine atoms), and a molecule of CF_4 can fit into its place in twelve ways. At the melting point, when there is equilibrium between the crystal and the liquid, equal numbers of molecules must be leaving the crystal and attaching themselves to it. The chance of leaving the crystal, under the influence of thermal agitation, is the same for a molecule of high symmetry as for one of low symmetry, whereas the chance of striking the crystal in suitable orientation to stick is greater for the molecule of high symmetry than for that of low symmetry. Hence substances with molecules of high symmetry crystallize more readily than those of low symmetry; that is, they have higher melting point. Relative to CF_2Cl_2 (symmetry number 2), this effect causes an increase in melting point of 57° for CF_4 and CCl_4 (symmetry number 12), and of about 14° for CF_3Cl and $CFCl_3$ (symmetry number 3).

15–6. *The Hydrogen Bond—the Cause of the Unusual Properties of Water*

The unusual properties of water mentioned above are due to the power of its molecules to attract one another especially strongly. This power is associated with a structural feature which is called the **hydrogen bond.**

The Abnormal Melting and Boiling Points of Hydrogen Fluoride, Water, and Ammonia.   The melting points and boiling points of the hydrides of some non-metallic elements are shown in Figure 15-8. The variation for a series of congeners is normal for the sequence CH_4, SiH_4, GeH_4, and SnH_4, but is abnormal for the other sequences. The curves through the points for H_2Te, H_2Se, and H_2S show the expected trend, but when extrapolated they indicate values of about −100° C and −80° C, respectively, for the melting point and boiling point of water. The observed value of the melting point is 100° greater, and that of the boiling point is 180° greater, than would be expected for water if it were a normal substance; and hydrogen fluoride and ammonia show similar, but smaller, deviations.

The Hydrogen Bond.   The hydrogen ion is a bare nucleus, with charge +1. If hydrogen fluoride, HF, had an extreme ionic structure, it could be represented as in A of Figure 15-9. The positive charge of the hydrogen ion could then strongly attract a negative ion, such as a fluoride ion, forming an $[F^-H^+F^-]^-$ or HF_2^- ion, as shown in B. This does indeed occur, and the stable ion HF_2^-, called the *hydrogen difluoride ion*, exists

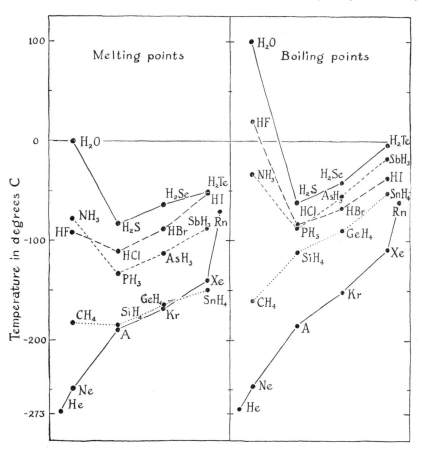

FIG. 15-8 *Melting points and boiling points of hydrides of non-metallic elements, showing abnormally high values for hydrogen fluoride, water, and ammonia, caused by hydrogen-bond formation.*

in considerable concentration in acidic fluoride solutions, and in salts such as KHF_2, potassium hydrogen difluoride. The bond holding this complex ion together, called the *hydrogen bond*, is weaker than ordinary ionic or covalent bonds, but stronger than ordinary van der Waals forces of intermolecular attraction.

Hydrogen bonds are also formed between hydrogen fluoride mole-

FIG. 15-9

The hydrogen fluoride molecule (A) *and the hydrogen difluoride ion, containing a hydrogen bond* (B).

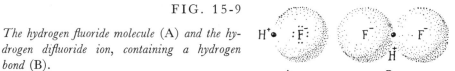

A   B

cules, causing the gaseous substance to be largely polymerized into the molecular species H_2F_2, H_3F_3, H_4F_4, H_5F_5, and H_6F_6. The last of these seems to be especially stable, probably because of its ability to form an extra hydrogen bond by assuming a ring structure (Fig. 15-10).

In a hydrogen bond the hydrogen ion is usually attached more strongly to one of the two electronegative atoms which it holds together

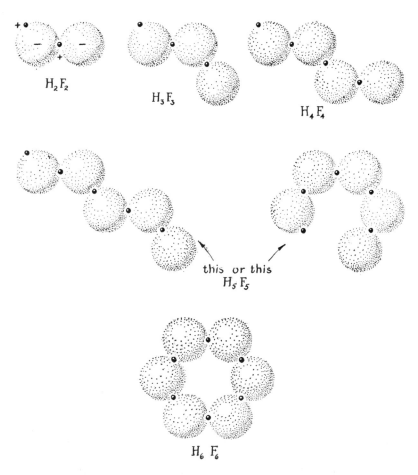

FIG. 15-10   *Some polymers of hydrogen fluoride.*

than to the other. The structure of the dimer of hydrogen fluoride may be represented by the formula

$$F^- \!\!-\!\! H^+ \text{---} F^- \!\!-\!\! H^+$$

in which the dashed line represents the hydrogen bonding.

Because of the electrostatic origin of the hydrogen bond, only the most

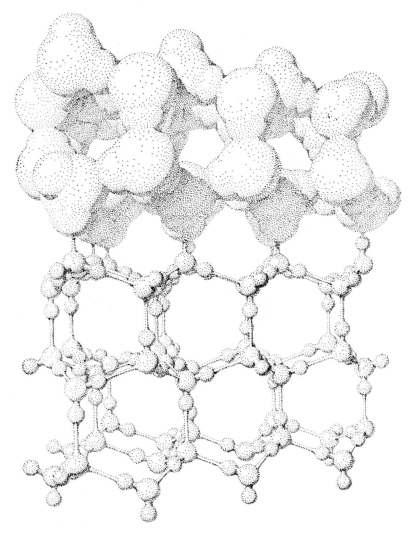

FIG. 15-11 *A small part of a crystal of ice. The molecules above are shown with approximately their correct size (relative to the interatomic distances). Note hydrogen bonds, and the open structure which gives ice its low density. The molecules below are indicated diagrammatically as small spheres for oxygen atoms and still smaller spheres for hydrogen atoms.*

electronegative atoms—fluorine, oxygen, nitrogen—form these bonds. Usually an unshared electron pair of the attracted atom approaches closely to the attracting hydrogen ion. Water is an especially suitable substance for hydrogen-bond formation, because each molecule has two attached hydrogen atoms and two unshared electron pairs, and hence can form four hydrogen bonds. The tetrahedral arrangement of the shared and unshared electron pairs causes these four bonds to extend in the four tetrahedral directions in space, and leads to the characteristic crystal structure of ice (Fig. 15-11). This structure, in which each molecule is surrounded by only four immediate neighbors, is a very open structure, and accordingly ice is a substance with abnormally low density. When ice melts, this tetrahedral structure is partially destroyed, and the water molecules are packed more closely together, causing water to have greater density than ice. Many of the hydrogen bonds remain, however, and aggregates of molecules with the open tetrahedral structure persist in water at the freezing point. With increase in temperature some of these aggregates break up, causing a further increase in density of the liquid; only at 4° C does the normal expansion due to increase in molecular agitation overcome this effect, and cause water to begin to show the usual decrease in density with increasing temperature.

The abnormally large dielectric constant of water (Chap. 9), which is responsible for the striking power of water to dissolve ionic substances, is due to its power to form hydrogen bonds. Two separate dipole molecules have much less power to neutralize an applied electric field than has the complex of the two, with dipole moment doubled. The only substances with dielectric constants greater than 40, and with great power to dissolve electrolytes, are water, liquid hydrogen fluoride, hydrogen peroxide, and liquid hydrogen cyanide (HCN). All of these substances polymerize through hydrogen-bond formation.

Exercises

15-1. Write the fundamental chemical equations for the softening of water by a zeolite, and the regeneration of the zeolite.

15-2. Write the fundamental chemical equations for the removal of most of the ionic impurities in water by the "ion-exchange" process. Why do you suppose this process is sometimes preferred to distillation by factories for the preparation of moderately pure water? What do you think is the simplest method of determining when the absorbers in tanks A and B of Figure 15-1 are saturated with ions and should be regenerated?

15-3. Why do thick layers of water have a stronger color than thin layers? What would be the apparent color of a very thin layer of bromine?

15-4. Is it true that a liquid made of heavy molecules has a higher boiling point than one made of light molecules because the gravitational attraction between heavy molecules is greater than the gravitational attraction between light molecules?

15-5. Describe briefly the forces responsible for the attraction between molecules.

15-6. Ethane, C_2H_6, boils at $-88.3°$ C, and hexafluorethane, C_2F_6, at $-79°$ C. What would you predict about the boiling point of CF_3CH_3?

15-7. What properties of solid, liquid, and gaseous hydrogen fluoride can you explain on the basis of the hydrogen bond?

15-8. Why are there no strong hydrogen bonds in crystalline phosphine, PH_3?

15-9. Explain the effect of the hydrogen bond on the density of ice and water.

15-10. Try to correlate all the pertinent information in this chapter and preceding chapters to explain why water is a good solvent for ionic salts.

Chapter 16

The Properties
of Solutions

One of the most striking properties of water is its ability to dissolve many substances, forming *aqueous solutions*. Solutions are very important kinds of matter—important for industry and for life. The ocean is an aqueous solution which contains thousands of components: ions of the metals and non-metals, complex inorganic ions, many different organic substances. It was in this solution that the first living organisms developed, and from it that they obtained the ions and molecules needed for their growth and life. In the course of time organisms were evolved which could leave this aqueous environment, and move out onto the land and into the air. They achieved this ability by carrying the aqueous solution with them, as tissue fluid, blood plasma, and intracellular fluids containing the necessary supply of ions and molecules.

The properties of solutions have been extensively studied, and it has been found that they can be correlated in large part by some simple laws. These laws and some descriptive information about solutions are discussed in the following sections.

16–1. *Types of Solutions. Nomenclature*

In Chapter 2 a *phase* was defined as a homogeneous part of a system, separated from other parts by physical boundaries. A **solution** *is a phase which consists of two or more molecular species that are not readily interconvertible*. These are called its *components*. Air is a *gaseous solution* of nitrogen, oxygen, carbon dioxide, water vapor, and the noble gases. Carbonated water is a *liquid solution* of water and carbon dioxide. (It contains other molecular species also—H_2CO_3, H^+, HCO_3^-—but since these are readily convertible into water and carbon dioxide they are not specified as additional components.) Coinage silver is a *solid solution* or *crystalline solution* of silver and copper.

Gaseous hydrogen fluoride contains several molecular species, HF, H_2F_2, H_3F_3, H_4F_4, etc.; but since these are readily interconvertible, it is customary not to consider it to be a gaseous solution. On the other hand, a gas containing the molecules O_2 and O_3 is considered to be a solution of oxygen and ozone, since the rate of interconversion of the two substances is small.

If one component of a solution is present in larger amount than the others, it may be called the **solvent;** the others are called **solutes.**

The concentration of a solute is often expressed as the number of grams per 100 g of solvent or the number of grams per liter of solution. It is often convenient to give the number of gram formula weights per liter of solution (the *formality*), the number of gram molecular weights per liter of solution (the *molarity*), or the number of equivalent weights per liter of solution (the *normality*). Sometimes these are referred to 1,000 g of solvent; they are then called the *weight-formality, weight-molarity,* and *weight-normality,* respectively.

Example 1.   A solution is made by dissolving 64.11 g of $Mg(NO_3)_2 \cdot 6H_2O$ in water enough to bring the volume to 1 l. Describe the solution.

   Answer.   The formula weight of $Mg(NO_3)_2 \cdot 6H_2O$ is 256.43; hence the solution is 0.25 F (0.25 formal) in this substance. The salt is, however, completely ionized in solution, to give magnesium ions Mg^{++} and nitrate ions NO_3^-. The solution is 0.25 M (0.25 molar) in Mg^{++} and 0.50 M in NO_3^-. It is also 0.50 N (0.50 normal) in Mg^{++} and 0.50 N in NO_3^-.

For some purposes concentrations of the components of a solution are described by values of their *mole fractions.* The mole fraction of a component or molecular species is the ratio of the number of moles of that component or molecular species to the total number of moles. The sum of the mole fractions of all the components or molecular species is thus equal to unity.

Example 2.   What are the mole fractions of the components of ordinary 95% ethyl alcohol?

   Answer.   Each 100 g of this solution contains 95 g of ethyl alcohol (C_2H_5OH, MW 46.05) and 5 g of water (H_2O, MW 18.02). The number of moles of alcohol per 100 g of solution is $95/46.05 =$

2.062; the number of moles of water is $5/18.02 = 0.278$. The total number of moles is 2.340. The mole fraction of alcohol is $x_1 = 2.062/2.340 = 0.881$; that of water is $x_2 = 0.278/2.340 = 0.119$. Note that $x_1 + x_2 = 1.000$.

It is worth noting that a 1 M aqueous solution cannot be made up accurately by dissolving one mole of solute in 1 l of water, because the volume of the solution is in general different from that of the solvent. Nor is it equal to the sum of the volumes of the components; for example, 1 l of water and 1 l of alcohol on mixing give 1.93 l of solution; there occurs a volume contraction of 3.5%. There is no reliable way of predicting the density of a solution; tables of experimental values for important solutions are given in reference books.

16–2. *Solubility*

An isolated system is in *equilibrium* when its properties, in particular the distribution of components among phases, remain constant with the passage of time.

If the system in equilibrium contains a solution and another phase which is one of the components of the solution in the form of a pure substance, the concentration of that substance in the solution is called the *solubility* of the substance. The solution is called a *saturated solution*.

For example, at 0° C a solution of borax containing 1.3 g of anhydrous sodium tetraborate, $Na_2B_4O_7$, in 100 g of water is in equilibrium with the solid phase $Na_2B_4O_7 \cdot 10H_2O$, sodium tetraborate decahydrate; on standing the system does not change, the composition of the solution remaining constant. The solubility of $Na_2B_4O_7 \cdot 10H_2O$ in water is hence 1.3 g of $Na_2B_4O_7$ per 100 g, or, correcting for the water of hydration, 2.5 g of $Na_2B_4O_7 \cdot 10H_2O$ per 100 g.

Change in the Solid Phase. The solubility of $Na_2B_4O_7 \cdot 10H_2O$ increases rapidly with increasing temperature; at 60° it is 20.3 g of $Na_2B_4O_7$ per 100 g (Fig. 16-1). If the system is heated to 70° and held there for some time, a new phenomenon occurs. A third phase appears, a crystalline phase with composition $Na_2B_4O_7 \cdot 5H_2O$, and the other solid phase disappears. At this temperature the solubility of the decahydrate is greater than that of the pentahydrate; a solution saturated with the decahydrate is supersaturated with respect to the pentahydrate, and will deposit crystals of the pentahydrate.* The process of solution of

* The addition of "seeds" (small crystals of the substance) is sometimes necessary to cause the process of crystallization to begin.

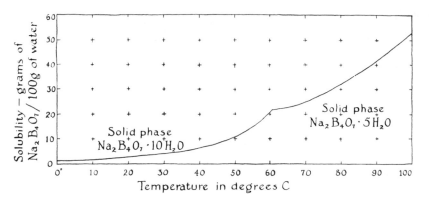

FIG. 16-1   *Solubility of sodium tetraborate in water.*

the unstable phase and crystallization of the stable phase will then continue until none of the unstable phase remains.*

In this case the decahydrate is less soluble than the pentahydrate below 61°, and is hence the stable phase below this temperature. The solubility curves of the two hydrates cross at 61°, the pentahydrate being stable in contact with solution above this temperature.

Change other than solvation may occur in the stable solid phase. Thus rhombic sulfur is less soluble in suitable solvents than is monoclinic sulfur at temperatures below 95.5° C, the transition temperature between the two forms; above this temperature the monoclinic form is the less

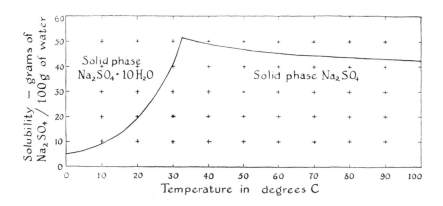

FIG. 16-2   *Solubility of sodium sulfate in water.*

* The third hydrate of sodium tetraborate, kernite, $Na_2B_4O_7 \cdot 4H_2O$, is more soluble than the other phases.

soluble. The principles of thermodynamics require that the temperature at which the solubility curves of the two forms cross be the same for all solvents, and be also the temperature at which the vapor-pressure curves intersect.

The Dependence of Solubility on Temperature. The solubility of a substance may either increase or decrease with increasing temperature. An interesting case is provided by sodium sulfate. The solubility of

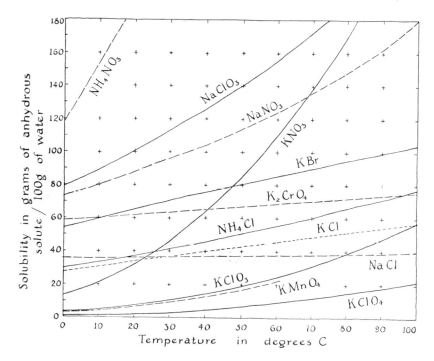

FIG. 16-3   *Solubility curves for some salts in water.*

$Na_2SO_4 \cdot 10H_2O$ (the stable solid phase below 32.4°) increases very rapidly with increasing temperature, from 5 g of Na_2SO_4 per 100 g of water at 0° to 55 g at 32.4°. Above 32.4° the stable solid phase is Na_2SO_4; the solubility of this phase decreases rapidly with increasing temperature, from 55 g at 32.4° to 42 g at 100° (Fig. 16-2).

Most salts show increased solubility with increase in temperature; a good number (NaCl, K_2CrO_4) change only slightly in solubility with increase in temperature; and a few, such as Na_2SO_4 and $Na_2CO_3 \cdot H_2O$, show decreased solubility (Figs. 16-3 and 16-4).

The principles of thermodynamics provide a quantitative relation between the change in solubility with temperature of a substance (its *temperature coefficient of solubility*) and its *heat of solution*, the heat evolved as the substance goes into solution in the solvent. If the heat of solution of a solid substance is positive (that is, if heat is evolved on solution) the solubility of the solid decreases with increasing temperature, and if the heat of solution is negative the solubility increases. This rule is a consequence of the principle of Le Châtelier. If a system containing

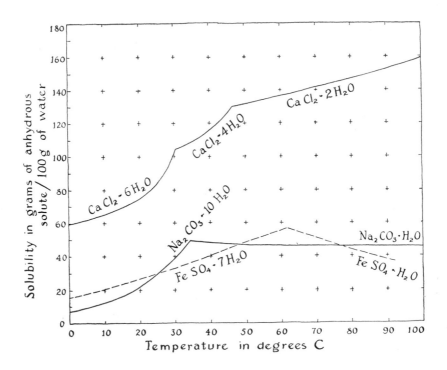

F I G. 1 6 - 4   *Solubility curves for salts forming two or three hydrates.*

solute and solution is in equilibrium at a certain temperature, and the temperature is raised, the equilibrium will shift in the direction that moves the system toward its original temperature. This shift will involve the transfer of more solute into the solution if the heat of solution is negative, or the reverse process if the heat of solution is positive. Consider a solid in equilibrium with its saturated solution at one temperature. Let the temperature be increased somewhat. If the heat of solution is negative (heat being absorbed on solution), the system would be cooled in case that some of the solid phase were to dissolve, and the temperature would then drop back toward the original temperature.

Hence this process will occur, and the solubility thus increases with increase in temperature.

Most salts, corresponding to their positive temperature coefficients of solubility, have negative heats of solution in water. For example, the heat of solution of $Na_2SO_4 \cdot 10H_2O$ in water is -19 kcal per gram formula weight. The formal heat of solution of sodium chloride is -1.3 kcal and that of Na_2SO_4 is 5.5 kcal.

The Dependence of Solubility on the Nature of Solute and Solvent. Substances vary greatly in their solubilities in various solvents. There are a few general rules about solubility, which, however, apply in the main to organic compounds. One of these rules is that *a substance tends to dissolve in solvents which are chemically similar to it*. For example, the hydrocarbon naphthalene, $C_{10}H_8$, has a high solubility in gasoline, which is a mixture of hydrocarbons, a somewhat smaller solubility in ethyl alcohol, C_2H_5OH, whose molecules consist of short hydrocarbon chains with hydroxyl groups attached, and a very small solubility in water, which is much different from a hydrocarbon. On the other hand, boric acid, $B(OH)_3$, a hydroxy compound, is moderately soluble in both water and alcohol, and insoluble in gasoline. In fact, the three solvents themselves show the same phenomenon—both gasoline and water are miscible with (soluble in) alcohol, whereas gasoline and water dissolve in each other only in very small amounts.

The explanation of these facts is the following. Hydrocarbon groups attract hydrocarbon groups only weakly, as is shown by the low melting and boiling points of hydrocarbons, relative to other substances with similar molecular weights. On the other hand, hydroxyl groups and water molecules show very strong intermolecular attraction; the melting point and boiling point of water are higher than those of any other substance with low molecular weight. This strong attraction is due to the partial ionic character of the O—H bonds, which places electrical charges on the atoms. The positively charged hydrogen atoms are then attracted to the negative oxygen atoms of other molecules, forming hydrogen bonds and holding the molecules firmly together (Chap. 15). The reason that the substances such as gasoline or naphthalene do not dissolve in water is that their molecules in solution would prevent water

molecules from forming as many of these strong
$$\begin{array}{ccc} H & & H \\ | & & | \\ O-H & - - - & O-H \end{array}$$
bonds as in pure water; on the other hand, boric acid is soluble in water because the rupture of the hydrogen bonds between water molecules

in pure water (as well as of the hydrogen bonds between boric acid molecules in the boric acid crystal) is compensated by the formation of strong hydrogen bonds between the water molecules and the hydroxyl groups of the boric acid molecules.

16–3. *Solubility of Salts and Hydroxides*

In the study of inorganic chemistry, especially qualitative analysis, it is useful to know the approximate solubility of common substances. The simple rules of solubility are given below. These rules apply to compounds of the common cations Na^+, K^+, NH_4^+, Mg^{++}, Ca^{++}, Sr^{++}, Ba^{++}, Al^{+++}, Cr^{+++}, Mn^{++}, Fe^{++}, Fe^{+++}, Co^{++}, Ni^{++}, Cu^{++}, Zn^{++}, Ag^+, Cd^{++}, Sn^{++}, Hg_2^{++}, Hg^{++}, and Pb^{++}. By "soluble" it is meant that the solubility is more than about 1 g per 100 ml (roughly 0.1 M in the cation), and by "insoluble" that the solubility is less than about 0.1 g per 100 ml (roughly 0.01 M); substances with solubilities within or close to these limits are described as *sparingly soluble*.

Class of mainly soluble substances:

All *nitrates* are soluble.

All *acetates* are soluble.

All *chlorides*, *bromides*, and *iodides* are soluble except those of silver, mercurous mercury, and lead. $PbCl_2$ and $PbBr_2$ are sparingly soluble in cold water (1 g per 100 ml at 20°) and more soluble in hot water (3 g, 5 g, respectively, per 100 ml at 100°).

All *sulfates* are soluble except those of barium, strontium, and lead. $CaSO_4$, Ag_2SO_4, and Hg_2SO_4 are sparingly soluble.

All salts of *sodium*, *potassium*, and *ammonium* are soluble except $NaSb(OH)_6$, $K_3Co(NO_2)_6$, K_2PtCl_6, $(NH_4)_2PtCl_6$, and $(NH_4)_3Co(NO_2)_6$.

Class of mainly insoluble substances:

All *hydroxides* are insoluble except those of the alkali metals, ammonium, and barium. $Ca(OH)_2$ and $Sr(OH)_2$ are sparingly soluble.

All normal *carbonates* and *phosphates* are insoluble, except those of the alkali metals and ammonium. Many hydrogen carbonates and phosphates, such as $Ca(HCO_3)_2$, $Ca(H_2PO_4)_2$, etc., are soluble.

All *sulfides* except those of the alkali metals, ammonium, and the alkaline-earth metals are insoluble.*

---

* The sulfides of aluminum and chromium are hydrolyzed by water, precipitating $Al(OH)_3$ and $Cr(OH)_3$.

16–4. The Solubility of Gases in Liquids: Henry's Law

Air is somewhat soluble in water: at room temperature (20° C) one liter of water dissolves 19.0 ml of air at 1 atm pressure. (The amount of dissolved air decreases with increasing temperature.) If the pressure is doubled, the solubility of the air is doubled. This proportionality of the solubility of air to its pressure illustrates *Henry's law*, which may be stated in the following way: *At constant temperature, the partial pressure in the gas phase of one component of a solution is, at equilibrium, proportional to the concentration of the component in the solution, in the region of low concentration.*

This is equivalent to saying that *the solubility of a gas in a liquid is proportional to the partial pressure of the gas.*

Example 3.   The solubility of atmospheric nitrogen* in water at 0° C is 23.54 ml/l, and that of oxygen is 48.89 ml/l. Air contains 79% N_2 and 21% O_2 by volume. What is the composition of the dissolved air?

Answer.   The solubilities of nitrogen and oxygen at partial pressures 0.79 and 0.21 atm respectively are $0.79 \times 23.54 = 18.60$ ml/l and $0.21 \times 48.89 = 10.27$ ml/l respectively. The composition of the dissolved air is hence $\dfrac{18.60}{18.60 + 10.27} = $ **64.4%** nitrogen and $\dfrac{10.27}{18.60 + 10.27} = $ **35.6%** oxygen.

The solubilities of most gases in water are of the order of magnitude of that of air. Exceptions are those gases which combine chemically with water or which dissociate largely into ions, including CO_2 (solubility 1,713 ml/l at 0° C), H_2S (4,670), and SO_2 and NH_3, which are extremely soluble.

The Partition of a Solute Between Two Solvents.   If a solution of iodine in water is shaken with chloroform, most of the iodine is transferred to the chloroform. The ratio of concentrations of iodine in the two phases, called the *distribution ratio*, is a constant in the range of small concentrations of the solute in each solution. For iodine in chloroform and water the value of this ratio at room temperature is 250; hence whenever a solution of iodine in chloroform is shaken with water or a solution in water is shaken with chloroform until equilibrium is reached, the iodine concentration in the chloroform phase is 250 times that in the water phase.

It is seen on consideration of the various equilibria that the distribution ratio of a solute between two solvents is equal to the ratio of the solubilities of the solute (as a crystalline or liquid phase) in the two solvents, provided that the solubilities are small. Moreover, the distribution ratio of a gaseous solute between two solvents is proportional to the ratio of its solubilities in the two solvents.

* 98.8% N_2 and 1.2% A.

The method of shaking a solution with an immiscible solvent is of great use in organic chemistry, especially the chemistry of natural products, for removing one of several solutes from a solution. In inorganic chemistry it is useful in another way—for determining concentrations of particular molecular species. Thus iodine combines with iodide ion to form the tri-iodide ion: $I_2 + I^- \longrightarrow I_3^-$. The concentration of molecular iodine, I_2, in a solution containing both I_2 and I_3^- can be determined by shaking with chloroform, analyzing the chloroform solution, and dividing by the distribution ratio. (Tri-iodide ion is not soluble in chloroform.)

16–5. *The Freezing Point and Boiling Point of Solutions*

It is well known that the freezing point of a solution is lower than that of the pure solvent; for example, in cold climates it is customary to add a solute such as alcohol or glycerol or ethylene glycol to the radiator water of automobiles to keep it from freezing. Freezing-point lowering by the solute also underlies the use of a salt-ice mixture for cooling, as in freezing ice cream; the salt dissolves in the water, making a solution, which is in equilibrium with ice at a temperature below the freezing point of water.

Let us consider what happens as a salt solution (concentration 1 formal, say) is cooled, with solid carbon dioxide, for example. The temperature falls to a little below the freezing point of the solution, $-3.4°$ C, and then, as ice begins to form, it rises to this value and remains constant. As ice continues to form, however, the salt concentration of the solution slowly increases, and its freezing point drops. When half of the water has frozen to ice the solution is 2 F in NaCl, and the temperature is $-6.9°$. Ice forms, the solution increases in concentration, and the temperature drops until it reaches the value $-21.1°$ C. At this temperature the solution becomes saturated with respect to the solute, which begins to crystallize out as the solid phase $NaCl \cdot 2H_2O$ (sodium chloride dihydrate). The system then remains at this temperature, called the *eutectic temperature*, as the solution freezes completely, without change in composition, to form a fine-grained mixture of two solid phases, ice and $NaCl \cdot 2H_2O$. This mixture is called the *eutectic mixture* or *eutectic*.

It is found by experiment that the freezing-point lowering of a dilute solution is proportional to the concentration of the solute. In 1883 the French chemist F. M. Raoult made the very interesting discovery that **the weight-molar freezing-point lowering produced by different solutes is the same for a given solvent.** Thus the following freezing points are observed for 0.1 M solutions of the following solutes in water:

Hydrogen peroxide	H_2O_2	$-0.186°$ C
Methanol	CH_3OH	-0.181

Ethanol	C_2H_5OH	-0.183
Dextrose	$C_6H_{12}O_6$	-0.186
Sucrose	$C_{12}H_{22}O_{11}$	-0.188

The *molar freezing-point constant* for water has the value $1.86°$ C, the freezing point of a solution containing c moles of solute per 1,000 g of water being -1.86 c in degrees C. For other solvents the values of this constant are shown in Table 16-1.

TABLE 16-1

SOLVENT	FREEZING POINT	MOLAR* FREEZING-POINT CONSTANT
Benzene...............	5.6° C	4.90° C
Acetic acid............	17	3.90
Phenol................	40	7.27
Camphor..............	180	40

* Molar = weight-molar, moles per 1,000 g of solvent.

The Determination of Molecular Weight by the Freezing-Point Method.   The freezing-point method is a very useful way of determining the molecular weights of substances in solution. Camphor, with its very large constant, is of particular value for the study of organic substances.

Example 4.   The freezing point of a solution of 0.244 g of benzoic acid in 20 g of benzene was observed to be $5.232°$ C, and that of pure benzene to be $5.478°$. What is the molecular weight of benzoic acid in this solution?

Solution.   The solution contains $\dfrac{0.244 \times 1,000}{20} = 12.2$ g of benzoic acid per 1,000 g of solvent. The number of moles of solute per 1,000 g of solvent is found from the observed freezing-point lowering $0.246°$ to be $\dfrac{0.246}{4.90} = 0.0502$. Hence the molecular weight is $\dfrac{12.2}{0.0502} = $ **243**. The explanation of this high value (the formula weight for benzoic acid, C_6H_5COOH, being 122.05) is that in this solvent the substance forms double molecules, $(C_6H_5COOH)_2$.

16–6. *Evidence for Electrolytic Dissociation*

One of the strongest arguments advanced by the Swedish chemist Arrhenius in 1887 in support of the theory of electrolytic dissociation was the fact that the freezing-point lowering of salt solutions is much larger than that calculated for undissociated molecules, the observed lowering for a salt such as NaCl or $MgSO_4$ in very dilute solution being just twice as great and for a salt such as Na_2SO_4 or $CaCl_2$ just three times as great as expected.

16–7. *Elevation of Boiling Point*

The boiling point of a solution is higher than that of the pure solvent by an amount proportional to the molar concentration of the solute. Values of the proportionality factor, the *molar boiling-point constant*, are given in Table 16-2 for some important solvents.

TABLE 16-2

SOLVENT	BOILING POINT	MOLAR BOILING-POINT CONSTANT
Water..............	100° C	0.52° C
Ethyl alcohol...........	78.5	1.19
Ethyl ether.............	34.5	2.11
Benzene..............	79.6	2.65

Boiling-point data for a solution can be used to obtain the molecular weight of the solute in the same way as freezing-point data.

16–8. *The Vapor Pressure of Solutions: Raoult's Law*

It was found experimentally by Raoult in 1887 that the partial pressure of solvent vapor in equilibrium with a dilute solution is directly proportional to the mole fraction of solvent in the solution. It can be expressed by the equation

$$p = p_0 x$$

in which p is the partial pressure of the solvent above the solution, p_0 is the vapor pressure of the pure solvent, and x is the mole fraction of solvent in the solution, as defined in the first section of this chapter. We may give a kinetic interpretation of this equation by saying that only x times as many solvent molecules can escape from the surface of a solution as from the corresponding surface of the pure solvent, and that accordingly equilibrium will be reached with the gas phase when the number of gas molecules striking the surface is x times the number striking the surface of the pure solvent at equilibrium.

Determination of Molecular Weight from Vapor Pressure.   Raoult's law permits the direct calculation of the effective molecular weight of a solute from data on the solvent vapor pressure of the solution, as shown by the following example.

Example 5.   A 10-g sample of an unknown non-volatile substance is dissolved in 100 g of benzene, C_6H_6. A stream of air is then bubbled through the solution, and the loss in weight of the solution (through saturation of the air with benzene vapor) is determined as 1.205 g. The same volume of air passed through pure benzene at the same temperature caused a loss of 1.273 g. What is the molecular weight of the solute?

   Answer.   The loss in weight by evaporation of benzene is proportional to the vapor pressure. Hence the mole fraction of benzene in the solution is $1.205/1.273 = 0.947$, and the mole fraction of solute is 0.053. The molecular weight of benzene, C_6H_6, is 78; and the number of moles of benzene in 100 g is 100/78. Let x be the molecular weight of the solute; the number of moles of solute in the solution (containing 10 g of solute) is $10/x$. Hence

$$\frac{10/x}{100/78} = \frac{0.053}{0.947}$$

or

$$x = \frac{78}{100} \times \frac{0.947}{0.053} \times 10 = \mathbf{139}$$

This is the molecular weight of the substance.

The Derivation of Freezing-Point Depression and Boiling-Point Elevation from Raoult's Law.   The laws of freezing-point lowering and boiling-point raising can be derived from Raoult's law in the following way. We first consider boiling-point raising. In Figure 16-5 the upper curve represents the vapor pressure of pure solvent as a function of the temperature. The temperature at which this becomes 1 atm is the boiling point of the pure solvent. The lower curve represents the vapor

pressure of a solution of a non-volatile solute; Raoult's law requires
that it lie below the curve for the pure solvent by an amount proportional to the molar concentration of solute, and that the same curve
apply for all solutes, the molar concentration being the only significant
quantity. This curve intersects the 1 atm line at a temperature higher
than the boiling point of the solvent by an amount proportional to the

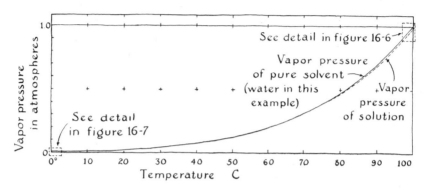

FIG. 16-5   *Vapor-pressure curves of water in the range from 0° C to 100° C.*

molar concentration of the solute (for dilute solutions), as expressed in
the boiling-point law (Fig. 16-6).

The argument for freezing-point lowering is similar. In Figure 16-7
the vapor-pressure curves of the pure solvent in the crystalline state
and the liquid state are shown intersecting at the freezing point of the
pure solvent. At higher temperatures the crystal has higher vapor pressure than the liquid, and is hence unstable relative to it, and at lower

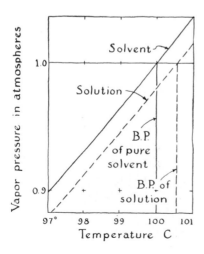

FIG. 16-6

*Vapor-pressure curves of water and an aqueous
solution near the boiling point, showing elevation of the boiling point of the solution.*

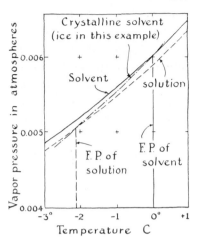

FIG. 16-7

Vapor-pressure curves of water, ice, and an aqueous solution near the freezing point, showing depression of the freezing point of the solution.

temperatures the stability relation is reversed. The solution vapor-pressure curve, lying below that of the liquid pure solvent, intersects the crystal curve at a temperature below the melting point of the pure solvent. This is the melting point of the solution.

Note that the assumption is made that the solid phase obtained on freezing the solution is pure solvent; if a crystalline solution is formed, as sometimes occurs, the freezing-point law does not hold.

16–9. *The Osmotic Pressure of Solutions*

If red blood corpuscles are placed in pure water they swell, become round, and finally burst. This is the result of the fact that the cell wall is permeable to water but not to some of the solutes of the cell solution (hemoglobin, other proteins); in the effort to reach a condition of equilibrium (equality of water vapor pressure) between the two liquids water enters the cell. If the cell wall were sufficiently strong, equilibrium would be reached when the hydrostatic pressure in the cell had reached a certain value, at which the water vapor pressure of the solution equals the vapor pressure of the pure water outside the cell. This equilibrium hydrostatic pressure is called the *osmotic pressure* of the solution.

A semi-permeable membrane is a membrane with very small holes in it, of such a size that molecules of the solvent are able to pass through but molecules of the solute are not. A useful semi-permeable membrane for measurement of osmotic pressure is made by precipitating cupric ferrocyanide, $Cu_2Fe(CN)_6$, in the pores of an unglazed porcelain cup, which gives the membrane mechanical support to enable it to withstand high pressures. Accurate measurements have been made in this way to over 250 atm. Cellophane membranes may also be used, if the osmotic pressure is not large.

It is found experimentally that the osmotic pressure of a dilute solution satisfies the equation

$$\pi V = n_1 R T$$

with n_1 the number of moles of solute (to which the membrane is impermeable) in volume V, π the osmotic pressure, R the gas constant, and T the absolute temperature. This relation was discovered by van't Hoff in 1887. It is striking that the equation is identical in form with the perfect-gas equation; van't Hoff emphasized the similarity of a dissolved substance and a gas.

It can be shown by the methods of thermodynamics that Raoult's law and the osmotic-pressure equation are related; the validity of one requires the validity of the other.

For inorganic substances and simple organic substances the osmotic-pressure method of determining molecular weight offers no advantages over other methods, such as the measurement of freezing-point lowering. It has, however, been found useful for substances of very high molecular weight; the molecular weight of hemoglobin was first reliably determined in this way by Adair in 1925. The value found by Adair, 68,000, has been verified by measurements made with the ultracentrifuge.

16–10. *The Activities of Ions*

During the early development of the ionic theory of electrolytic solutions it was recognized that the observed freezing-point lowering of these solutions, while greater than corresponding to undissociated solute molecules, is not so great as expected for complete ionization. For example, the freezing point of a 0.1 *F* solution of KBr is $-0.345°$ C. Since the freezing-point constant for water is $1.86°$, this lowering requires that there be effective 0.185 moles of solute, 85% more than the number of formulas KBr present, but not 100% more. For a number of years it was thought that facts such as this showed the salts to be only partially ionized; in this case KBr was said to be 85% ionized, the solution being said to be 0.085 *M* in K^+, 0.085 *M* in Br^-, and 0.015 *M* in undissociated KBr.

Then, about 1904, it was pointed out by A. A. Noyes that many properties of solutions of salts and strong acids (such as their color) suggest that they are completely ionized in dilute solution. This view has been generally accepted since 1923, when a quantitative theory of the interactions of ions in solution was developed by P. J. W. Debye and E. Hückel.

The explanation of the fact that a strong electrolyte such as potassium bromide produces a smaller freezing-point lowering than calculated for complete ionization is that there are strong electric forces operative between the ions, which decrease their effectiveness, so that the properties of their solutions are different from those of ideal solutions, except at extreme dilution. The interionic attraction reduces the *activity* of the ions to a value less than their concentration.

The factor by which the ion concentration is to be multiplied to obtain the ion activity is called the *activity coefficient*. For all strong electrolytes containing only univalent ions (HCl, NaCl, KNO_3, etc.) its values are approximately 0.80 at 0.1 *F*, 0.90 at 0.01 *F*, and 0.96 at 0.001 *F*, approaching 1 only in very dilute solutions. These activity coefficients are of significance in connection with chemical equilibrium, which is to be discussed later.

16–11. *Colloidal Solutions*

It was found by Thomas Graham in the years around 1860 that substances such as glue, gelatin, albumin, starch, etc., in solution diffuse very slowly, their diffusion rates being as small as one hundredth of those for ordinary solutes (salt, sugar, etc.). Graham also found that substances of these two types differ markedly in their ability to pass through a membrane such as parchment paper or collodion; if a solution of sugar and glue is put into a collodion bag and the bag is placed in a stream of running water, the sugar soon dialyzes through the bag into the water, and the glue remains behind. This process of *dialysis* gives a useful method of separating substances of these two kinds.

We now recognize that these differences in ability to pass through the pores of a membrane and in rates of diffusion are due to differences in size of the solute molecules. Graham thought that there was a deeper difference between ordinary, easily crystallizable substances and the slowly diffusing, non-dialyzing substances, which he was unable to crystallize. He named the substances of the latter class *colloids* (Greek *kolla*, glue), in contradistinction to ordinary *crystalloids*. It is now known that there is not a sharp line of demarcation between the two classes (many substances of large molecular weight have been crystallized), but it has been found convenient to retain the name "colloid" for substances of large molecular weight.

Some colloids consist of well-defined molecules, with constant molecular weight and definite molecular shape, permitting them to be piled in a crystalline array. Crystalline proteins include egg albumin (MW 43,000) and hemoglobin (MW 68,000). Even viruses, such as tobacco-mosaic virus, have been crystallized; their molecular weights range from 10,000,000 (bushy-stunt virus) to 2,000,000,000 (vaccinia virus). Colloidal solutions may also be made by dispersing in the solvent a solid or liquid substance which is normally insoluble, such as gold, ferric oxide, arsenious sulfide, etc. A colloidal solution of this sort consists of very small particles of the dispersed substance, so small that their temperature motion (Brownian movement) prevents them from settling out in the gravitational field of the earth.

It is possible to produce through centrifugal force an effective gravitational field of the order of magnitude of 500,000 times the earth's field in an *ultracentrifuge*, an instrument developed by the Swedish scientist The Svedberg, and improved in recent years, especially by J. W. Beams at the University of Virginia. In such a field dissolved particles of large molecular weight settle out rapidly, and molecular-weight values can be determined by observing the sedimentation rate or the equilibrium distribution, after centrifugation for a long time.

It is of interest in regard to the theory of ionization that an electric potential difference exists between the two ends of a solution of a salt such as lithium iodide (composed of a heavy ion and a light ion) in the earth's gravitational field or a centrifugal field.

Exercises

16-1.   A solution contains 10.00 g of anhydrous cupric sulfate and 100.0 g of water. What is the weight formality of this solution in $CuSO_4$? What is the weight formality in $CuSO_4 \cdot 5H_2O$? Are the volume formalities of this solution in $CuSO_4$ and $CuSO_4 \cdot 5H_2O$ equal? Why?

16-2.   Calculate the mole fraction of each component in the following solutions:
(a) 1.000 g of chloroform, $CHCl_3$, in 10.00 g of carbon tetrachloride, CCl_4
(b) 1.000 g of acetic acid, $C_2H_4O_2$, in 25.00 g of benzene, C_6H_6
(c) 1.000 g of acetic acid, $C_2H_4O_2$, in 25.00 g of benzene, recognizing that acetic acid actually exists in benzene solution as the dimer, $(C_2H_4O_2)_2$
(d) 5.00 g of toluene, $C_6H_5CH_3$, 5.00 g of xylene, $C_6H_4(CH_3)_2$, and 3.00 g of cyclohexane, C_6H_{12}

16-3.   The density of constant-boiling hydrochloric acid is 1.10 g/ml. It contains 20.24% HCl. Calculate the weight molarity, the volume molarity, and the mole fraction of HCl in the solution.

16-4.   Make qualitative predictions about the solubility of
(a) ethyl ether, $C_2H_5OC_2H_5$, in water, in alcohol, and in benzene
(b) hydrogen chloride in water and in gasoline

(c) ice in liquid hydrogen fluoride and in cooled gasoline

(d) stearic acid, $CH_3(CH_2)_{16}CO_2H$, in water, in ether, and in carbon tetrachloride

(e) sodium stearate, $(CH_3)(CH_2)_6CO_2^-Na^+$, in water and in carbon tetrachloride

(f) sodium stearate in an emulsion of gasoline in water

(g) decane, $C_{10}H_{22}$, in water and in gasoline

16-5. What can you say about the solubility in water of the substances $AgNO_3$, $PbCl_2$, PbI_2, Hg_2SO_4, $BaSO_4$, $Mg(OH)_2$, $Ba(OH)_2$, PbS, $NaSb(OH)_6$, K_2PtCl_6, KCl?

16-6. Apply Le Châtelier's principle to predict whether the melting point of ice under pressure greater than 1 atm is above or below $0°$ C.

16-7. (a) The density of sodium chloride is 2.16 g/ml, and that of its saturated aqueous solution, containing 311 g of NaCl per liter, is 1.197 g/ml. Would the solubility be increased or decreased by increasing the pressure? Give your calculations. (b) Make a similar prediction for another salt, obtaining data from reference books.

16-8. The vapor pressure of water has the following values (in mm of Hg) at the following temperatures:

$-10°$ C	2.15	$30°$ C	31.82
$-$ 5	3.16	40	55.32
0	4.58	50	92.51
5	6.34	60	149.4
10	9.21	70	233.7
15	12.79	80	355.1
20	17.54	90	525.8
25	23.76	100	760.0

(a) Make a graph of v.p. against temperature, and one of $\log_{10}$ v.p. against temperature. (b) Using the logarithmic graph, extrapolate to predict the boiling point of water under a pressure of 200 lbs. per sq. in. above atmospheric (1 atm = 14.696 lbs. per sq. in.). The experimental value is $191.5°$ C.

16-9. The volume of a sample of nitrous oxide collected over water at $23°$ C with atmospheric pressure 748.1 mm is 842 ml. What is the weight of nitrous oxide in the sample of gas, after correction for the vapor pressure of water?

16-10. What fractional change in volume occurs on saturating dry air with water vapor at $18°$ C? Refer to the data in Exercise 16-8.

16-11. How much water is there in a cubic meter of air at $25°$ C and 80% relative humidity? (Note: The relative humidity is the ratio of the partial pressure of the water vapor to the vapor pressure of liquid water at the same temperature. See Exercise 16-8 for data.)

16-12. Calculate approximately how much ethanol (C_2H_5OH) would be needed per gallon of radiator water to keep it from freezing at temperatures down to $10°$ F below the freezing point.

16-13. A solution containing 1 g of aluminum bromide in 100 g of benzene has a freezing point $0.099°$ below that of pure benzene. What are the apparent molecular weight and the correct formula of the solute?

16-14. The solubility of nitrogen at 1 atm partial pressure in water at 0° is 23.54 ml per l, and that of oxygen is 48.89. Calculate the amount by which the freezing points of air-saturated water and air-free water differ.

16-15. An aqueous solution of amygdalin (a sugar-like substance obtained from almonds) containing 96 g of solute per liter was found to have osmotic pressure 0.474 atm at 0° C. What is the molecular weight of the solute?

16-16. A 1% aqueous solution of gum arabic (simplest formula $C_{12}H_{22}O_{11}$) was found to have an osmotic pressure of 7.2 mm Hg at 25° C. What are the average molecular weight and degree of polymerization of the solute?

16-17. 100 ml of water containing 0.03 g of iodine in solution is shaken with 10 ml of chloroform. What percentage of the iodine remains in the water phase? If it had been shaken successively with two 5-ml portions of chloroform, how much would have remained? The distribution ratio of iodine between chloroform and water at 25° is 250.

16-18. The distribution ratio of iodine between carbon disulfide and water is 586. When a distribution experiment was made using 0.25 F KI solution instead of water, the amounts of dissolved iodine were found to be 0.0200 mole/l in the carbon disulfide and 0.0060 mole/l in the aqueous iodine solution. Assuming that in water the iodine is present as the dissolved molecular species I_2, calculate the concentrations of I_2 and I_3^- in the aqueous iodide solution.

Chapter 17

Sulfur, Selenium, and Tellurium

The sixth-group elements sulfur, selenium, and tellurium are much less electronegative than their congener oxygen (Chap. 5), and their chemical properties are correspondingly distinctive.

17–1. *The Oxidation States of Sulfur*

The principal oxidation states of sulfur are -2, 0, $+4$, and $+6$. These states are represented by many important substances, including those given in the diagram below.

$+6$	$\begin{cases} H_2SO_4 \\ SO_4^{--} \\ SO_3 \end{cases}$	sulfuric acid sulfate ion sulfur trioxide
$+4$	$\begin{cases} H_2SO_3 \\ SO_3^{--} \\ SO_2 \end{cases}$	sulfurous acid sulfite ion sulfur dioxide
0	S_8	sulfur
-1	Na_2S_2	sodium disulfide
-2	$\begin{cases} H_2S \\ S^{--} \end{cases}$	hydrogen sulfide sulfide ion

17–2. *Elementary Sulfur*

Orthorhombic and Monoclinic Sulfur.   Ordinary sulfur is a yellow solid substance which forms crystals with orthorhombic symmetry; it is called **orthorhombic sulfur** or, usually, **rhombic sulfur.** It is insoluble in water, but soluble in carbon disulfide (CS_2), carbon tetrachloride, and similar non-polar solvents, giving solutions from which well-formed crystals of sulfur can be obtained (Fig. 17-1). Some of its physical properties are given in Table 17-1.

TABLE 17-1   *Properties of Oxygen, Sulfur, Selenium, and Tellurium*

	ATOMIC NUMBER	MELTING POINT	BOILING POINT	DENSITY
Oxygen	8	$-218.4°$ C	$-183.0°$ C	1.429 g/l
Sulfur (orthorhombic)	16	$119.25°, 112.8°$	$444.6°$	2.07 g/cm^3
Selenium (gray)	34	$217°$	$688°$	4.79
Tellurium (gray)	52	$452°$	$1,390°$	6.25

At 112.8° C orthorhombic sulfur melts to form a straw-colored liquid. This liquid crystallizes in a monoclinic crystalline form, called β-sulfur or **monoclinic sulfur** (Fig. 17-1). The sulfur molecules in both orthorhombic sulfur and monoclinic sulfur, as well as in the straw-colored liquid, are S_8 molecules, with a staggered-ring configuration (Fig. 10-3). The formation of this large molecule (and of the similar molecules Se_8 and Te_8) is the expression of the bicovalence of the sixth-group elements by forming two single covalent bonds, instead of one double bond. Diatomic molecules S_2 are formed by heating sulfur vapor (S_8 at lower temperatures) to a high temperature, but these molecules are less stable than the large molecules containing single bonds. This fact is not iso-

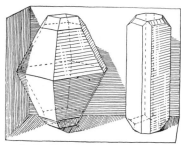

Orthorhombic   Monoclinic
      Sulfur

FIG. 17-1

Crystals of orthorhombic and monoclinic sulfur.

lated, but is an example of the generalization that stable double bonds and triple bonds are formed readily by the light elements carbon, nitrogen, and oxygen, but only rarely by the heavier elements. Carbon

disulfide, CS_2, with electronic structure : $\ddot{S}{=}C{=}\ddot{S}$:, and other compounds containing a carbon-sulfur double bond are the main exceptions to this rule.

Monoclinic sulfur is the stable form above 95.5° C, which is the *equilibrium temperature* (*transition temperature* or *transition point*) between it

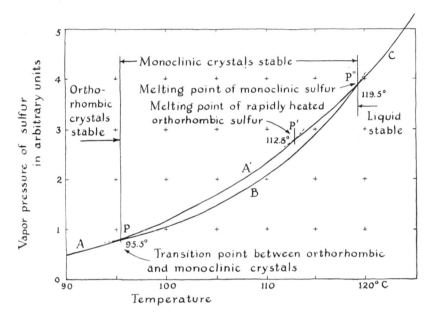

FIG. 17-2   *Vapor-pressure curves for sulfur.*

and the orthorhombic form. Monoclinic sulfur melts at 119.25° C. This is the true melting point of sulfur.

The equilibrium relations between the two crystalline forms of sulfur and the liquid may be clarified by Figure 17-2, which shows the vapor-pressure curves for the three phases plotted against the temperature. The curve A shows the vapor pressure of orthorhombic sulfur, B that of monoclinic sulfur, and C that of liquid sulfur. At a given temperature the phase with the smallest vapor pressure is the stable phase; if another phase, with larger vapor pressure, were present, it would evaporate, and the vapor would condense as the phase with smaller vapor pressure. Hence below 95.5° C the stable phase is orthorhombic sulfur, from 95.5° to 119.25° it is monoclinic sulfur, and above 119.25° (up to the boiling point) it is liquid sulfur. If orthorhombic sulfur is heated *very slowly*, it changes to monoclinic sulfur at the transition temperature 95.5°, and then melts at 119.25°.

Sometimes a transition between two crystalline phases occurs very rapidly. That between orthorhombic sulfur and monoclinic sulfur is rather slow, however, taking minutes or hours, and it is hence easy to superheat orthorhombic sulfur by heating it rapidly. If this is done, the vapor pressure of the crystals increases as shown by the curve A′, and at the point P′, where this curve crosses the vapor-pressure curve of the liquid, the crystals melt. The temperature at P′, 112.8° C, is the melting point of rapidly heated orthorhombic sulfur. It does not correspond to a true equilibrium: if the liquid is allowed to stand for a short time at a temperature between 112.8° and 119.25° it crystallizes as the phase stable at that temperature, monoclinic sulfur.

A rhombohedral form, containing S_6 molecules, also can be made.

Liquid Sulfur. Sulfur which has just been melted is a mobile, straw-colored liquid. The viscosity of this liquid is low because the S_8 molecules which compose it are nearly spherical in shape (Fig. 10-3) and roll easily over one another. When molten sulfur is heated to a higher temperature, however, it gradually darkens in color and becomes more viscous, finally becoming so thick (at 230°) that it cannot be poured out of its container. Most substances decrease in viscosity with increasing temperature, because the increased thermal agitation causes the molecules to move around one another more easily. The abnormal behavior of liquid sulfur results from the production of molecules of a different kind—long chains, containing scores of atoms. These very long molecules get entangled with one another, causing the liquid to be very viscous. The dark-red color is due to the ends of the chains, which consist of sulfur atoms with only one valence bond instead of the normal two.

The straw-colored liquid, S_8, is called λ-sulfur, and the dark-red liquid consisting of very long chains is called μ-sulfur. When this liquid is rapidly cooled by being poured into water it forms a rubbery *supercooled liquid*, insoluble in carbon disulfide. On standing for a few days at room temperature the long chains rearrange themselves into S_8 molecules, and the rubbery mass changes into an aggregate of crystals of orthorhombic sulfur.

Sulfur boils at 444.6°, forming vapor which contains S_8, S_6, and S_2 molecules. When cooled, the vapor condenses to form *flowers of sulfur*, which is only partially soluble in carbon disulfide, and consists of a mixture of molecular species.

The Mining of Sulfur.   Free sulfur occurs in large quantities in Sicily, Louisiana, and Texas. The Sicilian deposits consist of rock (clay, gypsum, limestone) mixed with about 20% free sulfur. The rock is heated by burning part of the sulfur, and molten sulfur is drawn off, and then purified by sublimation.

Over 80% of the world's production of sulfur is mined in Louisiana and Texas by a clever method, the Frasch process. The sulfur, mixed with limestone, occurs at depths of about one thousand feet, under strata of sand, clay, and rock. A boring is made to the deposit, and four

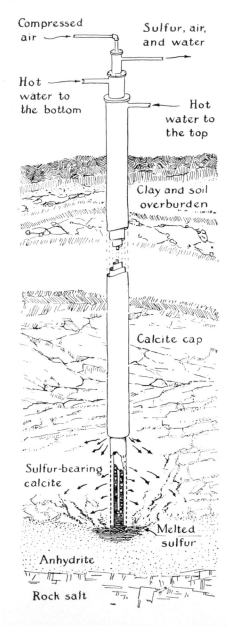

FIG. 17-3

The Frasch process for mining sulfur. (The mineral anhydrite which lies below the sulfur-calcite layer is anhydrous calcium sulfate, CaSO₄.)

concentric pipes are sunk (Fig. 17-3). Superheated water (155°) is pumped down the two outer pipes. This melts the sulfur, which collects in a pool around the open end. Air is forced down the innermost pipe, and a bubbly froth of air, sulfur, and water rises through the space between the innermost pipe and the next one. This mixture is allowed to flow into a very large wooden vat, where the sulfur hardens as a product 99.5% pure.

17–3. *Hydrogen Sulfide and the Sulfides of the Metals*

Hydrogen sulfide, H_2S, is analogous to water, its electronic structure

being $: \overset{\overset{\displaystyle H}{|}}{\underset{\cdot\cdot}{S}}$—H. It is far more volatile (m.p. $-85.6°$ C, b.p. $-60.7°$) than

water, because of its much smaller tendency to form hydrogen bonds. It is appreciably soluble in cold water (2.6 l of gas dissolving in 1 l of water at 20°), forming a slightly acidic solution. The solution is slowly oxidized by atmospheric oxygen, giving a milky precipitate of sulfur.

Hydrogen sulfide has a powerful odor, resembling that of rotten eggs. It is very poisonous, and care must be taken not to breathe the gas while using it in the analytical chemistry laboratory.

Hydrogen sulfide is readily prepared by action of hydrochloric acid on ferrous sulfide:

$$2HCl + FeS \longrightarrow FeCl_2 + H_2S \uparrow$$

The preparation is conveniently carried out in a Kipp generator; this apparatus permits the gas to be produced as it is used. It can also be obtained commercially under pressure in steel bottles or tanks.

The **sulfides** of the alkali and alkaline-earth metals are colorless substances easily soluble in water. The sulfides of most other metals are insoluble or only very slightly soluble in water, and their precipitation under varying conditions is an important part of the usual scheme of qualitative analysis for the metallic ions. Many metallic sulfides occur in nature; important sulfide ores include FeS, Cu_2S, CuS, ZnS, Ag_2S, HgS, and PbS.

The Polysulfides. Sulfur dissolves in a solution of an alkali or alkaline-earth sulfide, forming a mixture of polysulfides:

$$S^{--} + \tfrac{1}{8}S_8 \longrightarrow S_2^{--}, \text{ disulfide ion}$$
$$S^{--} + \tfrac{1}{4}S_8 \longrightarrow S_3^{--}, \text{ trisulfide ion}$$
$$S^{--} + \tfrac{3}{8}S_8 \longrightarrow S_4^{--}, \text{ tetrasulfide ion}$$

The disulfide ion has the structure $\left[\; :\overset{\cdot\cdot}{\underset{\cdot\cdot}{S}} - \overset{\cdot\cdot}{\underset{\cdot\cdot}{S}}\; :\right]^{--}$, analogous to that

of the peroxide ion, and the polysulfides have similar structures,

$$\left[\begin{array}{c} \overset{\cdot\cdot}{S} \\ \diagup \;\; \diagdown \\ :\!\overset{\cdot}{\underset{\cdot\cdot}{S}}\;\;\;\;\; \overset{\cdot}{\underset{\cdot\cdot}{S}}: \end{array} \right]^{--} , \left[\begin{array}{c} \overset{\cdot\cdot}{S}\;\;\;\;\; \overset{\cdot\cdot}{S}: \\ \diagup \diagdown \diagup \\ :\!\overset{}{\underset{\cdot\cdot}{S}}\;\;\;\;\; \overset{}{\underset{\cdot\cdot}{S}}: \end{array} \right]^{--} , \text{ etc.}$$

Hydrogen disulfide, H_2S_2, analogous to hydrogen peroxide, can be made by careful treatment of a disulfide with acid; however, the hydrogen polysulfides readily decompose to hydrogen sulfide and sulfur.

The common mineral *pyrite,* FeS_2, is ferrous disulfide.

17–4. *Sulfur Dioxide and Sulfurous Acid*

Sulfur dioxide, SO_2, is the gas formed by burning sulfur or sulfides, such as pyrite:

$$S + O_2 \longrightarrow SO_2$$
$$4FeS_2 + 11O_2 \longrightarrow 2Fe_2O_3 + 8SO_2 \uparrow$$

It is colorless, and has a characteristic choking odor.

Sulfur dioxide is conveniently made in the laboratory by adding a strong acid to solid sodium hydrogen sulfite:

$$HCl + NaHSO_3 \longrightarrow NaCl + H_2O + SO_2 \uparrow$$

It may be purified and dried by bubbling it through concentrated sul-furic acid, and, since it is over twice as dense as air, it may be collected by displacement of air.

A solution of **sulfurous acid,** H_2SO_3, is obtained by dissolving sulfur dioxide in water. Both sulfurous acid and its salts, the **sulfites,** are active reducing agents. They form sulfuric acid, H_2SO_4, and sulfates on oxidation by oxygen, the halogens, hydrogen peroxide, and similar oxidizing agents.

The electronic structure of sulfur dioxide is

$$\left\{ \begin{array}{cc} \overset{\cdot\cdot}{O}: & \overset{\cdot\cdot}{O}: \\ \diagup\;\overset{\cdot\cdot}{} & \diagup\!\!\diagup \\ :S & :S \\ \diagdown\!\!\diagdown & \diagdown \\ \underset{\cdot\cdot}{O}: & \overset{\cdot\cdot}{\underset{\cdot\cdot}{O}}: \end{array} \right\}$$

It is a resonating structure in which each sulfur-oxygen bond is a hybrid between a single bond and a double bond. In sulfurous acid one oxygen atom is replaced by two hydroxyl groups:

In each of these molecules the sulfur atom has one unshared pair of electrons; this is characteristic of atoms with oxidation number two less than the maximum.

Sulfur dioxide is used in great quantities in the manufacture of sulfuric acid, sulfurous acid, and sulfites. It destroys fungi and bacteria, and is used as preservative in the preparation of dried prunes, apricots, and other fruits. A solution of calcium hydrogen sulfite, $Ca(HSO_3)_2$, made by reaction of sulfur dioxide and calcium hydroxide, is used in the manufacture of paper pulp from wood. The solution dissolves lignin, a substance which cements the cellulose fibers together, and liberates these fibers, which are then processed into paper.

17–5. *Sulfur Trioxide*

Sulfur trioxide, SO_3, is formed in very small quantities when sulfur is burned in air. It is usually made by oxidation of sulfur dioxide by air, in the presence of a catalyst. The reaction

$$2SO_2 + O_2 \rightleftharpoons 2SO_3$$

is exothermic; it liberates 45 kcal of heat for two moles of sulfur trioxide produced. The principle of Le Châtelier accordingly requires that the equilibrium between the reactants and the product be shifted to the left (the direction that absorbs heat) when the temperature is raised. The nature of the equilibrium is such that at low temperatures a satisfactory yield can be obtained when the reaction proceeds nearly to equilibrium. However, the rate of the reaction is so small at low temperatures as to make the direct combination of the substances unsuitable as a commercial process, and at higher temperatures, where the rate is satisfactory, the yield is low because of the unfavorable equilibrium.

The solution to this problem was the discovery of catalysts (platinum, vanadium pentoxide) which speed up the reaction without affecting the equilibrium. The catalyzed reaction proceeds not in the gaseous mixture, but on the surface of the catalyst, as the gas molecules strike it. In practice sulfur dioxide, made by burning sulfur or pyrite, is mixed with air and passed over the catalyst at a temperature of 400–450° C. About 99% of the sulfur dioxide is converted into sulfur trioxide under these conditions. It is used mainly in the manufacture of sulfuric acid.

Sulfur trioxide is a corrosive gas, which combines vigorously with water to form sulfuric acid:

$$SO_3 + H_2O \longrightarrow H_2SO_4$$

It also dissolves readily in sulfuric acid, to form *oleum* or *fuming sulfuric acid*, which consists mainly of **disulfuric acid,** $H_2S_2O_7$ (also called **pyrosulfuric acid**):

$$SO_3 + H_2SO_4 \rightleftarrows H_2S_2O_7$$

Sulfur trioxide condenses at 44.5° to a colorless liquid, which freezes at 16.8° to transparent crystals. The substance is polymorphous, these crystals being the unstable form (the α-form). The stable form consists of silky asbestos-like crystals, which are produced when the α-crystals or the liquid stands for some time, especially in the presence of a trace of moisture. There exist also one or more other forms of the substance, which are hard to investigate because the changes from one form to another are very slow. The asbestos-like crystals slowly evaporate to SO_3 vapor at temperatures above 50°.

The Structure of Sulfur Trioxide and Its Derivatives.   The sulfur trioxide molecule in the gas phase, the liquid, and the α-crystals has the electronic structure

The molecule is planar, and each bond is a resonance hybrid, as indicated.

The properties of sulfur trioxide may be in large part explained as resulting from the instability of the sulfur-oxygen double bond. Thus by reaction with water the double bond can be replaced by two single bonds, in sulfuric acid:

$$
\begin{array}{ccc}
\text{H}\!-\!\ddot{\text{O}}: & & :\ddot{\text{O}}\!-\!\text{H} \\
& \diagdown \ \diagup & \\
& \text{S} & \\
& \diagup \ \diagdown & \\
:\!\ddot{\text{O}}: & & :\ddot{\text{O}}: \\
\end{array}
$$

The increased stability of the product is reflected in the large amount of heat evolved in the reaction. A second sulfur trioxide molecule can eliminate its double bond by combining with a molecule of sulfuric acid to form a molecule of disulfuric acid:

$$
\begin{array}{ccccc}
 & :\ddot{\text{O}}: & & :\ddot{\text{O}}: & \\
 & \diagdown & & \diagup & \\
 & & \text{S} & & \\
 & \diagup & & \diagdown & \\
\text{H}\!-\!\ddot{\text{O}}: & & :\ddot{\text{O}}: & & :\ddot{\text{O}}.\!-\!\text{H} \\
\diagdown & & \diagup & & \\
 & \text{S} & & & \\
\diagup & & \diagdown & & \\
:\!\ddot{\text{O}}: & & :\ddot{\text{O}}: & & \\
\end{array}
$$

Similarly, molecules of trisulfuric acid, $H_2S_3O_{10}$, tetrasulfuric acid, $H_2S_4O_{13}$, etc., can be formed (Fig. 17-4), culminating in a chain, $HO_3SO(SO_3)_\infty SO_3H$, of nearly infinite length—essentially a high polymer of sulfur trioxide, $(SO_3)_x$, with x large. *It is these very long molecules that constitute the asbestos-like crystalline form of sulfur trioxide.* We can understand why the crystals are fibrous, like asbestos—they consist of extremely long chain molecules, arranged together side by side, but easily separated into fibers, because, although the chains themselves are strong, the forces between them are relatively weak.

The molecular structures explain why the formation of the asbestos-like crystals, and also their decomposition to SO_3 vapor, are slow processes, whereas crystallization and evaporation are usually rapid. In this case these processes are really *chemical reactions,* involving the formation of new chemical bonds. The role of a trace of water in catalyzing the formation of the asbestos-like crystals can also be understood; the molecules of water serve to start the chains, which can then grow to great length.

17–6. *Sulfuric Acid and the Sulfates*

Sulfuric acid, H_2SO_4, is one of the most important of all chemicals, finding use throughout the chemical industry and related industries.

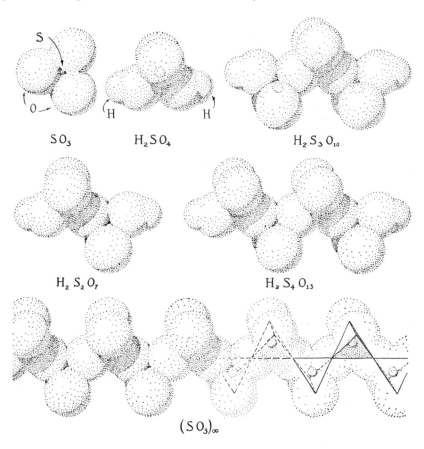

S O_3 H_2SO_4 $H_2S_3O_{10}$

$H_2S_2O_7$ $H_2S_4O_{13}$

$(SO_3)_\infty$

FIG. 17-4   *Sulfur trioxide and some oxygen acids of sulfur.*

It is a heavy, oily liquid (density 1.838 g/cm³), which fumes slightly in air, as the result of the liberation of traces of sulfur trioxide which then combine with water vapor to form droplets of sulfuric acid. When heated, pure sulfuric acid yields a vapor rich in sulfur trioxide, and then boils, at 338°, with the constant composition 98% H_2SO_4, 2% water. This is the ordinary "concentrated sulfuric acid" of commerce.

Concentrated sulfuric acid is very corrosive. It has a strong affinity for water, and a large amount of heat is liberated when it is mixed with water, as the result of the formation of hydronium ion:

$$H_2SO_4 + 2H_2O \rightleftharpoons 2H_3O^+ + SO_4^{--}$$

In diluting it, the concentrated acid should be poured into water in a thin stream, with stirring; water should never be poured into the acid, because it is apt to sputter and throw drops of acid out of the container. The diluted acid occupies a smaller volume than its constituents, the contraction being a maximum at $H_2SO_4 + 2H_2O$ [$(H_3O)^+_2 (SO_4)^{--}$].

The crystalline phases which form on cooling sulfuric acid containing varying amounts of sulfur trioxide or water are $H_2S_2O_7$, H_2SO_4, $H_2SO_4 \cdot H_2O$ [presumably $(H_3O)^+(HSO_4)^-$], $H_2SO_4 \cdot 2H_2O$ [$(H_3O)^+_2(SO_4)^{--}$], and $H_2SO_4 \cdot 4H_2O$.

The Manufacture of Sulfuric Acid. Sulfuric acid is made by two processes, the **contact process** and the **lead-chamber process,** which are now about equally important. In the contact process sulfur trioxide is made by the catalytic oxidation of sulfur dioxide (the name of the process refers to the fact that reaction occurs on contact of the gases with the solid catalyst). The gas containing sulfur trioxide is then bubbled through sulfuric acid, which absorbs the sulfur trioxide. Water is added at the proper rate, and 98% acid is drawn off.

The principle of the lead-chamber process is shown by the following experiment. A large flask is fitted with four inlet tubes and a small outlet tube. Three of the tubes come from wash bottles, and the fourth from a flask in which water may be boiled. When oxygen, sulfur dioxide, nitric oxide, and a small amount of water vapor are introduced into the large

flask, white crystals of nitrososulfuric acid,

$$\begin{array}{ccc} HO & & O-N=O \\ & \diagdown \, \diagup & \\ & S & \\ & \diagup \, \diagdown & \\ O & & O \end{array}$$

(sulfuric acid in which one hydrogen atom is replaced by the nitroso group,

$-\ddot{N}=\ddot{O}:$), are formed. When steam is sent into the flask by boiling the water in the small flask, the crystals react to form drops of sulfuric acid, liberating oxides of nitrogen. In effect, the oxides of nitrogen serve to catalyze the oxidation of sulfur dioxide by oxygen. The complex reactions which occur may be summarized as

$$2SO_2 + NO + NO_2 + O_2 + H_2O \longrightarrow 2HSO_4NO$$
$$2HSO_4NO + H_2O \longrightarrow 2H_2SO_4 + NO\uparrow + NO_2\uparrow$$

The oxides of nitrogen, NO and NO_2, which take part in the first reaction are released by the second reaction, and can serve over and over again.

In practice the reactions take place in large lead-lined chambers. The acid produced, called *chamber acid*, is from 65% to 70% H_2SO_4. It may be concentrated to 78% H_2SO_4 by the evaporation of water by the hot gases from the sulfur burner or pyrite burner. This process occurs as the acid trickles down over acid-resistant tile in a tower. A similar tower is used to remove the nitrogen oxides from the exhaust gases; the oxides of nitrogen are then reintroduced into the chamber.

The Chemical Properties and Uses of Sulfuric Acid.   The uses of sulfuric acid are determined by its chemical properties—as an **acid**, a **dehydrating agent**, and an **oxidizing agent**.

Sulfuric acid has a high boiling point, 330° C, which permits it to be used with salts of more volatile acids in the preparation of these acids. Nitric acid, for example, can be made by heating a nitrate, such as sodium nitrate, with sulfuric acid:

$$2NaNO_3 + H_2SO_4 \longrightarrow Na_2SO_4 + 2HNO_3\uparrow$$

It is also used for the manufacture of soluble phosphate fertilizers (Chap. 18), of ammonium sulfate for use as a fertilizer, of other sulfates, and of many chemicals and drugs. Steel is usually cleaned of iron rust (is "pickled") by immersion in a bath of sulfuric acid before it is coated with zinc, tin, or enamel. The use of sulfuric acid as the electrolyte in ordinary storage cells has been mentioned (Chap. 13).

Sulfuric acid has such a strong affinity for water as to make it an effective dehydrating agent. Gases which do not react with the substance may be dried by being bubbled through sulfuric acid. The dehydrating power of the concentrated acid is great enough to cause it to remove hydrogen and oxygen as water from organic compounds, such as sugar:

$$C_{12}H_{22}O_{11} \xrightarrow{} 12C + 11H_2O$$
sugar (sucrose) H_2SO_4

(The symbol $\xrightarrow[H_2SO_4]{}$ is used to show that H_2SO_4 assists in causing the reaction to go to the right.) Many explosives, such as glyceryl trinitrate (nitroglycerine), are made by reaction of organic substances with nitric acid, producing the explosive substance and water:

$$C_3H_5(OH)_3 + 3HNO_3 \longrightarrow C_3H_5(NO_3)_3 + 3H_2O$$
glycerine   glyceryl trinitrate

These reactions are made to proceed to the right by mixing the nitric acid with sulfuric acid, which by its dehydrating action favors the products.

Hot concentrated sulfuric acid is an effective oxidizing agent, the product of its reduction being sulfur dioxide. It will dissolve copper, and will even oxidize carbon:

$$Cu + 2H_2SO_4 \longrightarrow CuSO_4 + 2H_2O + SO_2 \uparrow$$
$$C + 2H_2SO_4 \longrightarrow CO_2 \uparrow + 2H_2O + 2SO_2 \uparrow$$

The solution of copper by hot concentrated sulfuric acid illustrates a general reaction—the solution of an unreactive metal in an acid under the influence of an oxidizing agent. The reactive metals, above hydrogen in the electromotive-force series, are oxidized to their cations by hydrogen ion, which is itself reduced to elementary hydrogen; for example,

$$Zn + 2H^+ \longrightarrow Zn^{++} + H_2 \uparrow$$

Copper is below hydrogen in the series, and does not undergo this reaction. It can be oxidized to cupric ion, however, by a stronger oxidizing agent, such as chlorine or nitric acid or, as illustrated above, hot concentrated sulfuric acid.

Sulfates.   Sulfuric acid combines with bases to form *normal sulfates*, such as K_2SO_4, potassium sulfate, and *hydrogen sulfates* or *acid sulfates* (sometimes called *bisulfates*), such as $KHSO_4$, potassium hydrogen sulfate.

The nearly insoluble sulfates occur as minerals: these include $CaSO_4 \cdot 2H_2O$ (*gypsum*), $SrSO_4$, $BaSO_4$ (*barite*), and $PbSO_4$. Barium sulfate is the least soluble of the sulfates, and its formation as a white precipitate is used as a test for sulfate ion.

Common soluble sulfates include $Na_2SO_4 \cdot 10H_2O$, $(NH_4)_2SO_4$, $MgSO_4 \cdot 7H_2O$ (Epsom salt), $CuSO_4 \cdot 5H_2O$ (blue vitriol), $FeSO_4 \cdot 7H_2O$, $(NH_4)_2Fe(SO_4)_2 \cdot 6H_2O$ (a well-crystallized, easily purified salt used in analytical chemistry in making standard solutions of ferrous ion), $ZnSO_4 \cdot 7H_2O$, $KAl(SO_4)_2 \cdot 12H_2O$ (alum), $NH_4Al(SO_4)_2 \cdot 12H_2O$ (ammonium alum), and $KCr(SO_4)_2 \cdot 12H_2O$ (chrome alum).

The Peroxysulfuric Acids.   Sulfuric acid contains sulfur in its highest oxidation state. When a strong oxidizing agent (hydrogen peroxide or an anode at suitable electrical potential) acts on sulfuric acid, the only oxidation which can occur is that of oxygen atoms, from -2 to -1. The products of this oxidation, *peroxysulfuric acid*, H_2SO_5, and *peroxydisulfuric acid*, $H_2S_2O_8$, have been mentioned near the end of Chapter 11. These acids and their salts are used as bleaching agents.

17–7. *The Thio or Sulfo Acids*

Sodium thiosulfate, $Na_2S_2O_3 \cdot 5H_2O$ (incorrectly called "hypo," from an old name, "sodium hyposulfite"), is a substance used in photography (Chap. 27). It is made by boiling a solution of sodium sulfite with free sulfur:

$$SO_3^{--} + S \longrightarrow S_2O_3^{--}$$

sulfite ion   thiosulfate ion

Thiosulfuric acid, $H_2S_2O_3$, is unstable, and sulfur dioxide and sulfur are formed when a thiosulfate is treated with acid.

The structure of the thiosulfate ion, $S_2O_3^{--}$, is interesting in that the two sulfur atoms are not equivalent. This ion is a sulfate ion, SO_4^{--}, in which one of the oxygen atoms has been replaced by a sulfur atom. The central sulfur atom may be assigned oxidation number $+6$, and the attached sulfur atom oxidation number -2.

Thiosulfate ion is easily oxidized, especially by iodine, to **tetrathionate ion,** $S_4O_6^{--}$:

$$2S_2O_3^{--} \longrightarrow S_4O_6^{--} + 2e^-$$

or

$$2S_2O_3^{--} + I_2 \longrightarrow S_4O_6^{--} + 2I^-$$

The structure of the tetrathionate ion is shown in Figure 17–5; it contains a disulfide group $-\overset{\cdot\cdot}{\underset{\cdot\cdot}{S}}-\overset{\cdot\cdot}{\underset{\cdot\cdot}{S}}-$ in place of the peroxide group of the peroxydisulfate ion. The oxidation of thiosulfate ion to tetrathionate ion is analogous to the oxidation of sulfide ion, S^{--}, to disulfide ion,

$$\left[:\overset{\cdot\cdot}{\underset{\cdot\cdot}{S}} - \overset{\cdot\cdot}{\underset{\cdot\cdot}{S}}: \right]^{--} , \text{ by the reaction}$$

$$2S^{--} \longrightarrow S_2^{--} + 2e^-$$

Thiosulfuric acid is representative of a general class of acids, called **thio acids** or **sulfo acids,** in which one or more oxygen atoms of an oxygen acid are replaced by sulfur atoms. For example, arsenic pentasulfide dissolves in a sodium sulfide solution to form the thioarsenate ion, AsS_4^{---}, completely analogous to the arsenate ion, AsO_4^{---}:

$$As_2S_5 + 3S^{--} \longrightarrow 2AsS_4^{---}$$

Arsenic trisulfide also dissolves, to form the thioarsenite ion:

$$As_2S_3 + 3S^{--} \longrightarrow 2AsS_3^{---}$$

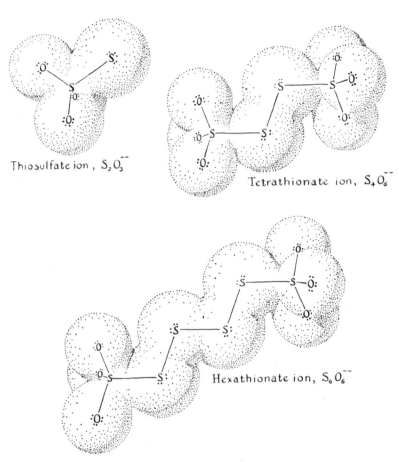

Thiosulfate ion, $S_2O_3^{--}$

Tetrathionate ion, $S_4O_6^{--}$

Hexathionate ion, $S_6O_6^{--}$

FIG. 17-5   *The thiosulfate ion and related ions.*

If disulfide ion, S_2^{--}, is present in the solution, the thioarsenite ion is oxidized to thioarsenate ion:

$$AsS_3^{---} + S_2^{--} \longrightarrow AsS_4^{---} + S^{--}$$

An alkaline solution of sodium sulfide and sodium disulfide (or of the ammonium sulfides) is used in the usual systems of qualitative analysis as a means of separating the precipitated sulfides of certain metals and metalloids. This separation depends upon the property of certain sulfides (HgS, As_2S_3, As_2S_5, Sb_2S_3, Sb_2S_5, SnS, SnS_2) to form thio anions (HgS_2^{--}, AsS_4^{---}, SbS_4^{---}, SnS_4^{----}), whereas others (Ag_2S, PbS, Bi_2S_3, CuS, CdS) remain undissolved.

17–8. *Selenium and Tellurium*

The elementary substances selenium and tellurium differ from sulfur in their physical properties in ways expected from their relative positions in the periodic table. Their melting points, boiling points, and densities are higher, as shown in Table 17-1.

The increase in metallic character with increase in molecular weight is striking. Sulfur is a non-conductor of electricity, as is the red allotropic form of selenium. The gray form of selenium has a small but measurable electric conductivity, and tellurium is a semi-conductor, with conductivity a fraction of 1% of that of metals. An interesting property of the

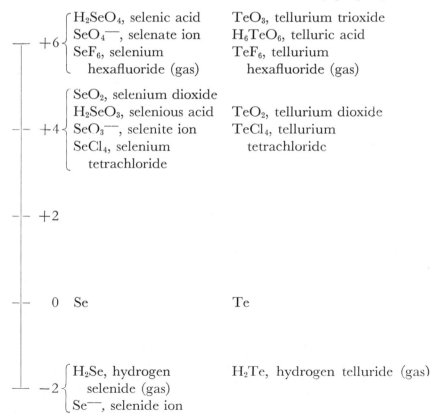

$+6$
H_2SeO_4, selenic acid
SeO_4^{--}, selenate ion
SeF_6, selenium hexafluoride (gas)

TeO_3, tellurium trioxide
H_6TeO_6, telluric acid
TeF_6, tellurium hexafluoride (gas)

$+4$
SeO_2, selenium dioxide
H_2SeO_3, selenious acid
SeO_3^{--}, selenite ion
$SeCl_4$, selenium tetrachloride

TeO_2, tellurium dioxide
$TeCl_4$, tellurium tetrachloride

$+2$

0 Se   Te

-2
H_2Se, hydrogen selenide (gas)
Se^{--}, selenide ion

H_2Te, hydrogen telluride (gas)

gray form of selenium is that its electric conductivity is greatly increased during exposure to visible light. This property is used in "selenium cells" for the measurement of light intensity.

Selenium is also used to impart a ruby-red color to glass, and to neutralize the green color in glass which is due to the presence of iron.

Selenium and tellurium are similar to sulfur in chemical properties, but are less electronegative (more metallic) in character. In addition, sexipositive tellurium shows increase in coordination number from 4 to 6, telluric acid being H_6TeO_6. Representative compounds are shown in the preceding chart.

Exercises

17-1. Write an oxidation-reduction equation for the formation of an acid of each of the important oxidation states of sulfur.

17-2. What order of solubility in a suitable organic solvent do you predict for
(a) orthorhombic sulfur, supercooled monoclinic sulfur, and supercooled λ-sulfur at 90° C
(b) superheated orthorhombic sulfur, monoclinic sulfur, and supercooled λ-sulfur at 100° C
(c) same as b at 115° C.
Remember that a saturated solution has the same vapor pressure of solute as the crystalline solute in equilibrium with it.

17-3. The density of orthorhombic sulfur is 2.07 g/cm³ and that of monoclinic sulfur is 1.96; apply Le Châtelier's rule to predict the effect of the application of pressure on the equilibrium temperature between the two forms.

17-4. Describe the Frasch process of mining sulfur.

17-5. What is the electronic structure of Na_2S_4?

17-6. What happens when a polysulfide is treated with acid?

17-7. Write chemical equations for the preparation of each of the substances H_2S, SO_2, and SO_3 by (a) a chemical reaction in which there is an oxidation or reduction of the sulfur atom; (b) a chemical reaction in which there is no change in the oxidation number of the sulfur.

17-8. Give the names and formulas of two natural sources of sulfur.

17-9. What is the role of a catalyst in the oxidation of SO_2 to SO_3?

17-10. Explain as fully as you can the properties of sulfur trioxide in terms of its electronic structure.

17-11. How would you make up a solution approximately 0.01 M in H^+ from concentrated sulfuric acid (98%, density 1.838 g/cm³)?

17-12. List all the examples that have been cited in this chapter and previous chapters of the use of concentrated sulfuric acid for the preparation of more volatile acids. Why cannot this method be applied to the preparation of hydrogen iodide gas?

17-13. Write chemical reactions illustrating the three important kinds of uses of sulfuric acid.

17-14. What is the electronic structure of pyrosulfuric acid?

17-15. What are the electronic structures of peroxysulfuric acid and peroxydisulfuric acid?

17-16. Write electronic-structure equations for
(a) sulfite ion and sulfur to give thiosulfate ion
(b) thiosulfate ion and iodine to give tetrathionate ion plus iodide ion.

17-17. A solution is made such that one liter contains 12.41 g of $Na_2S_2O_3 \cdot 5H_2O$. Exactly 35.00 ml of this solution is required to just decolorize 50.00 ml of a solution of I_3^- ion. What is the concentration of the I_3^- solution?

17-18. Give the names and formulas of the oxides and oxygen acids of selenium and tellurium.

Chapter 18

Nitrogen, Phosphorus, Arsenic, Antimony, and Bismuth

The properties of the elements of the fifth group of the periodic table change in a striking manner with increase in atomic number, from nitrogen to bismuth. Nitrogen is a stable, unreactive gas. Phosphorus, also a non-metallic substance, is unstable and very reactive. Arsenic, antimony, and bismuth are metalloids, with metallic character increasing in this order. The principal oxygen acid of nitrogen has the formula HNO_3, that of phosphorus the formula H_3PO_4, that of arsenic the formula H_3AsO_4, and that of antimony the formula $HSb(OH)_6$. The trichloride of nitrogen is an extremely unstable, highly explosive substance; the trichlorides of phosphorus, arsenic, antimony, and bismuth are stable compounds.

Many of the properties of these elements can be understood by the consideration of some of the properties of their atoms. Nitrogen is a very electronegative substance, its electronegativity (3 on the electronegativity scale) being exceeded only by the electronegativities of oxygen and fluorine. Phosphorus, arsenic, antimony, and bismuth have smaller electronegativities, with values 2.1, 2.0, 1.8, and 1.7, respectively. The increase in metallic character from nitrogen to bismuth and the great difference in stability of the trichlorides can be accounted for by the change in electronegativity. The stability of the ammonium ion, NH_4^+, has been discussed in Chapter 10. Nitrogen, like carbon and oxygen, tends to form multiple bonds, as in the elementary substance,

N≡N; phosphorus and its heavier congeners prefer to form only single bonds. The nitrogen atom is small, the single-bond covalent radius of nitrogen being 0.70 Å, and the atom can surround itself comfortably with only three oxygen atoms. Phosphorus, with covalent radius 1.10 Å, and arsenic, with covalent radius 1.21 Å, are large enough to surround themselves comfortably with four oxygen atoms, in a tetrahedral configuration, as in phosphoric acid, H_3PO_4, and arsenic acid, H_3AsO_4. The antimony atom has single-bond covalent radius 1.41 Å; it can surround itself with six oxygen atoms, in antimonic acid, $H[Sb(OH)_6]$.

18–1. *The Oxidation States of Nitrogen*

Compounds of nitrogen are known representing all oxidation levels from −3 to +5. Some of these compounds are shown in the following chart:

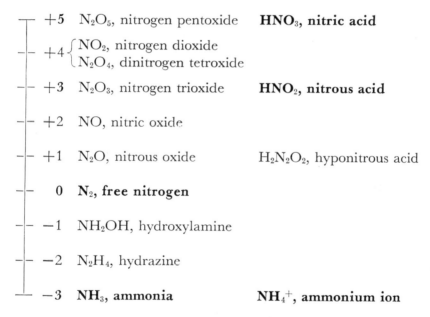

+5	N_2O_5, nitrogen pentoxide	**HNO$_3$, nitric acid**	
+4	NO_2, nitrogen dioxide N_2O_4, dinitrogen tetroxide		
+3	N_2O_3, nitrogen trioxide	**HNO$_2$, nitrous acid**	
+2	NO, nitric oxide		
+1	N_2O, nitrous oxide	$H_2N_2O_2$, hyponitrous acid	
0	**N$_2$, free nitrogen**		
−1	NH_2OH, hydroxylamine		
−2	N_2H_4, hydrazine		
−3	**NH$_3$, ammonia**	**NH$_4{}^+$, ammonium ion**	

It was mentioned in Chapter 6 that free nitrogen is surprisingly stable, and that this stability is responsible for the explosive properties of many nitrogen compounds. Usually a triple bond in a molecule causes the molecule to be less stable than molecules containing only single bonds; for example, acetylene, H—C≡C—H, is explosive, and sometimes undergoes violent detonation. The triple bond in the nitrogen molecule, : N≡N :, however, seems to be especially stable. It has been estimated that the nitrogen molecule is 110 kcal/mole more stable than it would be if its bond were normal, with the same energy as three single bonds.

An example of an unstable nitrogen compound is nitrogen trichloride,

$$: N \begin{matrix} \overset{..}{\underset{..}{Cl}} : \\ \diagup \\ \diagdown \end{matrix} \overset{..}{\underset{..}{Cl}} :. \quad \text{Whereas other non-metallic chlorides (such as } PCl_3, CCl_4$$

SCl_2, OCl_2) are stable, this substance explodes with great violence when jarred, with the evolution of a large amount of heat:

$$2NCl_3 \longrightarrow N_2 + 3Cl_2 + 110 \text{ kcal}$$

The amount of heat liberated is just equal to the extra stability of the nitrogen molecule.

Elementary nitrogen occurs in nature in the atmosphere, of which it constitutes 78% by volume. Compounds of nitrogen are made from free nitrogen by the action of lightning, which produces oxides of nitrogen which are carried into the soil by falling rain, and then become constituents of plants and animals. Nitrogen is also removed from the atmosphere by *nitrogen-fixing bacteria*, which live in nodules on the roots of some plants, especially the legumes—beans, peas, alfalfa, clover. In recent decades man has developed methods for the fixation of atmospheric nitrogen, described below.

18–2. *Ammonia and Its Compounds*

Ammonia, NH_3, is an easily condensable gas (b.p. $-33.35°$ C, m.p. $-77.7°$ C), readily soluble in water to produce an alkaline solution.

The solution of ammonia in water, called **ammonium hydroxide** solution (or sometimes *ammonia water* or *aqua ammonia*), contains the molecular species NH_3, NH_4OH (ammonium hydroxide), NH_4^+, and OH^-. Ammonium hydroxide is a weak base, and is only slightly ionized to **ammonium ion,** NH_4^+, and hydroxide ion:

$$NH_4OH \rightleftharpoons NH_4^+ + OH^-$$

In the ammonium hydroxide molecule the ammonium ion and the hydroxide ion are held together by a hydrogen bond.

The Preparation of Ammonia. Ammonia is easily made in the laboratory by heating an ammonium salt, such as ammonium chloride,

NH$_4$Cl, with a strong alkali, such as sodium hydroxide or calcium hydroxide:

$$2NH_4Cl + Ca(OH)_2 \longrightarrow CaCl_2 + 2H_2O + 2NH_3 \uparrow$$

The gas may also be made by warming concentrated (12 N) ammonium hydroxide.

The principal commercial method of production of ammonia is the **Haber process,** the direct combination of nitrogen and hydrogen under high pressure (several hundred atmospheres) in the presence of a catalyst (usually iron, containing molybdenum or other substances to increase the catalytic activity). The gases used must be specially purified, to prevent "poisoning" the catalyst. The reaction

$$N_2 + 3H_2 \rightleftharpoons 2NH_3$$

is exothermic, and accordingly, by Le Châtelier's principle, the yield of ammonia at equilibrium is less at a high temperature than at lower temperature. However, the gases react very slowly at low temperatures, and the reaction could be used as a commercial process only when a catalyst was found which speeded up the rate satisfactorily at 500° C. Even at this relatively low temperature the equilibrium is unfavorable if the gas mixture is under atmospheric pressure, less than 0.1% of the mixture being converted to ammonia (see Chap. 20). However, it is seen by Le Châtelier's principle that increase in the total pressure favors the formation of ammonia; at 500 atmospheres pressure the equilibrium mixture is over one-third ammonia, since the increased pressure would be partially reduced by the change in volume from 4 to 2.

Smaller amounts of ammonia are obtained as a by-product in the manufacture of coke and illuminating gas by the distillation of coal, and by the cyanamide process. In the *cyanamide process* a mixture of lime and coke is heated in an electric furnace, forming calcium acetylide (calcium carbide), CaC$_2$:

$$CaO + 3C \longrightarrow CO \uparrow + CaC_2$$

Nitrogen, obtained by fractionation of liquid air, is passed over the hot calcium acetylide, forming calcium cyanamide, CaCN$_2$:

$$CaC_2 + N_2 \longrightarrow CaCN_2 + C$$

Calcium cyanamide may be used directly as a fertilizer, or may be converted into ammonia by treatment with steam under pressure:

$$CaCN_2 + 3H_2O \longrightarrow CaCO_3 + 2NH_3$$

Ammonium Salts.   The ammonium salts are similar to the potassium salts and rubidium salts in crystal form, molar volume, color, and other properties. This similarity is due to the close approximation in size of the ammonium ion (radius 1.48 Å) to these alkali ions (radius of K^+, 1.33 Å, and of Rb^+, 1.48 Å). The ammonium salts are all soluble in water, and are completely ionized in aqueous solution.

Ammonium chloride, NH_4Cl, is used in dry batteries (Chap. 13) and as a flux in soldering and welding. Ammonium sulfate, $(NH_4)_2SO_4$, is an important fertilizer, and ammonium nitrate, NH_4NO_3, mixed with other substances, is used as an explosive.

Liquid Ammonia as a Solvent.   Liquid ammonia (boiling point $-33.4°$ C) has a high dielectric constant, and is a good solvent for salts, forming ionic solutions. It also has the unusual power of dissolving the alkali metals and alkaline-earth metals without chemical reaction, to form blue solutions which have an extraordinarily high electric conductivity and a metallic luster. These metallic solutions slowly decompose, with evolution of hydrogen, forming **amides,** such as sodium amide, $NaNH_2$:

$$2Na + 2NH_3 \longrightarrow 2Na^+ + 2NH_2^- + H_2 \uparrow$$

The amides are ionized in the solution into sodium ion and the amide

ion, $\left[\begin{array}{c} H \\ \ddot{N} \diagdown \\ \diagup \\ H \end{array} \right]$, which is analogous to the hydroxide ion in aqueous

systems. The ammonium ion in liquid ammonia is analogous to the hydronium ion (hydrated hydrogen ion) in aqueous systems.

Ammonium Amalgam.   The similarity of the ammonium ion to an alkali ion suggests that it might be possible to reduce ammonium ion to ammonium metal, NH_4. This has not been accomplished; however, a solution of ammonium metal in mercury, *ammonium amalgam*, can be made by cathodic reduction.

Hydrazine, N_2H_4, has the structure $\begin{array}{c} H-\ddot{N}-\ddot{N}-H \\ \diagup \qquad \diagdown \\ H \qquad\qquad H \end{array}$, in which nitrogen has oxidation number -2. It can be made by oxidizing ammonia with sodium hypochlorite. Hydrazine is a liquid with weak basic properties, similar to those of ammonia. It forms salts such as $(N_2H_5)^+Cl^-$ and $(N_2H_6)^{++}Cl_2^-$.

Hydroxylamine, NH_2OH, has the structure
$$\begin{array}{c} H-\overset{\cdot\cdot}{N}-\overset{\cdot\cdot}{O}: \\ \diagup \qquad \diagdown \\ H \qquad\qquad H \end{array}$$
, with uninegative nitro-

gen. It can be made by reducing nitric oxide or nitric acid under suitable conditions. It is a weak base, forming salts such as hydroxylammonium chloride, $(NH_3OH)^+Cl^-$.

18–3. *The Oxides of Nitrogen*

Nitrous oxide, N_2O, is made by heating ammonium nitrate:

$$NH_4NO_3 \longrightarrow 2H_2O + N_2O \uparrow$$

It is a colorless, odorless gas, which has the property of supporting combustion by giving up its atom of oxygen, leaving molecular nitrogen. When breathed for a short time the gas causes a condition of hysteria; this effect (discovered in 1799 by Humphry Davy) led to the use of the name *laughing gas* for the substance. Longer inhalation causes unconsciousness, and the gas, mixed with air or oxygen, is used as a general anesthetic for minor operations. The gas also finds use in making whipped cream; under pressure it dissolves in the cream, and when the pressure is released it fills the cream with many small bubbles, simulating ordinary whipped cream.

Nitric oxide, NO, can be made by reduction of dilute nitric acid (about 6 N) with copper or mercury:

$$3Cu + 8H^+ + 2NO_3^- \longrightarrow 3Cu^{++} + 4H_2O + 2NO \uparrow$$

When made in this way the gas usually contains impurities such as nitrogen and nitrogen dioxide. If the gas is collected over water, in which it is only slightly soluble, the nitrogen dioxide is removed by solution in the water.

A metal or other reducing agent may reduce nitric acid to any lower stage of oxidation, producing nitrogen dioxide, nitrous acid, nitric oxide, nitrous oxide, nitrogen, hydroxylamine, hydrazine, or ammonia (ammonium ion), depending upon the conditions of the reduction. Conditions may be found which strongly favor one product, but usually appreciable amounts of other products are also formed. Nitric oxide is produced preferentially under the conditions mentioned above.

Nitric oxide is a colorless, difficultly condensable gas (b.p. $-151.7°$, m.p. $-163.6°$ C). It combines readily with oxygen to form the red gas nitrogen dioxide, NO_2.

Dinitrogen trioxide, N_2O_3, can be obtained as a blue liquid by cooling an equimolar mixture of nitric oxide and nitrogen dioxide. It is the anhydride of nitrous acid, and produces this acid on solution in water:

$$N_2O_3 + H_2O \longrightarrow 2HNO_2$$

Nitrogen dioxide, NO_2, a red gas, and its dimer **dinitrogen tetroxide,** N_2O_4, a colorless, easily condensable gas, exist in equilibrium with one another:

$$2NO_2 \rightleftarrows N_2O_4$$
$$\text{red} \qquad \text{colorless}$$

The mixture of these gases may be made by adding nitric oxide to oxygen, or by reducing concentrated nitric acid with copper:

$$Cu + 4H^+ + 2NO_3^- \longrightarrow Cu^{++} + 2H_2O + 2NO_2 \uparrow$$

It is also easily obtained by decomposing lead nitrate by heat:

$$2Pb(NO_3)_2 \longrightarrow 2PbO + 4NO_2 \uparrow + O_2 \uparrow$$

The gas dissolves readily in water or alkali, forming a mixture of nitrate and nitrite.

Dinitrogen pentoxide, N_2O_5, the anhydride of nitric acid, can be made, as white crystals, by carefully dehydrating nitric acid with phosphorus pentoxide or by oxidizing nitrogen dioxide with ozone. It is unstable, decomposing spontaneously at room temperature into nitrogen dioxide and oxygen.

The **electronic structures** of the oxides of nitrogen are shown below. Most of these molecules are resonance hybrids, and the contributing structures are not all shown; for dinitrogen pentoxide, for example, the various single and double bonds may change places.

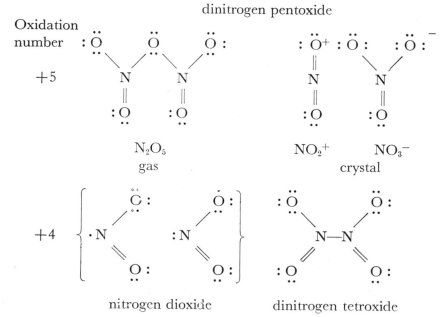

dinitrogen pentoxide

+3   dinitrogen trioxide

$$: \ddot{O} \qquad \ddot{O} \qquad \ddot{O} :$$

with N and N

+2 $\left\{ : \dot{N} = \ddot{O} : \qquad : \ddot{N} = \dot{O} : \right\}$ nitric oxide

+1 $\left\{ : \ddot{N} = N = \ddot{O} : \qquad : N \equiv N - \ddot{O} : \right\}$ nitrous oxide

We may well ask why it is that two of the most stable of these substances, NO and NO₂, are odd molecules, representing oxidation levels for nitrogen not occurring in other compounds, and also why N_2O_3 and N_2O_5, the anhydrides of the important substances HNO_2 and HNO_3, are so unstable that they decompose at room temperature. The answer to these questions probably is that the resonance of the odd electron between the two or three atoms of the molecule stabilizes the substances NO and NO₂ enough to make them somewhat more stable than the two anhydrides.

Nitrogen Oxide Cations.   The odd molecules nitric oxide, NO, and nitrogen dioxide, NO₂, can form stable cations by giving up one electron. The NO^+ cation contains a triple bond; its electronic structure is $: N \equiv O : ^+$. This cation is present in crystals of nitrosyl chlorostannate, $(NO)_2SnCl_6$, which is formed when nitrosyl chloride, NOCl, is added to tin tetrachloride, $SnCl_4$, and in many other crystals.

Crystals of NO_2ClO_4 contain the cation NO_2^+, which is linear, and has the structure $: \ddot{O} = N = \ddot{O} : ^+$, isoelectronic with carbon dioxide. It has also been shown that this cation is present in crystals of N_2O_5, together with the nitrate ion: crystalline dinitrogen pentoxide should be assigned the structural formula $NO_2^+NO_3^-$.

18–4. *Nitric Acid and the Nitrates*

Nitric acid, HNO_3, is a colorless liquid with melting point $-42°$ C, boiling point $86°$ C, and density 1.52 g/cm³. It is a strong acid, completely ionized to hydrogen ion and nitrate ion (NO_3^-) in aqueous solution; and it is a strong oxidizing agent.

Nitric acid can be made in the laboratory by heating sodium nitrate with sulfuric acid in an all-glass apparatus. The substance is also made commercially in this way, from natural sodium nitrate (Chile saltpeter), of which about 2,500,000 tons is exported from Chile each year.

The Manufacture of Nitric Acid from Ammonia.   Much nitric acid is also made by the oxidation of ammonia. This oxidation occurs in

several steps. Ammonia mixed with air burns on the surface of a platinum catalyst to form nitric oxide:

$$4NH_3 + 5O_2 \longrightarrow 4NO + 6H_2O$$

On cooling, the nitric oxide is further oxidized to nitrogen dioxide:

$$2NO + O_2 \longrightarrow 2NO_2$$

The gas is passed through a tower packed with pieces of broken quartz
through which water is percolating. Nitric acid and nitrous acid are
formed:

$$2NO_2 + H_2O \longrightarrow HNO_3 + HNO_2$$

As the strength of the acid solution increases, the nitrous acid decomposes:

$$3HNO_2 \rightleftharpoons HNO_3 + 2NO + H_2O$$

The nitric oxide is re-oxidized by the excess oxygen present, and again
enters the reaction.

The Fixation of Nitrogen as Nitric Oxide.   A method (the *arc process*)
formerly used for fixation of atmospheric nitrogen but now abandoned
is the direct combination of nitrogen and oxygen to nitric oxide at the
high temperature of the electric arc. The reaction

$$N_2 + O_2 \rightleftharpoons 2NO$$

is slightly endothermic, and the equilibrium yield of nitric oxide increases
with increasing temperature, from 0.4% at 1,500° to 5% at 3,000°. The
reaction was carried out by passing air through an electric arc in such
a way that the hot gas mixture was cooled very rapidly, thus "freezing"
the high-temperature equilibrium mixture. The nitric oxide was then
converted into nitric acid in the way described above.

Nitrates and Their Properties.   **Sodium nitrate,** $NaNO_3$, forms colorless crystals closely resembling crystals of calcite, $CaCO_3$ (Fig. 6-1).
This resemblance is not accidental. The crystals have the same structure, with Na^+ replacing Ca^{++} and NO_3^- replacing CO_3^{--}. The crystals
of sodium nitrate have the same property of *birefringence* (double refraction) as calcite. Sodium nitrate is used as a fertilizer, and for conversion
into nitric acid and other nitrates.

   The nitrate ion has a planar structure, with each bond a single-bond-
double-bond hybrid:

Potassium nitrate, KNO_3 (saltpeter), forms colorless orthorhombic crystals. It is used in pickling meat (ham, corned beef), in medicine, and in the manufacture of gunpowder, an intimate mixture of potassium nitrate, charcoal, and sulfur.

18–5. *Other Compounds of Nitrogen*

Nitrous acid, HNO_2, is formed together with nitric acid when nitrogen dioxide is dissolved in water. Nitrite ion can be made together with nitrate ion by solution of nitrogen dioxide in alkali:

$$2NO_2 + 2OH^- \longrightarrow NO_2^- + NO_3^- + H_2O$$

Sodium nitrite and potassium nitrite can be made also by decomposing the nitrates by heat:

$$2NaNO_3 \longrightarrow 2NaNO_2 + O_2$$

or by reduction with lead:

$$NaNO_3 + Pb \longrightarrow NaNO_2 + PbO$$

These nitrites are pale yellow crystalline substances, and their solutions are yellow.

The nitrite ion is a reducing agent, being oxidized to nitrate ion by bromine, permanganate ion, chromate ion, and similar oxidizing agents. It is also an oxidizing agent, able to oxidize iodide ion to iodine.

The electronic structure of the nitrite ion is

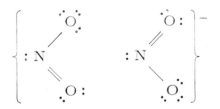

Hyponitrous Acid and the Hyponitrites.   Hyponitrous acid, $H_2N_2O_2$, is formed in small quantity by reaction of nitrous acid and hydroxylamine:

$$H_2NOH + HNO_2 \longrightarrow H_2N_2O_2 + H_2O$$

It is a very weak acid, with structure

$$\begin{array}{ccc} H-\overset{\cdot\cdot}{O}\overset{\cdot\cdot}{} & & \overset{\cdot\cdot}{O}\overset{\cdot\cdot}{}-H \\ \diagdown & & \diagup \\ & \underset{\cdot\cdot}{N}=\underset{\cdot\cdot}{N} & \end{array}$$

The acid decomposes to form nitrous oxide, N_2O; it is not itself formed in appreciable concentration by reaction of nitrous oxide and water. Its salts have no important uses.

Hydrogen Cyanide and Its Salts.   **Hydrogen cyanide,** HCN (structural formula H—C≡N :), is a gas which dissolves in water and acts as a very weak acid. It is made by treating a cyanide, such as potassium cyanide, KCN, with sulfuric acid, and is used as a fumigant and rat poison. It smells like bitter almonds and crushed fruit kernels, which in fact owe their odor to it. Hydrogen cyanide and its salts are very poisonous.

Cyanides are made by action of carbon and nitrogen on metallic oxides. For example, barium cyanide is made by heating a mixture of barium oxide and carbon to a red heat in a stream of nitrogen:

$$BaO + 3C + N_2 \longrightarrow Ba(CN)_2 + CO \uparrow$$

The cyanide ion, $[: C{\equiv}N :]^-$, is similar to a halide ion in its properties. By oxidation it can be converted to **cyanogen,** C_2N_2 (: N≡C—C≡N :), analogous to the halogen molecules F_2, Cl_2, etc.

The Cyanate Ion, Fulminate Ion, Azide Ion, and Thiocyanate Ion. By suitable procedures three anions can be made which are similar in structure to the carbon dioxide molecule $: \overset{\cdot\cdot}{O}{=}C{=}\overset{\cdot\cdot}{O} :$ and the nitrous oxide molecule $: \overset{\cdot\cdot}{N}{=}N{=}\overset{\cdot\cdot}{O} :$ (these structures are hybridized with other structures, such as $: O{=}C{-}\overset{\cdot\cdot}{\underset{\cdot\cdot}{O}} :$ and its analogs). These anions are

$$\left[: \overset{\cdot\cdot}{N}{=}C{=}\overset{\cdot\cdot}{O} : \right]^- \quad \text{cyanate ion}$$

$$\left[: \overset{\cdot\cdot}{C}{=}N{=}\overset{\cdot\cdot}{O} : \right]^- \quad \text{fulminate ion}$$

$$\left[: \overset{\cdot\cdot}{N}{=}N{=}\overset{\cdot\cdot}{N} : \right]^- \quad \text{azide ion}$$

A related ion is the thiocyanate ion, $\left[:\ddot{N}{=}C{=}\ddot{S}: \right]^{-}$, which forms a deep-red complex with ferric ion, used as a test for iron. The azide ion also forms a deep-red complex with ferric ion.

The fulminates and azides of the heavy metals are very sensitive explosives. Mercuric fulminate, $Hg(CNO)_2$, and lead azide, $Pb(N_3)_2$, are used as detonators.

18–6. *The Oxidation States of Phosphorus*

Phosphorus, like nitrogen and the other members of the fifth group, has oxidation states ranging from -3 to $+5$. The principal compounds of phosphorus are indicated in the following chart:

$+5$	P_4O_{10} (P_2O_5), phosphorus pentoxide	**H_3PO_4, phosphoric acid**	
$+4$			
$+3$	P_4O_6 (P_2O_3), phosphorus trioxide	**H_2HPO_3, phosphorous acid**	
$+1$		HH_2PO_2, hypophospho- rous acid	
0	P_4, P_∞, white phosphorus, red phosphorus		
-2	P_2H_4		
-3	PH_3, phosphine		

Phosphorus is less electronegative than nitrogen, but is a non-metallic element, its oxides being acid-forming and not amphoteric.* The quinquepositive oxidation state of phosphorus is more stable than that of nitrogen; phosphoric acid and the phosphates are not effective oxidizing agents. The oxygen acids of phosphorus contain one more oxygen atom (and two more hydrogen atoms) than the oxygen acids of nitrogen for corresponding oxidation levels. For example, the highest acid is H_3PO_4, corresponding to HNO_3:

* An amphoteric oxide is an oxide that can combine both with acids and with bases.

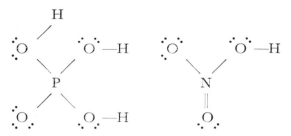

18–7. *Elementary Phosphorus*

Phosphorus occurs in nature mainly as the minerals *apatite*, $Ca_5(PO_4)_3F$, *hydroxyapatite*, $Ca_5(PO_4)_3(OH)$, and tricalcium phosphate (*phosphate rock*), ranging in composition from $Ca_3(PO_4)_2$ to hydroxyapatite. Hydroxyapatite is the main mineral constituent of the bones and teeth of animals, and complex organic compounds of phosphorus are essential constituents of nerve and brain tissue and of many proteins, and are involved significantly in the metabolic reactions of living organisms.

Elementary phosphorus is made by heating calcium phosphate with silica and carbon in an electric furnace. The silica forms calcium silicate, displacing phosphorus pentoxide, P_4O_{10}, which is then reduced by the carbon. The phosphorus leaves the furnace as vapor, and is condensed under water to *white phosphorus*.

Phosphorus vapor is tetratomic: the P_4 molecule has a structure with each atom having one unshared electron pair and forming a single bond with each of its three neighbors (Fig. 10-4).

At 1,600° C the vapor is dissociated slightly, forming a few percent of diatomic molecules P_2, with the structure $:P{\equiv}P:$, analogous to that of the nitrogen molecule.

Phosphorus vapor condenses at 280.5° C to liquid white phosphorus, which freezes at 44.1° C to solid white phosphorus, a soft, waxy, colorless material, soluble in carbon disulfide, benzene, and other non-polar solvents. Both solid and liquid white phosphorus contain the same P_4 molecules as the vapor.

White phosphorus is metastable, and it slowly changes to a stable form, *red phosphorus*, in the presence of light or on heating. White phosphorus usually has a yellow color because of partial conversion to the red form. The reaction takes several hours even at 250°. Red phosphorus is far more stable than the white form—it does not catch fire in air at temperatures below 240°, whereas white phosphorus ignites at about 40°, and oxidizes slowly at room temperature, giving off a white light ("phosphorescence"). Red phosphorus is not poisonous, whereas white phosphorus is very poisonous, the lethal dose being about 0.15 g; it causes necrosis of the bones, especially those of the jaw. White phosphorus burns are painful and slow to heal. Red phosphorus cannot be converted into white phosphorus except by vaporizing it. It is not appreciably soluble in any solvent. When heated to 500° or 600° red phosphorus slowly melts (if under pressure) or vaporizes, forming P_4 vapor.

Several other allotropic forms of the element are known. One of these, black phosphorus, is formed from white phosphorus under high pressure. It is still less reactive than red phosphorus.

The explanation of the properties of red and black phosphorus lies in their structure. These substances are *high polymers*, consisting of giant molecules extending throughout the crystal. In order for such a crystal to melt or to dissolve in a solvent a chemical reaction must take place. This chemical reaction is the rupture of some P—P bonds and formation of new ones. Such processes are very slow.

The Uses of Phosphorus.   Large amounts of phosphorus made from phosphate rock are burned and converted into phosphoric acid. Phosphorus is also used in making matches. White phosphorus is no longer used for this purpose because of its danger to the health of the workers. Ordinary matches are now made by dipping the ends of the match sticks into paraffin, and then into a wet mixture of phosphorus sulfide, lead dioxide (or other oxidizing agent), and glue. The heads of safety matches contain antimony trisulfide and potassium chlorate or dichromate, and the box is coated with a mixture of red phosphorus, powdered glass, and glue.

18–8. *Phosphine*

The hydrides of phosphorus are phosphine, PH_3 (with structure : P—H, with two other H attached), analogous to ammonia), P_2H_4 (P—P with H attached, analogous to hydrazine), and some solid hydrides, such as P_4H_2, with uncertain structure. Phosphine is not made by direct union of the elements. It is formed, together with the hypophosphite ion $H_2PO_2^-$, when white phosphorus is heated in a solution of alkali:

$$P_4 + 3OH^- + 3H_2O \longrightarrow 3H_2PO_2^- + PH_3 \uparrow$$

The gas made in this way, which contains a little P_2H_4, ignites spontaneously on contact with air and burns, forming white fumes of oxide. To avoid explosion, the air in the flask must be displaced by hydrogen or illuminating gas before the mixture in the flask is heated. Phosphine is exceedingly poisonous.

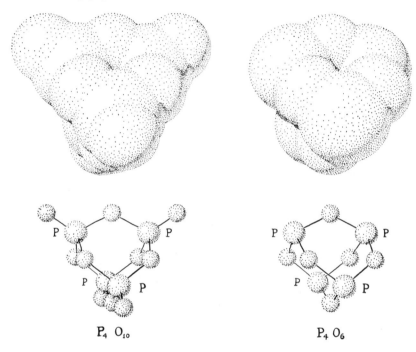

$$P_4 O_{10} \qquad\qquad P_4 O_6$$

FIG. 18-1   *Molecules of the oxides of phosphorus.*

Phosphine has far less affinity for hydrogen ion than has ammonia. Its only salts are phosphonium iodide, PH_4I, and phosphonium chloride, PH_4Cl. These salts decompose on contact with water, liberating phosphine.

18–9. *The Oxides of Phosphorus*

Phosphorus pentoxide, usually assigned the formula P_2O_5, consists of molecules P_4O_{10}, with the structure shown in Figure 18-1. It is formed when phosphorus is burned with a free supply of air. It reacts with water with great vigor, to form phosphoric acid, and it is used in the laboratory as a drying agent for gases.

Phosphorus trioxide, P_2O_3 or P_4O_6 (Fig. 18-1), is made, together with the pentoxide, by burning phosphorus with a restricted supply of air. It is much more volatile than the pentoxide (P_4O_6, m.p. 22.5° C, b.p. 173.1° C; P_4O_{10}, sublimes at 250°), and is easily purified by distillation in an apparatus from which air is excluded.

A third oxide, P_8O_{16}, is also known. It is formed, together with red phosphorus, when the trioxide vapor is heated to about 450°.

18–10. *Phosphoric Acid*

Pure *orthophosphoric acid*, H_3PO_4, is a deliquescent crystalline substance, with melting point 42° C. Commercial phosphoric acid is a viscous liquid. It is made by dissolving phosphorus pentoxide in water.

It was pointed out in the preceding chapter that phosphoric acid is a weak acid, its first dissociation constant being 0.75×10^{-2}. It is a stable substance, without effective oxidizing power.

Orthophosphoric acid forms three series of salts, with one, two, and three of its hydrogen atoms replaced by metal. The salts are usually made by mixing phosphoric acid and the metal hydroxide or carbonate, in proper proportion. *Sodium dihydrogen phosphate*, NaH_2PO_4 (also called *primary sodium phosphate*), is faintly acidic in reaction. It is used (mixed with sodium hydrogen carbonate) in baking powder, and also for treating boiler water, to prevent formation of scale. *Disodium hydrogen phosphate*, Na_2HPO_4 (*secondary sodium phosphate*), is slightly basic in reaction. *Trisodium phosphate*, Na_3PO_4 (*tertiary sodium phosphate*), is strongly basic. It is used as a detergent (for cleaning woodwork, etc.) and for treating boiler water.

Phosphates are valuable fertilizers. Phosphate rock [tricalcium phosphate, $Ca_3(PO_4)_2$, and hydroxyapatite] is too slightly soluble to serve as an effective source of phosphorus for plants. It is accordingly converted into the more soluble substance *calcium dihydrogen phosphate*, $Ca(H_2PO_4)_2$. This may be done by treatment with sulfuric acid:

$$Ca_3(PO_4)_2 + 2H_2SO_4 \longrightarrow 2CaSO_4 + Ca(H_2PO_4)_2$$

Enough water is added to convert the calcium sulfate to its dihydrate, gypsum, and the mixture of gypsum and calcium dihydrogen phosphate is sold as "superphosphate of lime." Sometimes the phosphate rock is treated with phosphoric acid:

$$Ca_3(PO_4)_2 + 4H_3PO_4 \longrightarrow 3Ca(H_2PO_4)_2$$

This product is much richer in phosphorus than the "superphosphate"; it is called "triple phosphate."

The Condensed Phosphoric Acids.   Phosphoric acid easily undergoes the process of *condensation*. Condensation is the reaction of two or more molecules to form larger molecules, either without any other products (in which case the condensation is also called *polymerization*), or with the elimination of small molecules, such as water. Condensation of two phosphoric acid molecules occurs by the reaction of two hydroxyl groups

$\overset{\cdot\cdot}{O}\overset{\cdot\cdot}{}$—H to form water and an oxygen atom held by single bonds to two phosphorus atoms.

When orthophosphoric acid is heated, it loses water and condenses to *diphosphoric acid* or *pyrophosphoric acid*, $H_4P_2O_7$:

$$2H_3PO_4 \rightleftharpoons H_4P_2O_7 + H_2O \uparrow$$

(The name *pyrophosphoric acid* is the one customarily used.) This acid is a white crystalline substance, with melting point 61° C. Its salts may be made by neutralization of the acid or by strongly heating the hydrogen orthophosphates or ammonium orthophosphates of the metals. Magnesium pyrophosphate is obtained in a useful method for quantitative analysis for either magnesium or orthophosphate. A solution containing orthophosphate ion may be mixed with a solution of magnesium chloride (or sulfate), ammonium chloride, and ammonium hydroxide. The very slightly soluble substance magnesium ammonium phosphate, $MgNH_4PO_4 \cdot 6H_2O$, then slowly precipitates. The precipitate is washed with dilute ammonium hydroxide, dried, and heated to a dull-red heat, causing it to form magnesium pyrophosphate, which is then weighed:

$$2MgNH_4PO_4 \cdot 6H_2O \longrightarrow Mg_2P_2O_7 + 2NH_3 + 13H_2O$$

The interconversion of pyrophosphates and phosphates is important in many bodily processes, including the metabolism of sugar. This reaction occurs at body temperature under the influence of special enzymes.

Larger condensed phosphoric acids also occur, such as $H_5P_3O_{10}$. Most important are those in which each phosphate tetrahedron is bonded by oxygen atoms to two other tetrahedra. These acids have the composition $(HPO_3)_x$, with $x = 3, 4, 5, 6, \cdots$. They are called the *metaphosphoric acids*. Among these acids are *tetrametaphosphoric acid* and *hexametaphosphoric acid*.

Metaphosphoric acid is made by heating orthophosphoric acid or pyrophosphoric acid. It is a viscous, sticky mass, which contains, in addition to ring molecules such as $H_4P_4O_{12}$, long chains approaching $(HPO_3)_\infty$ in composition. It is the long chains, which may also be condensed together to form branched chains, which, by becoming entangled, make the acid viscous and sticky.

The process of condensation may continue further, ultimately leading to phosphorus pentoxide.

The metaphosphates are used as water softeners. Sodium hexametaphosphate, $Na_6P_6O_{18}$, is especially effective for this purpose. The hexametaphosphate ion can combine with one or two calcium ions (or ferric ions) to form soluble complexes, $[CaP_6O_{18}]^{----}$ and $[Ca_2P_6O_{18}]^{--}$.

18–11. *Other Compounds of Phosphorus*

Phosphorous acid, H_2HPO_3, is a white substance, m.p. 74° C, which is made by dissolving phosphorus trioxide in cold water:

$$P_4O_6 + 6H_2O \longrightarrow 4H_2HPO_3$$

It may also be conveniently made by the action of water on phosphorus trichloride:

$$PCl_3 + 3H_2O \longrightarrow H_2HPO_3 + 3HCl$$

Phosphorous acid is an unstable substance. When heated it undergoes auto-oxidation-reduction to phosphine and phosphoric acid:

$$4H_2HPO_3 \longrightarrow 3H_3PO_4 + PH_3$$

The acid and its salts, the *phosphites*, are powerful reducing agents. Its reaction with silver ion is used as a test for phosphite ion; a black precipitate is formed, which consists of silver phosphate, Ag_3PO_4, colored black by metallic silver formed by reduction of silver ion. Phosphite ion also reduces iodate ion to free iodine, which can be detected by the starch test (blue color) or by its coloration of a small volume of carbon tetrachloride shaken with the aqueous phase.

Phosphorous acid is a weak acid, which forms two series of salts. Ordinary *sodium phosphite* is $Na_2HPO_3 \cdot 5H_2O$. *Sodium hydrogen phosphite*, $NaHHPO_3 \cdot 5H_2O$, also exists, but the third hydrogen atom cannot be replaced by a cation. It will be mentioned in Chapter 21 that the non-acidic character of this third hydrogen atom is due to its attachment directly to the phosphorus atom, rather than to an oxygen atom:

$$
\begin{array}{ccc}
\text{H} & & \ddot{\text{O}} \text{—H} \\
& \diagdown \quad \diagup & \\
& \text{P} & \\
& \diagup \quad \diagdown & \\
\ddot{\text{O}} & & \ddot{\text{O}} \text{—H}
\end{array}
$$

The phosphite ion is HPO_3^{--}, not PO_3^{---}.

Hypophosphorous Acid.   The solution remaining from the preparation of phosphine from phosphorus and alkali contains the *hypophosphite ion*, $H_2PO_2^-$. The corresponding acid, *hypophosphorous acid*, HH_2PO_2, can be prepared by using barium hydroxide as the alkali, thus forming barium hypophosphite, $Ba(H_2PO_2)_2$, and then adding to the solution the calculated amount of sulfuric acid, which precipitates barium sulfate and leaves the hypophosphorous acid in solution.

Hypophosphorous acid is a weak monoprotic acid, forming only one series of salts. The two non-acidic hydrogen atoms are bonded to the phosphorus atom:

$$
\begin{array}{ccc}
\text{H} & & \ddot{\text{O}} \text{—H} \\
& \diagdown \quad \diagup & \\
& \text{P} & \\
& \diagup \quad \diagdown & \\
\text{H} & & \ddot{\text{O}}
\end{array}
$$

The acid and the hypophosphite ion are powerful reducing agents, able to reduce the cations of copper and the more noble metals.

The Halides and Sulfides of Phosphorus.   By direct combination of the elements or by other methods the halides of terpositive phosphorus (PF_3, PCl_3, etc.) and of quinquepositive phosphorus (PF_5, PCl_5, etc.) can be formed. These halides are gases or easily volatile liquids or solids, which hydrolyze with water, forming the corresponding oxygen acids of phosphorus. The electronic structures of the phosphorus trihalides and pentahalides have been discussed in earlier chapters. These halides are useful in the preparation of inorganic and organic substances.

Phosphorus pentachloride with a little water forms *phosphorus oxychloride*, $POCl_3$, which is used as a chemical reagent. Phosphorus pentachloride reacts in general with the inorganic oxygen acids and organic substances containing hydroxyl groups, in such a way as to introduce a chlorine atom in place of the hydroxyl group —OH. Thus from sulfuric acid it produces chlorosulfuric acid, HSO_3Cl:

$$SO_2(OH)_2 + PCl_5 \longrightarrow SO_2(OH)Cl + POCl_3 + HCl$$

With an excess of phosphorus pentachloride the substance sulfuryl chloride, SO_2Cl_2, is formed:

$$SO_2(OH)_2 + 2PCl_5 \longrightarrow SO_2Cl_2 + 2POCl_3 + 2HCl$$

Sulfur and phosphorus combine when heated together to form various compounds, including P_2S_5, P_4S_7, and P_4S_3. The last of these, tetraphosphorus trisulfide, is used as a constituent of match heads.

18–12. *Arsenic, Antimony, and Bismuth*

Arsenic, antimony, and bismuth differ from their congeners nitrogen and phosphorus in the decreasing electronegativity which accompanies increasing atomic number. The principal compounds of these elements correspond to the oxidation states $+5$ and $+3$. The state -3 also occurs; it is represented by the gaseous hydrides AsH_3, SbH_3, and BiH_3, which, however, do not form salts analogous to the ammonium and phosphonium salts.

Representative compounds of the fifth-group elements are shown in the chart on page 392.

The oxides of arsenic are acidic; with water they form arsenic acid, H_3AsO_4, and arsenious acid, H_3AsO_3, which resemble the corresponding acids of phosphorus. Antimony pentoxide is also acidic, and its trioxide is amphoteric, behaving both as an acid and as a base (forming the antimony ion, Sb^{+++}). Bismuth trioxide is primarily a basic oxide, forming the ion Bi^{+++}; its acidic activity is slight.

Arsenic and Its Ores.   Elementary arsenic exists in several forms. Ordinary *gray arsenic* is a semi-metallic substance, steel-gray in color, with density 5.73 g/cm³ and melting point (under pressure) 814°. It sublimes rapidly at about 450°, forming gas molecules As_4 similar in structure to P_4. An unstable yellow crystalline form containing As_4 molecules, and soluble in carbon disulfide, also exists. The gray form has a covalent layer structure.

The chief minerals of arsenic include *orpiment*, As_2S_3 (from Latin *auripigmentum*, yellow pigment), *realgar*, AsS (a red substance), *arsenolite*,

	N	P	As	Sb	Bi
+5	N_2O_5 HNO_3	P_4O_{10} H_3PO_4 PCl_5	As_2O_5 H_3AsO_4 $AsCl_5$	Sb_2O_5 $HSb(OH)_6$ $SbCl_5$	Bi_2O_5
+4	NO_2				
+3	N_2O_3 HNO_2 NCl_3	P_4O_6 H_2HPO_3 PCl_3	As_4O_6 H_3AsO_3 $AsCl_3$	Sb_4O_6 H_3SbO_3 $SbCl_3$ Sb^{+++}	Bi_4O_6 $BiCl_3$ Bi^{+++}
+2	NO				
+1	N_2O $H_2N_2O_2$	HH_2PO_2			
0	N_2	P_4	As	Sb	Bi
−1	NH_2OH				
−2	N_2H_4	P_2H_4			
−3	NH_3 $NH_4{}^+$	PH_3 $PH_4{}^+$	AsH_3	SbH_3	BiH_3

As_4O_6, and *arsenopyrite*, FeAsS. Arsenic trioxide (arsenious oxide) is obtained by roasting ores of arsenic. The element is made by reducing the trioxide with carbon or by heating arsenopyrite:

$$4FeAsS \longrightarrow 4FeS + As_4 \uparrow$$

Arsenic is inert at room temperature, but ignites when heated, burning with a bluish flame to produce white clouds of the trioxide. It is oxidized to arsenic acid, H_3AsO_4, by hot nitric acid and other powerful oxidizing agents. Arsenic combines with many other elements, both metallic and non-metallic.

Arsenic is used with lead (0.5% As) in making lead shot. It makes the metal harder than pure lead, and also improves the properties of the molten metal—the shot are made by pouring the metal through a sieve at the top of a tall tower, which permits the liquid drops to assume a spherical form and then to harden before falling into water at the base of the tower.

Arsine.   Arsine, AsH_3, is a colorless, very poisonous gas with a garlic-like odor. It is made by reaction of a metallic arsenide, such as zinc arsenide, with acid:

$$Zn_3As_2 + 6HCl \longrightarrow 3ZnCl_2 + 2AsH_3 \uparrow$$

It also is formed by reduction of soluble arsenic compounds by zinc in acidic solution. This reaction is the basis of an important and sensitive test for arsenic, the *Marsh test*. The arsenic is deposited as a steel-gray or black mirror from the burning gas on to a cold glazed porcelain dish held in the flame. Antimony produces a velvety brown or black deposit, which is not soluble in sodium hypochlorite solution, whereas the arsenic deposit is. The antimony deposit, but not that of arsenic, dissolves in ammonium polysulfide solution. This test for arsenic will detect as small an amount as 1×10^{-6} g.

The Oxides and Acids of Arsenic.   *Arsenic trioxide* (arsenious oxide, As_4O_6) is a white solid substance which sublimes readily, and is easily purified by sublimation. Its molecules have the same structure as phosphorus trioxide, shown in Figure 18-1. It is a violent poison, and is used as an insecticide and for preserving skins.

Arsenic trioxide dissolves in water to form *arsenious acid*, H_3AsO_3. This acid differs from phosphorous acid in that all three of its hydrogen atoms are attached to oxygen atoms, and are replaceable by metal. It is a very weak acid. Cupric hydrogen arsenite, $CuHAsO_3$, and a cupric arsenite-acetate (called Paris green) are used as insecticides.

Arsenic pentoxide, As_2O_5, is not obtained by burning arsenic, but can be made by boiling arsenic trioxide with concentrated nitric acid. With water it forms *arsenic acid*, H_3AsO_4, which is closely similar to phosphoric acid. Sodium arsenate, Na_3AsO_4, is used as a weed killer, and other arsenates (especially of calcium and lead) are used as insecticides.

The toxicity of arsenic compounds to living organisms is utilized in chemotherapy; several organic compounds of arsenic have been discovered which are able to attack invading organisms, such as the spirochete of syphilis, when taken in amounts smaller than the amount poisonous to man.

Antimony. The principal ore of antimony is *stibnite*, Sb_2S_3, a steel-gray or black mineral which forms beautiful crystals. The metal is usually made by heating stibnite with iron:

$$Sb_2S_3 + 3Fe \longrightarrow 3FeS + 2Sb$$

Antimony is a brittle metal, silvery-gray in color. It has the property of expanding on freezing, and its main use is as a constituent of type metal (82% lead, 15% antimony, 3% tin), on which it confers this property, thus giving sharp reproductions of the mold.

The oxides and acids of antimony resemble those of arsenic, except that antimony in antimonic acid has coordination number 6, the formula of antimonic acid being $HSb(OH)_6$. A solution of potassium antimonate, $K^+[Sb(OH)_6]^-$, finds use as a test reagent for sodium ion; sodium antimonate, $NaSb(OH)_6$, one of the very few sodium salts with slight solubility in water (about 0.03 g per 100 g), is precipitated. The antimonate ion condenses to larger complexes when heated; this condensation may ultimately lead to macromolecular structures, such as that of dehydrated potassium antimonate, $KSbO_3$.

Antimony trioxide, Sb_4O_6, is amphoteric. In addition to reacting with bases to form antimonites, it reacts with acids to form antimony salts, such as antimony sulfate, $Sb_2(SO_4)_3$. The antimony ion Sb^{+++} hydrolyzes readily to form the *antimonyl ion*, SbO^+.

Antimony trichloride, $SbCl_3$, is a soft, colorless substance, which hydrolyzes with water, precipitating antimonyl chloride, $SbOCl$. The reaction may be reversed by adding hydrochloric acid, forming the complex anion $SbCl_4^-$. This anion can be oxidized by iodate ion to a similar complex anion of quinquevalent antimony:

$$5SbCl_4^- + 2IO_3^- + 12H^+ + 10Cl^- \longrightarrow 5SbCl_6^- + I_2 + 6H_2O$$

This reaction may be used for the quantitative determination of antimony.

Bismuth. Bismuth occurs in nature as the free element, and as the sulfide Bi_2S_3 and the oxide Bi_2O_3. The metal is won from its compounds by roasting and reducing the oxide with carbon. It is a brittle metal, with a silvery color showing a reddish tinge. It expands slightly on freezing. Its principal use is in making low-melting alloys (see Cadmium, Chap. 27).

The oxides of bismuth are basic, forming salts such as bismuth chloride, $BiCl_3 \cdot H_2O$, and bismuth nitrate, $Bi(NO_3)_3 \cdot 5H_2O$. These salts when dissolved in water hydrolyze, and precipitate the corresponding bismuthyl compounds, $BiOCl$ and $Bi(OH)_2NO_3$ (or $BiONO_3 \cdot H_2O$). The compounds of bismuth have found little use; bismuthyl nitrate and some other compounds are used to some extent in medicine.

Exercises

18-1. What are the commercial methods of preparing (a) nitrogen, (b) ammonia, (c) nitric acid, and (d) calcium cyanamide?

18-2. Describe laboratory methods of preparing (a) ammonia, (b) nitrous oxide, (c) nitric oxide, (d) dinitrogen trioxide, (e) nitrogen dioxide, (f) nitric acid, (g) sodium nitrite, (h) hydrazine, (i) ammonium amalgam.

18-3. Write the electronic structure of the nitrate ion.

18-4. Write a balanced chemical reaction to represent the formation of potassium sulfate, carbon dioxide, and nitrogen from potassium nitrate, carbon, and sulfur.

18-5. What chemical reaction takes place between nitrous acid and bromine? between nitrous acid and iodide ion?

18-6. What chemical reaction takes place between nitrogen dioxide and a solution of sodium hydroxide?

18-7. What is the electronic structure of hydrazine?

18-8. Balance the chemical reaction

$$N_2H_5^+ + Cr_2O_7^{--} \longrightarrow Cr^{+++} + N_2 \uparrow$$

18-9. What is the electronic structure of the azide ion?

18-10. How does the electronic structure of the cyanide ion compare with that of nitrogen?

18-11. Write the chemical equation for the reaction involved in the decolorizing of a blue solution of sodium in liquid ammonia.

18-12. Compare the chemical reaction of solutions of sodium amide and ammonium chloride in liquid ammonia with that of aqueous solutions of sodium hydroxide and hydrogen chloride.

18-13. What is the electronic structure of nitrous oxide?

18-14. What are possible electronic structures for nitrogen tetroxide?

18-15. What are the formulas and structures of the oxygen acids of the $+5$ oxidation states of the fifth-group elements?

18-16. What are the formulas and structures of the oxygen acids of the $+3$ oxidation states of the fifth-group elements [include $Bi(OH)_3$ in this tabulation]? How do the properties of these compounds vary with atomic number?

18-17. What are apatite and hydroxyapatite?

18-18. Write the chemical equation for the preparation of phosphorus in the electric furnace.

18-19. Compare the base strengths of PH_3 and NH_3. What generalization about tendency to share electrons with a proton will summarize all the facts you have learned about the basic and acidic strengths of NH_3, PH_3, H_2O, H_2S, H_2Se, HF, HCl?

18-20. Write the chemical equation for the condensation of orthophosphoric acid to pyrophosphoric acid. How may this chemical equilibrium be driven either to the right or to the left?

18-21. What is the structure of metaphosphoric acid?

18-22. Write a chemical equation for the reduction of Ag^+ by a solution of sodium phosphite.

18-23. Compare the properties of PCl_3 and $BiCl_3$.

18-24. Write chemical equations illustrating the acidic and the basic properties of the $+3$ oxidation state of antimony.

18-25. Which are the most metallic of the fifth-group elements?

18-26. Give the name and formula of an ore of antimony and an ore of arsenic.

18-27. Write a chemical equation for the preparation of Sb_2O_5 from Sb_2O_3.

18-28. What chemical reaction takes place when bismuth nitrate is dissolved in water?

Chapter 19

The Rate of
Chemical Reactions

19–1. *Factors Influencing the Rate of Reactions*

Two questions may be asked in the consideration of a proposed chemical process, such as the preparation of a useful substance. One question—"Are the stability relations such that it is possible for the reaction to occur?"—is answered by the use of chemical thermodynamics; a part of this subject is mentioned in the discussion of chemical equilibrium in following chapters. The second question, discussed in this chapter, is equally important; it is, "Under what conditions will the reaction proceed sufficiently rapidly for the method to be practicable?"

Every chemical reaction requires some time for its completion, but some reactions are very fast and some are very slow. Reactions between ions in solution without change in oxidation state are usually extremely fast. An example is the neutralization of an acid by a base, which proceeds as fast as the solutions can be mixed. Presumably nearly every time a hydronium ion collides with a hydroxide ion reaction occurs, and the number of collisions is very great, so that there is little delay in the reaction. The formation of a precipitate, such as that of silver chloride when a solution containing silver ion is mixed with a solution containing chloride ion, may require a few seconds, to permit the ions to diffuse together to form the crystalline grains of the precipitate:

$$Ag^+ + Cl^- \longrightarrow AgCl \downarrow$$

On the other hand, ionic oxidation-reduction reactions are sometimes very slow. An example is the oxidation of stannous ion by ferric ion:

$$2Fe^{+++} + Sn^{++} \longrightarrow 2Fe^{++} + Sn^{++++}$$

This reaction does not occur every time a stannous ion collides with one or two ferric ions. In order for reaction to take place, the collision must be of such a nature that electrons can be transferred from one ion to another, and collisions which permit this electron transfer to occur may be rare.

An example of a reaction which is extremely slow at room temperature is that between hydrogen and oxygen:

$$2H_2 + O_2 \longrightarrow 2H_2O$$

A mixture of hydrogen and oxygen can be kept for years without appreciable reaction.

The factors which determine the rate of a reaction are manifold. The rate depends not only upon the composition of the reacting substances, but also upon their physical form, the intimacy of their mixture, the temperature and pressure, the concentrations of the reactants, special physical circumstances such as irradiation with visible light, ultraviolet light, X-rays, neutrons, or other waves or particles, and the presence of other substances that affect the reaction but are not changed by it.

Homogeneous and Heterogeneous Reactions.   A reaction which takes place in a homogeneous system (consisting of a single phase) is called a **homogeneous reaction.** The most important of these reactions are those in gases (such as the formation of nitric oxide in the electric arc, $N_2 + O_2 \rightleftharpoons 2NO$), and those in liquid solutions. The effects of temperature, pressure, and the concentrations of the reactants on the rates of homogeneous reactions are discussed below.

A **heterogeneous reaction** is a reaction involving two or more phases. An example is the oxidation of carbon by potassium perchlorate:

$$KClO_4 + 2C \longrightarrow KCl + 2CO_2 \uparrow$$

This reaction and similar reactions occur when perchlorate propellants are burned. (These propellants, used for assisted take-off of airplanes and for propulsion of rockets, consist of intimate mixtures of very fine grains of carbon black and potassium perchlorate held together by a plastic binder.) Another example is the solution of zinc in acid:

$$\underline{Zn} + 2H^+ \longrightarrow Zn^{++} + H_2 \uparrow$$

In this reaction three phases are involved: the solid zinc phase, the solution, and the gaseous phase formed by the evolved hydrogen.

The Rate of Heterogeneous Reactions.   A heterogeneous reaction takes place at the surfaces (the *interfaces*) of the reacting phases, and it can be made to go faster by *increasing the extent of the surfaces*. Thus finely divided zinc reacts more rapidly with acid than does coarse zinc, and the rate of burning of a perchlorate propellant is increased by grinding the potassium perchlorate to a finer crystalline powder.

Sometimes a *reactant is exhausted* in the neighborhood of the interface, and the reaction is slowed down. Stirring the mixture then accelerates the reaction, by bringing fresh supplies of the reactant into the reaction region.

Catalysts may accelerate heterogeneous as well as homogeneous reactions. A small amount of cupric ion speeds up the solution of zinc in acid, and manganese dioxide increases the rate of evolution of oxygen from potassium chlorate.

The rates of nearly all chemical reactions depend greatly on the *temperature*. It is nearly universally true that reactions are speeded up by increase in temperature.

Special devices may be utilized to accelerate certain chemical reactions. The formation of a zinc amalgam on the surface of the grains of zinc by treatment with a small amount of mercury increases the speed of the reduction reactions.

The solution of zinc in acid is retarded somewhat by the bubbles of hydrogen, which prevent the acid from achieving contact with the zinc over its entire surface. This effect can be avoided by bringing a plate of unreactive metal, such as copper or platinum, into electrical contact with the zinc. The reaction then proceeds as two separate electron reactions. Hydrogen is liberated at the surface of the copper or platinum, and zinc dissolves at the surface of the zinc plate:

$$2H^+ + 2e^- \longrightarrow H_2 \uparrow \quad \text{at copper surface}$$
$$\underline{Zn \longrightarrow Zn^{++} + 2e^-} \quad \text{at zinc surface}$$

The electrons flow from the zinc plate to the copper plate through the electrical contact, and electric neutrality in the different regions of the solution is maintained by the migration of ions.

19–2. *Homogeneous Reactions*

Most actual chemical processes are very complicated, and the analysis of their rates is very difficult. As a reaction proceeds, the reacting substances are used up and new ones are formed; the temperature of the system is changed by the heat evolved or absorbed by the reaction; and other effects may occur which influence the reaction in a complex way. For example, when a drop of a solution of potassium permanganate is added to a solution containing hydrogen peroxide and sulfuric acid no detectable reaction may occur for several minutes. Then the reaction speeds up, and finally the rate may become so great as to decolorize a steady stream of permanganate solution as rapidly as it is poured into the reducing solution. This effect of the speeding-up of the reaction is due to the vigorous catalytic action of the products of reduction of permanganate ion: the reaction is extremely slow in the absence of the products, and is rapidly accelerated as soon as they are formed.

The *explosion* of a gaseous mixture, such as hydrogen and oxygen, and the *detonation* of a high explosive, such as glyceryl trinitrate (nitroglycerin), are interesting chemical reactions; but the analysis of the rates of these reactions is made very difficult because of the great changes in temperature and pressure which accompany them.

The great rate at which a chemical reaction may occur is illustrated by the rate at which a detonation surface moves through a specimen of glyceryl trinitrate or similar high explosive. This *detonation rate* is about 20,000 feet per second. A specimen of high explosive weighing several grams may accordingly be completely decomposed within a millionth of a second. Another reaction which can occur very rapidly is the fission of the nuclei of heavy atoms. The nuclear fission of several pounds of U^{235} or Pu^{239} may take place in a few millionths of a second in the explosion of an atomic bomb (see Chap. 33).

In order to obtain an understanding of the rates of reactions, chemists have attempted to simplify the problem as much as possible. A good understanding has been obtained of homogeneous reactions (in a gaseous or liquid solution) which take place at constant temperature. Experimental studies are made by placing the reaction vessel in a *thermostat*, which is held at a fixed temperature. The quantitative theory of reaction rate, discussed below, has special interest because of its relation to the theory of chemical equilibrium, which is treated in the following chapter.

19–3. *The Rate of a First-Order Reaction at Constant Temperature*

If a molecule, which we represent by the general symbol A, has a tendency to decompose spontaneously into smaller molecules

$$A \longrightarrow B + C$$

at a rate which is not influenced by the presence of other molecules, we expect that *the number of molecules which decompose by such a unimolecular process in unit time will be proportional to the number present*. If the volume of the system remains constant, the concentration of A will decrease at a rate proportional to this concentration. Let us use the symbol [A] for the concentration of A (in moles per liter). The rate of decrease in concentration with time is, in the language of the calculus, $\dfrac{-d[A]}{dt}$. For a unimolecular decomposition we accordingly may write the equation

$$- \frac{d[A]}{dt} = k[A] \tag{19-1}$$

as *the differential equation determining the rate of the reaction.** The factor k is called the *first-order rate constant*. A reaction of this kind is called a *first-order reaction*; **the order of a reaction is the sum of the powers of the concentration factors in the rate expression** (on the right side of the rate equation).

For example, the rate constant k may have the value 0.001, with the time t measured in seconds. The equation would then state that during each second 1/1,000 of the molecules present would decompose. Suppose that at the time $t = 0$ there were 1,000,000,000 molecules per milliliter in the reaction vessel. During the first second 0.1% of these molecules would decompose, and there would remain at $t = 1$ second only 999,000,000 molecules undecomposed. During the next second 999,000 molecules would decompose, and there would remain 998,001,000 molecules.† After some time (about 693 seconds) half of the molecules would have decomposed, and there would remain only 500,000,000 undecomposed molecules per milliliter. Of these about 500,000 would decompose during the next second, and so on. After another 693 seconds there would remain about 250,000,000 undecomposed molecules, and after still another 693 seconds there would remain about 125,000,000, and so on. During each period of 693 seconds the concentration of reactant is reduced to one-half its value at the beginning of the period.

This relation between concentration of reactant and the time t is shown by the curves in Figure 19-1. It is seen that each curve decreases by one-half its value during successive constant time intervals. The neg·

---

* Do not be discouraged by this equation even if you have not studied the calculus and are not familiar with any equations of this sort. The expression on the left of Equation 19-1 is the rate of the reaction—the amount of decrease of concentration of the reacting substance in unit time. The expression on the right shows that this rate of decrease is proportional to the concentration itself.

† These numbers are not precise. The molecules decompose at random, at the *average* rate given by Equation 19-1, and a small statistical fluctuation from this rate is to be expected.

ative slope of each curve at any point is proportional to the value of the curve at that point, as required by Equation 19-1.

The algebraic equation which expresses this relation is

$$[A] = [A]_0 e^{-kt} \tag{19-2}$$

This is the equation that is obtained by integrating Equation 19-1; it is equivalent to Equation 19-1. Equation 19-2 is called the *reaction-rate expression for a first-order reaction in the integrated form*. It states that the con-

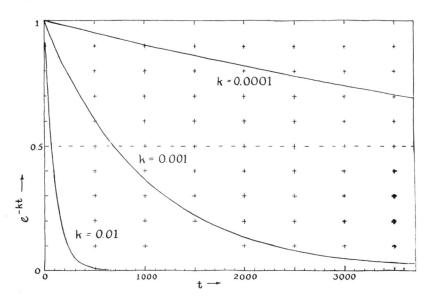

FIG. 19-1 *Curves showing decrease with time of the amount remaining of a substance decomposing by a first-order reaction, with indicated values of the reaction-rate constant.*

centration of the reactant at time t is equal to the concentration at time 0, $[A]_0$, multiplied by the exponential factor e^{-kt}. Here e is the base of natural logarithms, with value $2.718 \cdots$. The nature of this function can be seen from Figure 19-1.

The first-order character of a reaction may be tested by observing the rate of disappearance of reactant (the amount disappearing in a short time) at various concentrations, and comparing with Equation 19-1, or by observing the concentration itself for a particular sample for a long time, and comparing with Equation 19-2.

Examples of First-Order Reactions. Not many first-order reactions are known. One very important class of reactions of this type is **radio-**

active decomposition. Each nucleus of radium or other radioactive element decomposes independently of the presence of other atoms; and in consequence the rate of radioactive decay corresponds to Equation 19-1.

The time required for one-half of a first-order reactant to decompose

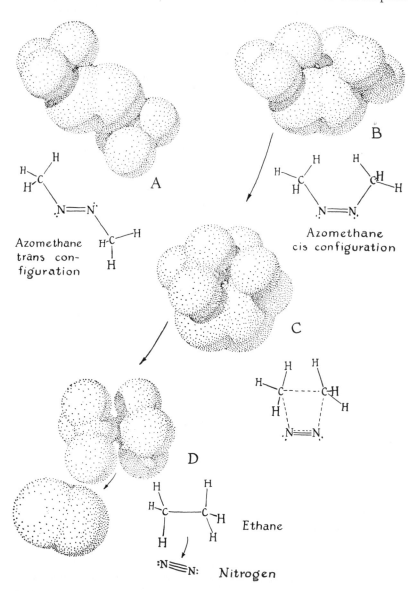

Azomethane
trans con-
figuration

A

B

Azomethane
cis configuration

C

D

Ethane

Nitrogen

FIG. 19-2   *The unimolecular decomposition of azomethane into nitrogen and ethane.*

is called its *half-life*. This time is 693 times the time required for 0.1% of the reactant to decompose. The half-life of radium itself is 1,733 years. Hence every $1,733/693 = 2\frac{1}{2}$ years 0.1% of the radium nuclei in a sample of radium undergo radioactive disintegration.

A representative first-order gas-phase chemical reaction is the decomposition of azomethane, CH_3—N=N—CH_3, into ethane and nitrogen:*

$$CH_3NNCH_3 \longrightarrow C_2H_6 + N_2$$

The molecular mechanism of this reaction is indicated in Figure 19-2. Most of the azomethane molecules have the configuration shown as A, with the methyl groups at opposite sides of the N=N axis. This is called the *trans* configuration. A few molecules have the *cis* configuration, B. If a molecule with the *cis* configuration collides very vigorously with another molecule, it may be set into very violent vibration, sufficient to bring the two carbon atoms close together, as shown in C. In this configuration the two N—C bonds tend to break, forming a C—C bond and another N—N bond. This tendency is indicated by the dashed valence-bond lines in C. The molecule C may either return to configuration B, or break the C—N bonds and separate into two molecules, D.

Two other first-order chemical reactions are the decomposition of nitrogen pentoxide, N_2O_5, into nitrogen dioxide and oxygen, and the decomposition of dimethyl ether, CH_3—O—CH_3, into methane, carbon monoxide, and hydrogen:

$$2N_2O_5 \longrightarrow 4NO_2 + O_2$$
$$CH_3OCH_3 \longrightarrow CH_4 + CO + H_2$$

It is to be noted that *the order of a reaction cannot be predicted from the stoichiometric over-all equation.* The equation for the N_2O_5 decomposition makes use of two molecules of the reactant, but the reaction is in fact a first-order reaction. This shows that the reaction takes place in steps; first there occurs a first-order decomposition, probably

$$N_2O_5 \longrightarrow NO_3 + NO_2$$

This is followed by other reactions, such as

$$2NO_3 \longrightarrow 2NO_2 + O_2$$

A simple method of studying the rate of a gaseous reaction in which the number of molecules of product is either greater or smaller than the number of molecules of reactant is the measurement of change in pres-

---

* Some other products also are formed, by other reactions of azomethane.

sure. The reactant is placed in the reaction vessel in the thermostat, and the gas pressure is then measured from time to time by a gauge. This method is illustrated by the following example.

Example 1.   At a given temperature a sample of dimethyl ether is found to have initial pressure [of pure $(CH_3)_2O$] of 300 mm Hg, and 10 seconds later the pressure has increased to 308.1 mm. How long would it take for the pressure to reach 600 mm, and how long would it then take for the pressure to change to 608.1 mm?

   Solution.   Let us answer the second question first. The reaction is

$$(CH_3)_2O \longrightarrow CH_4 + CO + H_2$$

Hence the number of molecules is tripled by the decomposition; the final pressure will be 900 mm. When half the ether has decomposed, the pressure will be 600 mm ($p_{ether} = 150$, $p_{CH_4} = 150$, $p_{CO} = 150$, $p_{H_2} = 150$). Since there is then only half as much ether present as initially, the rate of decomposition will be only half as great, and it will accordingly take **20 seconds** for the pressure to increase by 8.1 mm, which initially required 10 seconds.

   The first question is answered in the following way. From Equation 19-1 we derive

$$- \frac{dp_{ether}}{dt} = k p_{ether}$$

since the partial pressure of a gas at constant temperature is proportional to concentration. The increase in total pressure of 8.1 mm in 10 sec means a decrease of 4.05 mm in p_{ether} in 10 sec, or 0.405 mm per sec:

$$- \frac{dp_{ether}}{dt} = 0.405 \text{ mm/sec}$$

Hence

$$k = \frac{0.405}{300} = 0.00135 \text{ sec}^{-1}$$

The total pressure will reach 600 mm when p_{ether} has fallen to 150 mm from the initial value $p_0 = 300$ mm. Equation 19-2 is

$$p = p_0 e^{-kt}$$

In our case $\dfrac{p}{p_0} = 0.5$. Hence we want to find the value of t at which $e^{-kt} = $ **0.5.** The function e^{-x} has the value 0.5 when $x = 0.693$. (We have $-x = \ln 0.5$ or $x = \ln 2 = 2.303 \log 2 = 2.033 \times 0.301 = 0.693$.) Hence $kt = 0.693$ with $k = 0.00135$, or $t = 0.693/0.00135 = $ **513 sec.**

We may derive this answer in another way, using the statement in the text that the half-life is 693 times the time required for 0.1% decomposition. (This statement is proved in the preceding paragraph, where it is shown that $e^{-x} = \frac{1}{2}$ when $x = 0.693$.) In 10 seconds the partial pressure of dimethyl ether decreases from 300 mm to a value 4.05 mm less, a decrease of 1.35%. Hence there is 0.1% decomposition in $10/13.5 = 0.741$ seconds. The half-life of the ether is hence $693 \times 0.741 = $ **513 sec,** which is the answer.

19–4. *Reactions of Higher Order*

If reaction occurs by collision and interaction of two molecules A and B, the rate of the reaction will be proportional to the number of collisions. The number of collisions in unit volume is seen from simple kinetic considerations to be proportional to the product of the concentrations of A and B. Hence we may write as the differential rate expression for this second-order reaction

$$\text{rate of reaction} = -\frac{d[\text{A}]}{dt} = -\frac{d[\text{B}]}{dt} = k[\text{A}]\,[\text{B}] \qquad (19\text{-}3)$$

Here $-\dfrac{d[\text{A}]}{dt}$ is the rate of decrease in concentration of $[\text{A}]$ and $-\dfrac{d[\text{B}]}{dt}$ is that of $[\text{B}]$; they are equal, the reaction being $\text{A} + \text{B} \longrightarrow$ products. The factor k is the *second-order rate constant.*

It must again be emphasized that *the stoichiometric equation for a reaction does not determine its rate.* Thus the oxidation of iodide ion by persulfate ion

$$\text{S}_2\text{O}_8^{--} + 2\text{I}^- \longrightarrow 2\text{SO}_4^{--} + \text{I}_2$$

might be a third-order reaction, with rate proportional to $[\text{S}_2\text{O}_8^{--}]\,[\text{I}^-]^2$; it is in fact second-order, with rate proportional to $[\text{S}_2\text{O}_8^{--}]\,[\text{I}^-]$. In this case the slow, rate-determining reaction is the reaction between one persulfate ion and one iodide ion,

$$\text{S}_2\text{O}_8^{--} + \text{I}^- \longrightarrow \text{products}$$

This is followed by a rapid reaction between the products and another iodide ion.*

---

* The slow reaction probably produces the hypoiodite ion, IO^-.

Example 2.   In a solution of persulfate and iodide how would the rate of the reaction be changed by dilution with an equal amount of water?

Solution.   The concentrations $[S_2O_8{}^{--}]$ and $[I^-]$ would both be halved; hence the rate of reaction after dilution would be one-quarter the initial rate.

A general reaction with rate-determining equation

$$aA + bB + cC \longrightarrow \text{products}$$

(this step requiring the interaction of a molecules of substance A, b of B, and c of C) would proceed at the rate

$$\text{rate of reaction} = -\frac{d[A]}{dt} = k[A]^a\,[B]^b\,[C]^c \qquad (19\text{-}4)$$

In this expression the concentration of A occurs to the a power, that of B to the b power, and that of C to the c power. The order of this reaction would be $a + b + c$.

This equation is valid for gases at ordinary or low partial pressures and substances in solution at low concentrations.

The reaction-rate expression will be used in the following chapter in the discussion of chemical equilibrium.

19–5. *The Dependence of Reaction Rate on Temperature*

It is everyday experience that chemical reactions are accelerated by increased temperature. This is true, in fact, for almost all chemical reactions, and the dependence of the reaction rate on temperature is surprisingly similar for reactions of most kinds: *the rate of most reactions is approximately doubled for every 10° increase in temperature.*

This is a very useful rule. It is only a rough rule—the 10° factor for most reactions is close to 2, but occasionally it is as small as 1.5 or as large as 4. Reactions of very large molecules, such as proteins, may have even larger temperature factors; the rate of denaturation of ovalbumin (the process which occurs on boiling an egg) increases about fifty-fold for a 10° rise.

Example 3a.   In an experiment a sample of $KClO_3$ was 90% decomposed in 20 minutes; about how long would it have taken if the sample had been heated 20° hotter?

Answer.   About $1/4$ as long; a factor $1/2$ is introduced per 10° rise.

Example 3b. The reaction-rate constant for N_2O_5 decomposition at a certain temperature as found by experiment is 0.405 sec^{-1}. What would its value be at a temperature 5° higher?

    Answer. The relation between temperature and reaction-rate factor is an exponential one:

Rise	Factor
10°	2
20°	$2^2 = 4$
30°	$2^3 = 8$
40°	$2^4 = 16$

For 5° rise $(1/2 \times 10°)$ the factor is $2^{\frac{1}{2}} = 1.4$. Hence the constant becomes $1.4 \times 0.405 = 0.57$ sec^{-1}, and the reaction would proceed about 40% faster.

Spontaneous Combustion. Reactions such as the combustion of fuels proceed very rapidly when combustion is begun, but fuels may remain indefinitely in contact with air without burning. In these cases the rate of reaction at room temperature is extremely small. The process of lighting a fire consists in increasing the temperature of part of the fuel until the reaction proceeds rapidly; the exothermic reaction then liberates enough heat to raise another portion of the fuel to the kindling temperature, and in this way the process is continued.

    The oxidation of oil-soaked rags or other combustible material may occur rapidly enough at room temperature to produce heat enough to increase the temperature somewhat; this accelerates the oxidation, and causes further heating, until the mass bursts into flame. This process is called *spontaneous combustion.*

    The Arrhenius Equation: Activation Energy. The rate of a reaction is usually not determined completely by the number of molecular collisions in unit time. The fact that some reactions are very fast and other similar ones are very slow shows this, for the number of collisions is about the same for the slow reactions as for the fast ones: we must conclude that *in general only a fraction, sometimes a very small fraction, of molecular collisions lead to reaction.* It was suggested by Arrhenius that *in order to react, the colliding molecules* must have more than the average amount of energy.* This extra energy is called the *activation energy* of the reaction. It might be kinetic energy (the colliding molecules striking one another harder than for an average collision) or internal energy of the molecules.

    For example, the hydrogen molecule and the iodine molecule are known to have van der Waals radii of about 1.0 Å and 2.1 Å, respectively, so that on ordinary collision the H and I nuclei approach only to about 3.1 Å from one another. But the H—I distance in hydrogen iodide is 1.62 Å, and in order for the reaction $H_2 + I_2 \longrightarrow 2HI$ to

---

* Or, in the case of unimolecular decomposition, the decomposing molecule.

occur the nuclei must approach to nearly this distance. This occurs only on collision of an H_2 molecule and an I_2 molecule which are moving very fast toward one another. In this case the activation energy is the kinetic energy of the fast-moving molecules.

This concept leads to the equation

$$k = k'e^{-E_{act}/RT} \tag{19-5}$$

This expresses the dependence of the reaction-rate constant k of a reaction on the absolute temperature T. The activation energy per mole is E_{act}, and R is the gas constant. The values of the constant k' and of E_{act} are found by introducing the experimental values of k for two temperatures.

The derivation of this equation, including a slight dependence of k' on the temperature, requires the use of the methods of statistical mechanics. The factor $e^{-E_{act}/RT}$ is a consequence of the very general *Boltzmann principle*, which states that at equilibrium at temperature T the ratio of the number of molecules with large energy to the number of molecules with small energy involves the Boltzmann factor $e^{-E/RT}$, where E is the molar energy difference.

The factor k', multiplied by the concentration factors, determines essentially the number of collisions (with suitable mutual orientations of the molecules, etc.) in unit time, and the exponential factor (with value 1 for $E_{act} = 0$, and smaller values for larger activation energies) is the fraction of collisions in which the molecules have enough energy to react. The exponential form of this factor causes the rate to be increased by a certain factor per unit temperature rise. The normal factor of 2 per 10° rise corresponds to about 13,000 cal/mole for the energy of activation.

19–6. *Catalysis*

The study of the factors which affect the rate of reactions has become more and more important with the continued great development of chemical industry. A modern method of manufacturing toluene, used for making the explosive trinitrotoluene and for other purposes, may be quoted as an example. The substance methylcyclohexane, C_7H_{14}, occurs in large quantities in petroleum. At high temperature and low pressure this substance should decompose into toluene, C_7H_8, and hydrogen. The reaction is so slow, however, that the process could not be carried out commercially until the discovery was made that a certain mixture of oxides increases the rate of reaction enough for the process to be put into practice. Many examples of catalysis (the process of accelerating a reaction by use of a catalyst) have already been mentioned, and others are mentioned in later chapters.

It is thought that catalysts speed up reactions by bringing the reacting molecules together and holding them in configurations favorable to reaction. Unfortunately so little is known about the fundamental nature of catalytic activity that the search for suitable catalysts is largely empirical. The test of a catalytic reaction, as of any proposed chemical process, is made by trying it to see if it works.

19–7. *Photochemistry*

Many chemical reactions are caused to proceed by the effect of light; examples are the fading of dyes by sunlight, the explosion of a mixture of hydrogen and chlorine by light, and the conversion of carbon dioxide and water into carbohydrate and oxygen by plants, with chlorophyll as catalyst. Such reactions are called *photochemical reactions*.

One law of photochemistry (Grotthus, 1818) is that *only light which is absorbed is photochemically effective*. Hence a colored substance must be present in a system which shows photochemical reactivity with visible light. In the process of natural photosynthesis this substance is the green chlorophyll, and in the hydrogen-chlorine explosion it is chlorine.

The second law of photochemistry (formulated in 1912 by Einstein) is that *one molecule of reacting substance may be activated by the absorption of one light quantum*. A light quantum is the smallest amount of energy which can be removed from a beam of light by any material system (Chap. 8). Its magnitude depends on the frequency of the light: it is equal to $h\nu$, where h is Planck's constant, with value 6.6238×10^{-27} erg sec, and ν is the frequency of the light, equal to c/λ, with c the velocity of light and λ the wavelength of the light. In some systems, such as material containing rather stable dyes, many light quanta are absorbed by the molecules for each molecule decomposed; the fading of the dye by light is a slow and inefficient process in these materials. In some simple systems the absorption of one quantum of light results in the reaction or decomposition of one molecule. In other systems a *chain of reactions* may be set off by one light quantum. Examples are the photochemical reaction of hydrogen and chlorine or of hydrogen and bromine. A mixture of hydrogen and bromine illuminated with blue light produces hydrogen bromide, by photochemical reaction. Hydrogen is transparent to all visible light; bromine, which owes its red color to its strong absorption of blue light and violet light, is the photochemically active constituent in the mixture. The absorption of a quantum of blue light by a bromine molecule splits the molecule into two bromine atoms:

$$Br_2 + h\nu \longrightarrow 2Br$$

The bromine atoms then react with hydrogen molecules to form hydrogen bromide molecules and hydrogen atoms, and the hydrogen atoms react with bromine molecules to form hydrogen bromide molecules and more bromine atoms:

$$Br + H_2 \longrightarrow HBr + H$$
$$H + Br_2 \longrightarrow HBr + Br$$

These new bromine atoms then react as did those originally produced by the light, and thus a chain of reactions producing hydrogen bromide may be set up. Thousands of hydrogen bromide molecules may in this way be formed as a result of the absorption of a single quantum. The chain finally is broken through the recombination of bromine atoms to form bromine molecules; this reaction occurs on the collision of two bromine atoms with the wall of the vessel containing the gas or with another atom or molecule in the gas.

The photochemical decomposition of hydrogen bromide by light in the near ultraviolet region (around 2,500 Å) is a simple photochemical reaction, in which two molecules of hydrogen bromide are decomposed for every light quantum absorbed. The initial reaction is

$$HBr + h\nu \longrightarrow H + Br$$

The hydrogen atom then reacts with a second hydrogen bromide molecule:

$$H + HBr \longrightarrow H_2 + Br$$

These two reactions have produced two atoms of bromine. The two atoms of bromine combine with one another, on collision with another molecule or the wall, to form a molecule of bromine:

$$Br + Br \longrightarrow Br_2$$

The over-all reaction can accordingly be written in the following way:

$$2HBr + light\ quantum \longrightarrow H_2 + Br_2$$

The reaction does not occur in a single step, corresponding to the last equation, but in three steps, represented by the three preceding equations. The number of molecules decomposed per light quantum absorbed is called the *quantum yield*. In the photochemical decomposition of hydrogen bromide the quantum yield is 2.

A photochemical reaction of much geophysical and biological importance is the formation of ozone from oxygen. Oxygen is practically transparent to visible light and to light in the near ultraviolet region, but it strongly absorbs light in the far ultraviolet region—in the region from 1,600 Å to 1,800 Å. Each light quantum that is absorbed dissociates an oxygen molecule into two oxygen atoms:

$$O_2 + h\nu \longrightarrow 2O$$

A thermal reaction (a reaction that can take place in the dark, and does not require absorption of a light quantum) then follows:

$$O + O_2 \longrightarrow O_3$$

Accordingly there are produced two molecules of ozone, O_3, for each light quantum absorbed. In addition, however, the ozone molecules can be destroyed by combining with oxygen atoms, or by a photochemical reaction. The reaction of combining with oxygen atoms is

$$O + O_3 \longrightarrow 2O_2$$

The reactions of photochemical production of ozone and destruction of ozone lead to a photochemical equilibrium, which maintains a small concentration of ozone in the oxygen being irradiated. The layer of the atmosphere in which the major part of the ozone is present is about 15 miles above the earth's surface; it is called the *ozone layer*.

The geophysical and biological importance of the ozone layer results from the absorption of light in the near ultraviolet region, from 2,400 Å to 3,000 Å, by the ozone. The photochemical reaction is

$$O_3 + h\nu \longrightarrow O + O_2$$

This reaction permits ozone to absorb ultraviolet light so strongly as to remove practically all of the ultraviolet light from the sunlight before it reaches the earth's surface. The ultraviolet light which it absorbs is photochemically destructive toward many of the organic molecules necessary in life processes, and if the ultraviolet light of sunlight were not prevented by the ozone layer from reaching the surface of the earth life in its present form could not exist.

Another interesting photochemical reaction is the darkening of silver halide grains in a photographic emulsion. Pure silver halides are not very sensitive; adsorbed material and the gelatin of the emulsion increase the sensitivity. After a grain has been in part decomposed by photochemical action, the decomposition can be completed by chemical development (Chap. 27).

Blueprint paper provides another interesting example. This is made by treating paper with a solution of potassium ferricyanide and ferric citrate. Under the action of light the citrate ion reduces the ferric ion to ferrous ion, which combines with ferricyanide to form the insoluble blue compound $KFeFe(CN)_6 \cdot H_2O$ (Prussian blue). The unreacted substances are then washed out of the paper with water.

Exercises

19-1.   If the rate of solution of zinc in hydrochloric acid is proportional to the surface area of the zinc, how much more rapidly will a thousand cubes of zinc each weighing a milligram dissolve than a single cube weighing one gram?

19-2. By what factor would the percentage decomposition in given time of a sample of N_2O_5 (which decomposes unimolecularly) be increased by compressing to half the volume with temperature held constant?

19-3. In an investigation of the second-order gas reaction

$$2NO_2 = 2NO + O_2$$

the pressure changed from 100 to 101 mm in 12 sec, starting from pure NO_2. How long would it take, later on, to change from 125 to 126 mm?

19-4. Azomethane gas decomposes according to the first-order reaction

$$CH_3NNCH_3 \longrightarrow C_2H_6 + N_2$$

(a) In a reaction at 287° C, with initial pressure (of azomethane only) 160 mm, what would the final total pressure be? (b) When the total pressure reached 161.6 mm, after 100 seconds, what fraction of the azomethane had decomposed? (c) Using the equation $\dfrac{-dp_{az}}{dt} = kp_{az}$ (p_{az} = partial pressure of azomethane), calculate k (in sec^{-1}) at 287° C from the above data. (d) How long would it take for half the azomethane to decompose? (e) If the initial pressure were 80 mm, how long would it take for half the azomethane to decompose, at the same temperature?

19-5. The reduction of ferric ion by stannous ion in neutral solution was shown by A. A. Noyes to be third-order, corresponding to the reaction

$$2Fe^{+++} + Sn^{++} = 2Fe^{++} + Sn^{++++}$$

At certain concentrations 1% of the iron is reduced in 10 seconds. (a) How long would it take to reduce 1% of the iron if $[Sn^{++}]$ were doubled? (b) How long would it take to reduce 1% of the iron if $[Fe^{+++}]$ were doubled? (c) About how long would it take, at the original concentrations, if the temperature were raised 30°?

19-6. Professor Ramsperger reported the values 1.00×10^{-4} at 287.3° C and 20.8×10^{-4} at 327.4° C for the first-order rate constant of the azomethane decomposition. (a) From these data determine the 10° rate-constant factor. (b) Predict a value for the rate constant at 20° C. (c) Calculate how long it would take for a sample to decompose to the extent of 1% at 20° and at 327.4° C.

19-7. The half-life period of radium (the time required for half of a sample to decompose) is 1,733 years. What is the reaction-rate constant for the reaction? What fraction decomposes in one day?

19-8. The half-life period of C^{11}, made artificially and used in biological researches, is 20 min. How much of a sample remains after 3 hours?

19-9. A sample contains initially equal numbers of atoms of C^{11}, with half-life 20 min., and of C^{14}, with half-life about 5,568 years. (a) What is the initial ratio of activities of C^{11} to C^{14} (that is, of rate of decomposition)? (b) What is the ratio of activities after 6 hours? after 12 hours?

19-10. How long would it take before a mole of radium atoms disintegrates until only one or two radium atoms are left?

19-11.   Calculate the half-life in years of the plutonium isotope of mass number 239, Pu^{239}, from the measurement that one microgram (10^{-6} g) of plutonium emits 140,000 alpha particles per minute. Each plutonium atom emits one alpha particle as it decomposes.

19-12.   Automobile tires when stored age through oxidation and other reactions of the rubber. By what factor would the safe period of storage be multiplied by lowering the temperature of the storage room 10° F?

19-13.   Ozone gas decomposes according to the equation $2O_3 \longrightarrow 3O_2$. At one temperature, with ozone present at an initial pressure of 1.000 atm, the pressure rose to 1.012 atm in one minute. About how long would it take for the pressure to change from 1.000 to 1.012 atm at a temperature 15° C higher?

19-14.   If it is necessary to store oil-soaked rags, how should this be done?

19-15.   How does light cause the reaction between hydrogen and chlorine to take place? Would ultraviolet light with wavelength 1,000 Å, which causes the dissociation of hydrogen molecules into hydrogen atoms, initiate the reaction between hydrogen and chlorine?

19-16.   What molecular processes can you imagine that would prevent a single quantum of light from causing all of the chlorine and all of the hydrogen in a vessel from combining?

19-17.   We know that catalysts in the body cause carbohydrates (sugars), such as $C_6H_{12}O_6$, to react with oxygen to form carbon dioxide and water. In plants, due to the presence of chlorophyll, carbon dioxide and water are converted by a photochemical reaction to sugar and oxygen. Are these statements inconsistent with the statement that a catalyst can affect only the rate of a reaction and not its equilibrium? Why not?

Chapter 20

Chemical
Equilibrium

20–1. *Equilibrium in Homogeneous Systems*

Sometimes a chemical reaction begins, continues for a while, and then stops before any one of the reactants is used up; *the reaction has reached equilibrium.* An example is the reaction of cupric ion and ammonia in aqueous solution to form the complex ion $Cu(NH_3)_4^{++}$. If some ammonium hydroxide solution (which contains some ammonia molecules in solution) is added to a dilute solution of a cupric salt the color of the solution changes from pale blue, the color of hydrated cupric ion, $Cu(H_2O)_4^{++}$, to a deeper blue, because of the formation of the deep-blue ammonia complex. However, neither all of the ammonia nor all of the hydrated copper ion has been used up; this is shown by the fact that the deep-blue color can be made more intense by adding either more cupric salt or more ammonia to the solution.

The equilibrium results from the fact that the rates of the two reactions

$$Cu(H_2O)_4^{++} + 4NH_3 \longrightarrow Cu(NH_3)_4^{++} + 4H_2O$$

and

$$Cu(NH_3)_4^{++} + 4H_2O \longrightarrow Cu(H_2O)_4^{++} + 4NH_3$$

are comparable in magnitude; at equilibrium these rates are equal. From the arguments of the preceding chapter we might write the two equations

$$\text{forward rate} = k_1 \, [Cu(H_2O)_4^{++}] \, [NH_3]^4$$

and

$$\text{backward rate} = k_2 \, [Cu(NH_3)_4^{++}] \, [H_2O]^4$$

for the rates of the forward and backward reactions, assuming that each of the reactions occurs in one step. At equilibrium these rates are equal; cupric ion is still reacting with ammonia molecules to form the complex, and the complex is still decomposing, but just as much cupric ammonia complex is being decomposed in unit time as is being formed. Hence we write

$$\text{forward rate} = \text{backward rate}$$

$$k_1 \, [Cu(H_2O)_4{}^{++}] \, [NH_3]^4 = k_2 \, [Cu(NH_3)_4{}^{++}] \, [H_2O]^4$$

or

$$\frac{[Cu(NH_3)_4{}^{++}] \, [H_2O]^4}{[Cu(H_2O)_4{}^{++}] \, [NH_3]^4} = \frac{k_1}{k_2} = K \tag{20-1}$$

The quantity K, which is the ratio of the rate constants for the forward and backward reactions, is called the **equilibrium constant** of the reaction of formation of the cupric ammonia complex.

We now see why the reaction does not go to completion. If it were to go to completion, either one or the other of the molecular species $Cu(H_2O)_4{}^{++}$ and NH_3 would be all used up: its concentration would be zero. This would make the concentration-ratio expression become infinite, which could be the value of $K = k_1/k_2$ only if k_1 were infinite or k_2 were zero. This is, however, not the case—both reactions take place with finite rate.

We also see why the concentration of the ammonia complex is increased by adding either cupric ion or ammonia. If either the concentration $[Cu(H_2O)_4{}^{++}]$ or $[NH_3]$ is increased, the rate of the forward reaction increases, becoming greater than that of the backward reaction; hence the forward reaction proceeds until the concentration ratio of Equation 20-1 is again equal to the equilibrium constant K.

Equilibria of this sort are very important in chemistry. Many industrial processes have been made practicable by the discovery of a way of shifting an equilibrium so as to produce a satisfactory amount of a desired product. In this chapter we discuss quantitatively the principles of chemical equilibrium and the methods of shifting the equilibrium of a system in one direction or the other.

20–2. *Stable Equilibrium and Metastable Equilibrium*

If a reaction which is possible for a system proceeds extremely slowly under the existing conditions, it may be convenient to ignore that reaction in the discussion of chemical equilibrium. For example, a burning jet of hydrogen continues to burn when the jet is introduced into pure chlorine:

$$H_2 + Cl_2 \longrightarrow 2HCl$$

Nevertheless, the rate of this reaction at room temperature (and in the absence of bright light) is so small that a mixture of hydrogen and chlorine can be kept for many days before a detectable amount of hydrogen chloride is formed. A system of this sort is said to be in **metastable equilibrium.** If a catalyst is introduced, accelerating the forward and reverse reactions

$$H_2 + Cl_2 \rightleftarrows 2HCl$$

the system approaches a state of true equilibrium or **stable equilibrium.**

A system may be in metastable equilibrium with respect to one reaction and in stable equilibrium with respect to another. For example, a system initially containing a gaseous mixture of hydrogen, chlorine, and liquid water would very soon closely approach equilibrium with respect to water vapor and liquid water, through the evaporation of water until the partial pressure of water vapor in the gaseous phase became essentially equal to the vapor pressure of liquid water at the temperature of the system. It would also soon reach equilibrium between the gases hydrogen and chlorine and their solutions in the water. After a somewhat longer time the chlorine would reach equilibrium with its products of hydrolysis:

$$Cl_2 + H_2O \rightleftarrows HClO + H^+ + Cl^-$$

These equilibria could be observed and studied even though no reaction occurred between hydrogen and chlorine; the system would be in stable equilibrium with respect to these reactions, and in metastable equilibrium with respect to the reaction

$$H_2 + Cl_2 \rightleftarrows 2HCl$$

An isolated system in equilibrium must be *isothermal;* that is, all parts of the system must be at the same temperature, since otherwise heat would flow from the hotter regions to the colder regions. It must also be *isopiestic,* with all regions at the same pressure (except for the very small pressure differences due to gravity). It is sometimes convenient to discuss a system in a state which does not change with time, but which may involve a steady flow of heat or of matter into or out of the system. Such a system is said to be in a *steady state.* An example is a gas or solution in a vessel which is kept warm at the top and cold at the bottom. It is found by experiment that the concentrations or partial pressures of the constituents of the system are not the same at the top as at the bottom, when a steady state is reached.

20–3. *The General Equation for the Equilibrium Constant*

For a general reaction

$$a\text{A} + b\text{B} + \cdots \rightleftarrows d\text{D} + e\text{E} + \cdots$$

we may write the rate expressions

$$\left.\begin{array}{l} \text{forward rate} = k_1 \, [\text{A}]^a \, [\text{B}]^b \cdots \\ \text{backward rate} = k_2 \, [\text{D}]^d \, [\text{E}]^e \cdots \end{array}\right\} \ (20\text{-}2)$$

Hence at equilibrium, when the two rates are equal, the following equation holds:

$$\frac{[\text{D}]^d \, [\text{E}]^e \cdots}{[\text{A}]^a \, [\text{B}]^b \cdots} = K \tag{20-3}$$

with K, the equilibrium constant, equal to k_1/k_2. The equation holds when the concentrations of the reactants and products are small; deviations are observed at large concentrations.

It is not necessary to assume that the forward and backward reactions occur with such mechanisms as to lead to the above rate expressions. Even if the reactions take place in steps, with rates involving powers of the reactant concentrations different from the coefficients in the over-all stoichiometric equation, the equilibrium expression 20-3 is valid. *This expression is, in fact, a consequence of the laws of thermodynamics, and its validity is not dependent on the reaction-rate arguments which we have presented.*

Equation 20-3 is the equilibrium expression for a homogeneous system (a solution or gas) at constant temperature. The value of the equilibrium constant K depends on the temperature. The way in which it changes with changing temperature is discussed later.

It is customary to write the concentration ratio as in Equation 20-3 for an equation such as Equation 20-2; namely, *the product concentrations (to the appropriate powers) are written in the numerator and the reactant concentrations in the denominator.* This is a useful convention.

If the concentration of one substance in a system initially at equilibrium is increased, the forward or reverse reaction will take place until the concentrations have changed in such a way as to restore the equality of the concentration ratio to the equilibrium constant. In particular a reaction can be driven farther toward completion by increasing the concentration of one or more of the reactants and driven back by increasing that of one or more of the products.

The equilibrium expression 20-3 was discovered by two Norwegian chemists, Guldberg and Waage, in 1864. The underlying law is often called the *law of chemical equilibrium* or *law of mass action*. The arguments used by Guldberg and Waage were similar to those given above.

The usefulness of the equilibrium expression can be shown by making some calculations with its aid.

Example.   Acetic acid, $HC_2H_3O_2$ (the acid in vinegar), is a weak acid, only a fraction of its molecules being ionized in aqueous solution. The concentration of hydrogen ions in a 1 N solution of acetic acid is found to be the same as in a 0.0042 N solution of hydrochloric acid. Would the solution of acetic acid become more acidic or less acidic if some sodium acetate were added to it?

Answer.   It would become less acidic, for the following reason. Acetic acid ionizes according to the equation

$$HC_2H_3O_2 \rightleftarrows H^+ + C_2H_3O_2^-$$

The equilibrium expression for this equation is

$$K = \frac{[H^+]\,[C_2H_3O_2^-]}{[HC_2H_3O_2]}$$

This expression must have the same value after the sodium acetate is added as before. The sodium ions, Na^+, from the added sodium acetate have no effect. The acetate ions, $C_2H_3O_2^-$, however, increase the value of $[C_2H_3O_2^-]$, so that the ratio $\dfrac{[H^+]\,[C_2H_3O_2^-]}{[HC_2H_3O_2]}$ on the right side of the equilibrium equation becomes greater than the constant K. Hence a reaction must occur, and must continue until this ratio is reduced to the value K. This involves decreasing $[H^+]$ and $[C_2H_3O_2^-]$, and increasing $[HC_2H_3O_2]$, which occurs if some of the ions combine to form the un-ionized acid:

$$H^+ + C_2H_3O_2^- \longrightarrow HC_2H_3O_2$$

Hence some of the hydrogen ion will be used up, and the solution will become less acidic.

This qualitative conclusion can, of course, be reached simply by the application of the principle of Le Châtelier (Chap. 15) to the system. The equilibrium equation, however, permits quantitative calculations to be made.

20–4. *The Equilibrium Constant Expressed*
in Partial Pressures

Since at constant temperature the concentrations of molecular species in a gas are proportional to the partial pressures, the equilibrium expression for a gaseous reaction may be written as

$$\frac{p_D^d p_E^e \cdots}{p_A^a p_B^b \cdots} = K$$

In general the numerical value of K depends on whether concentrations or partial pressures are used, and on the units chosen for measuring concentration or pressure.

Example 1. The equilibrium constant (with partial pressures in atm) for the reaction

$$H_2 + I_2(g) \rightleftarrows 2HI$$

has the value 808 at room temperature (25° C). To what extent does hydrogen iodide decompose at room temperature?

   Solution. We are given that

$$\frac{p^2_{HI}}{p_{H_2} p_{I_2}} = 808$$

On decomposition HI forms equal amounts of H_2 and I_2; hence we may put

$$x = p_{H_2} = p_{I_2}$$

Then

$$x^2 = \frac{p^2_{HI}}{808}$$

or

$$x = \frac{p_{HI}}{28.4}$$

The partial pressure of H_2 and that of I_2 are hence 3.52% that of HI. Since two molecules of HI on reaction form only one of H_2 and one of I_2, there must have been 7.04% more HI present initially than when equilibrium is reached. Hence the extent of decomposition of the hydrogen iodide is 7.04/107.04 = 0.066, or **6.6%**.

   It is of interest that *the extent of decomposition in this case is independent of the total pressure*. This results from the fact that there is no change in the total number of molecules on reaction, and hence the numerator and denominator of the equilibrium expression are of the same degree. Multiplying all the partial pressures by the same factor does not change the value of the equilibrium expression. On the other hand, in the following example it is shown that the amount of decomposition of ammonia

$$2NH_3 \rightleftarrows N_2 + 3H_2$$

is strongly dependent on the pressure; here four molecules are formed from two.

In Example 1 the equilibrium constant has been written for the reaction of formation of HI from the elements. If the decomposition or dissociation reaction

$$2HI \rightleftarrows H_2 + I_2(g)$$

were written, the equilibrium constant would be

$$K_{\text{dissociation}} = \frac{p_{H_2}p_{I_2}}{p^2_{HI}}$$

and its value would be the reciprocal of that for the formation reaction. This equilibrium constant is called the **dissociation constant** of hydrogen iodide into the elements.

Example 2.   At 500° C the equilibrium constant for the formation of ammonia by the reaction

$$N_2 + 3H_2 \rightleftarrows 2NH_3$$

has the value 1.50×10^{-5}, expressed in terms of partial pressures in atmospheres. What fraction of a stoichiometric mixture of nitrogen and hydrogen could be converted to ammonia with the total pressure kept at 1 atm? at 500 atm?

Solution.   The equilibrium equation for this reaction is

$$\frac{p^2_{NH_3}}{p_{N_2}p^3_{H_2}} = 1.50 \times 10^{-5}$$

The problem states that

$$p_{H_2} = 3p_{N_2}$$

because the stoichiometric ratio N_2 to $3H_2$ is specified for these gases. The total pressure is the sum of the partial pressures of the three gases:

$p_{N_2} + p_{H_2} + p_{NH_3} = p_{total}$

Let

$x = p_{NH_3}$

Then

$p_{N_2} + p_{H_2} = p_{total} - x$

and

$p_{N_2} = \frac{1}{4} (p_{total} - x)$
$p_{H_2} = \frac{3}{4} (p_{total} - x)$

Therefore

$$\frac{x^2}{\frac{27}{256} (p_{total} - x)^4} = 1.50 \times 10^{-5}$$

$$\frac{x^2}{(p_{total} - x)^4} = 1.58 \times 10^{-6}$$

$x = 1.26 \times 10^{-3} \times (p_{total} - x)^2$

This quadratic equation might be solved directly. It is seen, however, that when p_{total} is small x is small compared with p_{total}. Hence as a first approximation we neglect x in comparison with p_{total} in the term on the right where these quantities are subtracted, obtaining

$x \cong 0.00126 \times p^2_{total}$

For total pressure 1 atm this gives $x = p_{NH_3} = 0.00126$ atm. Remembering that two molecules of ammonia are formed from four molecules of the reactants, we see that only **0.25%** of the gas mixture is converted into ammonia.

For $p_{total} = 500$ atm this approximate method gives $x = p_{NH_3} = 0.00126 \times 500^2 = 315$ atm, which is not negligible compared with $p_{total} = 500$ atm. Direct solution of the quadratic equation gives $p_{NH_3} = 152$ atm, which leads to $p_{N_2} = 87$ atm and $p_{H_2} = 261$ atm. From these values it is calculated that at this total pressure **46.6%** of the original mixture is converted into ammonia. This calculation shows why high pressures are used in the manufacture of ammonia from the elements (Chap. 18). In practice the reaction is carried out at about 500° C and 500 atm.

The principles of homogeneous equilibrium have many important applications to the chemistry of solutions. Some of these, including the discussion of weak acids and bases, the hydrolysis of salts, and the formation of complex ions, are treated in later chapters.

Application of the Principle of Le Châtelier. It is seen that the principle of Le Châtelier (Chap. 15) may be applied in several ways to systems such as those just discussed. If the partial pressure of H_2 or I_2 in a system initially at equilibrium is increased, the reaction will proceed in such direction as to decrease this partial pressure toward the original value; that is, hydrogen and iodine will combine to HI until the partial-pressure quotient again becomes equal to the equilibrium constant.

If the pressure of the system is changed there occurs no change in the H_2-I_2-HI equilibrium, because the reaction is not accompanied by change in pressure. But change in total pressure of the system causes a shift in the ammonia equilibrium in the direction which tends to restore the original pressure; hence increase in pressure causes formation of more ammonia. In industrial plants for the fixation of atmospheric nitrogen by the ammonia process pressures as high as 1,000 atm are used, in order that the yield be large. In the manufacture of toluene by the dehydrogenation of methylcyclohexane, on the other hand, the pressure is kept low in order to obtain a large yield; here the reaction is

$$C_7H_{14}(g) \rightleftharpoons C_7H_8(g) + 3H_2$$

It is interesting to note that the addition of nitrogen to the N_2-H_2-NH_3 system causes the equilibrium to shift in such a way as to use up a part of the added nitrogen if the volume of the system is kept constant during the addition of extra nitrogen. If, on the other hand, the pressure is kept constant, so that the other gases are diluted, the equilibrium may shift in the opposite direction. *In applying the principle of Le Châtelier partial pressures or concentrations of substances are the significant variables, and not the amounts of substances.* In the above case the addition of extra nitrogen at constant total pressure increases the partial pressure of nitrogen and decreases that of hydrogen, and the effect of this decrease is more important at some ratios of the two gases than the effect of the increase for nitrogen.

Effect of Catalysts. It is a consequence of the laws of thermodynamics —the impossibility of perpetual motion—that *a system in equilibrium is not changed by the addition of a catalyst*. The catalyst may increase the rate at which the system approaches its final equilibrium state, but it cannot change the value of the equilibrium constant. Under equilibrium conditions a catalyst has the same effect on the rate of the backward reaction as on that of the corresponding forward reaction.

It is true that a system which has stood unchanged for a long period of time, apparently in equilibrium, may undergo reaction when a small amount of a catalyst is added. Thus a mixture of hydrogen and oxygen at room temperature remains apparently unchanged for a very long period of time; however, if some finely divided platinum (platinum black) is placed in the gas, chemical reaction begins and continues until very little of one of the reacting gases remains. In this case the system in absence of the catalyst is not in equilibrium with respect to the reaction $2H_2 + O_2 \rightleftharpoons 2H_2O$, but only in metastable equilibrium, the rate of formation of water being so small that true equilibrium would not be approached in a millennium. Because of the possibility of metastable equilibrium it is necessary in practice to apply the following **equilibrium criterion**: *A system is considered to have reached equilibrium with respect to a certain reaction when the same final state is reached by approach by the reverse reaction as by the forward reaction.*

20–5. *Equilibrium in Heterogeneous Systems*

For heterogeneous systems, with more than one phase present, the equilibrium conditions are closely related to those for homogeneous systems. There are two important principles which apply.

1. *The activity of a substance in a system at equilibrium has the same value for each phase of the system of which the substance is a component.* For example, in the system ice–water–water-vapor at $0°$ C the activity of water is the same for all three phases. Activity is usually expressed as partial pressure or as concentration; in this case the vapor pressure of ice and the vapor pressure of liquid water are both equal to the partial pressure of water vapor in the gas phase. If some ether were also present, forming another liquid phase, the amount of water dissolved in the ether would be such as to give the same partial pressure of water for the ether-water phase as for the other phases.

2. *The activity of a substance present in a system as a pure liquid or crystalline phase is constant at constant temperature.* In any system in which there is ice, for example, at $-10°$ C, the activity of water has the same value, equal to the vapor pressure of ice at this temperature. We have already made use of this principle in the discussion of freezing-point lowering.

Since the activity of a pure liquid or crystalline phase is constant at constant temperature, the equilibrium constant for a reaction may be written without including the substance composing this phase.

Let us consider, for example, the decomposition of silver oxide:

$$2Ag_2O(s) \rightleftharpoons 4Ag(s) + O_2$$

We might write as the equilibrium constant

$$\frac{p_{O_2}p^4_{Ag}}{p^2_{Ag_2O}} = K_1$$

Since, however, p_{Ag} and p_{Ag_2O} are constants, the simplified equation

$$p_{O_2} = K$$

may be written. This states that at equilibrium at constant temperature the partial pressure of oxygen produced by partial decomposition of silver oxide is constant. At 400° C, for example, the decomposition constant of Ag_2O has the value 110 mm. Hence silver oxide held at this temperature would decompose so long as the partial pressure of oxygen in the gas in contact with the solid were less than 110 mm. Since the partial pressure of oxygen in air is 160 mm, finely divided silver at 400° C would combine with atmospheric oxygen to form the oxide. At 426° C the dissociation pressure of the oxide reaches 160 mm; hence at temperatures above this silver remains unoxidized in air.

Water and Dilute Solutions.   Since the partial pressure of water in dilute aqueous solutions is nearly the same as that for pure water, and is hence nearly constant at constant temperature, it is customary to omit the activity of water in the equilibrium expression for dilute aqueous solutions.

A very important reaction is the neutralization reaction

$$H_3O^+ + OH^- \rightleftarrows 2H_2O(l)$$

or the ionization reaction of water

$$2H_2O(l) \rightleftarrows H_3O^+ + OH^-$$

The equilibrium constant for this is

$$\frac{[H_3O^+]\,[OH^-]}{[H_2O]^2} = K_1$$

in which $[H_2O]$ represents the activity of water in the solution. The product of K_1 and $[H_2O]^2$ may be taken as another constant, K:

$$[H_3O^+]\,[OH^-] = K$$

The value of K is 1.0×10^{-14} mole²/l² at 25° C. *Hence in pure water both hydronium ions, H_3O^+, and hydroxide ions, OH^-, have the concentration 10^{-7} moles per liter, and in acid or basic solutions the product of the concentrations of these two ions equals 10^{-14}.* This is discussed further in the following chapter.

Solubility Product. An interesting case of equilibrium is that involving a solid substance and ions in solution. Let us consider, for example, lead chloride, $PbCl_2$. This salt has solubility 0.99 g per 100 ml or 0.0356 gfw/l at 20° C. The equilibrium between the solid salt and its ions in the solution corresponds to the reaction

$$PbCl_2(s) \rightleftharpoons Pb^{++} + 2Cl^-$$

and the equilibrium expression is

$$[Pb^{++}]\,[Cl^-]^2 = K$$

This equilibrium constant is called the **solubility product** of the salt. Its value at 20° is $0.0356 \times 0.0712^2 = 1.81 \times 10^{-4}$.

The form of the solubility-product expression is seen to be such as to make the solubility of the salt in a solution containing either chloride ion or lead ion much less than that in pure water. This *common-ion effect* is very important in qualitative analysis. A detailed discussion of solubility products and their uses will be given in Chapter 22.

Hydrates and Ammoniates. Sometimes reference is made to the water vapor pressure of a hydrated crystal, such as $CuSO_4 \cdot 5H_2O$. This is hardly correct; actually the crystal $CuSO_4 \cdot 5H_2O$ exists in stable equilibrium with water vapor over a wide range of partial pressure at constant temperature; at 50° C, for example, the partial pressure of water vapor in equilibrium with the crystal may be anywhere between 45.4 mm and 87.7 mm.

Let us consider the loss of water by $CuSO_4 \cdot 5H_2O$. It is found by experiment that on loss of water by this crystal the hydrate $CuSO_4 \cdot 3H_2O$ is first formed, the reaction being

$$CuSO_4 \cdot 5H_2O \rightleftharpoons CuSO_4 \cdot 3H_2O + 2H_2O$$

The equilibrium expression for this reaction is

$$p^2_{H_2O} = K'$$

or

$$p_{H_2O} = K$$

This constant K has the value 45.4 mm at 50° C; at this value of p_{H_2O}, and only at this value, the two solid hydrates $CuSO_4 \cdot 5H_2O$ and $CuSO_4 \cdot 3H_2O$ can remain in equilibrium at this temperature. K can be called the equilibrium water vapor pressure of the pentahydrate and the trihydrate.

For values of p_{H_2O} above 45.4 mm at 50° C, $CuSO_4 \cdot 3H_2O$ is not stable;

it is converted completely into the pentahydrate. At $p_{H_2O} = 87.7$ mm a liquid phase is formed, the saturated aqueous solution of the salt; this value, 87.7 mm, is the partial pressure of water which corresponds to the equilibrium

$$CuSO_4 \cdot xH_2O(l) \rightleftharpoons CuSO_4 \cdot 5H_2O(s) + (x - 5)H_2O(g)$$

At values of p_{H_2O} greater than 87.7 mm $CuSO_4 \cdot 5H_2O$ is unstable relative to the solution of the salt.

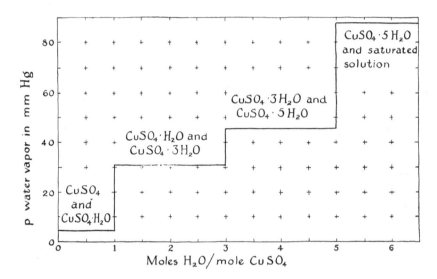

FIG. 20-1   *Partial pressure of water vapor in equilibrium with copper sulfate and its crystalline hydrates and saturated solution.*

Two other equilibrium water vapor pressures are shown by the system $CuSO_4$-H_2O at 50° C. These are 30.9 mm, for the reaction

$$CuSO_4 \cdot 3H_2O(s) \rightleftharpoons CuSO_4 \cdot H_2O(s) + 2H_2O(g)$$

and 4.5 mm, for the reaction

$$CuSO_4 \cdot H_2O(s) \rightleftharpoons CuSO_4(s) + H_2O(g)$$

The stability regions of the hydrates are hence the following:

$CuSO_4$	0 to 4.5 mm
$CuSO_4 \cdot H_2O$	4.5 to 30.9
$CuSO_4 \cdot 3H_2O$	30.9 to 45.4
$CuSO_4 \cdot 5H_2O$	45.4 to 87.7
$CuSO_4 \cdot xH_2O(l)$	above 87.7

These are indicated in Figure 20-1.

The curves which represent the boundaries of these stability ranges as functions of the temperature may intersect. Thus the curve for $CuSO_4 \cdot 5H_2O$-$CuSO_4 \cdot 3H_2O$ reaches that for $CuSO_4 \cdot 5H_2O$-solution at 95.7° C. Above this temperature the phase $CuSO_4 \cdot 5H_2O$ has no region of stability, and the phase in equilibrium with the solution is $CuSO_4 \cdot 3H_2O$.

Similar regions of stability, bounded by transition pressures of ammonia, are shown by crystalline ammoniates, such as $CuSO_4 \cdot 5NH_3$, $CuSO_4 \cdot 4NH_3$, $CuSO_4 \cdot 2NH_3$. The stability relations of a hydrate-ammoniate, such as $Cu(NH_3)_4SO_4 \cdot H_2O$, are more complex.

20–6. *The Conditions under Which a Reaction Proceeds to Completion*

A reaction such as the synthesis of hydrogen iodide

$$H_2 + I_2 \rightleftharpoons 2HI$$

does not proceed to completion; the relative amounts of the three substances must correspond to the equilibrium expression, and even under the most favorable conditions the conversion to the product is not complete.

Some reactions, in particular heterogeneous reactions, may proceed to completion, one of the reacting substances being used up completely. An example has just been discussed: one hydrate is completely transformed into another when the partial pressure of water has a suitable value.

The conditions under which a given reaction may proceed to completion or sufficiently near to completion for the purpose at hand can usually be found by considering the equilibrium problem which is involved. Some important classes of reactions are discussed in the following paragraphs.

A condensed-phase reaction may proceed to completion if a gas is formed and drawn off. Thus zinc placed in acid reacts to form hydrogen; if this is allowed to escape, the reaction will proceed until all of the zinc has dissolved or all of the acid has been used.

Usually a salt and an acid do not react completely. However, a reaction such as

$$H_2SO_4 + 2NaCl \rightleftharpoons Na_2SO_4 + 2HCl$$

can be made to go to completion by heating the system and driving off hydrogen chloride. Sulfuric acid and phosphoric acid, with high boiling points, can be used in this way in making the more volatile acids from their salts. On the other hand, sulfuric acid or phosphoric acid can be made from a sulfate or phosphate by heating it with the still less volatile silicic acid (silica).

A reaction in solution may proceed to completion if a slightly soluble substance or slightly ionized substance is formed. In general, when solutions of strong electrolytes are mixed no reaction occurs. If, however, the ionic concentrations are such that the solubility product of a substance is exceeded, reaction occurs until the ionic concentration product equals the solubility product, and if the solubility of the substance is small this will carry the reaction essentially to completion. Similarly, if a slightly ionized substance (such as water itself) is formed the reaction will proceed to an approximation to completion determined by the smallness of the degree of ionization of the substance. Examples of these effects will be discussed quantitatively in the following chapters.

20–7. *The Effect of Change of Temperature on Equilibrium*

A reaction that evolves heat as the reaction proceeds is called an exothermic reaction, and one that absorbs heat is called an endothermic reaction.

From the principle of Le Châtelier we can predict that *increase in temperature will drive a reaction further toward completion (by increasing the equilibrium constant) if the reaction is endothermic and will drive it back (by decreasing the equilibrium constant) if the reaction is exothermic.*

This principle is of great practical importance. For example, the synthesis of ammonia is exothermic (the heat evolved is 11.0 kcal per mole of ammonia formed); hence the yield is made a maximum by keeping the temperature as low as possible. The commercial process became practicable when catalysts were found that cause the reaction to proceed sufficiently rapidly at low temperatures.

The reaction

$$N_2 + O_2 \rightleftharpoons 2NO$$

is, on the other hand, endothermic (21.6 kcal of heat is absorbed per mole of NO formed); hence in order to fix atmospheric nitrogen by forming nitric oxide a very high temperature is needed. The temperature used in practice, that of an electric arc, is about 2,000° C.

20–8. *The Phase Rule—a Method of Classifying*
All Systems in Equilibrium

We have so far discussed a number of examples of systems in equilibrium. These examples include, among others, a crystal or a liquid in equilibrium with its vapor (Chap. 2), a crystal and its liquid in equilibrium with its vapor at its melting point (Chap. 2), a solution in equilibrium with the vapor of the solvent and with the frozen solvent (Chap. 16),

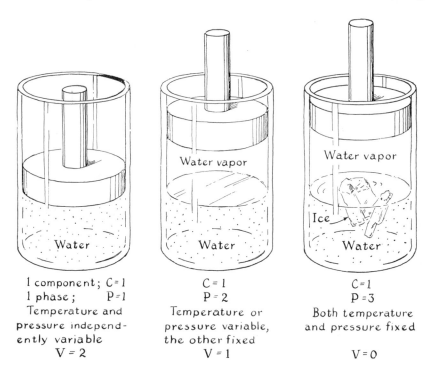

1 component; $C=1$ $C=1$ $C=1$
1 phase; $P=1$ $P=2$ $P=3$
Temperature and   Temperature or   Both temperature
pressure independ-   pressure variable,   and pressure fixed
ently variable   the other fixed
      $V=2$ $V=1$ $V=0$

FIG. 20-2   *A simple system illustrating the phase rule.*

silver oxide and metallic silver in equilibrium with oxygen (this chapter), and salt hydrates in equilibrium with water vapor (this chapter).

These systems appear to be quite different from one another. However, it was discovered by a great American theoretical physicist, Professor J. Willard Gibbs of Yale University (1839–1903), that a simple, unifying principle holds for all systems in equilibrium. This principle is called the *phase rule*.

The phase rule is a relation between the number of independent components, the number of phases, and the variance of a system in equilibrium. The independent components (or, briefly, the components) of a system are the substances that must be added to realize the system. The phases have been defined earlier (Chaps. 1 and 16). Thus a system containing ice, water, and water vapor consists of three phases but only one component (water-substance), since any two of the phases can be formed from the third. The *variance* of the system is the number of independent ways in which the system can be varied; these ways may include varying the temperature and the pressure, and also varying the composition of any solutions (gaseous, liquid, or crystalline) which exist as phases in the system.

The nature of the phase rule can be induced from some simple examples. Consider the system represented in Figure 20-2. It is made of water-substance (water in its various forms), in a cylinder with movable piston (to permit the pressure to be changed), placed in a thermostat with changeable temperature. If only one phase is present both the pressure and the temperature can be arbitrarily varied over wide ranges: the variance is 2. For example, liquid water can be held at any temperature from its freezing point to its boiling point under any applied pressure. But if two phases are present the pressure is automatically determined by the temperature: the variance is reduced to 1. For example, pure water vapor in equilibrium with water at a given temperature has a definite pressure, the vapor pressure of water at that temperature. And if three phases are present in equilibrium, ice, water, and water vapor, both the temperature and the pressure are exactly fixed: the variance is 0. This condition is called the *triple point* of ice, water, and water vapor. It occurs at temperature $+0.0099°$ C and pressure 4.58 mm of mercury.

We see that for this simple system, with one component, the sum of the number of phases and the variance is equal to 3. It was discovered by Gibbs that for every system in equilibrium the sum of the number of phases and the variance is 2 greater than the number of components:

number of phases + variance = number of components + 2

or, using the abbreviations P, V, and C,

$$P + V = C + 2$$

This is the phase rule.

Let us now consider its application. We ask: Is it ever possible for four phases to exist together in equilibrium? The answer is seen to be that it is, provided that there are at least two components. If there are only two components the four phases can co-exist only at exactly fixed temperature and pressure. For example, we might add copper sulfate to the water in our system. The components would then be two in number ($C = 2$). When ice, liquid solution, and water vapor were present ($P = 3$), the temperature could still be varied somewhat, by varying the concentration of copper sulfate in the liquid solution. The variance would then be 1, with three phases. On lowering the temperature there would ultimately be formed crystals of copper sulfate pentahydrate, $CuSO_4 \cdot 5H_2O$. The system would then be at fixed temperature, fixed pressure, and fixed composition of solution ($V = 0$), as determined by the phase rule for $C = 2$ and $P = 4$.

You may find it worth while to consider some other examples of systems in equilibrium, in order to see how the phase rule applies to them. The salt hydrates, with water vapor pressures as shown in Figure 20-1, are interesting; remember that the variance is at least 1, because the diagram as drawn corresponds to an arbitrarily chosen temperature (50° C).

Exercises

20-1. Write equilibrium expressions for the following reactions:

(a) $H_2O \rightleftharpoons H^+ + OH^-$

(b) $2CO_2 \rightleftharpoons 2CO + O_2$

(c) $2C + O_2 \rightleftharpoons 2CO$

(d) $CH_4 + 2O_2 \rightleftharpoons CO_2 + 2H_2O(g)$

(e) $2Cr_2O_7^{--} + 28H^+ + 6Sn^{++} \rightleftharpoons 4Cr^{+++} + 6Sn^{++++} + 14H_2O$

(f) $4FeS + 7O_2 \rightleftharpoons 2Fe_2O_3 + 4SO_2$

20-2. What is the numerical value of the equilibrium constant for the formation of HI (Example 1, this chapter) with partial pressures expressed in mm of Hg? What is it in terms of concentrations in moles per liter?

20-3. (a) What is the numerical value of the equilibrium constant for the formation of NH_3 (Example 2) with partial pressures expressed in mm of Hg? What is it in terms of concentrations in moles per liter? (b) Derive a relation valid at any temperature for calculating the equilibrium constant for the ammonia equilibrium using concentrations in moles per liter from the equilibrium constant using partial pressures.

20-4. At temperatures around 800° C iodine vapor is partially dissociated into atoms. If the partial pressure of I_2 is doubled, by what factor is the partial pressure of I changed?

20-5. Give in detail the calculation of the fractions of the gas mixture converted into ammonia at 1 atm and 500 atm total pressure from the values of p_{NH_3} given in Example 2.

20-6. (a) Calculate the partial pressure of ammonia at 1 atm total pressure which would be obtained at 500° C with an originally equimolar mixture of nitrogen and hydrogen. (b) What ratio of the two gases at this total pressure would give the largest yield of ammonia?

20-7. The vapor pressure of $I_2(s)$ at 25° C is 0.308 mm. (a) What is the numerical value of the equilibrium constant for the reaction

$$H_2 + I_2(s) = 2HI$$

at this temperature (see Example 1)? (b) What is the partial pressure of hydrogen in equilibrium with crystalline iodine and hydrogen iodide at one atmosphere?

20-8. The equilibrium constant for the reaction

$$2BaO(s) + O_2 = 2BaO_2(s)$$

has the following values, in atm:

t	K
697° C	0.086
737	.186
794	.497
835	.945
853	1.220

(a) Plot K as a function of t. (b) Over what temperature range would BaO take up oxygen from air? (c) Over what range would BaO_2 evolve oxygen at 1 atm pressure?
This has been used as a commercial method for obtaining oxygen from air.

20-9. The dissociation pressure of calcium carbonate has the following values:

t	p_{CO_2}
600° C	10 mm
800	180
840	320
880	580
896	760
910	1,000

(a) At what temperature would carbon dioxide begin to be given off from the substance heated in the air? (b) heated in a covered crucible? (c) heated in a lime-kiln in which hot flue gases (CO_2, N_2) from burning coke pass by the limestone?

20-10. The equilibrium water vapor pressures for calcium chloride at 20° C are

$CaCl_2—CaCl_2 \cdot 2H_2O$	0.00045 atm
$CaCl_2 \cdot 2H_2O—CaCl_2 \cdot 4H_2O$	.00326
$CaCl_2 \cdot 4H_2O—CaCl_2 \cdot 6H_2O$	.00497

(a) What fraction of the water vapor in saturated air at 20° C would fail to be picked up by anhydrous calcium chloride? The vapor pressure of water at 20° C is 17.54 mm. (b) What fraction would fail to be picked up after the drying agent had been used until its weight had increased by 10%? (c) After what increase in weight of the drying agent should a calcium chloride drying tube or desiccator be refilled? (d) In an experiment air is drawn through a calcium chloride drying tube, over a sample which is giving off water, and through another drying tube. How much error is introduced in the determination of the water given off by the sample through the failure of the second drying tube to dry the air completely?

20-11.   Trimethyl aluminum polymerizes in the gas phase according to the equation

$$2(CH_3)_3Al \rightleftarrows (CH_3)_6Al_2$$

(Chemists do not yet know the electronic structure of this dimer of trimethyl aluminum.) At $100°$ C and a total pressure of 97.2 mm of Hg the observed density of the vapor of trimethyl aluminum is 0.536 g/l. Calculate the equilibrium constant for the association of trimethyl aluminum. (A. W. Laubengayer and W. F. Gilliam, *J. Am. Chem. Soc.*, **63,** 477, 1941.)

20-12.   Solid ammonium hydrosulfide dissociates according to the equation

$$NH_4HS(s) \rightleftarrows NH_3(g) + H_2S(g)$$

At $25°$ C the sublimation pressure of solid NH_4HS is 501 mm of Hg. What is the partial pressure of H_2S over solid NH_4HS if the partial pressure of NH_3 is adjusted to be 1.000 atm?

20-13.   The fatty acids such as acetic acid dimerize in benzene solution due to the formation of two hydrogen bonds:

$$2CH_3COOH \rightleftarrows H_3C—C \overset{\displaystyle O- - -H—O}{\underset{\displaystyle O—H- - -O}{\Big\langle}} C—CH_3$$

If the freezing-point depression of a solution of 0.1350 g of acetic acid in 100 g of benzene, C_6H_6, is $0.0612°$ C, calculate the equilibrium constant for this dimerization, with concentrations expressed in moles per 1,000 g of benzene (see Chap. 16).

20-14.   Derive the equilibrium expressions for such equilibria as

$$NH_4HS(s) \rightleftarrows NH_3(g) + H_2S(g)$$
$$PbCl_2(s) \rightleftarrows Pb^{++} + 2Cl^-$$

by considering the rate of evaporation or solution and the rate of condensation or precipitation as functions of the surface area of the solid and the concentrations of the various components.

Chapter 21

Acids and Bases

It is useful to give a further discussion of acids and bases after the consideration of the basic principles of chemical equilibrium, because the phenomenon of chemical equilibrium is important in determining many of the properties of acids and bases.

In Chapter 5 an acid was defined as a hydrogen-containing substance which dissociates on solution in water to produce hydrogen ions, and a base was defined as a substance containing the hydroxide ion, OH^-, or the hydroxyl group, $-OH$, which can dissociate in aqueous solution as the hydroxide ion. It was pointed out that acidic solutions have a characteristic sharp taste, due to the hydrogen ion, H^+, or, rather, the hydronium ion, H_3O^+, and that basic solutions have a characteristic brackish taste, due to the hydroxide ion.

In Chapter 9 it was mentioned that the ordinary mineral acids (hydrochloric acid, nitric acid, sulfuric acid) are completely ionized (dissociated) in solution, producing one hydrogen ion for every acidic hydrogen atom in the formula of the acid, whereas other acids, such as acetic acid, produce only a much smaller number of hydrogen ions. Acids such as acetic acid are called *weak acids*. The reason that a 1 F solution of acetic acid does not have nearly so sharp a taste, and does not react nearly so vigorously with an active metal, such as zinc, as a 1 F solution of hydrochloric acid is that the 1 F solution of acetic acid contains a great number of undissociated molecules $HC_2H_3O_2$, and only a relatively small number of ions H^+ (that is, H_3O^+—we shall continue to follow the practice of using the symbol H^+, for convenience) and $C_2H_3O_2^-$. There exists in a solution of acetic acid a steady state, corresponding to the equation

$$HC_2H_3O_2 \rightleftarrows H^+ + C_2H_3O_2^-$$

In order to understand the properties of acetic acid it is necessary to formulate the equilibrium expression for this steady state; by use of this equilibrium expression the properties of acetic acid solutions of different concentrations can be predicted.

The general principles of chemical equilibrium can be similarly used in the discussion of a weak base, such as ammonium hydroxide, and also of salts formed by weak acids and weak bases. In addition, these principles are important in providing an understanding of the behavior of *indicators*, the colored substances that were described in Chapter 5 as useful for determining whether a solution is acidic, neutral, or basic. These principles are of further importance in permitting a discussion of the relation between the concentrations of hydrogen ion and hydroxide ion in the same solution.

21–1. *Hydrogen-Ion Concentration*

Pure water has a very small but measurable electric conductivity, which is about one ten-millionth that of a 1 N solution of an acid or base. This suggests that the ionization of water

$$2H_2O \rightleftarrows H_3O^+ + OH^-$$

gives hydrogen ions (hydronium ions) and hydroxide ions in concentration about 10^{-7} M. Refined measurements of the electric conductivity of water and of dilute solutions of hydrochloric acid, sodium hydroxide, and sodium chloride have provided the value 1.00×10^{-7} for $[H^+]$ and $[OH^-]$ in pure water at 25° C. *

Instead of saying that the concentration of hydrogen ion in pure water is 1×10^{-7}, it is customary to say that the pH of pure water is 7. **The pH is the negative common logarithm of the hydrogen-ion concentration:**

$$pH = -\log [H^+] \tag{21-1}$$

or

$$[H^+] = 10^{-pH} = \text{antilog} (-pH) \tag{21-2}$$

Example.   What is the pH of a solution with $[H^+] = 2 \times 10^{-5}$?
   Solution.   The log of 2×10^{-5} is $0.301 - 5 = -4.699$. Hence the pH of the solution is **4.699.**

---

* The extent of ionization depends on the temperature; at 0° the concentrations $[H^+]$ and $[OH^-]$ are 0.83×10^{-7}, and at 100° 6.9×10^{-7}.

Second Example.   What is the hydrogen-ion concentration of a solution with $pH = 0$?

   Solution. $[H^+] = $ antilog $0 = 1$. Hence a solution $1\ M$ in H^+ has $pH\ 0$.

With use of the equilibrium expression

$$[H^+]\,[OH^-] = K_W = 1.00 \times 10^{-14} \text{ at } 25° \text{ C} \tag{21-3}$$

discussed in the preceding chapter the hydroxide-ion concentration can be calculated for a solution of given pH. Thus a solution with $pH\ 14$ has $[H^+] = 10^{-14}$ and hence $[OH^-] = 1$. Acidic solutions have pH less than 7, and alkaline solutions have pH greater than 7.

   A very satisfactory method of determining the pH of a solution is by use of a hydrogen-ion concentration indicator, with which the electric potential of a cell with cell reaction involving hydrogen ion is measured. The theory underlying this procedure will be discussed in Chapter 32. Modern glass-electrode pH meters are now available which cover the pH range from 0 to 14 with an accuracy approaching 0.01. Less precise determinations of pH are made by use of indicators, organic substances which change color as the pH changes. The behavior of indicators is the topic which we discuss next.

21–2. *Indicators*

The change in color of an indicator as the pH of the solution changes is not sharp, but extends over a range of one or two pH units. This is the result of the existence of chemical equilibrium between the two differently colored forms of the indicator, and the dependence of the color on the hydrogen-ion concentration is due to the participation of hydrogen ion in the equilibrium. Thus the red form of litmus may be represented by the formula HIn and the blue form by In^-, resulting from the dissociation reaction

$$\underset{\substack{\text{red}\\\text{Acid form}}}{HIn} \rightleftarrows H^+ + \underset{\substack{\text{blue}\\\text{Alkaline form}}}{In^-} \tag{21-4}$$

In alkaline solutions, with $[H^+]$ very small, the equilibrium is shifted to the right, and the indicator is converted almost entirely into the basic form (blue for litmus); in acid solutions, with $[H^+]$ large, the equilibrium is shifted to the left, and the indicator assumes the acid form.

   Let us calculate the relative amount of the two forms as a function of $[H^+]$. The equilibrium expression for the reaction 21-4 is

$$\frac{[\text{H}^+]\,[\text{In}^-]}{[\text{HIn}]} = K_{\text{In}} \tag{21-5}$$

in which K_{In} is the equilibrium constant for the indicator. We rewrite this as

$$\frac{[\text{HIn}]}{[\text{In}^-]} = \frac{[\text{H}^+]}{K_{\text{In}}} \tag{21-6}$$

This equation shows how the ratio of the two forms of the indicator depends on $[\text{H}^+]$. When the two forms are present in equal amounts the ratio $[\text{HIn}]/[\text{In}^-]$ has the value 1, and hence $[\text{H}^+] = K_{\text{In}}$; the indicator

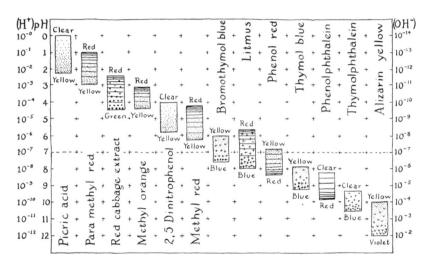

FIG. 21-1   *Color changes of indicators.*

constant K_{In} is thus the value of the hydrogen-ion concentration at which the change in color of the indicator is half completed. The corresponding $p\text{H}$ value is called the pK of the indicator.

Now if the $p\text{H}$ is decreased by one unit the value of $[\text{H}^+]$ becomes ten times K_{In} and the ratio $[\text{HIn}]/[\text{In}^-]$ then equals 10. Thus at a $p\text{H}$ value one less than pK of the indicator (its midpoint) the acid form of the indicator predominates over the basic form in the ratio 10 : 1; 91% of the indicator is then in the acid form, and 9% in the basic form. Over a range of two $p\text{H}$ units the indicator changes from 91% acid form to 91% basic form. For most indicators the color change detectable by the eye occurs over a range of about 1.2 to 1.8 units.

Indicators differ in their pK values; pure water, with $p\text{H}$ 7, is neutral to litmus (pK 6.8), acidic to phenolphthalein (pK 8.8), and alkaline to methyl orange (pK 3.7).

A chart showing the color changes and effective pH ranges of several indicators is given in Figure 21-1. The approximate pH of a solution can be found by finding by test the indicator toward which the solution shows a neutral reaction. Test paper, made with a mixture of indicators and showing several color changes, is now available with which the pH of a solution can be estimated to within about 1 unit over the pH range 1 to 13.

In titrating a weak acid or a weak base the indicator must be chosen with care. The way of choosing the proper indicator is described in the following section.

It is seen that an indicator behaves as a weak organic acid; the equilibrium expression for an indicator is the same as that for an ordinary weak acid, as discussed in the following section.

An indicator may be a weak base rather than a weak acid:

$$\text{InOH} \rightleftarrows \text{In}^+ + \text{OH}^-$$
Alkaline form   Acid form

The equilibrium expression for this basic dissociation combined with that for the dissociation of water is equivalent to the acid equilibrium equation 21-5, which can accordingly be used for all indicators.

21-3. *Weak Acids and Bases*

Ionization of a Weak Acid.   A 0.1 N solution of a strong acid such as hydrochloric acid is 0.1 M in hydrogen ion, since this acid is very nearly completely dissociated into ions except in very concentrated solutions. On the other hand, a 0.1 N solution of acetic acid contains hydrogen ions in much smaller concentration, as is seen by testing with indicators, observing the rate of attack of metals, or simply by tasting. Acetic acid is a weak acid; the acetic acid molecules hold their protons so firmly that not all of them are transferred to water molecules to form hydronium ions; instead, there is an equilibrium reaction

$$\text{HC}_2\text{H}_3\text{O}_2 + \text{H}_2\text{O} \rightleftarrows \text{H}_3\text{O}^+ + \text{C}_2\text{H}_3\text{O}_2^-$$

or, ignoring the hydration of the proton,

$$\text{HC}_2\text{H}_3\text{O}_2 \rightleftarrows \text{H}^+ + \text{C}_2\text{H}_3\text{O}_2^-$$

The equilibrium expression for this reaction is

$$\frac{[\text{H}^+]\,[\text{C}_2\text{H}_3\text{O}_2^-]}{[\text{HC}_2\text{H}_3\text{O}_2]} = K$$

In general, for an acid HA in equilibrium with ions H$^+$ and A$^-$, the equilibrium expression is

$$\frac{[H^+]\,[A^-]}{[HA]} = K_A \tag{21-7}$$

The constant K_A, characteristic of the acid, is called its **acid constant** or **ionization constant**.

Values of acid constants are found experimentally by measuring the pH of solutions of the acids. A table of values is given later in this chapter.

Example. The pH of a 0.1 N solution of acetic acid is found by experiment to be 2.874. What is the acid constant?

    Solution. To calculate the acid constant we note that the ionization of $HC_2H_3O_2$ produces H^+ and $C_2H_3O_2^-$ in equal quantities, and since the amount of hydrogen ion resulting from the dissociation of water is negligible compared with the total amount present, we have $[H^+] = [C_2H_3O_2^-] = \text{antilog}\ (-2.874) = 1.34 \times 10^{-3}$. The concentration $[HC_2H_3O_2]$ is hence $0.100 - 0.001 = 0.099$, and the acid constant has the value $K_A = (1.34 \times 10^{-3})^2/0.099 = $ **1.80×10^{-5}**.

The hydrogen-ion concentration of a weak acid (containing no other electrolytes which react with it or its ions) in 1 N concentration is approximately equal to the square root of its acid constant, as is seen from the following example.

Example. What is $[H^+]$ of a 1 N solution of HCN, which has $K_A = 4 \times 10^{-10}$? of a 1 N solution of acetic acid?

    Solution. Let $x = [H^+]$. Then we have $[CN^-] = x$ and $[HCN] = 1 - x$, and the equilibrium equation is

$$\frac{x^2}{1 - x} = K_A = 4 \times 10^{-10}$$

We know that x is going to be much smaller than 1, since this weak acid is only slightly ionized; hence we replace $1 - x$ by 1 (neglecting the small difference between $[HCN]$ and the total cyanide concentration), obtaining

$x^2 = 4 \times 10^{-10}$
$x = \mathbf{2 \times 10^{-5}} = [H^+]$

The neglect of the ionization of water is also seen to be justified, since $[H^+]$ is 200 times the value for pure water.

For acetic acid we obtain similarly the result

$$[H^+] = [C_2H_3O_2^-] = (1.8 \times 10^{-5})^{\frac{1}{2}} = 4.2 \times 10^{-3}$$

Successive Ionizations of a Polyprotic Acid.   A polyprotic acid has several acid constants, corresponding to dissociation of successive hydrogen ions. For phosphoric acid, H_3PO_4, there are three equilibrium expressions:

$$H_3PO_4 \rightleftarrows H^+ + H_2PO_4^-$$

$$K_1 = \frac{[H^+][H_2PO_4^-]}{[H_3PO_4]} = 7.5 \times 10^{-3} = K_{H_3PO_4}$$

$$H_2PO_4^- \rightleftarrows H^+ + HPO_4^{--}$$

$$K_2 = \frac{[H^+][HPO_4^{--}]}{[H_2PO_4^-]} = 6.2 \times 10^{-8} = K_{H_2PO_4^-}$$

$$HPO_4^{--} \rightleftarrows H^+ + PO_4^{---}$$

$$K_3 = \frac{[H^+][PO_4^{---}]}{[HPO_4^{--}]} = 10^{-12} = K_{HPO_4^{--}}$$

Note that these constants have the dimension of concentration, mole/l.

The ratio of successive ionization constants for a polybasic acid is usually about 10^{-5}, as in this case. We see that with respect to its first hydrogen phosphoric acid is a moderately strong acid—considerably stronger than acetic acid. With respect to its second hydrogen it is weak, and to its third very weak.

Ionization of a Weak Base.   A weak base dissociates in part to produce hydroxide ions:

$$MOH \rightleftarrows M^+ + OH^-$$

The corresponding equilibrium expression is

$$\frac{[M^+][OH^-]}{[MOH]} = K_B \tag{21-8}$$

The constant K_B is called the *base constant* of the base.

Ammonium hydroxide is the only common weak base. Its base constant has the value 1.81×10^{-5} at $25°$ C. The hydroxides of the alkali metals and the alkaline-earth metals are strong bases.

Example.   What is the pH of a 0.1 F solution of ammonium hydroxide?
   Solution.   Our fundamental equation is

$$\frac{[NH_4^+][OH^-]}{[NH_4OH]} = K_B = 1.81 \times 10^{-5} \tag{21-9}$$

Since the ions NH_4^+ and OH^- are produced in equal amounts by the dissociation of the base and the amount of OH^- from dissociation of water is negligible, we put

$$[NH_4^+] = [OH^-] = x$$

The concentration of NH_4OH is accordingly $0.1 - x$, and we obtain the equation

$$\frac{x^2}{0.1 - x} = 1.81 \times 10^{-5}$$

(Here we have made the calculation as though all the undissociated solute were NH_4OH. Actually there is some dissolved NH_3 present; however, since the equilibrium $NH_3 + H_2O = NH_4OH$ is of such a nature that the ratio $[NH_4OH]/[NH_3]$ is constant, we are at liberty to write the equilibrium expression for the base as shown above [Eq. 21-9], with the symbol $[NH_4OH]$ representing the total concentration of undissociated solute, including the molecular species NH_3 as well as NH_4OH.)

Solving this equation, we obtain the result

$$x = [OH^-] = [NH_4^+] = 1.34 \times 10^{-3}$$

The solution is hence only slightly alkaline—its hydroxide-ion concentration is the same as that of a 0.00134 N solution of sodium hydroxide.

This value of $[OH^-]$ corresponds to $[H^+] = 1.00 \times 10^{-14}/1.34 \times 10^{-3} = \mathbf{7.46 \times 10^{-12}}$, as calculated from the water equilibrium equation

$$[H^+][OH^-] = 1.00 \times 10^{-14}$$

The corresponding pH is **11.127,** which is the answer to the problem.

21–4. *The Titration of Weak Acids and Bases; the Hydrolysis of Salts*

A solution containing, say, 0.2 mole of a strong acid such as hydrochloric acid in a liter has $[H^+] = 0.2$ and pH $= 0.7$. The addition of a strong base, such as 0.2 N NaOH, causes the hydrogen-ion concentration to diminish through neutralization by the added hydroxide ion. When 990 ml of strong base has been added the excess of acid over base is $0.2 \times 10/1{,}000 = 0.002$ mole, and since the total volume is very close to 2 1 the value of $[H^+]$ is 0.001, and the pH is 3. When 999 ml has been added, and the neutralization reaction is within 0.1% of completion, the values are $[H^+] = 0.0001$ and $pH = 4$. At $pH = 5$ the reaction is within 0.001% of completion and at pH 6 within 0.0001%. Finally pH 7, neutrality, is reached when an amount of strong base has been added exactly equivalent to the amount of strong acid present. A very small excess of strong base causes the pH to increase beyond 7.

We see that to obtain the most accurate results in titrating a strong acid and a strong base an indicator with indicator constant about 10^{-7}

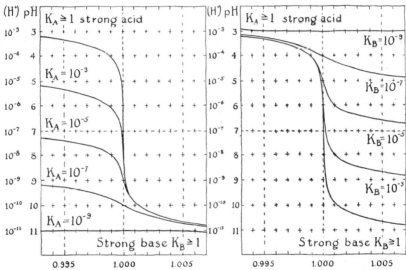

Ratio of equivalents of base to acid in titration of a 0.2N acid with a 0.2 N base, either acid or base being strong

FIG. 21-2   *Acid-base titration curves.*

($pK = 7$) should be chosen, such as litmus or bromthymol blue. The titration curve calculated above, and given in Figure 21-2, shows, however, that the choice of an indicator is in this case not crucial; any indicator with pK between 4 (methyl orange) and 10 (thymolphthalein) could be used with error less than 0.2%.

In titrating a weak acid (with a strong base) or a weak base (with a strong acid) greater care is needed in the selection of an indicator. Let us consider the titration of 0.2 N acetic acid, a moderately weak acid with $K_A = 1.80 \times 10^{-5}$, with 0.2 N sodium hydroxide. When an amount of the alkali equivalent to that of the acid has been added the resultant solution is the same as would be obtained by dissolving 0.1 mole of the salt $NaC_2H_3O_2$ in a liter of water. The solution of this salt is not neutral, with pH 7, however, but is alkaline. Let us consider what happens when $NaC_2H_3O_2$ is dissolved in water. This salt, like most salts, is completely dissociated into ions, Na^+ and $C_2H_3O_2^-$. The acetate ion and hydrogen ion are in equilibrium with undissociated acetic acid, and the reaction

$$H^+ + C_2H_3O_2^- \rightleftarrows HC_2H_3O_2$$

occurs to some extent. This uses some of the H^+, and reduces $[H^+]$ below 10^{-7}. To retain the water equilibrium

$$[H^+][OH^-] = 10^{-14}$$

some water dissociates:

$$H_2O \rightleftarrows H^+ + OH^-$$

This increases the OH^- concentration, and the solution becomes basic. The effect can be said to be due to the reaction

$$C_2H_3O_2^- + H_2O \rightleftarrows HC_2H_3O_2 + OH^- \tag{21-10}$$

which is the sum of the two reactions given above. This reaction of an anion of a weak acid with water to form the undissociated acid and hydroxide ion, which makes a solution of a salt of a strong base and a weak acid basic, is called the *hydrolysis* of the salt.

A salt of a strong acid and a weak base hydrolyzes analogously to give an acidic solution.

Our problem of selecting a suitable indicator for acetic acid is to be solved by calculating the pH of a 0.1 N $NaC_2H_3O_2$ solution; a suitable indicator has pK equal to this pH value.

To make this calculation we use the two equilibrium expressions

$$\frac{[H^+][C_2H_3O_2^-]}{[HC_2H_3O_2]} = 1.80 \times 10^{-5} = K_A$$

and

$$[H^+][OH^-] = 1.00 \times 10^{-14} = K_W$$

Our solution contains Na^+, $C_2H_3O_2^-$, $HC_2H_3O_2$, and OH^- in appreciable concentrations, and H^+ in extremely small concentration (less than 10^{-7}, since the solution is basic). We know that $[Na^+]$ is 0.1, since the solution is 0.1 N $NaC_2H_3O_2$. Moreover, the electric neutrality of the solution requires that

$$[C_2H_3O_2^-] + [OH^-] = 0.1$$

(neglecting $[H^+]$), and the composition of the solution requires that

$$[HC_2H_3O_2] + [C_2H_3O_2^-] = 0.1$$

From the last two equations we obtain

$$[HC_2H_3O_2] = [OH^-]$$

Now let us put

$$[HC_2H_3O_2] = [OH^-] = x$$

and

$$[C_2H_3O_2^-] = 0.1 - [OH^-] = 0.1 - x$$

We eliminate $[H^+]$ from the equilibrium equations by dividing one by the other, obtaining

$$\frac{[HC_2H_3O_2][OH^-]}{[C_2H_3O_2^-]} = \frac{K_W}{K_A} = \frac{1.00 \times 10^{-14}}{1.80 \times 10^{-5}}$$

or

$$\frac{x^2}{0.1 - x} = 5.56 \times 10^{-10}$$

which on solution gives

$$x = 0.75 \times 10^{-5}$$

Hence $[OH^-] = 0.75 \times 10^{-5}$ and $[H^+] = 1.34 \times 10^{-9}$.

The pH of the solution of sodium acetate is hence 8.87. By reference to Figure 21-1 we see that *phenolphthalein, with $pK = 9$, is the best indicator to use for titrating a moderately weak acid such as acetic acid.*

The complete titration curve, showing the pH of the solution as a function of the amount of strong base added, can be calculated in essentially this way. Its course is shown in Figure 21-2 ($K_A = 10^{-5}$). We see that the solution has pH 7 when there is 1% excess of acid; hence if litmus were used as the indicator an error of 1% would be made in the titration.

To titrate a weak base such as ammonium hydroxide the indicator methyl orange (pK 3.8) may be used.

It is possible by suitable selection of indicators to titrate separately a strong acid and a weak acid or a strong base and a weak base in a mixture of the two. Let us consider, for example, a solution of sodium hydroxide and ammonium hydroxide. If strong acid is added until the pH is 11.1, which is that of 0.1 N ammonium hydroxide solution, the strong base will be within 1% of neutralization (Fig. 21-2). Hence by using alizarine yellow (pK 11) as indicator the concentration of strong base can be determined, and then by a second titration with methyl orange the concentration of ammonium hydroxide can be found.

The Hydrolysis of Salts of Metals Other than the Alkalies and Alkaline Earths. The metal hydroxides other than the alkalies and alkaline earths are weak bases. Accordingly, metal salts of strong acids, such as $FeCl_3$, $CuSO_4$, $KAl(SO_4)_2 \cdot 12H_2O$ (alum), etc., hydrolyze to produce acid solutions; the sour taste of these salts is characteristic. It is interesting that the hydrolysis of a metal salt need not produce the hydroxide of the metal, but may produce a soluble complex cation; thus the hydrolysis of alum or of aluminum sulfate or nitrate takes place primarily according to the following equation:

$$Al^{+++} + H_2O \rightleftarrows AlOH^{++} + H^+$$

The complex cation $AlOH^{++}$ is only partially dissociated, and so at equilibrium there exist in the solution in appreciable concentrations all the ions which take part in this reaction, Al^{+++}, $AlOH^{++}$, and H^+. The concentration of hydrogen ion produced in this way is such as to make a solution of any salt of aluminum and a strong acid acidic.

A second hydrolysis reaction

$$AlOH^{++} + H_2O \rightleftarrows Al(OH)_2{}^+ + H^+$$

and a third

$$Al(OH)_2{}^+ + H_2O \rightleftarrows Al(OH)_3 + H^+$$

occur to smaller extents. The complex ions $AlOH^{++}$ and $Al(OH)_2{}^+$ remain in solution, whereas the hydroxide $Al(OH)_3$ is only very slightly soluble and precipitates if more than a very small amount is formed (its solubility is about 10^{-8} mole per liter). This final step in the hydrolysis of aluminum salts leads to precipitation only if the hydrogen-ion concentration of the solution is made small (less than about 10^{-3}) by addition of basic substances.

It will be recalled from the discussion in Chapter 9 that the aluminum ion in aqueous solution is hydrated, having the formula $Al(H_2O)_6{}^{+++}$, with the six water molecules arranged octahedrally about the aluminum ion. The hydrolysis of aluminum salts may be most accurately represented by the equations

$$Al(H_2O)_6{}^{+++} \rightleftarrows Al(H_2O)_5OH^{++} + H^+$$
$$Al(H_2O)_5OH^{++} \rightleftarrows Al(H_2O)_4(OH)_2{}^+ + H^+$$
$$Al(H_2O)_4(OH)_2{}^+ \rightleftarrows Al(H_2O)_3(OH)_3 + H^+ \rightleftarrows$$
$$Al(OH)_3 \downarrow + 3H_2O + H^+$$

In the process of hydrolysis the hydrated ions of aluminum lose protons, forming successive hydroxide complexes; the final neutral complex then loses water to form the insoluble hydroxide $Al(OH)_3$.

The hydrolysis of ferric salts is so common that the color of ferric ion, $Fe(H_2O)_6^{+++}$, is usually masked by that of the hydroxide complexes. Ferric ion is nearly colorless; it seems to have a very pale violet color, seen in crystals of ferric alum, $KFe(SO_4)_2 \cdot 12H_2O$, and ferric nitrate, $Fe(NO_3)_3 \cdot 9H_2O$, and in ferric solutions strongly acidified with nitric or perchloric acid. Solutions of ferric salts ordinarily have the characteristic yellow-to-brown color of the hydroxide complexes $Fe(H_2O)_5OH^{++}$ and $Fe(H_2O)_4(OH)_2^+$, or even the red-brown color of colloidal particles of hydrated ferric hydroxide.

Polyprotic Acids.   The acid constants for successive hydrogens of a polyprotic acid decrease in value, usually by a factor of about 10^{-5}, as mentioned earlier for phosphoric acid. Sulfuric acid is a strong acid with respect to the first hydrogen* ($K_{H_2SO_4} = 10^3$) and only moderately strong with respect to the second ($K_{HSO_4^-} = 1.2 \times 10^{-2}$). Sulfurous acid is moderately strong ($K_{H_2SO_3} = 1.2 \times 10^{-2}$) and its ion is weak ($K_{HSO_3^-} = 1 \times 10^{-7}$).

From these values we can say what the acidities of solutions of salts of these acids should be. A solution of $NaHSO_4$ would be neutral so far as hydrolysis is concerned, since $NaOH$ and H_2SO_4 are both strong; but the ion HSO_4^- is itself a moderately strong acid, and it would ionize

$$HSO_4^- \rightleftarrows H^+ + SO_4^{--}$$

to give an acid solution, with pH about 2 (for 0.1 F solution), thus making a solution of this salt acid. The normal salt Na_2SO_4 would be slightly basic (pH about 7.5, interpolated from Fig. 21-2) because of a small amount of hydrolysis resulting from the relative weakness of HSO_4^-.

The salt sodium hydrogen sulfite, $NaHSO_3$, would tend to hydrolyze slightly to produce H_2SO_3 and OH^-, but the ion HSO_3^- would also dissociate into H^+ and SO_3^{--}, and this effect is determinative, making the solution slightly acidic (pH about 5).

We see that the pH of a solution of a normal salt [Na_3PO_4, $NaC_2H_3O_2$, $(NH_4)_2SO_4$, NH_4CN] is determined by the extent of hydrolysis, which depends on the dissociation constants of the acid and base (the last constant only for polyprotic acids; e.g., $K_3 = K_{HPO_4^{--}}$ for Na_3PO_4). If the acid is stronger (for its last hydrogen) than the base the solution is acidic, and if the base is the stronger the solution is basic. Three of the above normal salts, Na_3PO_4, $NaC_2H_3O_2$, and NH_4CN, are basic, and $(NH_4)_2SO_4$ is acidic.

* This value for K is a rough one, estimated from certain experimental data for strong sulfuric acid.

The *p*H of a solution of an "acid" salt is determined by two effects: first, hydrolysis, and second, the dissociation of the hydrogen-containing anion to produce hydrogen ion. In the case of $NaHSO_3$, discussed above, the second effect is the greater, and the solution is acidic. For $NaHCO_3$, with $K_{H_2CO_3} = 4.3 \times 10^{-7}$ (weak) and $K_{HCO_3^-} = 4.7 \times 10^{-11}$ (very weak), the effect of hydrolysis is the greater, and the solution is basic.

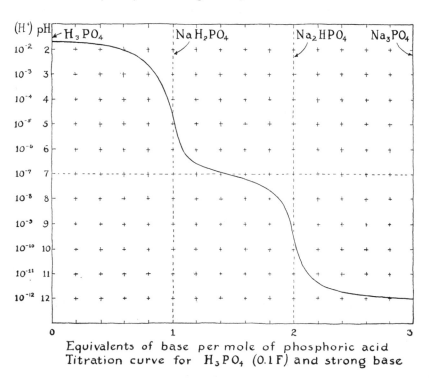

Equivalents of base per mole of phosphoric acid
Titration curve for H_3PO_4 (0.1 F) and strong base

FIG. 21-3   *Titration curve for phosphoric acid and a strong base.*

This conclusion is seen to be reasonable in the following way. Hydrolysis is seen from Figure 21-2 to give *p*H 10 for a salt of an acid with $K_A = 10^{-7}$, neglecting dissociation of HCO_3^-. On the other hand, ionization of a 0.1 *N* solution of HCO_3^-, neglecting hydrolysis, would give *p*H 6. The change from neutrality is greater for the first effect than the second, and accordingly we expect the solution to be basic. The exact value of the *p*H would be found by solving the equilibrium equations simultaneously; this gives *p*H = 8.3.

The complete *p*H curve for the titration of phosphoric acid with a strong base is given in Figure 21-3. In the midway region of neutralization of each hydrogen the *p*H changes only slowly, whereas in the region corresponding to the compositions NaH_2PO_4 and Na_2HPO_4 it changes very rapidly. We see that this acid could be titrated either with respect to its first hydrogen, with use of an indicator with pK about 4.5, or with respect to the first and second hydrogens, with use of an indicator with pK about 9.5.

Hydrolysis in General.   The word "hydrolysis" is used not only in the above way but also in referring to more general chemical reactions in which a molecule or ion is converted into two or more molecules or ions by reaction with water. The examples discussed above are cases of *anion hydrolysis* and *cation hydrolysis*, such as

$$C_2H_3O_2^- + H_2O \rightleftarrows HC_2H_3O_2 + OH^-$$
$$Al^{+++} + H_2O \rightleftarrows AlOH^{++} + H^+$$

In addition, a reaction such as

$$PCl_5 + 4H_2O \rightleftarrows H_3PO_4 + 5HCl$$

or

$$\underset{\text{calcium carbide}}{CaC_2} + 2H_2O \rightleftarrows Ca(OH)_2 + \underset{\text{acetylene}}{H_2C_2}$$

is also classed as a hydrolytic reaction. From the more general concepts of acids and bases discussed later a relation can be seen between such reactions as these and the hydrolysis of anions and cations.

Not all reactions involving water are classed as hydrolytic reactions. Thus the reaction of water with a molecule or ion such as calcium oxide

$$CaO + H_2O \rightleftarrows Ca(OH)_2$$

is usually called *hydration*.

21–5. *Buffered Solutions*

Very small amounts of strong acid or base suffice to change the hydrogen-ion concentration of water in the slightly acidic to slightly basic region; one drop of strong concentrated acid added to a liter of pure water makes it appreciably acidic, increasing the hydrogen-ion concentration by a factor of 5,000, and two drops of strong alkali then makes it basic, decreasing the hydrogen-ion concentration by a factor of over a million. Yet there are solutions to which large amounts of strong acid or base can be added with only very small resultant change in hydrogen-ion concentration. Such solutions are called **buffered solutions.** Blood and other physiological solutions are buffered; the pH of blood changes only slowly from its normal value (about 7.4) on addition of acid or base. Important among the buffering substances in blood are the serum proteins, which contain basic and acidic groups which can combine with the added acid or base.

A drop of concentrated acid, which when added to a liter of pure water increases $[H^+]$ 5,000-fold (from 10^{-7} to 5×10^{-4}), produces an increase in $[H^+]$ of less than 1% (from 1.00×10^{-7} to 1.01×10^{-7}, for example) when added to a liter of a buffered solution such as the phosphate buffer made by dissolving 0.2 gfw of phosphoric acid in a liter of water and adding 0.3 gfw of sodium hydroxide.

This is a half-neutralized phosphoric acid solution; its principal ionic constituents and their concentrations are Na^+, 0.3 M; HPO_4^{--}, 0.1 M; $H_2PO_4^-$, 0.1 M; H^+, about 10^{-7} M. From the titration curve of Figure 21-3 we see that this solution is a good buffer; to change its pH from 7 to 6.5 (tripling the hydrogen-ion or hydroxide-ion concentration) about one-twentieth of an equivalent of strong acid or base is needed per liter, whereas this amount of acid or base in water would cause a change of 5.7 pH units (an increase or decrease of $[H^+]$ by the factor 500,000). Such a solution, usually made by dissolving the two well-crystallized salts KH_2PO_4 and $Na_2HPO_4 \cdot 2H_2O$ in water, is widely used for buffering in the neutral region (pH 5.3–8.0).* Other useful buffers are made with sodium citrate and hydrochloric acid (pH 1–3.5), acetic acid and sodium acetate (pH 3.6–5.6), boric acid and sodium hydroxide (pH 7.8–10.0), and glycine and sodium hydroxide (pH 8.5–13).

The behavior of a buffer can be understood from the equilibrium equation for the acid dissociation. Let us consider the case of acetic acid and sodium acetate. The solution contains $HC_2H_3O_2$ and $C_2H_3O_2^-$ in equal or comparable concentrations. The equilibrium expression

$$\frac{[H^+][C_2H_3O_2^-]}{[HC_2H_3O_2]} = K_A$$

may be rewritten as

$$[H^+] = \frac{[HC_2H_3O_2]}{[C_2H_3O_2^-]} K_A$$

This shows that when $[C_2H_3O_2^-]$ and $[HC_2H_3O_2]$ are equal, as in an equimolar mixed solution of $HC_2H_3O_2$ and $NaC_2H_3O_2$, the value of $[H^+]$ is just that of K_A, 1.80×10^{-5}, and hence the pH is 4.74. A 1 : 5 mixture of $HC_2H_3O_2$ and $NaC_2H_3O_2$ has $[H^+] = \frac{1}{5}K_A$ and pH 5.44, and a 5 : 1

---

* A concentrated neutral buffer solution containing one half gfw of each salt per liter may be kept in the laboratory to neutralize either acid or base spilled on the body.

mixture has $[H^+] = 5K_A$ and pH 4.04. By choosing a suitable ratio of $HC_2H_3O_2$ to $NaC_2H_3O_2$ any desired hydrogen-ion concentration in this neighborhood can be obtained.

It is seen from the equilibrium expressions that *the effectiveness of a buffer depends on the concentrations of the buffering substances;* a tenfold dilution of the buffer decreases by the factor 10 the amount of acid or base per liter which can be added without causing the pH to change more than the desired amount.

For the phosphate buffer in the pH-7 region the equilibrium constant of interest is that for the reaction

$$H_2PO_4^- \rightleftarrows HPO_4^{--} + H^+$$

The value of $K_{H_2PO_4^-}$ is 6.2×10^{-8}; this is accordingly the value of $[H^+]$ expected for a solution with $[H_2PO_4^-] = [HPO_4^{--}]$.

If the buffered solution is dilute, this is its hydrogen-ion concentration. Because the activities of ions are affected by other ions, however, there is appreciable deviation from the calculated values in salt solutions as concentrated as 0.1 M. This fact accounts for the discrepancies between the pH values calculated from equilibrium constants and those given in the buffer tables.

21–6. *The Strengths of the Oxygen Acids*

The oxygen acids, which consist of oxygen atoms O and hydroxyl groups OH attached to a central atom [$HClO_4 = ClO_3(OH)$, $H_2SO_4 = SO_2(OH)_2$, etc.], vary widely in strength, from very strong acids such as perchloric acid, $HClO_4$, to very weak ones such as boric acid, H_3BO_3. It is often useful to know the approximate strengths of these acids. Fortunately there have been formulated some simple and easily remembered rules regarding these acid strengths.

Before discussing these rules, let us review the nomenclature of the oxygen acids.

The Nomenclature of the Oxygen Acids.   The common oxygen acid of each element is given a name obtained from the name of the element with the use of the **ending "ic"** (as shown at the top of page 452). In most cases the oxidation state of the central atom in this **"ic" acid** has the highest positive value corresponding to the position in the periodic table: B^{3+}, C^{4+}, N^{5+}, Si^{4+}, P^{5+}, S^{6+}. Chloric, bromic, and iodic acids, containing quinquevalent halogen, are, for historical reasons, exceptions. The oxygen acid of septivalent chlorine, $HClO_4$, is called

H_2CO_3	HNO_3		
Carbonic acid	Nitric acid		
			$HClO_4$
H_4SiO_4	H_3PO_4	H_2SO_4	Perchloric acid
Silicic acid	Phosphoric acid	Sulfuric acid	$HClO_3$
			Chloric acid
H_4GeO_4	H_3AsO_4	H_2SeO_4	
Germanic acid	Arsenic acid	Selenic acid	$HBrO_3$
			Bromic acid
$H_2Sn(OH)_6$	$HSb(OH)_6$	H_6TeO_6	H_5IO_6
Stannic acid	Antimonic acid	Telluric acid	Periodic acid
			(Paraperiodic acid)
			HIO_3
			Iodic acid

perchloric acid, and that of septivalent iodine, H_5IO_6, is called periodic acid (or sometimes paraperiodic acid); perbromic acid does not exist.

The number of oxygen atoms surrounding the central atom is called its **coordination number.** We see that these atoms have, for their maximum valence, the coordination numbers shown in Table 21-1. An ion

TABLE 21-1

PERIOD	CN	CONFIGURATION
First-row elements...............	3	Planar triangle
Second-row elements............	4	Tetrahedron
Third-row elements.............	4	Tetrahedron
Fourth-row elements............	6	Octahedron

such as BO_3^{---}, the borate ion, has a planar triangular structure,

; an ion such as PO_4^{---} or AsO_4^{---} is tetra-

hedral, with the four oxygen atoms arranged at the corners of a regular tetrahedron about the central atom; $Sb(OH)_6^-$ and IO_6^{5-} have a regular octahedral configuration.

The reason for the change in coordination number is that the first-row atoms are so small that only three oxygen atoms can be fitted around them. The second-row and third-row atoms are larger, and can accommodate four oxygen atoms, and the still larger **fourth-row atoms can** hold six.

By loss of water, without change in valence of the central atom, these acids can be converted into related acids which are given special names in which the suffix "ic" is retained:

$$4H_3BO_3 - 5H_2O \longrightarrow H_2B_4O_7, \text{ tetraboric acid}$$
$$nH_3BO_3 - nH_2O \longrightarrow (HBO_2)_n, \text{ metaboric acid } (n \geqq 3)$$
$$2H_4SiO_4 - H_2O \longrightarrow H_6Si_2O_7, \text{ disilicic acid}$$
$$nH_4SiO_4 - nH_2O \longrightarrow (H_2SiO_3)_n, \text{ metasilicic acid } (n \geqq 3)$$
$$2H_3PO_4 - H_2O \longrightarrow H_4P_2O_7, \text{ pyrophosphoric acid}$$
$$nH_3PO_4 - nH_2O \longrightarrow (HPO_3)_n, \text{ metaphosphoric acid } (n \geqq 3)$$
$$2H_2SO_4 - H_2O \longrightarrow H_2S_2O_7, \text{ pyrosulfuric acid}$$

Acids in which the central atom has oxidation number 2 less than for the "ic" acids are the **"ous" acids:** examples are

HNO_2, nitrous acid	N^{+++}
H_3PO_3, phosphorous acid	P^{+++}
H_2SO_3, sulfurous acid	S^{++++}
$HClO_2$, chlorous acid	Cl^{+++}

The ending "ous" is retained when the central atom has still lower valence, and the **prefix "hypo"** is added:

$H_2N_2O_2$, hyponitrous acid	N^+
H_3PO_2, hypophosphorous acid	P^+
$HClO$, hypochlorous acid	Cl^+

Salts of the "ic" acids are given the **ending "ate,"** and those of the "ous" acids the **ending "ite":**

Na_3PO_4, sodium phosphate
$Na_6P_6O_{18}$, sodium hexametaphosphate
Na_2SO_3, sodium sulfite

The Rules Expressing the Strengths of the Oxygen Acids. The strengths of these oxygen acids are expressed approximately by the following two rules:

Rule 1. The successive acid constants K_1, K_2, K_3, $\cdots$ are in the ratios $1 : 10^{-5} : 10^{-10} : \cdots$.

We have already noted the examples of phosphoric acid

$$K_{H_3PO_4} = 7.5 \times 10^{-3} \qquad K_{H_2PO_4^-} = 6.2 \times 10^{-8}$$
$$K_{HPO_4^{--}} = 10^{-12}$$

and sulfurous acid

$$K_{H_2SO_3} = 1.2 \times 10^{-2} \qquad K_{HSO_3^-} = 1 \times 10^{-7}$$

The rule holds well for all the acids of the class under consideration.

Rule 2. The value of the first ionization constant is determined by the value of m in the formula $XO_m(OH)_n$: *if m is zero* [*no excess of oxygen atoms over hydrogen atoms, as in* $B(OH)_3$] *the acid is very weak, with* $K_1 \leq 10^{-7}$; *for* $m = 1$ *the acid is weak, with* $K_1 \cong 10^{-2}$; *for* $m = 2$ ($K_1 \cong 10^3$) *or* $m = 3$ ($K_1 \cong 10^8$) *the acid is strong.*

Note the occurrence here of the factor 10^5. The applicability of this rule is shown by the tables on the following pages.

The second rule can be understood in the following way. The force attracting H^+ to ClO^- to form $ClOH$ (hypochlorous acid) is that of an O—H valence bond. But the force between H^+ and either one of the two oxygen atoms of the ion ClO_2^- to form $ClOOH$ (chlorous acid) may be smaller than that for an O—H valence bond because the total attraction for the proton is divided between the two oxygen atoms, and hence this acid (of the second class) may well be expected to be more highly dissociated than hypochlorous acid. An acid of the third class would be still more highly dissociated, since the total attraction for the proton would be divided among three oxygen atoms.

With use of these rules we can answer questions as to the hydrolysis of salts or the choice of indicators for titration without referring to tables of acid constants.

Example.   What reaction of litmus would be expected to solutions of the following salts: $NaClO$, $NaClO_2$, $NaClO_3$, $NaClO_4$?

>   **Solution.**   The corresponding acids are shown by the rule to be very weak, weak, strong, and very strong, respectively. Hence $NaClO$ and $NaClO_2$ would through hydrolysis give basic solutions, and the other two salts would give neutral solutions.

Second Example.   What indicator could be used for titrating periodic acid, H_5IO_6?

>   **Solution.**   This acid has one extra oxygen atom, and is hence of the second class, as is phosphoric acid. We accordingly refer to Figures 21-3 and 21-1, and see that methyl orange should be satisfactory for titrating the first hydrogen or phenolphthalein for titrating the first two hydrogens.

First class: Very weak acids $X(OH)_n$ or H_nXO_n (first acid constant about 10^{-7} or less)

	K_1
Hypochlorous acid, HClO	3.2×10^{-8}
Hypobromous acid, HBrO	2×10^{-9}
Hypoiodous acid, HIO	1×10^{-11}
Silicic acid, H_4SiO_4	1×10^{-10}
Germanic acid, H_4GeO_4	2.6×10^{-9}
Boric acid, H_3BO_3	5.8×10^{-10}
Arsenious acid, H_3AsO_3	6×10^{-10}
Antimonous acid, H_3SbO_3	10^{-11}
Telluric acid, H_6TeO_6	1.6×10^{-9}

Second class: Weak acids $XO(OH)_n$ or H_nXO_{n+1} (first acid constant about 10^{-2})

	K_1
Chlorous acid, $HClO_2$	10^{-2}
Sulfurous acid, H_2SO_3	1.2×10^{-2}
Phosphoric acid, H_3PO_4	0.75×10^{-2}
Phosphorous acid,* H_2HPO_3	1.6×10^{-2}
Hypophosphorous acid,* HH_2PO_2	1×10^{-2}
Arsenic acid, H_3AsO_4	0.5×10^{-2}
Periodic acid, H_5IO_6	2.3×10^{-2}
Nitrous acid, HNO_2	0.45×10^{-3}
Acetic acid, CH_3COOH	1.8×10^{-5}
Carbonic acid,† H_2CO_3	0.45×10^{-6}

Third class: Strong acids $XO_2(OH)_n$ or H_nXO_{n+2} (first acid constant about 10^3, second acid constant about 10^{-2})

	K_1	K_2
Chloric acid, $HClO_3$	Large	
Sulfuric acid, H_2SO_4	Large	1.2×10^{-2}
Selenic acid, H_2SeO_4	Large	1×10^{-2}

Fourth class: Very strong acids $XO_3(OH)_n$ or H_nXO_{n+3} (first acid constant about 10^8)

| Perchloric acid, $HClO_4$ | Very strong |
| Permanganic acid, $HMnO_4$ | Very strong |

* It is known that phosphorous acid has the structure

$$H-\overset{\displaystyle O}{\underset{\displaystyle OH}{\overset{|}{\underset{|}{P}}}}-OH$$

and hypophosphorous acid the structure

$$H-\overset{\displaystyle O}{\underset{\displaystyle H}{\overset{|}{\underset{|}{P}}}}-OH;$$

the hydrogen atoms which are bonded to the phosphorus atom are not counted in applying the rule.

† The low value for K_1 for carbonic acid is due in part to the existence of some of the un-ionized acid in the form of dissolved CO_2 molecules rather than H_2CO_3. The proton dissociation constant for the molecular species H_2CO_3 is about 2×10^{-4} (see, for example, A. R. Olson and P. V. Youle, *J. Amer. Chem. Soc.*, **62**, 1027, 1940).

Other Acids. There is no simple way of remembering the strengths of acids other than those discussed above. HCl, HBr, and HI are strong, but HF is weak, with $K_A = 6.7 \times 10^{-4}$. The homologs of water are weak acids, with the following reported acid constants:

	K_1	K_2
Hydrosulfuric acid, H_2S	1.1×10^{-7}	1.0×10^{-14}
Hydroselenic acid, H_2Se	1.7×10^{-4}	1×10^{-11}
Hydrotelluric acid, H_2Te	2.3×10^{-3}	1×10^{-11}

The hydrides NH_3, PH_3, etc., function as bases by adding protons rather than as acids by losing them.

Oxygen acids which do not contain a single central atom have strengths corresponding to reasonable extensions of our rules, as shown by the following examples:

Very weak acids ($K_1 = 10^{-7}$ or less)

	K_1	K_2
Hydrogen peroxide, HO—OH	2.4×10^{-12}	
Hyponitrous acid, HON—NOH	9×10^{-8}	1×10^{-11}

Weak acids ($K_1 = 10^{-2}$)

	K_1	K_2
Oxalic acid, HOOC—COOH	5.9×10^{-2}	6.4×10^{-5}

The following acids are not easily classified:

	K_1
Hydrocyanic acid, HCN	4×10^{-10}
Cyanic acid, HOCN	Strong
Thiocyanic acid, HSCN	Strong
Hydrazoic acid, HN_3	1.8×10^{-5}

21–7. *More General Concepts of Acids and Bases*

In recent years several more general concepts of acids and bases have been introduced. They are useful for some purposes, such as the discussion of non-aqueous solutions. One of these concepts, due to Brönsted, is that an acid is any molecular or ionic species which can give up a proton (which is a *proton donor*), and a base is any one which can take up a proton (which is a *proton acceptor*). Thus NH_4^+ is called an acid, since it can give up a proton:

$$NH_4^+ \rightleftharpoons NH_3 + H^+$$

and NH_3 is called a base, since this reaction can be reversed. Any acid anion, such as the acetate ion, could be called a base from this point of view.

The Brönsted concept provides a simple way of discussing hydrolysis, as is illustrated by the following example. The acetate ion is a base of significant strength, since the equilibrium

$$C_2H_3O_2^- + H^+ \rightleftharpoons HC_2H_3O_2$$

favors the product $HC_2H_3O_2$. Hence a solution of sodium acetate is expected to be basic in reaction. This explanation of hydrolysis is an interesting alternative to that given in an earlier section of this chapter.

Another, still more general concept was introduced by G. N. Lewis. He called a base anything which has available an unshared pair of electrons (such as NH_3) and an acid anything which could attach itself to such a pair of electrons (such as H^+, to form NH_4^+, or BF_3, to form

$$\begin{array}{ccc} F & H & \\ | & | & \\ F-B-N-H \\ | & | & \\ F & H & \end{array}$$

). This concept explains many phenomena, such as the effect of certain substances other than hydrogen ion in changing the color of indicators. Another interesting application of the concept is its explanation of salt formation by reaction of acidic oxides and basic oxides, as in the formation of calcium silicate by fusion of calcium oxide and silica:

$$2CaO + SiO_2 \longrightarrow Ca_2SiO_4$$

Acid Strength and Condensation.   It is observed that the tendency of oxygen acids to condense to larger molecules is correlated with their acid strengths. Very strong acids, such as $HClO_4$ and $HMnO_4$, condense only with difficulty, and the substances formed, Cl_2O_7 and Mn_2O_7, are very unstable. Less strong acids, such as H_2SO_4, form condensation products such as $H_2S_2O_7$, pyrosulfuric acid, on strong heating, but these products are not stable in aqueous solution. Phosphoric acid forms pyrophosphate ion and other condensed ions in aqueous solution, but these ions easily hydrolyze to the orthophosphate ion; other weak acids behave similarly. The very weak oxygen acids, including silicic acid (Chap. 30) and boric acid, condense very readily, and their condensation products are very stable substances.

This correlation is reasonable. The un-ionized acids contain oxygen atoms bonded to hydrogen atoms, and the condensed acids contain oxygen atoms bonded to two central atoms:

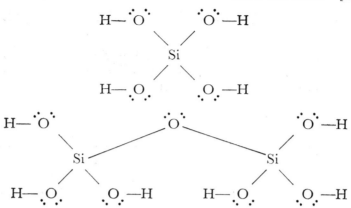

It is hence not surprising that stability of the un-ionized acid (corresponding to small acid strength) should be correlated with stability of the condensed molecules.

Exercises

21-1. Which of these oxides are acid anhydrides and which basic anhydrides? Write an equation for each representing its reaction with water.

P_2O_3 Fe_2O_3 Na_2O Mn_2O_7 RaO
Cl_2O B_2O_3 Al_2O_3 MnO SO_2
Cl_2O_7 CO_2 I_2O_5 TeO_3 SO_3
N_2O_5 Cu_2O MgO SiO_2 As_2O_3

21-2. How many grams of each of the following substances would be needed to make up 1 l of 0.1 N acid or base?

$NaOH$ CaO $NaHC_2O_4 \cdot H_2O$ H_2SO_4 $KHSO_4$ I_2O_5

21-3. What is the normality of a solution of a strong acid 25.00 ml of which is rendered neutral by 28.35 ml of 0.1013 N NaOH solution?

21-4. The poisonous *botulinus* organism does not grow in canned vegetables if the pH is less than 4.5. Some investigators (*Journal of Chemical Education*, **22**, 409, 1945) have recommended that in home canning of non-acid foods, such as beans, without a pressure canner a quantity of hydrochloric acid be added. The amount of hydrochloric acid recommended is 25 ml of 0.5 N hydrochloric acid per pint jar.

   Calculate the pH that this solution would have, assuming it originally to be neutral, and neglecting the buffering action of the organic material. Also calculate the amount of baking soda ($NaHCO_3$), measured in teaspoonfuls, that would be required to neutralize the acid after the jar is open. One teaspoon equals 4 grams of baking soda.

21-5. What is the pH of 1 N HCl? of 0.1 N HCl? of 10 N HCl? of 0.1 N NaOH? of 10 N NaOH?

21-6. Calculate the hydrogen-ion concentration in the following solutions:

(a) 1 F $HC_2H_3O_2$, $K = 1.8 \times 10^{-5}$
(b) 0.06 F HNO_2, $K = 0.45 \times 10^{-3}$
(c) 0.004 F NH_4OH, $K_B = 1.8 \times 10^{-5}$
(d) 0.1 F HF, $K = 6.7 \times 10^{-4}$

21-7. What are the pH values of the solutions of Exercise 21-6?

21-8. Calculate the concentrations of the various ionic and molecular species in a solution prepared by mixing equal volumes of 1 N $NaOH$ and 0.5 N NH_4OH.

21-9. Calculate the pH of a solution that is 0.1 F in HNO_2 and 0.1 F in HCl.

21-10. Calculate the concentrations of the various ionic and molecular species in the following solutions:

(a) 0.1 F H_2Se ($K_1 = 1.7 \times 10^{-4}$, $K_2 = 1 \times 10^{-11}$)
(b) 0.01 F H_2CO_3 ($K_1 = 4.5 \times 10^{-7}$, $K_2 = 6 \times 10^{-11}$)
(c) 1 F H_2CrO_4 ($K_1 = 5.9 \times 10^{-2}$, $K_2 = 3.2 \times 10^{-7}$)
(d) 0.5 F H_3PO_4 ($K_1 = 7.5 \times 10^{-3}$, $K_2 = 2 \times 10^{-7}$, $K_3 = 1 \times 10^{-12}$)
(e) 1 F H_2SO_4 ($K_2 = 1.20 \times 10^{-2}$)
(f) 0.01 F H_2SO_4

21-11. Calculate the pH of a solution that is

(a) 0.1 F in NH_4Cl, 0.1 F in NH_4OH
(b) 0.05 F in NH_4Cl, 0.15 F in NH_4OH
(c) 1.0 F in $HC_2H_3O_2$, 0.3 F in $NaC_2H_3O_2$
(d) prepared by mixing 10 ml 1 F $HC_2H_3O_2$ with 90 ml 0.05 F $NaOH$

21-12. Calculate the pH of a solution that is prepared from

(a) 10 ml 1 F HCN, 10 ml 1 F $NaOH$
(b) 10 ml 1 F NH_4OH, 10 ml 1 F HCl
(c) 10 ml 1 F NH_4OH, 10 ml 1 F NH_4Cl

21-13. Calculate the concentration of the various ionic and molecular species in

(a) 0.4 F NH_4Cl
(b) 0.1 F $NH_4C_2H_3O_2$
(c) 0.1 F $NaHCO_3$
(d) 0.1 F Na_2CO_3

21-14. Calculate the concentration of the various ionic and molecular species in a solution that is

(a) 0.3 F in HCl, and 0.1 F in H_2S
(b) buffered to a pH of 4, and 0.1 F in H_2S
(c) 0.2 F in KHS
(d) 0.2 F in K_2S

21-15. Calculate the equilibrium constant for the reaction

$$Cu^+ + Fe^{+++} \rightleftarrows Cu^{++} + Fe^{++}$$

from the equilibrium constants given below for the two reactions

$$Fe^{++} + Co^{+++} \rightleftarrows Fe^{+++} + Co^{++} \quad K = 1.1 \times 10^{18}$$
$$Cu^+ + Co^{+++} \rightleftarrows Cu^{++} + Co^{++} \quad K = 1.6 \times 10^{25}$$

21-16. Calculate the equilibrium constant for the reaction

$$NH_4^+ + C_2H_3O_2^- + H_2O \rightleftarrows NH_4OH + HC_2H_3O_2$$

from the known equilibrium constants for the reactions

$$NH_4OH \rightleftarrows NH_4^+ + OH^-$$
$$HC_2H_3O_2 \rightleftarrows H^+ + C_2H_3O_2^-$$
$$H_2O \rightleftarrows H^+ + OH^-$$

21-17. Boric acid loses only one hydrogen ion. In 0.1 M H_3BO_3, $[H^+] = 1.05 \times 10^{-5}$. Calculate the ionization constant for boric acid.

21-18. A patent medicine for stomach ulcers contains 2.1 g of $Al(OH)_3$ per 100 ml. How far wrong is the statement on the label that the preparation is "capable of combining with 16 times its volume of $N/10$ HCl"?

21-19. Which of these substances form acidic solutions, which neutral, and which basic? Write equations for the reactions which give excess H^+ or OH^-.

NaCl	$(NH_4)_2SO_4$	$CuSO_4 \cdot 5H_2O$
NaCN	$NaHSO_4$	$FeCl_2$
Na_3PO_4	NaH_2PO_4	$KAlSO_4 \cdot 12H_2O$
NH_4Cl	Na_2HPO_4	$Zn(ClO_4)_2$
NH_4CN	$KClO_4$	BaO

21-20. Approximately how much acetic acid must be added to a 0.1 N solution of sodium acetate to make the solution neutral?

21-21. What indicators should be used in titrating the following acids?

	K_A
HNO_2	4.5×10^{-4}
H_2S (first hydrogen)	1.1×10^{-7}
HCN	4×10^{-10}

21-22. With what indicators could you titrate separately for HCl and $HC_2H_3O_2$ in a solution containing both acids?

21-23. What relative weights of KH_2PO_4 and $Na_2HPO_4 \cdot 2H_2O$ should be taken to make a buffered solution with pH 6.0?

21-24. Carbon dioxide, produced by oxidation of substances in the tissues, is carried by the blood to the lungs. Part of it is in solution as carbonic acid, and part as hydrogen carbonate ion, HCO_3^-. If the pH of the blood is 7.4, what fraction is carried as the ion?

21-25. The value of K_1 for H_2S is 1.1×10^{-7}. What is the ratio $[H_2S]/[HS^-]$ at pH 8? If hydrogen sulfide at 1 atm pressure is 0.1 F soluble in acid solution, what would be its solubility at pH 8?

21-26. Estimate the acid constants of H_2SeO_4, H_3AsO_4, H_5IO_6, HOCl, and H_3AsO_3, without reference to the text.

21-27. What chemical reactions take place when water is added to pyrosulfuric acid and to pyrophosphoric acid? Which of these reactions takes place the more readily?

Chapter 22

Solubility Product
and Precipitation

22–1. *The Effect of Other Solutes on the Solubility of a Substance*

In many cases the solubility of a substance is not changed very much by the addition of other substances (in small concentrations) to the solution. For example, ordinarily a non-electrolytic (non-ionizing) solute, such as sugar or iodine, has little effect on the solubility of a salt in water, and conversely a salt such as sodium nitrate has little effect on the solubility of iodine in water. Also the presence of a salt which has no ion in common with another salt whose solubility is under consideration produces only a rather small effect on the solubility of the second salt, usually a small increase; this small increase is due to the electrostatic interaction of the ions in the solution, which decreases their activity somewhat, as discussed in Section 16–10.

Sometimes, however, the solubility of a substance is greatly changed by the presence of other solutes. For example, iodine is very much more soluble in a solution containing iodide ion than in pure water, and potassium perchlorate is much less soluble in a solution containing either another potassium salt or another perchlorate than in pure water. The *increased* solubility of iodine is due to the *formation of a complex*, the triiodide ion I_3^-; this phenomenon is discussed in Chapter 23. The other effect, the *decrease* in solubility of a salt by another salt with a *common ion*, is the subject of the discussion in the following sections of this chapter.

22-2. *The Solubility-Product Principle*

In discussing chemical equilibrium in Chapter 20 we learned that in a saturated solution of potassium perchlorate the ion-concentration product is constant (at a given temperature):

$$[K^+][ClO_4^-] = K_{SP} \text{ at saturation}$$

The constant K_{SP} is called the *solubility-product constant* of the salt, or simply its *solubility product*.

The constancy of this product follows from the equilibrium expression

$$\frac{[K^+][ClO_4^-]}{[KClO_4]} = K$$

for the ionization reaction

$$KClO_4 = K^+ + ClO_4^-$$

We replace $[KClO_4]$ by a constant, which is justified whenever the solution is in equilibrium with pure crystalline $KClO_4$, *and only then.* **The solubility-product principle applies only to saturated solutions of the salt.** The product $[K^+][ClO_4^-]$ can, of course, have any value less than K_{SP} for an unsaturated solution.

Potassium perchlorate has at 0° the solubility 7.5 g/l in water. The ion concentrations $[K^+]$ and $[ClO_4^-]$ are hence both equal to $7.5/138.56 = 0.054$ M, and K_{SP} is equal to $0.054^2 = 29.0 \times 10^{-4}$ mole²/l². This value can now be used to calculate the solubility of potassium perchlorate in a solution of another potassium salt or another perchlorate. Its solubility in such a solution is less than in pure water, because of the action of the ion (K^+ or ClO_4^-) already present in the solution. This decrease in solubility is said to result from the **common-ion effect.**

Let us consider, for example, a solution initially 0.2 F in KCl. The initial ion concentrations are

$$[K^+] = [Cl^-] = 0.200$$

Now let this solution be saturated with $KClO_4$. If x moles of $KClO_4$ dissolve per liter, the final ion concentrations are

$$[K^+] = 0.200 + x$$
$$[Cl^-] = 0.200$$
$$[ClO_4^-] = x$$

The solubility-product principle is then expressed by the equation

$$[K^+][ClO_4^-] = (0.200 + x)x = K_{SP} = 29.0 \times 10^{-4}$$

On solution for x this gives $x = 0.014$. Hence $[K^+] = 0.214$ and $[ClO_4^-] = 0.014$. The solubility of potassium perchlorate in 0.2 F KCl solution is accordingly 0.014 formula weights per liter, which is only about one-fourth of its solubility in pure water.

The common-ion effect may be extremely great for rather insoluble salts. Thus K_{SP} for silver chloride is 1.7×10^{-10}, and correspondingly the solubility of AgCl in pure water is the square root of this number; that is, 1.3×10^{-5} M. In 0.1 F NaCl it is only 1.7×10^{-9} M, which is one ten-thousandth as great. It is seen that the common-ion effect can be used to remove all but traces of silver ion from a solution, by increasing the chloride-ion concentration.

Values of the solubility product are given for many salts in the table at the end of this chapter. Some of its uses are illustrated in the following examples.

The reliability of calculations made with use of the principle is determined mainly by the total concentration of ions in the solution. In very dilute solutions (0.001 F) the calculations are reliable to within about 4%. In more concentrated solutions, in which the activity coefficients of the ions are considerably less than unity, the actual solubilities of salts are usually somewhat larger than calculated. This increased solubility amounts for salts consisting of singly charged ions (such as K^+, Cl^-) to about 10% for 0.01 F solutions and about 20% for 0.1 F solutions.

22–3. *Examples of Solubility Calculations*

For some systems the solubility-product principle must be combined with other equilibrium expressions in solubility calculations. In the following examples some simple and some complex systems are discussed. (Additional examples, dealing with systems in which complex ions are formed, are treated in the following chapter.)

Example 1.   The solubility of mercurous chloride (calomel), Hg_2Cl_2, is 3.0×10^{-5} g per 100 ml. What is its solubility product? What volume of 0.01 F NaCl solution would be needed to dissolve the amount of mercurous chloride which would be dissolved by 1 l of pure water?

  Solution.   The solubility is 3.0×10^{-4} g/l or $3.0 \times 10^{-4}/472.1 = 0.64 \times 10^{-6}$ formula weight per liter. (472.1 is the formula weight of Hg_2Cl_2.) The mercurous ion is Hg_2^{++} (Chap. 27), and the molecule Hg_2Cl_2 dissociates into one Hg_2^{++} ion and two Cl^- ions. The ion concentrations are hence

$[Hg_2^{++}] = 0.64 \times 10^{-6}$
$[Cl^-] = 1.28 \times 10^{-6}$

and the solubility product is

$$K_{SP} = [Hg_2^{++}][Cl^-]^2 = 1.0 \times 10^{-18}$$

In 1 liter of pure water 0.64×10^{-6} formula weight of calomel can be dissolved. In 0.01 F NaCl solution $[Cl^-]$ equals 0.01; hence if this solution is saturated with calomel, the mercurous-ion concentration is given by the equation

$$[Hg_2^{++}](0.01)^2 = K_{SP} = 1.0 \times 10^{-18}$$

or

$$[Hg_2^{++}] = 1.0 \times 10^{-14}$$

The solubility of calomel in this salt solution is hence $1.0 \times 10^{-14}/0.64 \times 10^{-6} = 1.6 \times 10^{-8}$ times smaller than in pure water, and a volume of 0.64×10^8 1 (that is, 64 million liters) would be required to dissolve the 0.003 g of calomel which will dissolve in one liter of pure water.

Example 2. Effect of *pH* on Solubility. In the purification and clarification of water for domestic use aluminum sulfate is sometimes added to produce a gelatinous precipitate of aluminum hydroxide, to which suspended particles cling. If the *p*H of the water is 7.0, how much aluminum ion remains in solution? The solubility product of $Al(OH)_3$ is 1.9×10^{-33}.

Solution. At *p*H 7 the value of $[OH^-]$ is 1.0×10^{-7}. Hence

$$[Al^{+++}](1.0 \times 10^{-7})^3 = 1.9 \times 10^{-33}$$
$$[Al^{+++}] = 1.9 \times 10^{-12}$$

There hence remains 1.9×10^{-12} gram atom or, multiplying by the atomic weight of aluminum (27), 0.51×10^{-10} gram of aluminum ion in solution per liter of water.

22–4. *The Solution of Carbonates in Acid; Hard Water*

The normal carbonates of metals other than the alkalies and ammonium are only slightly soluble in water. We all know, however, that carbonates dissolve easily in acid. This is due in part to the fact that carbon dioxide produced by the reaction escapes from the solution, thus diminishing the carbonate-ion concentration. It is also due in large measure to the existence of most of the carbonate ion in acid solution in the form of HCO_3^- or H_2CO_3 rather than CO_3^{--}; only the last enters into the solubility-product expression of a normal carbonate, and accordingly a larger amount of carbonate can be dissolved by an acidic solution than by a neutral or basic solution before the ion-concentration product equals the solubility product of the carbonate.

This is responsible for the solution of limestone by acid ground water; the quantitative discussion of this effect is given in the following paragraph.

Quantitative Treatment of the Solubility of Carbonates.   The solubility product of $CaCO_3$ is 4.8×10^{-9}.

The solubility of the substance in solutions sufficiently alkaline for all carbonate to exist as the carbonate ion CO_3^{--} is hence 7×10^{-5} mole/l or 0.001 g/l.

In water with pH 7 the ion species HCO_3^- predominates over CO_3^{--}; the equilibrium expression

$$\frac{[H^+][CO_3^{--}]}{[HCO_3^-]} = K_{HCO_3^-} = 4.7 \times 10^{-11}$$

leads to

$$\frac{[CO_3^{--}]}{[HCO_3^-]} = \frac{4.7 \times 10^{-11}}{[H^+]}$$

or

$$[CO_3^{--}]/[HCO_3^-] = 4.7 \times 10^{-4} \text{ for } [H^+] = 10^{-7}$$

Moreover, with $K_{H_2CO_3} = 4.3 \times 10^{-7}$, the ratio $[HCO_3^-]/[H_2CO_3]$ equals 4.3 at pH 7. Hence in neutral solution the total carbonate is divided in the ratios 19% H_2CO_3, 81% HCO_3^-, and only 0.038% CO_3^{--}, the total carbonate concentration being 2,600 times the CO_3^{--} concentration. The equilibrium expression

$$[Ca^{++}][CO_3^{--}] = 4.8 \times 10^{-9}$$

can accordingly be rewritten as

$$[Ca^{++}] \text{ [total carbonate]} = 4.8 \times 10^{-9} \times 2,600 = 1.25 \times 10^{-5}$$

If no calcium ion or carbonate were initially present, the two concentrations $[Ca^{++}]$ and [total carbonate] resulting from solution of $CaCO_3$ would be equal and each would equal $\sqrt{1.25 \times 10^{-5}} = 0.035$ mole/l or 0.35 g/l, which is 51 times that in alkaline solutions. In acid solutions the solubility is much greater still.

Some natural waters are acid because of the presence of a large amount of dissolved carbon dioxide. On heating such water carbon dioxide is driven off, and the hydrogen-ion concentration of the water becomes much less. Even though the total carbonate concentration is decreased, the concentration of CO_3^{--} may be increased greatly because of the increased ionization of HCO_3^- resulting from the change in pH. This may cause the product $[Ca^{++}][CO_3^{--}]$ to reach the solubility product, resulting in the deposition of $CaCO_3$. Water of this kind, from which the dissolved calcium can be precipitated by boiling, is said to have *temporary hardness*. In practice this hardness is removed by adding lime, $Ca(OH)_2$, which neutralizes the acid, and causes all the calcium to precipitate as carbonate.

Permanently hard waters are those containing calcium ion (perhaps with magnesium ion or iron ion) and sulfate or chloride ion instead of carbonate. Such waters may be softened by the addition of sodium carbonate; the sodium ion which remains in solution is unobjectionable.

The use of zeolites and of artificial macromolecular base-exchange agents for the softening of water has been described in Chapter 15.

The solubilities of salts of other weak acids, such as phosphates, acetates, sulfides, etc., are also dependent on hydrogen-ion concentration. A discussion of sulfides is given in the following sections.

22–5. *The Precipitation of Sulfides*

In the systems of qualitative analysis for the metal ions a very important procedure is sulfide precipitation, with the aid of which about fifteen of the twenty-three or twenty-four metals commonly tested for are precipitated. The great usefulness of sulfides in qualitative analysis depends on two factors—the great range of the solubility products of the sulfides and the great range of concentrations of the sulfide ion S^{--} which can be obtained by varying the acidity of the solution.

Some solubility products of interest are the following:

	K_{SP}		K_{SP}
HgS	10^{-54}	ZnS	10^{-24}
CuS	10^{-40}	FeS	10^{-22}
CdS	10^{-28}	CoS*	10^{-21}
PbS	10^{-28}	NiS*	10^{-21}
SnS	10^{-28}	MnS*	10^{-16}

* CoS and NiS are probably dimorphous; the less soluble forms, with K_{SP} about 10^{-27}, are not easily precipitated from acid solutions. MnS is dimorphous; the value given is for the usual flesh-colored form, the green form having $K_{SP} = 10^{-22}$.

The acid constants for H_2S are

$$K_{H_2S} = \frac{[H^+][HS^-]}{[H_2S]} = 1.1 \times 10^{-7}$$

$$K_{HS^-} = \frac{[H^+][S^{--}]}{[HS^-]} = 1.0 \times 10^{-14}$$

From these equations we obtain

$$\frac{[H^+]^2[S^{--}]}{[H_2S]} = 1.1 \times 10^{-21}$$

or

$$[S^{--}] = \frac{1.1 \times 10^{-21}\,[H_2S]}{[H^+]^2}$$

Now in the system of qualitative analysis part of the procedure consists in saturating a solution of appropriately adjusted hydrogen-ion concentration with hydrogen sulfide. In a saturated solution (with $p_{H_2S} = 1$ atm) the value of $[H_2S]$ is about 0.1 M. The foregoing equation hence for this case becomes

$$[S^{--}] = \frac{1.1 \times 10^{-22}}{[H^+]^2}$$

We see that by changing the pH from 0 ($[H^+] = 1$) to 12 ($[H^+] = 10^{-12}$) the sulfide-ion concentration can be varied throughout the great range from 10^{-22} to over 1.

In the Noyes-Swift procedure the metals of the hydrogen sulfide group are precipitated from 0.3 N acid solution. Let us use the solubility products given above to predict which of these sulfides would be precipitated. With $[H^+] = 0.3$ we have $[S^{--}] = 10^{-21}$. Now about 0.5 or 1 mg of metal in 100 ml of solution is the smallest amount which should escape detection in a system of qualitative analysis. The concentration of metal corresponding to this, assuming atomic weight 50 or 100, is $[M^{++}] = 10^{-4}$. Hence, if the solubility product of a sulfide MS were 10^{-25} or smaller, any quantity of the ion M^{++} greater than 0.5 or 1 mg per 100 ml would be precipitated under these conditions. From the table we see that Hg^{++}, Cu^{++}, Cd^{++}, Pb^{++}, and Sn^{++} should precipitate with the H_2S group, and that Zn^{++}, Fe^{++}, Co^{++}, Ni^{++}, and Mn^{++} should not. This is correct— the hydrogen sulfide group consists of the ions Hg^{++}, Cu^{++}, Cd^{++}, Pb^{++}, Sn^{++}, Sn^{4+}, As^{3+}, As^{5+}, Sb^{+++}, Sb^{5+}, and Bi^{+++}. The solubility products for the sulfides SnS_2, As_2S_3, As_2S_5, Sb_2S_3, Sb_2S_5, and Bi_2S_3 have values compatible with their inclusion in this group.

After separation of the precipitate by filtration, the filtrate is made neutral or basic by adding ammonium hydroxide. With $[H^+]$ less than

TABLE 22-1　　*Solubility-Product Constants at Room Temperature* $(18°\text{--}25° C)$

HALIDES	K_{SP}	HALIDES	K_{SP}
AgCl	1.6×10^{-10}	Hg_2I_2*	1×10^{-28}
AgBr	5×10^{-13}	MgF_2	6×10^{-9}
AgI	1×10^{-16}	PbF_2	3.2×10^{-8}
BaF_2	1.7×10^{-6}	$PbCl_2$	1.7×10^{-5}
CaF_2	3.4×10^{-11}	$PbBr_2$	6.3×10^{-6}
CuCl	1×10^{-7}	PbI_2	9×10^{-9}
CuBr	1×10^{-8}	SrF_2	3×10^{-9}
CuI	1×10^{-12}	TlCl	2.0×10^{-4}
Hg_2Cl_2*	1×10^{-18}	TlBr	4×10^{-6}
Hg_2Br_2*	5×10^{-23}	TlI	6×10^{-8}

CARBONATES	K_{SP}	CARBONATES	K_{SP}
Ag_2CO_3	8×10^{-12}	$FeCO_3$	2×10^{-11}
$BaCO_3$	5×10^{-9}	$MnCO_3$	9×10^{-11}
$CaCO_3$	4.8×10^{-9}	$PbCO_3$	1×10^{-13}
$CuCO_3$	1×10^{-10}	$SrCO_3$	1×10^{-9}

CHROMATES	K_{SP}	CHROMATES	K_{SP}
Ag_2CrO_4	1×10^{-12}	$PbCrO_4$	2×10^{-14}
$BaCrO_4$	2×10^{-10}	$SrCrO_4$	3.6×10^{-5}

HYDROXIDES	K_{SP}	HYDROXIDES	K_{SP}
$Al(OH)_3$	1×10^{-33}	$Fe(OH)_3$	1×10^{-38}
$Ca(OH)_2$	8×10^{-6}	$Mg(OH)_2$	6×10^{-12}
$Cd(OH)_2$	1×10^{-14}	$Mn(OH)_2$	1×10^{-14}
$Co(OH)_2$	2×10^{-16}	$Ni(OH)_2$	1×10^{-14}
$Cr(OH)_3$	1×10^{-30}	$Pb(OH)_2$	1×10^{-16}
$Cu(OH)_2$	6×10^{-20}	$Sn(OH)_2$	1×10^{-26}
$Fe(OH)_2$	1×10^{-15}	$Zn(OH)_2$	1×10^{-15}

| SULFIDES: see Section 22-5. | | | |

SULFATES	K_{SP}	SULFATES	K_{SP}
Ag_2SO_4	1.2×10^{-5}	Hg_2SO_4*	6×10^{-7}
$BaSO_4$	1×10^{-10}	$PbSO_4$	2×10^{-8}
$CaSO_4 \cdot 2H_2O$	2.4×10^{-5}	$SrSO_4$	2.8×10^{-7}

* The solubility-product expressions for mercurous salts involve the concentration $[Hg_2^{++}]$.

10^{-7}, $[S^{--}]$ becomes greater than 10^{-8}. Under these conditions any sulfide MS with K_{SP} less than 10^{-12} would precipitate; this class includes the sulfides of Zn^{++}, Fe^{++}, Co^{++}, Ni^{++}, and Mn^{++}.

A more detailed discussion of sulfide precipitations is given in Swift, *System of Chemical Analysis*.

More complete tables of values of solubility-product constants may be found in handbooks and reference books (see end of Chap. 1). An extensive table (App. III) and discussion of the experimental data on which the values depend are given by W. M. Latimer, *The Oxidation States of the Elements and Their Potentials in Aqueous Solution*, Prentice-Hall, New York, 1952.

Exercises

22-1. The value of K_{SP} for AgBr is 5.0×10^{-13}. What is its solubility?

22-2. The solubility of MgF_2 is 0.075 g/l. What is K_{SP} for this salt?

22-3. The value of K_{SP} for $PbCl_2$ is 1.7×10^{-5}. What is its solubility in water? in 0.05 F NaCl?

22-4. From the solubility of Ag_2CrO_4, 0.0030 g per 100 ml, calculate its solubility product, and from this its solubility in 0.01 F $AgNO_3$ and in 0.01 F K_2CrO_4.

22-5. The silver halides have the following solubility products:

AgCl $\quad$ 1.6×10^{-10}
AgBr $\quad$ 5.0×10^{-13}
AgI $\quad$ 1.0×10^{-16}

What would happen if a silver chloride precipitate were allowed to stand in a solution of sodium iodide? if a silver iodide precipitate were allowed to stand in a solution of sodium chloride?

22-6. The values of K_{SP} for AgCl and Ag_2CrO_4 are 1.6×10^{-10} and 1.0×10^{-12}, respectively. Which will precipitate first when a drop of Ag^+ solution is added to a solution which contains 0.1 F NaCl and 0.1 F Na_2CrO_4? If additional Ag^+ is added (say from a 0.1 F solution), when will the other precipitate begin to form?

Look up the color of Ag_2CrO_4 in a reference book; suggest a method for the determination of Ag^+ or Cl^- on the basis of these calculations.

22-7. A solution is in equilibrium with a $PbCrO_4$ precipitate and a $BaCrO_4$ precipitate. What is the concentration ratio $[Pb^{++}]/[Ba^{++}]$ calculated for the dissolved cations? (This calculation is insufficient, because these two chromates actually form solid solutions.)

22-8. Organic chemists sometimes shake a halide with silver oxide to prepare a hydroxide. The same method may be used to convert an inorganic halide into the hydroxide, such as CsCl into CsOH. Explain this reaction with use of the solubility product of Ag_2O, which is $[Ag^+] [OH^-] \times 2.0 = 10^{-8}$. What percent of iodide ion would remain unreplaced by hydroxide ion after this treatment?

22-9. Using the data of Exercise 22-8, calculate the solubilities of Ag_2O in solutions buffered at pH 7, 8, and 9.

22-10. How much silver acetate would dissolve in one liter of a citrate buffer with pH 3.9? in a phosphate buffer with pH 6.0? $K_{SP} = 3.6 \times 10^{-3}$ for $AgC_2H_3O_2$; be sure to consider the equilibrium $HC_2H_3O_2 = H^+ + C_2H_3O_2^-$ in solving this problem.

22-11. The value of K_{SP} for $BaCO_3$ is 5×10^{-9}. What are the solubilities of this salt in solutions buffered at pH 12, 8, 7, and 6?

22-12. What happens when solid $BaCO_3$ is shaken up with pure distilled water, initially at pH 7?

22-13. The value of K_{SP} for calcium oxalate, CaC_2O_4, is 2×10^{-9}; for $H_2C_2O_4$ (oxalic acid) $K_1 = 0.059$ and $K_2 = 6 \times 10^{-5}$. What is the solubility of CaC_2O_4 in pure water? Show that the hydrolysis of $C_2O_4^{--}$ can be neglected in this problem. What is the solubility of CaC_2O_4 in a solution buffered at pH 5?

22-14. Show that the value $K_{SP} = 10^{-74}$ for Bi_2S_3 is compatible with the inclusion of bismuth in the hydrogen sulfide group.

22-15. Calculate the weights of the ions Hg^{++}, Cu^{++}, Cd^{++}, Pb^{++}, and Sn^{++} which would remain in solution in 100 ml of 0.3 N acid after hydrogen sulfide precipitation.

22-16. From the qualitative consideration of the equilibria involved predict which solvent will dissolve the greater amount of solute, and give your reasons:

(a) $BaCO_3$ in water or 1 F $HC_2H_3O_2$
(b) $Al(OH)_3$ in water or 1 F HCl
(c) $BaSO_4$ in 1 F $HC_2H_3O_2$ or 1 F HNO_3
(d) $AgC_2H_3O_2$ in 0.1 F HNO_3 or 0.1 F $NaC_2H_3O_2$
(e) Ag_2CrO_4 in 0.1 F $AgNO_3$ or 0.1 F K_2CrO_4
(f) $Fe(OH)_3$ in 0.1 F NH_4Cl or 0.1 F NH_4OH
(g) CO_2 in water or 1 F HCl
(h) $Mg(OH)_2$ in water or 1 F NH_4Cl
(i) $Ca_3(PO_4)_2$ in 1 F $HC_2H_3O_2$ or 1 F HCl

22-17. A test for magnesium ion may be made by adding to the solution (50 ml volume) about 5 ml of 15 N NH_4OH and 15 ml of 1 N Na_2HPO_4; in the presence of Mg^{++} a white precipitate, NH_4MgPO_4, is formed. (a) Write the solubility-product expression for ammonium magnesium phosphate. (b) Ammonium magnesium phosphate is moderately soluble in water, yet the test carried out as directed above is satisfactory if as much as $\frac{1}{2}$ mg of Mg^{++} is present. Moreover, the above test is not satisfactory if NH_4OH is replaced by NH_4Cl, although the latter gives a larger concentration of ammonium ions. Explain these facts by consideration of the equilibria involved.

Chapter 23

Complex Ions

23–1. *The Nature of Complex Ions*

An ion which contains several atoms, such as the sulfate ion, SO_4^{--}, is called a *complex ion*. Familiar examples of complex ions other than those of the oxygen acids are the deep blue cupric ammonia complex ion, $Cu(NH_3)_4^{++}$, which is formed by adding ammonium hydroxide to a solution of cupric salt, the ferrocyanide ion, $Fe(CN)_6^{----}$, the ferricyanide ion, $Fe(CN)_6^{---}$, and the triiodide ion, I_3^-. Even the hydrated metal ions such as $Al(H_2O)_6^{+++}$ are properly considered to be complex ions.

Complex ions are important in the methods of separation used in qualitative and quantitative chemical analysis and in various industrial processes. Their structure and properties are discussed in detail in this chapter.

23–2. *Ammonia Complexes*

A solution of a cupric salt is blue in color. This blue color is due to the absorption of yellow and red light, and consequent preferential transmission of blue light. The molecular species which absorbs the light is the *hydrated copper ion*, probably $Cu(H_2O)_4^{++}$. Crystalline hydrated cupric salts such as $CuSO_4 \cdot 5H_2O$ are blue, like the aqueous solution, whereas anhydrous $CuSO_4$ is white.*

When a few drops of sodium hydroxide solution are added to a cupric solution a blue precipitate is formed. This is cupric hydroxide, $Cu(OH)_2$,

---

* The crystal structure of $CuSO_4 \cdot 5H_2O$ shows that in the crystal four water molecules are attached closely to the cupric ion, and the fifth is more distant.

which precipitates when the ion-concentration product $[Cu^{++}]$ $[OH^-]^2$ reaches the solubility product of the hydroxide. [Here the symbol Cu^{++} is used, as is conventional, for the ion species $Cu(H_2O)_4^{++}$.] Addition of more sodium hydroxide solution leads to no further change.

If ammonium hydroxide is added in place of sodium hydroxide the same precipitate of $Cu(OH)_2$ is formed. On addition of more ammonium hydroxide, however, the precipitate dissolves, giving a clear solution with a deeper and more intense blue color than the original cupric solution.*

The solution of the precipitate cannot be attributed to increase in hydroxide-ion concentration, because sodium hydroxide does not cause it, nor to ammonium ion, because ammonium salts do not cause it. There remains undissociated NH_4OH or NH_3, which might combine with the cupric ion. It has in fact been found that the new deep-blue ion species formed by addition of an excess of ammonium hydroxide is the **cupric ammonia complex** $Cu(NH_3)_4^{++}$, similar to the hydrated cupric ion except that the four water molecules have been replaced by ammonia molecules. This complex is sometimes called the *cupric tetrammine complex*, the word *ammine* meaning an attached ammonia molecule.

Salts of this complex ion can be crystallized from ammonia solution. The best-known one is **cupric tetrammine sulfate monohydrate,** $Cu(NH_3)_4SO_4 \cdot H_2O$, which has the same deep-blue color as the solution.

The reason that the precipitate of cupric hydroxide dissolves in an excess of ammonium hydroxide can be given in the following way. A precipitate of cupric hydroxide is formed because the concentration of cupric ion and the concentration of hydroxide ion are greater than the values corresponding to the solubility product of cupric hydroxide. If there were some way for copper to be present in the solution without exceeding the solubility product of cupric hydroxide, then precipitation would not occur. In the presence of ammonia, copper exists in the solution not as the cupric ion (that is, the hydrated cupric ion), but principally as the cupric ammonia complex, $Cu(NH_3)_4^{++}$. This complex is far more stable than the hydrated cupric ion. The reaction of formation of the cupric ammonia complex is

$$Cu^{++} + 4NH_3 \rightleftarrows Cu(NH_3)_4^{++}$$

We see from the equation for the reaction that the addition of ammonia to the solution causes the equilibrium to shift to the right, more of the cupric ion being converted into cupric ammonia complex as more and

---

* In describing color the adjective "deep" refers not to intensity but to shade; deep blue tends toward indigo.

more ammonia is added to the solution. When sufficient ammonia is present a large amount of copper may exist in the solution as cupric ammonia complex, at the same time that the cupric-ion concentration is less than that required to cause precipitation of cupric hydroxide. When ammonia is added to a solution in contact with the precipitate of cupric hydroxide the cupric ion in the solution is converted to cupric ammonia complex, causing the solution to be unsaturated with respect to cupric hydroxide. The cupric hydroxide precipitate then dissolves, and if enough ammonia is present the process continues until the precipitate has dissolved completely.

This process of **solution of a slightly soluble substance through formation of a complex by one of its ions** is the basis of some of the most important practical applications of complex formation. Several examples are mentioned later in this chapter.

The nickel ion forms two rather stable ammonia complexes. When a small amount of ammonium hydroxide solution is added to a solution of a nickel salt (green in color) a pale-green precipitate of nickel hydroxide, $Ni(OH)_2$, is formed. On addition of more ammonium hydroxide solution this dissolves to give a blue solution, which with still more ammonium hydroxide changes color to light blue-violet.

The light blue-violet complex is shown to be the **nickel hexammine**

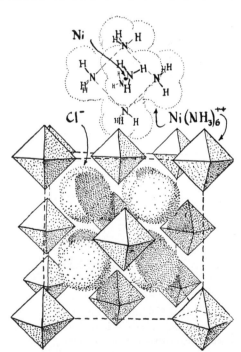

FIG. 23-1

The structure of crystalline nickel hexammine chloride, $Ni(NH_3)_6Cl_2$. The crystal contains octahedral nickel hexammine ions and chloride ions.

ion, $Ni(NH_3)_6^{++}$, by the facts that the same color is shown by crystalline $Ni(NH_3)_6Cl_2$ and other crystals containing six ammonia molecules per nickel ion, and that X-ray studies have revealed the presence in these crystals of octahedral complexes in which the six ammonia molecules are situated about the nickel ion at the corners of a regular octahedron. The structure of crystalline $Ni(NH_3)_6Cl_2$ is shown in Figure 23-1.

The blue complex is probably the **nickel tetramminedihydrate ion,** $Ni(NH_3)_4(H_2O)_2^{++}$. Careful studies of the change in color with increasing ammonia concentration indicate that the ammonia molecules are added one by one, and that all the complexes $Ni(H_2O)_6^{++}$, $Ni(H_2O)_5NH_3^{++}$, $Ni(H_2O)_4(NH_3)_2^{++}$, $Ni(H_2O)_3(NH_3)_3^{++}$, $Ni(H_2O)_2(NH_3)_4^{++}$, $Ni(H_2O)(NH_3)_5^{++}$, and $Ni(NH_3)_6^{++}$ exist.

Several metal ions form ammonia complexes with sufficient stability to put the hydroxides into solution. Others, such as aluminum and iron, do not. The formulas of the stable complexes are given below. There is no great apparent order about the stability or composition of the complexes, except that often the unipositive ions add two, the bipositive ions four, and the terpositive ions six ammonia molecules. This rule is explained by the electroneutrality principle (Sec. 10–8); if the metalnitrogen bonds have 50% ionic character, these formulas lead to zero electric charge on the metal atom.

The **silver ammonia complex,** $Ag(NH_3)_2^+$, is sufficiently stable for ammonium hydroxide to dissolve precipitated silver chloride by reducing the concentration of silver ion, $[Ag^+]$, below the value required for precipitation by the solubility product of AgCl. A satisfactory test for silver ion is the formation with chloride ion of a precipitate which is soluble in ammonium hydroxide.

Stable Ammonia Complexes

$Cu(NH_3)_2^+$	$Cu(NH_3)_4^{++}$	$Co(NH_3)_6^{+++}$
$Ag(NH_3)_2^+$	$Zn(NH_3)_4^{++}$	$Cr(NH_3)_6^{+++}$
$Au(NH_3)_2^+$	$Cd(NH_3)_4^{++}$	
	$Hg(NH_3)_2^{++}$	
	$Hg(NH_3)_4^{++}$	
	$Ni(NH_3)_4^{++}$	
	$Ni(NH_3)_6^{++}$	
	$Co(NH_3)_6^{++}$	

Notes: (1) Cobaltous ammonia ion is easily oxidized by air to cobaltic ammonia ion. (2) Chromic ammonia ion forms only slowly, and is decomposed by boiling, to give chromium hydroxide precipitate.

23–3. Cyanide Complexes

Another important class of complex ions includes those formed by the metal ions with cyanide ion. The common cyanide complexes are given in the following list.

Cyanide Complexes

$Cu(CN)_2^-$	$Zn(CN)_4^{--}$	$Fe(CN)_6^{---}$
$Ag(CN)_2^-$	$Cd(CN)_4^{--}$	$Co(CN)_6^{---}$
$Au(CN)_2^-$	$Hg(CN)_4^{--}$	$Au(CN)_4^-$
	$Mn(CN)_6^{----}$	
	$Fe(CN)_6^{----}$	
	$Co(CN)_6^{----}$	

Some of these complexes are very stable; the stability of the **argentocyanide ion,** $Ag(CN)_2^-$, for example, is so great that addition of sulfide does not cause silver sulfide to precipitate, even though the solubility product of silver sulfide is very small. The **ferrocyanide ion,** $Fe(CN)_6^{----}$, **ferricyanide ion,** $Fe(CN)_6^{---}$, and **cobalticyanide ion,** $Co(CN)_6^{---}$, are so stable that they are not appreciably decomposed by strong acid. The others are decomposed by strong acid, with the formation of hydrocyanic acid, HCN.

An interesting illustration of the stability of the ferrocyanide complex is provided by the old method of making potassium ferrocyanide, $K_4Fe(CN)_6$, by strongly heating nitrogenous organic material (such as dried blood and hides) with potassium hydroxide and iron filings.

The **cobaltocyanide ion,** $Co(CN)_6^{----}$, is, like the cobaltous ammonia complex, a very strong reducing agent; it is able to decompose water, liberating hydrogen, as it changes into cobalticyanide ion.

An interesting practical use of cyanide complexes occurs in the extraction of gold and silver from ores by the **cyanide process.** Gold is a noble metal, with oxidation-reduction potential such that it is insoluble in acids other than aqua regia (see the following section). It usually occurs as native gold, the elementary substance, distributed in fine grains through quartz or other rock. The solution of the gold is effected by utilizing the great stability of the **auric cyanide complex,** $Au(CN)_4^-$. The powdered ore is treated with a solution of sodium cyanide in the presence of air, and the gold goes into solution as $Au(CN)_4^-$, atmospheric oxygen being the agent which oxidizes the gold from the zero-valent to the terpositive state:

$$4Au + 16CN^- + 6H_2O + 3O_2 \longrightarrow 4Au(CN)_4^- + 12OH^-$$

Silver ores are also leached by the cyanide process. For native silver the reaction is similar to that for gold:

$$4Ag + 8CN^- + 2H_2O + O_2 \longrightarrow 4Ag(CN)_2^- + 4OH^-$$

Oxygen is not needed for leaching of silver ores in which the silver is present as compounds; a representative reaction for this case, for the silver mineral cerargyrite, AgCl, is

$$AgCl + 2CN^- \longrightarrow Ag(CN)_2^- + Cl^-$$

The gold and silver are usually regained from the leaching solution by electrolytic deposition or by replacement by zinc or aluminum.

Cyanide solutions are used in the **electroplating** of gold, silver, zinc, cadmium, and other metals. In these solutions the concentrations of uncomplexed metal ions are very small, and this favors the production of a uniform, fine-grained deposit. Other complex-forming anions (tartrate, citrate, chloride, hydroxide) are also used in plating solutions.

23–4. *Complex Halides and Other Complex Ions*

Nearly all anions can enter into complex formation with metal ions. Thus stannic chloride, $SnCl_4$, forms with chloride ion the stable **hexachlorostannate ion,** $SnCl_6^{--}$, which with cations crystallizes in an extensive series of salts. Various complexes of this kind are discussed below.

Chloride Complexes.   Many chloride complexes are known; representative are the following:

$$CuCl_2(H_2O)_2, \ CuCl_3(H_2O)^-, \ CuCl_4^{--}$$
$$AgCl_2^-, \ AuCl_2^-$$
$$HgCl_4^{--}$$
$$CdCl_4^{--}, \ CdCl_6^{----}$$
$$SnCl_6^{--}$$
$$PtCl_6^{--}$$
$$AuCl_4^-$$

The cupric chloride complexes are recognizable in strong hydrochloric acid solutions by their green color. The crystal $CuCl_2 \cdot 2H_2O$ is bright-green, and X-ray studies have shown that it contains the complex molecule $CuCl_2(H_2O)_2$. The ion $CuCl_3(H_2O)^-$ is usually written $CuCl_3^-$; it is highly probable that the indicated water molecule is present, and, indeed, the ion $Cu(H_2O)_3Cl^+$ very probably also exists in solution.

The stability of the **tetrachloroaurate ion** $AuCl_4^-$ is responsible for the ability of aqua regia, a mixture of nitric and hydrochloric acids, to dissolve gold, which is not significantly soluble in the acids separately. Nitric acid serves as the oxidizing agent which oxidizes gold to the terpositive state, and the chloride ions provided by the hydrochloric acid further the reaction by combining with the auric ion to form the stable complex:

$$\text{Au} + 4\text{HCl} + 3\text{HNO}_3 \longrightarrow \text{HAuCl}_4 + 3\text{NO}_2 \uparrow + 3\text{H}_2\text{O}$$

The solution of platinum in aqua regia likewise results in the stable **hexachloroplatinate ion,** PtCl_6^{--}.

Other Halide Complexes.   The bromide and iodide complexes closely resemble the chloride complexes, and usually have similar formulas.

Fluoride ion is more effective than the other halide ions in forming complexes. Important examples are the **tetrafluoroborate ion,** BF_4^-, the **hexafluorosilicate ion,** SiF_6^{--}, the **hexafluoroaluminate ion,** AlF_6^{---}, and the **ferric hexafluoride ion,** FeF_6^{---}.

The **triiodide ion,** I_3^-, is formed by dissolving iodine in an iodide solution. Similar complexes exist, including the **dibromoiodide** and **dichloroiodide ions,** IBr_2^- and ICl_2^-.

Complexes with Thiosulfate, Nitrite, etc.   A useful complex is that formed by thiosulfate ion, $\text{S}_2\text{O}_3^{--}$, and silver ion. Its formula is $\text{Ag}(\text{S}_2\text{O}_3)_2^{---}$, and its structure is

$$
\left[
\begin{array}{c}
: \ddot{\text{O}} : \qquad\qquad : \ddot{\text{O}} : \\
| \qquad\qquad\qquad | \\
: \ddot{\text{O}} - \text{S} - \ddot{\text{S}} - \text{Ag} - \ddot{\text{S}} - \text{S} - \ddot{\text{O}} : \\
| \qquad\qquad\qquad | \\
: \ddot{\text{O}} : \qquad\qquad : \ddot{\text{O}} :
\end{array}
\right]^{---}
$$

analogous to

$$[\text{H}_3\text{N}-\text{Ag}-\text{NH}_3]^+$$

and

$$[: \text{N}\equiv\text{C}-\text{Ag}-\text{C}\equiv\text{N} :]^-$$

This complex ion is sufficiently stable to cause silver chloride and bromide to be soluble in thiosulfate solutions, and this is the reason that sodium thiosulfate solution ("hypo") is used after development of a photographic film or paper to dissolve away the unreduced silver halide, which if allowed to remain in the emulsion would in the course of time darken through long exposure to light.

Of the nitrite complexes, that with cobaltic ion, $Co(NO_2)_6^{---}$, called the **cobaltinitrite ion** or **hexanitritocobaltic ion,** is the most familiar. **Potassium cobaltinitrite,** $K_3Co(NO_2)_6$, is one of the least soluble potassium salts, and its precipitation on addition of sodium cobaltinitrite reagent is commonly used as a test for potassium ion.

Ferric ion and thiocyanate ion combine to give a product with an intense red color; this reaction is used as a test for ferric ion. The red color seems to be due to various complexes, ranging from $Fe(H_2O)_5NCS^{++}$ to $Fe(NCS)_6^{---}$. The azide ion, NNN^-, gives a similar color with ferric ion

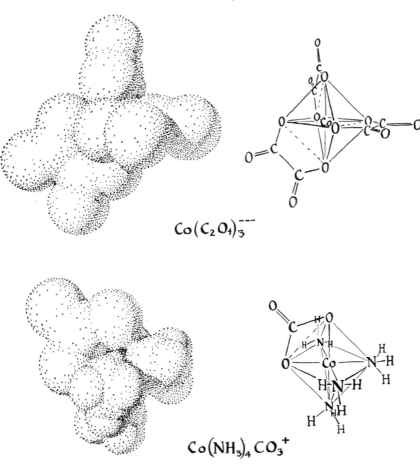

$$Co(C_2O_4)_3^{---}$$

$$Co(NH_3)_4CO_3^+$$

FIG. 23-2   *The structure of the cobaltic trioxalate ion,* $Co(C_2O_4)_3^{---}$, *and the cobaltic tetrammine carbonate ion,* $Co(NH_3)_4CO_3^+$. *Two oxygen atoms of each oxalate group or carbonate group are bonded to cobalt, and occupy two of the six corners of the octahedron. These corners must be adjacent, connected by an edge of the octahedron.*

The Chromic and Cobaltic Complexes.   Tervalent chromium and cobalt combine with cyanide ion, nitrite ion, chloride ion, sulfate ion, oxalate ion, water, ammonia, and many other ions and molecules to form a very great number of complexes, with a wide range of colors, which are nearly the same for corresponding chromic and cobaltic complexes. Most of these complexes are stable, and are formed and decomposed slowly. Representative are the members of the series

$$Cr(NH_3)_6^{+++} \qquad\qquad Cr(NH_3)_5Cl^{++} \qquad\qquad Cr(NH_3)_4Cl_2^{+}$$
yellow   purple   green

$$Cr(NH_3)_3Cl_3 \qquad\qquad\qquad Cr(NH_3)_2Cl_4^{-}$$
violet   orange-red

and

$$Co(NH_3)_6^{+++} \qquad\qquad Co(NH_3)_5H_2O^{+++} \quad \cdots \quad Co(H_2O)_6^{+++}$$
yellow   rose-red   purple

A group such as oxalate ion, $C_2O_4^{--}$, or carbonate ion, CO_3^{--}, may occupy two of the six coordination places in an octahedral complex; examples are $Co(NH_3)_4CO_3^{+}$ and $Cr(C_2O_4)_3^{---}$. The structure of these complexes is shown in Figure 23-2.

The often puzzling color changes shown by chromic solutions are due to reactions involving these complexes. Solutions containing chromic ion, $Cr(H_2O)_6^{+++}$, are purple in color; on heating they become green, because of the formation of complexes such as $Cr(H_2O)_4Cl_2^{+}$ and $Cr(H_2O)_5SO_4^{+}$. At room temperature these green complexes slowly decompose, again forming the purple solution.

23–5. *Hydroxide Complexes*

If sodium hydroxide is added to a solution containing zinc ion a precipitate of zinc hydroxide is formed:

$$Zn^{++} + 2OH^- \rightleftharpoons Zn(OH)_2$$

This hydroxide precipitate is, of course, soluble in acid; *it is also soluble in alkali.* On addition of more sodium hydroxide the precipitate goes back into solution, this process occurring at hydroxide-ion concentrations from 0.1 M to 1 M.

To explain this phenomenon we might postulate the formation of a complex ion, remembering the solubility of cupric hydroxide and nickel hydroxide in ammonium hydroxide with formation of ammonia complexes. This is indeed the explanation; the complex ion which is formed is the **zincate ion,** $Zn(OH)_4^{--}$, by the reaction

$$Zn(OH)_2 + 2OH^- \rightleftharpoons Zn(OH)_4^{--}$$

The ion is closely similar to other complexes of zinc, such as $Zn(H_2O)_4^{++}$, $Zn(NH_3)_4^{++}$, and $Zn(CN)_4^{--}$, with hydroxide ions in place of water or ammonia molecules or cyanide ions. The ion $Zn(H_2O)(OH)_3^-$ is also formed to some extent.

Recalling that the hydrolysis of zinc salts produces the cation $Zn(H_2O)_3OH^+$, we see that the molecular species that exist in zinc solutions of different pH values are the following:

Acidic solution $\quad\begin{cases} Zn(H_2O)_4^{++} \\ Zn(H_2O)_3(OH)^+ \end{cases}$

Neutral solution $\quad Zn(H_2O)_2(OH)_2 \qquad Zn(OH)_2 \downarrow$

Basic solution $\quad\begin{cases} Zn(H_2O)(OH)_3^- \\ Zn(OH)_4^{--} \end{cases}$

The conversion of each complex into the following one occurs by removal of a proton from one of the four water molecules of the tetrahydrated zinc ion. The precipitate of zinc hydroxide is formed by loss of water from the neutral complex $Zn(H_2O)_2(OH)_2$.

The precipitate $Zn(OH)_2$ also fits into the system of complexes, despite the difference of its formula from the general expression ZnX_4. Two molecules of $Zn(H_2O)_2(OH)_2$ can combine with loss of one molecule of water to form the larger complex

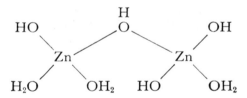

In this complex, $Zn_2(H_2O)_3(OH)_4$, each zinc ion is surrounded by four oxygen atoms (of OH^- or H_2O), exactly as in the hydrated zinc cation or the zincate anion; the loss of water without decrease in coordination number is achieved by the dual role played by one hydroxide oxygen atom, which serves as part of the coordination tetrahedron for both zinc ions. By continuing this process all of the tetrahedra can be linked together into an infinite framework, in which each tetrahedron shares its corners with four other tetrahedra. This is the structure of the $Zn(OH)_2$ precipitate.

Amphoteric Hydroxides. A hydroxide, such as zinc hydroxide, which can combine with acids to form salts and also with bases to form salts is called an *amphoteric hydroxide*. The amphoteric properties of a metal hydroxide are determined by the stability of the hydroxide complex of the metal.

The principal common amphoteric hydroxides and their anions* are the following:

$Zn(OH)_2$	$Zn(OH)_4^{--}$	zincate ion
$Al(OH)_3$	$Al(OH)_4^{-}$	aluminate ion
$Cr(OH)_3$	$Cr(OH)_4^{-}$	chromite ion
$Pb(OH)_2$	$Pb(OH)_3^{-}$	plumbite ion
$Sn(OH)_2$	$Sn(OH)_3^{-}$	stannite ion

In addition the following hydroxides evidence acidic properties by combining with hydroxide ion to form complex anions:

$Sn(OH)_4$	$Sn(OH)_6^{--}$	stannate ion
$As(OH)_3$	$As(OH)_4^{-}$	arsenite ion
$As(OH)_5$	AsO_4^{---}	arsenate ion
$Sb(OH)_3$	$Sb(OH)_4^{-}$	antimonite ion
$Sb(OH)_5$	$Sb(OH)_6^{-}$	antimonate ion

Except for arsenate ion, and possibly arsenite ion, the anions are hydroxide complexes as indicated.

The hydroxides of this second set are not properly described as amphoteric, despite their acidic properties, because they do not have basic properties. These hydroxides do not combine with strong acids in general, but dissolve in acid only in the presence of anions, such as chloride ion, with which they can form complexes, such as the chlorostannate ion, $SnCl_6^{--}$.

The hydroxides listed above form hydroxide complex anions to a sufficient extent to make them soluble in moderately strong alkali. Other common hydroxides have weaker acidic properties: $Cu(OH)_2$ and $Co(OH)_2$ are only slightly soluble in very strong alkali, and $Cd(OH)_2$, $Fe(OH)_3$, $Mn(OH)_2$, and $Ni(OH)_2$ are effectively insoluble. The common analytical method of separation of Al^{+++}, Cr^{+++}, and Zn^{++} from Fe^{+++}, Mn^{++}, Co^{++}, and Ni^{++} with use of sodium hydroxide is based on these facts.

---

* Because of the difficulty of determining the amount of hydration of an ion in aqueous solutions, chemists have been slow to accept these formulas; the older formulas are ZnO_2^{--}, AlO_2^{-}, etc.

It is possible that plumbite ion and stannite ion contain more hydroxide groups than indicated.

23–6. *Sulfide Complexes*

Sulfur, which is directly below oxygen in the periodic table of the elements, has many similar properties with it. One of these is the property of combining with another atom to form complexes; there exist *sulfo acids* (thio acids) of many elements similar to the oxygen acids. An example is **sulfophosphoric acid,** H_3PS_4, which corresponds exactly in formula to phosphoric acid, H_3PO_4. This sulfo acid is not of much importance; it is unstable, and hydrolyzes in water to phosphoric acid and hydrogen sulfide:

$$H_3PS_4 + 4H_2O \longrightarrow H_3PO_4 + 4H_2S$$

But other sulfo acids, such as **sulfarsenic acid,** H_3AsS_4, are stable, and are of use in analytical chemistry and in chemical industry.

All of the following arsenic acids are known:

$$H_3AsO_4 \quad H_3AsO_3S \quad H_3AsO_2S_2 \quad H_3AsOS_3 \quad H_3AsS_4$$

The structure of the five complex anions AsO_4^{---}, AsO_3S^{---}, $AsO_2S_2^{---}$, $AsOS_3^{---}$, and AsS_4^{---} is the same: an arsenic atom surrounded tetrahedrally by four other atoms, oxygen or sulfur.

Some metal sulfides are soluble in solutions of sodium sulfide or ammonium sulfide because of formation of a complex sulfo anion. The important members of this class are HgS, As_2S_3, Sb_2S_3, As_2S_5, Sb_2S_5, and SnS_2, which react with sulfide ion in the following ways:

$$HgS + S^{--} \rightleftharpoons HgS_2^{--}$$
$$As_2S_3 + 3S^{--} \rightleftharpoons 2AsS_3^{---}$$
$$Sb_2S_3 + 3S^{--} \rightleftharpoons 2SbS_3^{---}$$
$$As_2S_5 + 3S^{--} \rightleftharpoons 2AsS_4^{---}$$
$$Sb_2S_5 + 3S^{--} \rightleftharpoons 2SbS_4^{---}$$
$$SnS_2 + S^{--} \rightleftharpoons SnS_3^{--}$$

Mercuric sulfide is soluble in a solution of sodium sulfide and sodium hydroxide (to repress hydrolysis of the sulfide, which would decrease the sulfide-ion concentration), but not in a solution of ammonium sulfide and ammonium hydroxide, in which the sulfide-ion concentration is smaller. The other sulfides listed are soluble in both solutions. CuS, Ag_2S, Bi_2S_3, CdS, PbS, ZnS, CoS, NiS, FeS, MnS, and SnS are not soluble in sulfide solutions, but most of these form complex sulfides by fusion with Na_2S or K_2S. Although SnS is not soluble in Na_2S or $(NH_4)_2S$ solutions, it dissolves in solutions containing both sulfide and disulfide, Na_2S_2 or $(NH_4)_2S_2$, or sulfide and peroxide. The disulfide ion, S_2^{--}, or peroxide oxidizes the tin to the stannic level, and the sulfostannate ion is then formed:

$$SnS + S_2^{--} \rightleftarrows SnS_3^{--}$$

Many schemes of qualitative analysis involve separation of the copper-group sulfides (PbS, Bi_2S_3, CuS, CdS) from the tin-group sulfides (HgS, As_2S_3, As_2S_5, Sb_2S_3, Sb_2S_5, SnS, SnS_2) by treatment with Na_2S-Na_2S_2 solution, which dissolves only the tin-group sulfides.

23–7. *The Quantitative Treatment of Complex Formation*

The quantitative theory of chemical equilibrium, as discussed in earlier chapters, can be applied in a straightforward manner to problems involving the formation of complexes. Some of the ways in which this can be done are exemplified in the following paragraphs.

Example 1.   Ammonium hydroxide is added to a cupric solution until a precipitate is formed, and the addition is continued until part of the precipitate has dissolved to give a deep-blue solution. What would be the effect of dissolving some ammonium chloride in the solution?

Solution.   The weak base NH_4OH is partially ionized and is in equilibrium with dissolved ammonia:

$$NH_3 + H_2O \rightleftarrows NH_4OH \rightleftarrows NH_4^+ + OH^-$$

Addition of NH_4Cl would increase $[NH_4]^+$, which would shift the equilibrium to the left, producing more NH_3 and decreasing the hydroxide-ion concentration. The precipitate $Cu(OH)_2$ is in equilibrium with the solution according to the reaction

$$\underline{Cu(OH)_2} + 4NH_3 \rightleftarrows Cu(NH_3)_4^{++} + 2OH^-$$

Both the increase of $[NH_3]$ and the decrease of $[OH^-]$ caused by addition of NH_4Cl to the solution would shift this reaction to the right; hence more of the precipitate would dissolve.

Example 2.   Would a precipitate of AgCl be formed if 1 ml of 1 F $AgNO_3$ were added to 100 ml of a solution 1 M in CN^- and 1 M in Cl^-? The solubility product of AgCl is 1.6×10^{-10} and the complex-formation constant of $Ag(CN)_2^-$ is

$$\frac{[Ag(CN)_2^-]}{[Ag^+][CN^-]^2} = 1 \times 10^{21}$$

Solution. With $[CN^-] = 1$, the ratio $[Ag^+]/[Ag(CN)_2^-]$ has the value 1×10^{-21}. Hence, if all the added silver ion were in solution the value of $[Ag(CN)_2^-]$ would be 10^{-2} (since except for a minute amount the total silver present would be in the form of this complex), and the value of $[Ag^+]$ would be $10^{-2} \times 10^{-21} = 10^{-23}$. Now the product $[Ag^+][Cl^-]$ equals 10^{-23} if $[Ag^+] = 10^{-23}$ and $[Cl^-] = 1$; the product of these values is very much smaller than the solubility product, so that the solution is far from saturated with respect to AgCl, and no precipitate would form.

TABLE 23-1 *Ammonia Concentrations Producing 50% Conversion of Metal Ions to Complexes*

METAL ION	COMPLEX ION	AMMONIA CONCENTRATION
Cu^+	$Cu(NH_3)_2^+$	5×10^{-6}
Ag^+	$Ag(NH_3)_2^+$	2×10^{-4}
Zn^{++}	$Zn(NH_3)_4^{++}$	5×10^{-3}
Cd^{++}	$Cd(NH_3)_4^{++}$	5×10^{-2}
	$Cd(NH_3)_6^{++}$	10
Hg^{++}	$Hg(NH_3)_2^{++}$	2×10^{-9}
	$Hg(NH_3)_4^{++}$	2×10^{-1}
Cu^{++}	$Cu(NH_3)_4^{++}$	5×10^{-4}
Ni^{++}	$Ni(NH_3)_4^{++}$	5×10^{-2}
	$Ni(NH_3)_6^{++}$	5×10^{-1}
Co^{++}	$Co(NH_3)_6^{++}$	1×10^{-1}
Co^{+++}	$Co(NH_3)_6^{+++}$	1×10^{-6}

In the accompanying tables there are given values of equilibrium constants or equivalent constants for the reactions of formation of some complexes. The values of equilibrium constants must be used with some caution in making calculations. Thus for the reaction

$$Cu^{++} + 4NH_3 \rightleftharpoons Cu(NH_3)_4^{++}$$

we would write

$$K = \frac{[Cu(NH_3)_4^{++}]}{[Cu^{++}][NH_3]^4}$$

as the equilibrium constant, and expect the concentration ratio $[Cu(NH_3)_4^{++}]/[Cu^{++}]$ to vary with the fourth power of the ammonia concentration. This is true, however, only as an approximation, because the reaction is more complicated than this. Actually the ammonia molecules attach themselves to the copper ion one at a time (replacing water molecules), and an accurate treatment would require that there be considered the four successive equilibria

$$Cu(H_2O)_4{}^{++} + NH_3 \rightleftarrows Cu(H_2O)_3NH_3{}^{++} + H_2O$$
$$Cu(H_2O)_3NH_3{}^{++} + NH_3 \rightleftarrows Cu(H_2O)_2(NH_3)_2{}^{++} + H_2O$$
$$Cu(H_2O)_2(NH_3)_2{}^{++} + NH_3 \rightleftarrows CuH_2O(NH_3)_3{}^{++} + H_2O$$
$$CuH_2O(NH_3)_3{}^{++} + NH_3 \rightleftarrows Cu(NH_3)_4{}^{++} + H_2O$$

The consequence of the existence of these intermediate complexes is that the formation of the final product takes place over a larger range of values of the ammonia concentration than it would otherwise. If the complex were formed in one step the change from 1% to 99% conversion would require only a tenfold increase in $[NH_3]$; it is found by experiment, however, that the ammonia concentration must be increased 10,000-fold to produce this conversion, as followed by the color change.

TABLE 23-2   *Ion Concentrations Producing 50% Conversion of Metal Ions to Complexes*

METAL ION	COMPLEX ION	ION CONCENTRATION
Cu^+	$Cu(CN)_2{}^-$	1×10^{-8}
	$CuCl_2{}^-$	4×10^{-3}
Ag^+	$Ag(CN)_2{}^-$	3×10^{-11}
	$AgCl_2{}^-$	3×10^{-3}
	$Ag(NO_2)_2{}^-$	4×10^{-2}
	$Ag(S_2O_3)_2{}^{---}$	3×10^{-7}
Zn^{++}	$Zn(CN)_4{}^{--}$	1×10^{-4}
Cd^{++}	$Cd(CN)_4{}^{--}$	6×10^{-5}
	$CdI_4{}^{--}$	3×10^{-2}
Hg^{++}	$Hg(CN)_4{}^{--}$	5×10^{-11}
	$HgCl_4{}^{--}$	9×10^{-5}
	$HgBr_4{}^{--}$	4×10^{-6}
	$HgI_4{}^{--}$	1×10^{-8}
	$Hg(SCN)_4{}^{--}$	3×10^{-6}

23–8. *The Structural Chemistry of Complexes*

The concept of the coordination of ions or groups in a definite geometric arrangement about a central ion was developed shortly after the beginning of the present century by the Swiss chemist Alfred Werner to account for the existence and properties of compounds such as K_2SnCl_6, $Co(NH_3)_6I_3$, etc. Before Werner's work these compounds had been assigned formulas such as $SnCl_4 \cdot 2KCl$ and $CoI_3 \cdot 6NH_3$, and had been classed as "molecular compounds," of unknown nature. Werner showed that the properties of the complexes of Cr^{+++}, Co^{+++}, Sn^{++++}, and other atoms with coordination number 6 could be explained by the postulate

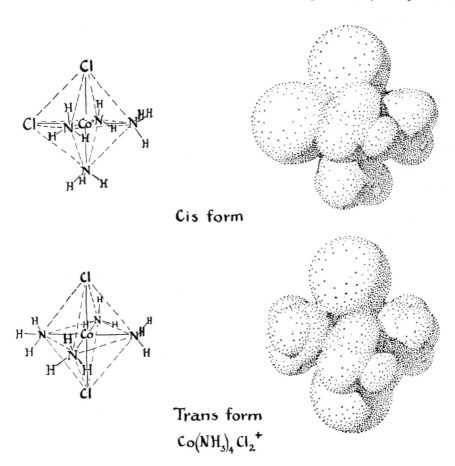

Cis form

Trans form

$$Co(NH_3)_4Cl_2^+$$

FIG. 23-3 *The cis and trans isomers of the cobaltic tetrammine dichloride ion,*
$Co(NH_3)_4Cl_2^+$. In the cis form the two chlorine atoms occupy adjacent corners of
the coordination octahedron about the cobalt atom, and in the trans form the two
chlorine atoms occupy opposite corners.

that the six attached groups are arranged about the central atom at the corners of a circumscribed regular octahedron.

One important property which Werner explained in this way is the existence of *isomers*, different substances with the same chemical composition. For example, there are two complexes with the formula

$Co(NH_3)_4Cl_2^+$, one violet in color and one green. Werner identified these two complexes with the cis and trans structures shown in Figure 23-3. In the cis form the chloride ions are in adjacent positions, and in the trans form in opposite positions. Werner identified the violet complex with the cis configuration through the observation that it could be made easily from the carbonate-ammonia complex $Co(NH_3)_4CO_3^+$, for which only the cis form is possible (Fig. 23-2).

Complexes MX_4 are sometimes tetrahedral in configuration $[Zn(CN)_4^{--}, Zn(NH_3)_4^{++}]$, and sometimes square and planar $[Ni(CN)_4^{--}, Cu(NH_3)_4^{++}, PdCl_4^{--}]$.

It is interesting that in many complexes the number of electrons about the central atom, including two electrons for each bond to the attached atoms, is equal to the number in a noble gas. Thus in

$$\left[\begin{array}{c} NH_3 \\ \cdot\cdot \\ H_3N : Zn : NH_3 \\ \cdot\cdot \\ NH_3 \end{array} \right]^{++}$$

the 28 electrons of the zinc ion Zn^{++} and the 8 electrons of the four bonds total 36, the number in krypton; in this complex the zinc atom has achieved the krypton electronic structure. Similarly, in the ferrocyanide ion, $Fe(CN)_6^{----}$, the iron atom has the krypton complement of 36 electrons. In some other complexes there is a deficiency of electrons about the central atom: $Cu(NH_3)_4^{++}$, 35; $Ni(CN)_4^{--}$, 34; $Fe(CN)_6^{---}$, 35; $Cr(NH_3)_6^{+++}$, 33. Only rarely is there an excess, and this leads to instability; thus, although cobaltous ion Co^{++} is stable, its complexes such as $Co(CN)_6^{----}$ and $Co(NH_3)_6^{++}$, with 37 electrons about the cobalt atom, are so unstable that they are very easily oxidized by atmospheric oxygen to the corresponding cobaltic complexes, and in the absence of oxygen they reduce water, liberating hydrogen.

In recent years a great amount of information about the structure of complexes has been gathered by use of X-rays, magnetic measurements, and other modern methods. This information about the configuration of the atoms in the complexes has been correlated with their chemical properties in such a way as to bring reasonable order into this field of chemistry.

The **metal carbonyls,** complexes of metals with carbon monoxide, are interesting substances of some practical importance. In the Mond process of obtaining pure nickel from iron-nickel ores the ore is reduced with hydrogen to metallic nickel under conditions such that the iron oxide is not reduced. Carbon monoxide is then passed through the reduced ore at room temperature; it combines with the nickel to form nickel carbonyl:

$$Ni + 4CO \longrightarrow Ni(CO)_4$$

Nickel carbonyl is a gas. It is passed into a decomposer heated to 150° C; the gas decomposes, depositing pure metallic nickel, and the liberated carbon monoxide is returned to be used again.

Exercises

23-1. Discuss the effects of adding to three portions of a cupric solution (a) NH_4OH, (b) $NaOH$, (c) NH_4Cl. Write equations for reactions.

23-2. To three portions of a solution containing Ni^{++} and Al^{+++} there are added (a) $NaOH$, (b) NH_4OH, (c) $NaOH + NH_4OH$. What happens in each case?

23-3. Is silver chloride more or less soluble in 1 F NH_4OH than in a solution 1 F in NH_4Cl and 1 F in NH_4OH? Why? (Note that there are two opposing effects— one resulting from the change in degree of ionization of NH_4OH and the other from the increase in concentration of chloride ion. Which of these effects is the larger?)

23-4. Write the equation for the principal chemical reaction involved in fixing a photographic film.

23-5. For each of the following cases state in which of the two solutions the substance is more soluble, and why. Write equations for reactions.

$KClO_4$ in 1 F K_2SO_4 or 1 F Na_2SO_4
$AgC_2H_3O_2$ in 0.1 F $NaC_2H_3O_2$ or 0.1 F $HC_2H_3O_2$
$Al(OH)_3$ in 1 F $NaOH$ or 1 F NH_4OH
$Cu(OH)_2$ in 1 F $NaOH$ or 1 F NH_4OH
$Cu(OH)_2$ in 1 F NH_4OH or 1 F $NH_4OH + 1$ $F NH_4Cl$

23-6. From the complex constant of $Ag(S_2O_3)_2^{---}$ (obtained from Table 23-2) and the solubility product of $AgBr$ calculate the thiosulfate-ion concentration needed to dissolve 5 g of $AgBr$ per liter.

23-7. Arrange the following solutions in order of ability to dissolve $AgCl$, using data from Tables 23-1 and 23-2: 0.1 F $NaNO_2$, 0.1 F $Na_2S_2O_3$, 0.1 F $NaCN$.

23-8. Will 0.1 g of $AgBr$ dissolve in 100 ml of 1 $F NH_4OH$ solution? (K_{SP} for $AgBr = 5 \times 10^{-13}$.)

23-9. Write the chemical equation for the solution of platinum in aqua regia. Explain why platinum dissolves in aqua regia but not in either hydrochloric acid or nitric acid alone.

23-10. Would sodium cyanide be an effective and satisfactory substitute for sodium thiosulfate as a fixer? See Table 23-2 for data.

23-11. Perchlorate ion is generally found to be the weakest complexing reagent of the common anions. Which solution will be more acidic, $0.1\ F\ Zn(ClO_4)_2$ or $0.1\ F$ $ZnCl_2$?

23-12. How many structural isomers of the octahedral complex $Co(NH_3)_3Cl_3$ are there?

23-13. How many isomers of the tetrahedral complex $Zn(NH_3)_2Cl_2$ are there? of the planar, square complex $Pt(NH_3)_2Cl_2$?

23-14. If each CO molecule donates two electrons to the nickel atom in $Ni(CO)_4$, what is the electron configuration of the nickel atom in this molecule? Predict the probable formula for iron carbonyl, remembering that the atomic number of iron is 2 less than that of nickel.

23-15. What concentration of NH_3 is there in a solution that is $1\ F$ in NH_4Cl? Is much $Hg(NH_3)_2^{++}$ formed when $1\ F\ NH_4Cl$ is added to an Hg^{++} solution?

Chapter 24

The Nature of
Metals and Alloys

24–1. *The Metallic Elements*

About seventy-four of the ninety-eight elementary substances are metals. A metal may be defined as a substance which has large conductivity of electricity and of heat, has a characteristic luster, called metallic luster, and can be hammered into sheets (is malleable) and drawn into wire (is ductile); in addition, the electric conductivity increases with decrease in temperature.*

The metallic elements may be taken to include lithium and beryllium in the first short period of the periodic table, sodium, magnesium, and aluminum in the second short period, the thirteen elements from potassium to gallium in the first long period, the fifteen from rubidium to antimony in the second long period, the twenty-nine from cesium to bismuth in the first very long period (including the fourteen rare-earth metals), and the twelve from francium to californium. The metallic elements thus comprise three-quarters of all the elements, and many of their compounds have important uses.

The metals themselves and their alloys are of great usefulness to man, because of the properties characteristic of metals. Our modern

---

* Sometimes there is difficulty in classifying an element as a metal, a metalloid, or a nonmetal. For example, the element tin can exist in two forms, one of which, the common form, called white tin, is metallic, whereas the other, gray tin, has the properties of a metalloid. The next element in the periodic table, antimony, exists in only one crystalline form, with the electric and thermal properties of a metal, and with metallic luster, but very brittle, rather than malleable and ductile. We shall consider both tin and antimony to be metals, although antimony is sometimes classed with the metalloids.

civilization is based upon iron and steel, and valuable alloy steels are made which involve the incorporation with iron of vanadium, chromium, manganese, cobalt, nickel, molybdenum, tungsten, and other metals. The importance of these alloys is due primarily to their hardness and strength. These properties are a consequence of the presence in the metals of very strong bonds between the atoms. For this reason it is of especial interest to us to understand the nature of the forces that hold the metal atoms together in metals and alloys.

24–2. The Structure of Metals

In a non-metal or metalloid the number of atoms that each atom has as its nearest neighbors is determined by its valence. For example, the io-

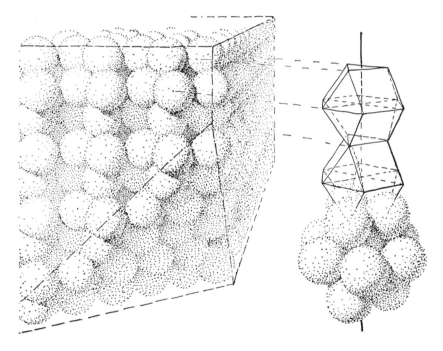

FIG. 24-1   *The hexagonal close-packed arrangement of spheres. Many metals crystallize with this structure.*

dine atom, which is univalent, has only one other iodine atom close to it in a crystal of iodine: the crystal, like liquid iodine and iodine vapor, is composed of diatomic molecules. In a crystal of sulfur there are S_8 molecules, in which each sulfur atom has two nearest neighbors, to each of which it is attached by one of its two valence bonds. In diamond the quadrivalent carbon atom has four nearest neighbors. On the other hand, the univalent potassium atom in potassium metal, the bivalent calcium atom in calcium metal, and the quadrivalent titanium atom in titanium metal do not have only one, two, and four nearest neighbors, respectively, but have, instead, eight or twelve nearest neighbors. We may state that one of the characteristic features of a metal is that each atom has a large number of neighbors; the number of small interatomic distances is greater than the number of valence bonds.

Most metals crystallize with an atomic arrangement in which each atom has surrounded itself with the maximum number of atoms that is geometrically possible. There are two common metallic structures that correspond to the closest possible packing of spheres of constant size. One of these structures, called the cubic closest-packed structure, has been described in Chapter 2. The other structure, called hexagonal closest packing, is represented in Figure 24-1. It is closely similar to the cubic closest-packed structure; each atom is surrounded by twelve equidistant neighbors, with, however, the arrangement of these neighbors slightly different from that in cubic closest packing. About fifty of the seventy-four metals have the cubic closest-packed structure or the hexagonal closest-packed structure, or both.

Another common structure, assumed by about twenty metals, is the body-centered cubic structure. This structure, shown as Figure 24-2, is based upon a cubic unit of structure containing two atoms, one with the coordinates 0, 0, 0 and the other with the coordinates 1/2, 1/2, 1/2. Each atom has eight nearest neighbors, at the distance $\sqrt{3}\,a_0/2$, and six next-nearest neighbors, at the distance a_0. These six next-nearest neighbors are thus 15% more distant than the eight nearest neighbors; in

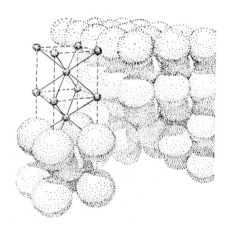

FIG. 24-2

The atomic arrangement in α-iron (body-centered arrangement).

discussing the structure it is difficult to decide whether to describe each atom as having ligancy 8 or ligancy 14.

Some of the metals have more complex structures. An example is given in Figure 24-3, which represents the crystal structure of white tin. White tin is tetragonal in symmetry. Each atom is surrounded by six nearest neighbors, at the corners of a distorted octahedron; four of these neighbors are at a somewhat smaller distance than the other two. Tin is the only element that crystallizes with this structure.

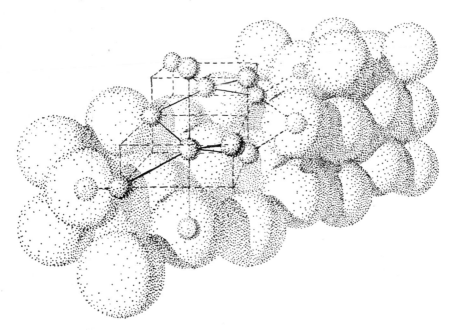

FIG. 24-3   *The crystal structure of white tin. Each atom is surrounded by six neighbors, at the corners of a distorted octahedron.*

The periodicity of properties of the elements, as functions of the atomic number, is well illustrated by the observed values of the interatomic distances in the metals, as shown in Figure 24-4. These values are half of the directly determined interatomic distances for the metals with a cubic closest-packed or hexagonal closest-packed structure. For other metals a small correction has been made; it has been observed, for example, that a metal such as iron or titanium, which crystallizes in a modification with a closest-packed structure and also a modification with the body-centered cubic structure, has contact interatomic distances about 3% less in the latter structure than in the former, and accordingly a correction of 3% can be made for body-centered cubic structures, to convert the interatomic distances over to ligancy 12.

We may well expect that the strongest bonds would have the shortest interatomic distances, and it is accordingly not surprising that the large interatomic distances shown in Figure 24-4 are those for soft metals, such as potassium; the smallest ones, for chromium, iron, nickel, etc., refer to the hard, strong metals.

Let us consider the first six metals of the first long period, potassium, calcium, scandium, titanium, vanadium, and chromium. The first of these metals, potassium, is a soft, light metal with low melting point. The second metal, calcium, is much harder and denser, and has a much

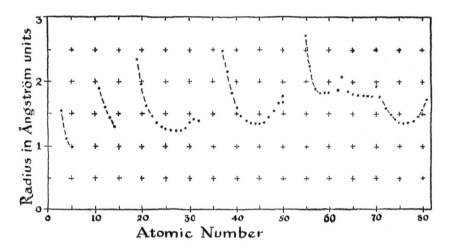

FIG. 24-4   *The atomic radii of metals, plotted against atomic number.*

higher melting point. Similarly, the third metal, scandium, is still harder, still denser, and melts at a still higher temperature; and this change in properties continues through titanium, vanadium, and chromium. The successive changes in properties may be correlated with the decrease in interatomic distance from potassium to chromium. The decrease in interatomic distance may be illustrated in another way by calculating a quantity called the ideal density, equal to 50/(gram-atomic volume). This ideal density, which is inversely proportional to the gram-atomic volume of the metal, is the density that these six metals would have if they all had the same atomic weight, 50, and crystallized in the closest-packed structure, with the interatomic distances represented in Figure 24-4. We see from Figure 24-5 that the ideal density increases steadily from its minimum value of about 1 for potassium to a value of

about 7 for chromium, and many other properties of the metals, including hardness and tensile strength, show a similar steady increase through
this series of six metals.

There is a very simple explanation of this change in properties in
terms of the electronic structure of the metals. The potassium atom has
only one electron outside of its completed argon shell. It could use this
electron to form a single covalent bond with another potassium atom,

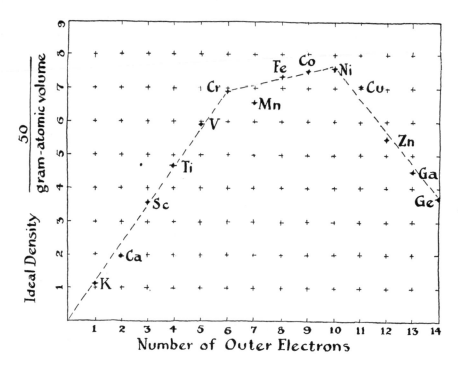

FIG. 24-5   *A graph of the ideal density of the metals of the first long period.*
The ideal density is defined here as the density that these metals would have in
case that their atomic weight was equal to 50.

as in the diatomic molecules K_2 that are present, together with monatomic molecules K, in potassium vapor. In the crystal of metallic
potassium each potassium atom has a number of neighboring atoms, at
the same distance. It is held to these neighbors by its single covalent
bond, which resonates among the neighbors. Thus the bond between
each potassium atom and each of its nearest neighbors is a fraction of a
single bond; the potassium atom, which is able to form only one single
bond, does not concentrate this bond onto a single neighbor, as does

the iodine atom in the molecule I_2, but instead permits its one valence bond to resonate about among all of its nearest neighbors.

In metallic calcium there are *two* valence electrons per calcium atom, permitting each atom to form two bonds with its neighbors. These two bonds resonate among the calcium-calcium positions, giving a total bonding power in the metal twice as great as that in potassium. The increase in valence from one for potassium to two for calcium accordingly explains the decrease in interatomic distance, the increase in density, the increase in hardness, and the increase in melting point.

Similarly, in scandium, with *three* valence electrons, the bonding is three times as strong as in potassium, and so on to chromium, where, with *six* valence electrons, the bonding is six times as strong. The increase in strength of the bonds from scandium to chromium is reflected by increase in hardness, strength, melting point, and other properties.

This increase does not continue in the same way beyond chromium. Instead, the strength, hardness, and other properties of the transition metals remain essentially constant for the five elements chromium, manganese, iron, cobalt, and nickel, as is indicated by the small change in ideal density in Figure 24-5. (The low value for manganese is due to the unusual crystal structure of this metal, shown by no other element.)

Metallic Valence. It is reasonable to conclude from the discussion given above of the properties of the elements in the sequence from potassium to chromium that these metals use all of their electrons outside of the argon shell, of eighteen electrons, to form metallic bonds. If we define the metallic valence as the number of electrons involved in forming bonds in a metal, then the metallic valence has the value 1 for potassium, 2 for calcium, 3 for scandium, 4 for titanium, 5 for vanadium, and 6 for chromium.

We may interpret the change in the curve of Figure 24-5 at chromium as resulting from the retention of the maximum value 6 for the metallic valence through the series from chromium to nickel. It is interesting that the metallic valence of chromium, 6, corresponds to the oxidation number $+6$ that is characteristic of the chromates and dichromates, rather than to the lower oxidation number $+3$ shown in the chromic salts, and that the metals manganese, iron, cobalt, and nickel also have the metallic valence 6, although nearly all of their compounds represent the oxidation state $+2$ or $+3$. The valuable physical properties of these metals are the result of their high metallic valence.

The values of the metallic valence can be discussed by consideration of the available orbitals. For the outer electrons of these elements the available orbitals are the five $3d$ orbitals, the $4s$ orbital, and the three $4p$ orbitals. These nine orbitals, when occupied by electron pairs, can hold eighteen electrons, which, with the eighteen electrons of the argon shell, make thirty-six, the electron number of krypton. Each of the nine orbitals may be occupied by an unshared electron pair, which does not contribute to the bonding, or by a bonding electron, or, in the case of the ferromagnetic metals, by a nonbonding magnetic electron. However, the nine orbitals in the metal are not all available for this purpose. The properties of a metal indicate that the valence bonds in the metal resonate among the different positions in an unsynchronized manner. For example, we

$$\begin{array}{ccccccc}
\text{K—K} & & \text{K} & \text{K} & & \overset{-}{\text{K}}\text{—K} \\
& & | & | & & | \\
\text{K—K} & & \text{K} & \text{K} & & \text{K} \;\; \overset{+}{\text{K}}
\end{array}$$

FIG. 24-6   **a**   **b**   **c**

might have the distribution of valence bonds represented by *a* in the crystal of potassium metal, shown in Figure 24-6. This could resonate to the distribution of bonds shown as *b*, if the two bonds change their places simultaneously. However, there is evidence that it is characteristic of metals for the valence bonds to resonate independently, and if one of the bonds in *a* shifts, a structure such as that shown in *c* results. Here the potassium atom represented as K^- is forming one extra bond; it is holding two electrons, instead of its normal value one. The potassium atom diagonally opposite it, represented as K^+, has no electrons attached to it. The atom K^- needs to have an extra orbital available, in order that the second valence bond may resonate onto it. Since there are, all together, nine stable orbitals available to the potassium atom, this requirement of an extra orbital, the *metallic orbital*, does not cause any difficulty for potassium. It does, however, cause difficulty for elements such as copper.

Let us consider a copper atom in a copper crystal. Copper has atomic number 29, and thus the atom has eleven electrons outside of the argon shell. It has available nine stable orbitals, of which one, however, must be reserved to serve as the metallic orbital. We may discuss the valence of the copper atom by distributing its eleven outer electrons among the eight orbitals. If we place one electron in each of the eight orbitals, we have three left over. These may be introduced into three of the orbitals, which are then occupied by unshared electron pairs, which do not contribute to the bonding. The other five orbitals contain one valence electron apiece. Accordingly, the metallic valence of copper is indicated by these considerations to be five.

The assumptions that there are nine stable orbitals, that one must be reserved in a metal to serve as the metallic orbital, and that the metallic valence cannot be greater than six lead to the following values of the metallic valence in the sequence from potassium to germanium:

K	Ca	Sc	Ti	V	Cr	Mn	Fe	Co	Ni	Cu	Zn	Ga	Ge
1	2	3	4	5	6	6	6	6	6	5	4	3	2

The change in metallic valence from 1 for potassium to 6 for chromium, remaining constant at 6 through nickel, and then decreasing to 2 for germanium, accounts in a rough way for the change in properties of the metals through this sequence of elements.

Mechanical Properties of Metals.   Most metals are malleable and ductile. Instead of being smashed into splinters when struck by a hammer, a piece of metal is flattened into a sheet or foil. A crystal of a metal must hence be able to deform itself without breaking.

If a crystal of sodium chloride is deformed in such a way that the ions are moved about one ionic diameter relative to one another, then sodium ions become adjacent to sodium ions and chloride ions to chloride ions, and the repulsion of the ions of like sign causes the crystal to break into pieces. In a metal, however, the atoms are all of the same kind, and any atom can form bonds with any other atom. Moreover, the valence bonds, which resonate easily from one position to another in the crystal, can still form between neighboring atoms even if the crystal is deformed, and accordingly a crystal of a metal remains strong during deformation.

The way in which a crystal of a metal changes its shape is by *slip along glide planes*. For example, the metal zinc has the hexagonal closest-packed structure indicated in Figure 24-1. The distance between the hexagonal layers of atoms is somewhat larger than for ideal closest packing—the distance between neighboring zinc atoms in the same hexagonal layer is 2.66 Å, whereas that between atoms in adjacent layers is 2.91 Å. Accordingly, we might expect it to be easy for a hexagonal layer to slip over another hexagonal layer. If a single crystal of zinc is made in the form of a round wire, with the hexagonal layers at an angle, as shown in the upper part of Figure 24-7, and the ends of the wire are pulled, the wire stretches out into a ribbon, through slip along the hexagonal planes, as illustrated on the right side of Figure 24-7. Photomicrographs of a metal that has been subjected to strain often show traces of these glide planes.

The slip along a glide plane does not occur by the simultaneous motion of a whole layer of atoms relative to an adjacent layer. Instead, the atoms move one at a time. There is a flaw in the structure, where an atom is missing. The atom to one side of this flaw (which is called a *dislocation*) moves to occupy the space, and leaves a space where it was; that is, the dislocation moves in the opposite direction to the atom. When the dislocation has moved all the way across the crystal grain, the whole row of atoms has moved, and the lower part of the crystal has slipped one atomic diameter in the direction of the strain.

It is found by experiment that a small amount of impurity in a metal may make it brittle. For example, copper containing sulfur or arsenic is brittle, rather than malleable and ductile. One way in which the foreign atoms may produce brittleness is by interfering with the motion of dislocations through the crystal; when the dislocation reaches a sulfur atom or other foreign atom in the copper crystal it may be stopped, and the slip may thus be prevented from continuing.

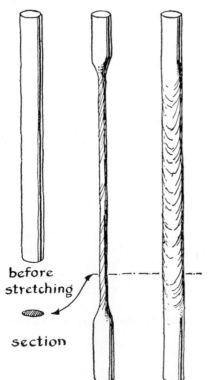

before
stretching

section

side   front

FIG. 24-7

The deformation of a rod of zinc into a ribbon, through slip along glide planes.

Similarly, if a piece of copper is hammered until the large crystal grains are broken up into small crystal grains, the crystal boundaries may interfere with slip by stopping the motion of the dislocations. Presumably this is the mechanism of the hardening of copper and other metals by cold work (by hammering them or otherwise working them in the cold).

Pure aluminum is a soft, malleable, and ductile metal. For some purposes an alloy of aluminum that is stronger, tougher, and less ductile is needed. Aluminum alloys of this sort can be made by incorporating small amounts of other metals, such as copper and magnesium. An alloy containing about 4% copper and 0.5% magnesium may strengthen the aluminum through the formation of hard, brittle crystals of the inter-metallic compound $MgCu_2$. These minute crystals, interspersed through the crystals of aluminum, can serve to key the glide planes of aluminum so effectively as to improve the mechanical properties of the alloy significantly over those of the pure metal.

24–3. Metallurgy—the Winning and Refining of Metals

Metals are obtained from ores. An ore is a mineral or natural material that may be profitably treated for the extraction of one or more metals. The process of extracting a metal from the ore is called winning the metal. Refining is the purification of the metal that has been extracted from the ore. Metallurgy is the science and art of winning and refining metals, and preparing them for use.

Many different kinds of processes are used for winning metals. The simplest processes are those used to obtain the metals which occur in nature in the elementary state. Thus nuggets of gold and of the platinum metals may be picked up by hand, in some deposits, or may be separated by a hydraulic process, when the nuggets occur mixed with lighter materials in a placer deposit.*

A quartz vein containing native gold distributed through it may be treated by pulverizing the quartz in a stamp mill, and then treating the pulverized material with mercury. The gold dissolves in the mercury, which is easily separated from the quartz because of its great density, and the gold can be recovered from the amalgam (the solution in mercury) by distilling off the mercury, leaving a residue of gold.

The chemical process usually involved in the winning of metals is reduction of a compound of the metal, the ore, to the free metal. The principal reducing agent that is used is carbon, often in the form of coke. An example is the reduction of tin dioxide, SnO_2, with carbon, described below; another example is the reduction of iron oxide with coke, in a blast furnace, described in the following chapter. Occasion-

---

* A placer deposit is a glacial deposit or alluvial deposit, as of sand or gravel, containing gold or other valuable material.

ally other reducing agents than carbon are used; thus antimony is won from stibnite, Sb_2S_3, by heating it with iron:

$$Sb_2S_3 + 3Fe \longrightarrow 3FeS + 2Sb$$

The strongly electropositive metals, such as the alkali metals, the alkaline-earth metals, and aluminum, are obtained from the ores by electrolysis, as described in Chapter 13.

Some metals, such as titanium and the rare-earth metals, are obtained by reduction of their oxides by a more active metal. The alkali metals, calcium, and aluminum are used as reducing agents for this purpose (see the discussion of the aluminothermic method of preparing metals, in the chapter on chromium and manganese, Chap. 25).

The principal methods of winning representative metals from their ores are described in the following sections.

The impure metals that are obtained from the ores are purified in various ways. Distillation is used for mercury, and sublimation for tin, antimony, mercury, cadmium, and zinc. The electrolytic refining of copper has been described in Chapter 13. An unusual method of refining a metal is used in the Mond process for nickel (Sec. 23-8).

The Metallurgy of Copper.   The principal ores of copper are *native copper*, Cu; *cuprite*, Cu_2O; *chalcocite*, Cu_2S; *chalcopyrite*, $CuFeS_2$; *malachite*, $Cu_2CO_3(OH)_2$; and *azurite*, $Cu_3(CO_3)_2(OH)_2$.

An ore containing native copper may be treated by grinding and then washing away the gangue (the associated rock or earthy material), and melting and casting the copper. Oxide and carbonate ores may be leached with dilute sulfuric acid, to produce a cupric solution from which the copper can be deposited by electrolysis (Chap. 13). High-grade oxide and carbonate ores may be reduced by heating the ores with coke mixed with a suitable flux. (A flux is a material, such as limestone, which combines with the silicate minerals of the gangue to form a slag which is liquid at the temperature of the furnace, and can be easily separated from the metals.)

The most important ores of copper are sulfide ores, which are smelted by a complex process. Low-grade ores are first concentrated, by a process such as *flotation*. The finely ground ore is treated with a mixture of water and a suitable oil. The oil wets the sulfide minerals, and the water wets the silicate minerals of the gangue. Air is then blown through to produce a froth, which contains the oil and the sulfide minerals. Concentration is effected by skimming off the froth.

The concentrate or the rich sulfide ore is then roasted in a furnace through which air is passing. This removes some of the sulfur as sulfur dioxide, and leaves a mixture of Cu_2S, FeO, SiO_2, and other substances. The roasted ore is then mixed with limestone, to serve as a flux, and is heated in a furnace. The iron oxide and silica combine with the limestone to form a slag, and the cuprous sulfide melts and can be drawn off. This impure cuprous sulfide is called *matte*. It is then reduced by blowing air through the molten material:

$$Cu_2S + O_2 \longrightarrow SO_2 \uparrow + 2Cu$$

Some copper oxide is also formed by the blast of air, and this is reduced by stirring the molten metal with poles of green wood. The copper obtained in this way has a characteristic appearance, and is called *blister copper*. It contains about 1% iron, gold, silver, and other impurities, and is usually refined electrolytically, as described in Chapter 13.

The Metallurgy of Silver.   The principal ores of silver are *native silver*, Ag; *argentite*, Ag_2S; and *cerargyrite* or *horn-silver*, AgCl. The **cyanide process** of winning the metal from these ores is widely used. This process involves treating the crushed ore with a solution of sodium cyanide, NaCN, for about two weeks, with thorough aeration to oxidize the native silver. The reactions producing the soluble complex ion $Ag(CN)_2^-$ have been given in Sec. 23-3. The silver is then obtained from the solution by reduction with metallic zinc:

$$Zn + 2Ag(CN)_2^- \longrightarrow 2Ag \downarrow + Zn(CN)_4^{--}$$

The **amalgamation process** is used for native silver. The ore is treated with mercury, which dissolves the silver. The liquid amalgam is then separated from the gangue and distilled, the mercury collecting in the receiver and the silver remaining in the retort.

Silver is obtained as a by-product in the refining of copper and lead. The sludge from the electrolytic refining of copper may be treated by simple chemical methods to obtain its content of silver and gold. The small amount of silver in lead is obtained by an ingenious method, the **Parkes process.** This involves stirring a small amount (about 1%) of zinc into the molten lead. Liquid zinc is insoluble in liquid lead, and the solubility of silver in liquid zinc is about 3,000 times as great as in liquid lead. Hence the partition constant between the two liquids (Chap. 16) is 3,000, and accordingly most of the silver dissolves in the zinc. The zinc-silver phase comes to the top, solidifies as the crucible cools, and is lifted off. The zinc can then be distilled away, leaving the silver. Gold present in the lead is also obtained by this process.

The Metallurgy of Gold. Gold is obtained from its ores, such as gold-bearing quartz, by pulverizing the ore and washing it over plates of copper coated with a layer of amalgam. The gold dissolves in the amalgam, which is then scraped off and separated by distillation. The tailings (ore after the first process) may then be treated with cyanide solution, and the gold be won from the cyanide solution by electrolysis or treatment with zinc:

$$4Au + 8CN^- + O_2 + 2H_2O \longrightarrow 4Au(CN)_2^- + 4OH^-$$
$$2Au(CN)_2^- + Zn \longrightarrow 2Au \downarrow + Zn(CN)_4^{--}$$

The Metallurgy of Zinc. The principal ore of zinc is *sphalerite* or *zincblende*, ZnS. Less important ores include *zincite*, ZnO; *smithsonite*, $ZnCO_3$; *willemite*, Zn_2SiO_4; *calamine*, $Zn_2SiO_3(OH)_2$; and *franklinite*, Fe_2ZnO_4.

Many ores of zinc are concentrated by flotation before smelting. Sulfide ores and carbonate ores are then converted to oxide by roasting:

$$2ZnS + 3O_2 \longrightarrow 2ZnO + 2SO_2 \uparrow$$
$$ZnCO_3 \longrightarrow ZnO + CO_2 \uparrow$$

The zinc oxide is mixed with carbon and heated in a fire-clay retort to a temperature high enough to vaporize the zinc:

$$ZnO + C \longrightarrow Zn \uparrow + CO \uparrow$$

The zinc vapor is condensed in fire-clay receivers. At first the zinc is condensed in the cool condenser as a fine powder, called *zinc dust*, which contains some zinc oxide. After the receiver becomes hot the vapor condenses to a liquid, which is cast in ingots called *spelter*. Spelter contains small amounts of cadmium, iron, lead, and arsenic. It can be purified by careful redistillation.

The zinc oxide can also be reduced by electrolysis. It is dissolved in sulfuric acid, and electrolyzed with aluminum sheets as cathodes. The deposited zinc, which is about 99.95% pure, is stripped off the cathodes, melted, and cast into ingots, for use where pure zinc is needed, as in the production of brass. The sulfuric acid is regenerated in the process, as is seen from the reactions:

Solution of zinc oxide: $ZnO + 2H^+ \longrightarrow Zn^{++} + H_2O$
Cathode reaction: $Zn^{++} + 2e^- \longrightarrow Zn \downarrow$
Anode reaction: $H_2O \longrightarrow \frac{1}{2}O_2 \uparrow + 2H^+ + 2e^-$
Over-all reaction: $ZnO \longrightarrow Zn \downarrow + \frac{1}{2}O_2 \uparrow$

The Metallurgy of Cadmium.   The principal ore of cadmium is *greenockite*, CdS. Cadmium occurs to the amount of about 1% in many zinc ores, and it is obtained mainly as a by-product in the smelting and refining of zinc. Cadmium is more volatile than zinc, and in the reduction of zinc oxide containing cadmium oxide it is concentrated in the first portions of dust collected in the receivers.

The Metallurgy of Mercury.   Mercury occurs in nature as the native metal, in small globules of pure mercury and as crystalline silver amalgam. Its most important ore is the red mineral *cinnabar*, HgS. Cinnabar is smelted simply by heating it in a retort in a stream of air, and condensing the mercury vapor in a receiver:

$$HgS + O_2 \longrightarrow Hg \uparrow + SO_2 \uparrow$$

Mercury which has been contaminated with other metals can be purified by squeezing it through chamois-skin, which removes solid impurities, and then pouring it in a stream of fine droplets through a dilute solution of nitric acid and mercurous nitrate, which dissolves the more active metals.

The Metallurgy of Tin.   The principal ore of tin is *cassiterite*, SnO$_2$, the main deposits of which are in Colombia, the East Indies, and Cornwall, England. The crude ore is ground and washed in a stream of water, which separates the lighter gangue from the heavy cassiterite. The ore is then roasted, to oxidize the sulfides of iron and copper to products (sulfates) which are removed by leaching with water. The purified ore is then mixed with carbon and reduced in a reverberatory furnace (a furnace in which hot gases heat the material from above—see Chap. 26). The crude tin produced in this way is remelted at a gentle heat, and the pure metal flows away from the higher-melting impurities, chiefly compounds of iron and arsenic. Some tin is purified by electrolysis.

The Metallurgy of Lead.   The principal ore of lead is *galena*, PbS, which occurs, often in beautiful cubic crystals, in large deposits in the United States, Spain, and Mexico. The ore is first roasted until part of it has been converted into lead oxide, PbO, and lead sulfate, PbSO$_4$. The supply of air to the furnace is then cut off, and the temperature is raised. Metallic lead is then produced by the reactions

$$PbS + 2PbO \longrightarrow 3Pb + SO_2 \uparrow$$
$$PbS + PbSO_4 \longrightarrow 2Pb + 2SO_2 \uparrow$$

Some lead is also made by heating galena with scrap iron:

$$PbS + Fe \longrightarrow Pb + FeS$$

Silver is often removed from lead by the Parkes process, described above. Some pure lead is made by electrolytic refining.

24–4. *The Nature of Alloys*

An *alloy* is a metallic material containing two or more elements. It may be homogeneous, consisting of a single phase, or heterogeneous, consisting of a mixture of phases. An example of a homogeneous alloy is coinage silver. An ordinary sample of coinage silver consists of small crystal grains, each of which is a solid solution of copper and silver, with structure of the sort represented in Figure 4-5. Another example is the alloy obtained by melting together magnesium and tin in the ratio corresponding to the formula Mg_2Sn. This alloy consists of crystal grains of the *intermetallic compound* Mg_2Sn. Often, however, alloys contain two phases, and sometimes more.

A discussion of the structure of some alloys will be given in later sections of this chapter and in the following chapters. The discussion is based upon a general principle which has been found to have great value in this field, as well as in other fields of chemistry. This principle is the *phase rule*, which we have discussed in Chapter 20. It is stated there that it was discovered by J. Willard Gibbs that for every system in equilibrium the sum of the number of phases and the variance is 2 greater than the number of components:

number of phases + variance = number of components + 2

or, using the abbreviations *P*, *V*, *C:*

P + V = C + 2

We may mention again that the number of phases in the system is the number of kinds of materials present, separated from one another by physical boundaries; the number of components is the number of different substances required to reproduce the system; and the variance is the number of independent ways in which the system can be varied, including varying the temperature and the pressure, and also varying the composition of any solutions (gaseous, liquid, or crystalline) which exist as phases in the system.

As a first application of the phase rule, we may ask ourselves what the maximum number of phases is that can be in equilibrium with one another, at the arbitrary pressure 1 atm, if the alloy is a binary alloy, composed of two metallic elements. To answer the question we may rewrite the phase rule as

$$P = C + 2 - V$$

The number of components is 2, for the binary alloy. The variance cannot be less than 1, because the pressure is arbitrarily fixed at 1 atm, which means that pressure represents one of the independent ways in which the system can be varied. The maximum value of the quantity $C + 2 - V$ is accordingly $2 + 2 - 1 = 3$. Hence it is possible for three phases to be in equilibrium with one another in a binary alloy at arbitrarily chosen pressure; however, the temperature cannot be arbitrarily chosen, under these circumstances. If we ask how many phases can be in equilibrium with one another in a binary alloy at arbitrary pressure and arbitrary temperature, the answer is 2. Examples are given in the following sections.

The Binary System Arsenic-Lead.   The phase diagram for the binary system arsenic-lead is shown as Figure 24-8. In this diagram the vertical coordinate is the temperature, in degrees centigrade. The diagram corresponds to the pressure of 1 atm. The horizontal coordinate is the composition of the alloy, represented along the bottom of the diagram in atomic percentage of lead, and along the top in weight percentage of lead. The diagram shows the temperature and composition corresponding to the presence in the alloy of different phases.

The range of temperatures and compositions represented by the region above the lines AB and BC is a region in which a single phase is present, the liquid phase, consisting of the molten alloy. The region included in the triangle ADB represents two phases, a liquid phase and a solid phase consisting of crystals of arsenic. The triangle BEC similarly represents a two-phase region, the two phases being the liquid and crystalline lead. The range below the horizontal line DBE consists of the two phases crystalline arsenic and crystalline lead, the alloy being a mixture of small grains of the two elements.

Let us apply the phase rule to an alloy in the one-phase region above the line ABC. Here we have a system of two components, and, in this region, one phase; the phase rule states that the variance should be 3. The three quantities describing the system which may be varied in this region are the pressure (taken arbitrarily in this diagram as 1 atm, but capable of variation), the temperature, which may be varied through the range permitted by the boundaries of the region, and the composition of the molten alloy, which may similarly be varied through the range of compositions permitted by the boundaries of the region.

An alloy in the region *ADB*, such as that represented by the point *P*, at 35 atomic percent lead and 400° C, lies in a two-phase region, and the variance is accordingly stated by the phase rule to be 2. The pressure and the temperature are the two variables; the phase rule hence states that it is not possible to vary the composition of the phases present in

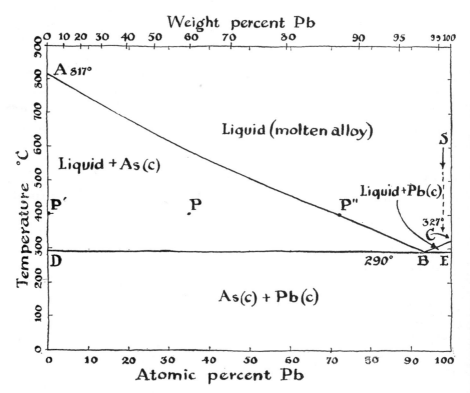

FIG. 24-8 *Phase diagram for the binary system arsenic-lead.*

the alloy. The phases are crystalline arsenic, represented by the point *P'* directly to the left of *P*, and the molten alloy, with the composition *P''* directly to the right of *P*. The composition of the molten alloy in equilibrium with crystalline arsenic at 400° C and 1 atm pressure is definitely fixed at *P''*; it cannot be varied.

The only conditions under which three phases can be in equilibrium with one another at the arbitrary pressure 1 atm are represented by the point *B*. With three phases in equilibrium with one another for this two-component system, the phase rule requires that there be only one arbitrary variable, which we have used in fixing the pressure arbitrarily at 1 atm. Correspondingly we see that the composition of the liquid is fixed at that represented by the point *B*, 93 atomic percent lead, and the composition of the two solid phases is fixed, these phases being pure arsenic and pure lead. The temperature is also fixed, at the value 290° C, corresponding to the point *B*. This point is called the *eutectic point*, and the corresponding alloy is called the *eutectic alloy*, or simply the *eutectic*. The word "eutectic" means melting easily; the eutectic has a sharp melting point. When a liquid alloy with the eutectic composition is cooled, it crystallizes completely on reaching the temperature 290°, forming a mixture of very small grains of pure arsenic and pure lead, with a fine texture. When this alloy is slowly heated, it melts sharply at the temperature 290°.

The lines in the phase diagram are the boundaries separating a region in which one group of phases are present from a region in which another group of phases are present. These boundary lines can be located by various experimental methods, including the measurement of the temperature at which transitions occur from one phase to another. If a crucible filled with pure arsenic is heated to a temperature above the melting point of the arsenic, 817° C, and the system is then allowed to cool, it would be noted, by means of a thermometer or thermocouple in the molten arsenic, that the temperature decreases steadily with time until the value 817° C is reached, and then remains constant at that value for several minutes, while the arsenic is freezing. After all of the molten arsenic has frozen, the temperature will again decrease steadily, until room temperature is reached. If, however, a mixture of 35 atomic percent lead and 65 atomic percent arsenic is heated to make the molten alloy with this composition, and this melt is allowed to cool, a somewhat different behavior is observed. The cooling will proceed uniformly until a temperature of about 590° C is reached. At this temperature the rate of cooling will be decreased somewhat, because arsenic will begin to crystallize out of the melt, and the energy of crystallization liberated by the arsenic will help to keep the system warm. The reason that the alloy begins to freeze at a lower temperature than pure arsenic is the same as the reason that a salt solution or sugar solution freezes at a temperature lower than the freezing point of pure water, as discussed in Chapter 16. The slope of the line *AB* is a measure of the *freezing-point depression* of molten arsenic by dissolved lead. As arsenic begins to crystallize out of the molten alloy, the composition of the melt changes, and a lower temperature is required to cause more arsenic to crystallize out. The crystallization of arsenic alone continues until the temperature reaches the eutectic temperature, 290° C, and the composition of the melt reaches the eutectic value, represented by point *B*. When this state is reached, the temperature of the crystallizing alloy stays constant until the eutectic melt has completely crystallized into a fine-grained mixture of crystalline arsenic and crystalline lead. The solid alloy then consists of large primary crystals of arsenic embedded in a fine-grained eutectic mixture of arsenic crystals and lead crystals.

If a molten alloy of arsenic and lead with the eutectic composition is cooled, the temperature drops at a regular rate until the eutectic temperature, 290° C, is reached; the liquid then crystallizes into the solid eutectic alloy, the temperature remaining constant until crystallization is complete. The cooling curves obtained for the eutectic composition are accordingly similar to those of the pure metal. The eutectic has a constant melting point, just as has either one of the pure elementary substances.

The effect of the phenomenon of depression of the freezing point in causing the eutectic melting point to be lower than the melting point of the pure metals can be intensified by the use of additional components. Thus an alloy with eutectic melting point 70° C can be made by melting together 50 weight percent bismuth (m.p. 271° C), 27% lead (m.p. 327.5° C), 13% tin (m.p. 232° C), and 10% cadmium (m.p. 321° C), and the melting point can be reduced still further, to 47° C, by the incorporation in this alloy of 18% of its weight of indium (m.p. 155° C).

It is now possible, in terms of this phase diagram, to discuss a phenomenon mentioned in Chapter 18. It was stated there that a small amount, about 0.5% by weight, of arsenic is added to lead used to make lead shot, in order to increase the hardness of the shot and also to improve the properties of the molten material. Lead shot is made by dripping the molten alloy through a sieve. The fine droplets freeze during their passage through the air, and are caught in a tank of water after they have solidified. If pure lead were used, the falling drops would solidify rather suddenly on reaching the temperature 327° C. A falling drop tends not to be perfectly spherical, but to oscillate between prolate and oblate ellipsoidal shapes, as you may have noticed by observing drops of water dripping from a faucet; and hence the shot made of pure lead might be expected not to be perfectly spherical in shape. But the alloy containing 0.5% arsenic by weight, represented by the arrow *S*, would begin to freeze on reaching the temperature 320° C, and would continue to freeze, forming small crystals of pure lead, until the eutectic temperature 290° C is reached. During this stage of its history the drop would consist of a sludge of lead crystals in the molten alloy, and this sluggish sludge would be expected to be drawn into good spherical shape by the action of the surface-tension forces of the liquid.

The Binary System Lead-Tin.   The phase diagram for the lead-tin system of alloys is shown as Figure 24-9. This system rather closely resembles the system arsenic-lead, except for the fact that there is an appreciable solubility of tin in crystalline lead and a small solubility of lead in crystalline tin. The phase designated α (alpha) is a solid solution of tin in lead, the solubility being 19.5 weight percent at the

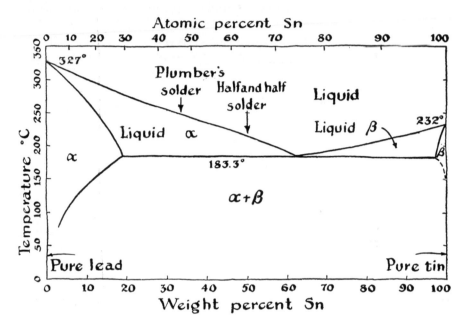

FIG. 24-9   *Phase diagram for the binary system lead-tin.*

eutectic temperature and dropping to 2% at room temperature. The phase β (beta) is a solid solution of lead in tin, the solubility being about 2% at the eutectic temperature and extremely small at room temperature. The eutectic composition is about 62 weight percent tin, 38 weight percent lead.

The composition of *solder* is indicated by the two arrows, corresponding to ordinary plumbers' solder and to half-and-half solder. The properties of solder are explained by the phase diagram. The useful property of solder is that it permits a wiped joint to be made. As the solder cools it forms a sludge of crystals of the α phase in the liquid alloy, and the mechanical properties of this sludge are such as to permit it to be handled by the plumber in an effective way. The sludge corresponds to transition through the region of the phase diagram in which liquid and the α phase are present together. For plumbers' solder the temperature range involved is about 70°, from 250° C to 183° C, the eutectic temperature.

The Binary System Silver-Gold.   The metals silver and gold are completely miscible with one another not only in the liquid state but also in the crystalline state. A solid alloy of silver and gold consists of a single phase, homogeneous crystals with the cubic closest-packed

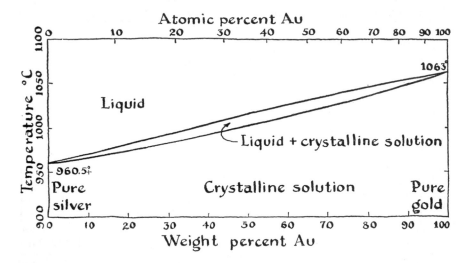

FIG. 24-10   *Phase diagram for the binary system silver-gold, showing the formation of a complete series of crystalline solutions.*

structure, described for copper in Chapter 2, with gold and silver atoms occupying the positions in this lattice essentially at random. The phase diagram shown as Figure 24-10 represents this situation. It is seen that the addition of a small amount of gold to pure silver does not depress the freezing point, in the normal way, but instead causes an increase in the temperature of crystallization.

The alloys of silver and gold, usually containing some copper, are used in jewelry, in dentistry, and as a gold solder.

The Binary System Silver-Strontium.   A somewhat more complicated binary system, that formed by silver and strontium, is represented in Figure 24-11. It is seen that four intermetallic compounds are formed, their formulas being Ag_4Sr, Ag_5Sr_3, $AgSr$, and Ag_2Sr_3. These compounds and the pure elements form a series of eutectics; for example, the alloy containing 25 weight percent strontium is the eutectic mixture of Ag_4Sr and Ag_5Sr_3.

Some other binary systems are far more complicated than this one. As many as a dozen different phases may be present, and these phases may involve variation in composition, resulting from the formation of

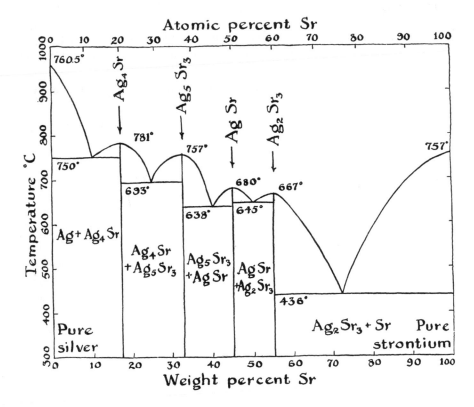

FIG. 24-11   *Phase diagram for the binary system silver-strontium, showing the formation of four intermetallic compounds.*

solid solutions. Ternary alloys (formed from three components) and alloys involving four or more components are, of course, still more complex.

It is seen that the formulas of intermetallic compounds, such as Ag_4Sr, do not correspond in any simple way to the usually accepted valences of the element. Compounds such as Ag_4Sr can be described by saying that the strontium atom uses its two valence electrons in forming bonds with the silver atoms which surround it, and that the silver atoms then use their remaining valence electrons in forming bonds with other silver atoms. Some progress has been made in developing a valence theory of the structure and properties of intermetallic compounds and of alloys in general, but this field of chemistry is still far from its final form.

Exercises

24-1. Discuss the metallic valence of the elements rubidium, strontium, and yttrium. What would you predict about change in hardness, density, strength, and melting point in this series of elements?

24-2. Would you predict palladium to be more dense or less dense than silver? than cadmium?

24-3. Describe the metallurgy of tin and of lead. Why cannot metallic tin be prepared by the same process that is used for metallic lead?

24-4. What are the principal ores of copper, silver, gold, zinc, tin, lead?

24-5. Define alloy, intermetallic compound, phase, variance, eutectic, triple point, binary system.

24-6. State the phase rule, and give an application of it.

24-7. Cadmium (m.p. 321° C) and bismuth (m.p. 271° C) do not form solid solutions nor compounds with one another. Their eutectic point lies at 61 weight percent bismuth and 146° C. Sketch their phase diagram, and label each region to show what phases are present.

24-8. Describe the structure of the alloy that would be obtained by cooling a melt of silver containing 10 atomic percent strontium (see Fig. 24-11).

Chapter 25

Chromium and Manganese, and Related Metals

In this chapter and in the two following chapters we shall discuss the chemistry of the transition metals—the elements that occur in the central region of the long periods of the periodic table. These elements and their compounds have great practical importance. Their chemical properties are complex and interesting.

The chemistry of chromium and manganese and their congeners will be discussed in the present chapter, and also the preceding elements scandium, titanium, and vanadium, and their congeners, as well as the rare-earth metals. Iron, cobalt, nickel, and the palladium and platinum metals are treated in Chapter 26, and copper, zinc, gallium, and germanium and their congeners in the following chapter.

25–1. *The Nature of the Transition Metals*

The long periods of the periodic system can be described as short periods with ten additional elements inserted. The first three elements of the long period between argon and krypton, which are the metals potassium, calcium, and scandium, resemble their congeners of the preceding short period, sodium, magnesium, and aluminum, respectively. Similarly, the last three elements in the sequence, the non-metals arsenic, selenium, and bromine, resemble their preceding congeners, phosphorus, sulfur, and chlorine, respectively. The first and the last of the intervening elements, titanium (in group IVa) and germanium (in group IVb), are both similar in their properties to silicon, the second-period element in group IV. The remaining elements of the long period, vanadium, chromium, manganese, iron, cobalt, nickel, copper, zinc, and gallium, have no lighter congeners; they are not similar in their properties to any lighter elements.

The properties of these elements accordingly suggest that the long period can be described as involving the introduction of ten elements in the center of the series. The introduction of these elements is correlated with the insertion of ten additional electrons into the M shell (five electron pairs occupying the five $3d$ orbitals), converting it from a shell of eight electrons, as in the argon atom, to a shell of eighteen electrons. It is convenient to describe the long period as involving ten *transition metals*, corresponding to the ten $3d$ electrons. There is some arbitrariness about the selection of these ten elements, inasmuch as both titanium, in group IVa, and germanium, in IVb, are sufficiently similar to silicon to make it difficult to differentiate between them. We shall for convenience consider the ten elements from titanium, group IVa, to gallium, group IIIb, as constituting the ten transition elements in the first long period, and shall take the heavier congeners of these elements as the transition elements in the later series.

The chemical properties of the transition elements do not change so strikingly with change in atomic number as do those of the other elements. In the series potassium, calcium, scandium the normal salts of the elements correspond to the maximum oxidation numbers given by the positions of the elements in the periodic system: 1 for potassium, 2 for calcium, and 3 for scandium; the sulfates, for example, of these elements are K_2SO_4, $CaSO_4$, $Sc_2(SO_4)_3$. The fourth element, titanium, tends to form salts representing the oxidation numbers lower than its maximum, 4; although compounds such as titanium dioxide, TiO_2, and titanium tetrachloride, $TiCl_4$, can be prepared, most of the compounds of titanium represent lower oxidation states, $+2$ or $+3$. The same tendency is shown by the succeeding elements. The compounds of vanadium, chromium, and manganese representing the maximum oxidation numbers, $+5$, $+6$, and $+7$, respectively, are strong oxidizing agents, and are easily reduced to compounds in which these elements have oxidation number $+2$ or $+3$. The oxidation numbers $+2$ and $+3$ continue to be the important ones for the succeeding elements, iron, cobalt, nickel, copper, and zinc.

A striking characteristic of most of the compounds of the transition metals is their *color*. Nearly every compound formed by vanadium, chromium, manganese, iron, cobalt, nickel, and copper is strongly colored, the color depending not only on the atomic number of the metallic element but also on its state of oxidation, and, to some extent, on the nature of the non-metallic element or acidic radical with which the metal is combined. It seems clear that the color of these compounds is associated with the presence of an incomplete M shell of electrons— that is, with an M shell containing less than its maximum number of electrons, eighteen. When the M shell is completed, as in the compounds of bipositive zinc ($ZnSO_4$, etc.) and of unipositive copper ($CuCl$, etc.), the substances are, in general, colorless. Another property characteristic of incompleted inner shells is paramagnetism, the property of a substance of being attracted into a strong magnetic field. Nearly all of the compounds of the transition elements in oxidation states corresponding to the presence of incompleted inner shells are strongly paramagnetic.

The winning and refining of some of the transition metals from their ores have been discussed in the preceding chapter, as well as the nature of the metals and their alloys.

25–2. *Chromium*

The Oxidation States of Chromium.   The principal oxidation states of chromium are represented in the following diagram:

$+6$ **CrO_3, $CrO_4{}^{--}$, $Cr_2O_7{}^{--}$** $\begin{cases} \text{chromium trioxide} \\ \text{chromate ion} \\ \text{dichromate ion} \end{cases}$

$+3$ **Cr_2O_3, Cr^{+++}** $\begin{cases} \text{chromic oxide} \\ \text{chromic ion} \end{cases}$

$+2$ **Cr^{++}**   chromous ion

0 **Cr**   metallic chromium

The maximum oxidation number, $+6$, corresponds to the position of the element in the periodic table (group VIa). The terpositive and bipositive ions are similar to the ions formed by the other transition elements, such as the ferric ion, Fe^{+++}, and ferrous ion, Fe^{++}. It is likely that these ions are formed because the transition atoms contain a number of electrons in the same shell ($3d$); two or three of these electrons can be easily removed by an oxidizing agent, but not more, because the attraction of a more highly charged ion for the electrons becomes too great. (The compounds of sexivalent chromium contain covalent bonds, which neutralize part of the positive charge of the chromium atom.)

Ores of Chromium.   The most important ore of chromium is *chromite*,* $FeCr_2O_4$. The element was not known to the ancients, but was discovered in 1798 in lead chromate, $PbCrO_4$, which occurs in nature as the mineral *crocoite*.

Metallic Chromium.   The metal can be prepared by reducing chromium trioxide with metallic aluminum. The two reactants in the form of fine powder are mixed, and the mixture is ignited. The heat liberated by the reaction is great enough to produce molten chromium:

$$2Al + Cr_2O_3 \longrightarrow Al_2O_3 + 2Cr$$

(The general method of producing a metal by reduction of its oxide by aluminum is called the *aluminothermic process*.) Metallic chromium is also made by electrolytic reduction of compounds, usually chromic acid in aqueous solution.

Chromium is a silvery-white metal, with a bluish tinge. It is a very strong metal, with a high melting point, 1,830° C. Because of its high melting point it resists erosion by the hot powder gases in big guns, the linings of which are accordingly sometimes plated with chromium.

Although the metal is more electropositive than iron, it easily assumes a "passive" (unreactive) state, by becoming coated with a thin layer of oxide, which protects it against further chemical attack. This property and its pleasing color are the reasons for its use for plating iron and brass objects, such as plumbing fixtures.

The *alloys* of chromium are very important, especially the ferrous alloys (alloy steels). The chromium steels are very hard, tough, and strong. They are used for armor plate, projectiles, safes, etc. Ordinary *stainless steel* contains 14–18% chromium (and usually 8% nickel).

The Chromates and Dichromates.   Chromium in its highest oxidation state ($+6$) does not form a basic hydroxide, $Cr(OH)_6$; the corresponding

---

* Chromite is an oxide of bipositive iron and terpositive chromium (sometimes called a *mixed oxide*, although it is not a mixture). Its formula is sometimes written as $FeO \cdot Cr_2O_3$.

oxide, CrO_3, a red substance called **chromium trioxide**, has acid properties. It dissolves in water to form a red solution of **dichromic acid**, $H_2Cr_2O_7$:

$$2CrO_3 + H_2O \longrightarrow H_2Cr_2O_7 \rightleftharpoons 2H^+ + Cr_2O_7^{--}$$

The salts of dichromic acid are called **dichromates:** they contain the dichromate ion, $Cr_2O_7^{--}$. Sexivalent chromium also forms another important series of salts, the **chromates,** which contain the ion CrO_4^{--}.

The chromates and dichromates are made by a method which has general usefulness for preparing salts of an acidic oxide—the method of *fusion with an alkaline hydroxide or carbonate*. The carbonate functions as a basic oxide by losing carbon dioxide when heated strongly. Potassium carbonate is preferred to sodium carbonate because potassium chromate and potassium dichromate crystallize well from aqueous solution, and can be easily purified by recrystallization, whereas the corresponding sodium salts are deliquescent and are difficult to purify.

A mixture of powdered chromite ore and potassium carbonate slowly forms potassium chromate, K_2CrO_4, when strongly heated in air. The oxygen of the air oxidizes chromium to the sexipositive state, and also oxidizes the iron to ferric oxide:

$$4FeCr_2O_4 + 8K_2CO_3 + 7O_2 \longrightarrow 2Fe_2O_3 + 8K_2CrO_4 + 8CO_2 \uparrow$$

Sometimes the oxidation reaction is aided by the addition of an oxidizing agent, such as potassium nitrate, KNO_3, or potassium chlorate, $KClO_3$. The potassium chromate, a yellow substance, can be dissolved in water and recrystallized.

On addition of an acid, such as sulfuric acid, to a solution containing chromate ion, CrO_4^{--}, the solution changes from yellow to orange-red in color, because of the formation of dichromate ion, $Cr_2O_7^{--}$:

$$\underset{\text{yellow}}{2CrO_4^{--}} + 2H^+ \rightleftharpoons \underset{\text{orange-red}}{Cr_2O_7^{--}} + H_2O$$

The reaction can be reversed by the addition of a base:

$$\underset{\text{orange-red}}{Cr_2O_7^{--}} + 2OH^- \rightleftharpoons \underset{\text{yellow}}{2CrO_4^{--}} + H_2O$$

At an intermediate stage* both chromate ion and dichromate ion are present in the solution, in chemical equilibrium.

---

* There is also present in the solution some hydrogen chromate ion, $HCrO_4^-$:

$$H^+ + CrO_4^{--} \rightleftharpoons HCrO_4^-$$

The chromate ion has a tetrahedral structure. The formation of dichromate ion involves the removal of one oxygen ion O^{--} (as water), by combination with two hydrogen ions, and its replacement by an oxygen atom of another chromate ion (see Fig. 25-1).

Both chromates and dichromates are strong oxidizing agents, the chromium being easily reduced from $+6$ to $+3$ in acid solution. **Potas-**

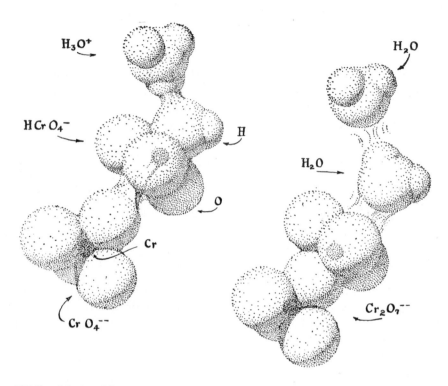

FIG. 25-1   *The reaction of a hydrogen chromate ion, a chromate ion, and a hydronium ion to form a dichromate ion and water.*

sium dichromate, $K_2Cr_2O_7$, is a beautifully crystallizable, bright-red substance used considerably in chemistry and industry. A solution of this substance or of chromium trioxide, CrO_3, in concentrated sulfuric acid is a very strong oxidizing agent which serves as a cleaning solution for laboratory glassware. Large amounts of **sodium dichromate,** $Na_2Cr_2O_7 \cdot 2H_2O$, are used in the tanning of hides, to produce "chrome-tanned" leather. The chromium forms an insoluble compound with the leather protein.

Lead chromate, $PbCrO_4$, is a bright yellow,* practically insoluble substance which is used as a pigment (chrome yellow).

Compounds of Terpositive Chromium.   When ammonium dichromate, $(NH_4)_2Cr_2O_7$, a red salt resembling potassium dichromate, is ignited, it burns to form a green powder, **chromic oxide,** Cr_2O_3:

$$(NH_4)_2Cr_2O_7 \longrightarrow N_2 \uparrow + 4H_2O \uparrow + Cr_2O_3$$

This reaction involves the reduction of the dichromate ion by ammonium ion. Chromic oxide is also made by heating sodium dichromate with sulfur, and leaching out the sodium sulfate with water:

$$Na_2Cr_2O_7 + S \longrightarrow Na_2SO_4 + Cr_2O_3$$

It is a very stable substance, which is resistant to acids and has a very high melting point. It is used as a pigment (chrome green).

Reduction of a dichromate in aqueous solution produces *chromic ion*, Cr^{+++} or $[Cr(H_2O)_6]^{+++}$, which has a violet color. The salts of this ion are similar in formula to those of aluminum. **Chrome alum,** $KCr(SO_4)_2 \cdot 12H_2O$, forms large violet octahedra.

Chromic chloride, $CrCl_3 \cdot 6H_2O$, forms several kinds of crystals, varying in color from violet to green, the solutions of which have similar colors. These different colors are due to the formation of stable complex ions:

$[Cr(H_2O)_6]^{+++}$ violet
$[Cr(H_2O)_5Cl]^{++}$ green
$[Cr(H_2O)_4Cl_2]^{+}$ green

In each of these complex ions there are six groups (water molecule or chloride ion) attached to the chromium ion.

Chromic hydroxide, $Cr(OH)_3$, is obtained as a pale, grayish-green, flocculent precipitate when ammonium hydroxide or sodium hydroxide is added to a chromic solution. The precipitate dissolves in an excess of sodium hydroxide, forming the *chromite anion*, $Cr(OH)_4^-$:

$$Cr(OH)_3 + OH^- \longrightarrow Cr(OH)_4^-$$

---

* The fact that large crystals of lead chromate are red and the powdered substance is yellow is not an isolated phenomenon, but an example of a general principle. The color of a material results from the preferential absorption of light of certain wavelengths from a beam of light passing through the material. Much of the light from a large crystal has passed through the crystal, whereas that from a powder has been reflected from the surface, and has passed through only a few small grains. It is for this reason that a powdered substance is lighter in color than the same substance as large crystals.

Chromic ion can be oxidized to chromate ion or dichromate ion by strong oxidizing agents, such as sodium peroxide in alkaline solution.

Chromous Compounds.   Chromic solutions are reduced by zinc in acid solution or by other strong reducing agents to *chromous ion*, Cr^{++} or $[Cr(H_2O)_6]^{++}$, which is blue in color. This solution and solid chromous salts are very strong reducing agents, and must be protected from the air.

25–3. *The Congeners of Chromium*

The three heavier elements in group VIa, molybdenum, tungsten, and uranium, have all found important special uses.

Molybdenum.   The principal ore of molybdenum is *molybdenite*, MoS_2, which occurs especially in a great deposit near Climax, Colorado. This mineral forms shiny black plates, closely similar in appearance to graphite.

Molybdenum metal is used to make filament supports in radio tubes and for other special uses. It is an important constituent of alloy steels.

The chemistry of molybdenum is complicated. It forms compounds with oxidation numbers $+6$, $+5$, $+4$, $+3$, and $+2$. **Molybdenum trioxide,** MoO_3, is a yellow-white substance made by roasting molybdenite. It dissolves in alkalies to produce molybdates, such as **ammonium molybdate,** $(NH_4)_6Mo_7O_{24} \cdot 4H_2O$. This reagent is used to precipitate orthophosphates, as the substance $(NH_4)_3PMo_{12}O_{40} \cdot 18H_2O$.

Tungsten (Wolfram).   Tungsten is a strong, heavy metal, with very high melting point (3,370° C). It has important uses, as filaments in electric light bulbs, for electric contact points in spark plugs, as electron targets in X-ray tubes, and, in tungsten steel (which retains its hardness even when very hot), as cutting tools for high-speed machining.

The principal ores of tungsten are *scheelite*, $CaWO_4$, and *wolframite*, $(Fe,Mn)WO_4$.*

Tungsten forms compounds in which it has oxidation number $+6$ (tungstates, including the minerals mentioned above), $+5$, $+4$, $+3$, and $+2$. **Tungsten carbide,** WC, is a very hard compound which is used for the cutting edge of high-speed tools.

Uranium.   Uranium is the rarest metal of the chromium group. Its principal ores are *pitchblende*, U_3O_8, and *carnotite*, $K_2U_2V_2O_{12} \cdot 3H_2O$. Its

---

* The formula $(Fe,Mn)WO_4$ means a solid solution of $FeWO_4$ and $MnWO_4$, in indefinite ratio.

most important oxidation state is $+6$ [sodium diuranate, $Na_2U_2O(OH)_{12}$; uranyl nitrate, $UO_2(NO_3)_2 \cdot 6H_2O$; etc.].

Before 1942 uranium was said to have no important uses. In 1942, however, exactly one hundred years after the metal was first isolated, uranium became one of the most important of all elements. It was discovered in that year that uranium could be made a source of nuclear energy, liberated in tremendous quantity at the will of man. A discussion of the present significance of uranium is given in Chapter 33.

25–4. *Manganese*

The Oxidation States of Manganese.   The principal oxidation states of manganese are represented in the following diagram:

$+7$	MnO_4^-, Mn_2O_7	{	permanganate ion, manganese heptoxide
$+6$	MnO_4^{--}		manganate ion
$+4$	MnO_2		manganese dioxide
$+3$	Mn_2O_3, Mn^{+++}	{	manganese trioxide, manganic ion
$+2$	Mn^{++}		manganous ion
0	Mn		metallic manganese

The maximum oxidation number, $+7$, corresponds to the position of the element in the periodic table (group VIIa).

Ores of Manganese.   The principal ore of manganese is *pyrolusite*, MnO_2. Pyrolusite occurs as a black massive mineral and also as very fine black powder. When pyrolusite is added to glass in the process of manufacture, the ferrous ion often present in ordinary glass, which colors it green, is oxidized to ferric ion, which is nearly colorless. The mineral finds considerable use in thus decolorizing glass, and its name is derived from this use (Greek *pyr*, fire, and *luo*, I dissolve).

Less important ores are *braunite*, Mn_2O_3 (containing some silicate); *manganite*, $MnO(OH)$; and *rhodochrosite*, $MnCO_3$.

Metallic Manganese. Impure manganese can be made by reducing manganese dioxide with carbon:

$$MnO_2 + 2C \longrightarrow Mn + 2CO \uparrow$$

Manganese is also made by the aluminothermic process:

$$3MnO_2 + 4Al \longrightarrow 2Al_2O_3 + 3Mn$$

Manganese alloy steels are usually made from special high-manganese alloys prepared by reducing mixed oxides of iron and manganese with coke in a blast furnace (see Chap. 27). The high-manganese alloys (70–80% Mn, 20–30% Fe) are called *ferromanganese*, and the low-manganese alloys (10–30% Mn) are called *spiegeleisen*.

Manganese is a silvery-gray metal, with a pinkish tinge. It is reactive, and displaces hydrogen even from cold water. Its principal use is in the manufacture of alloy steel.

Manganese Dioxide. Manganese dioxide is the only important compound of quadripositive manganese. This substance has many uses, most of which depend upon its action as an oxidizing agent (with change from Mn^{+4} to Mn^{+2}) or as a reducing agent (with change from Mn^{+4} to Mn^{+6} or Mn^{+7}).

Manganese dioxide oxidizes hydrochloric acid to free chlorine, and is used for this purpose:

$$MnO_2 + 2Cl^- + 4H^+ \longrightarrow Cl_2 \uparrow + Mn^{++} + 2H_2O$$

Its oxidizing power also underlies its use in decolorizing glass (as mentioned above), and in the ordinary dry cell (see Chap. 13).

The Manganates and Permanganates. When manganese dioxide is heated with potassium hydroxide in the presence of air it is oxidized to **potassium manganate,** K_2MnO_4. Potassium manganate is made from manganese dioxide in this way:

$$2MnO_2 + 4KOH + O_2 \longrightarrow 2K_2MnO_4 + 2H_2O \uparrow$$

It is a green salt, which can be dissolved in a small amount of water to give a green solution, containing potassium ion and the *manganate ion*, MnO_4^{--}. The manganates are the only compounds of Mn^{+6}. They are powerful oxidizing agents, and are used to a small extent as disinfectants.

The manganate ion can be oxidized to *permanganate ion*, MnO_4^-, which contains Mn^{+7}. The electron reaction for this process is

$$MnO_4^{--} \longrightarrow MnO_4^- + e^-$$

In practice this oxidation is carried out electrolytically (by cathodic oxidation) or by use of chlorine:

$$2MnO_4^{--} + Cl_2 \longrightarrow 2MnO_4^- + 2Cl^-$$

The process of auto-oxidation-reduction is also used; manganate ion is stable in alkaline solution, but not in neutral or acidic solution. The addition of any acid, even carbon dioxide (carbonic acid), to a manganate solution causes the production of permanganate ion and the precipitation of manganese dioxide:

$$\underset{\text{green}}{3MnO_4^{--}} + 4H^+ \longrightarrow \underset{\text{magenta}}{2MnO_4^-} + MnO_2 \downarrow + 2H_2O$$

When hydroxide is added to the mixture of the purple solution and the brown or black precipitate, a clear green solution is again formed, showing that the reaction is reversible.

This reaction serves as another example of Le Châtelier's principle: the addition of hydrogen ion, which occurs on the left side of the equation, causes the reaction to shift to the right.

Potassium permanganate, $KMnO_4$, is the most important chemical compound of manganese. It occurs as deep purple-red prisms, which dissolve readily in water to give a solution intensely colored with the magenta color characteristic of permanganate ion. The substance is a powerful oxidizing agent, which is used as a disinfectant. It is an important chemical reagent.

On reduction in acidic solution the permanganate ion accepts five electrons, to form the manganous ion:

$$MnO_4^- + 5e^- + 8H^+ \longrightarrow Mn^{++} + 4H_2O$$

In neutral or basic solution it accepts three electrons, to form a precipitate of manganese dioxide:

$$MnO_4^- + 3e^- + 4H^+ \longrightarrow MnO_2 \downarrow + 2H_2O$$

A one-electron reduction to manganate ion can be made to take place in strongly basic solution:

$$MnO_4^- + e^- \longrightarrow MnO_4^{--}$$

Permanganic acid, $HMnO_4$, is a strong acid which is very unstable.

Its anhydride, **manganese heptoxide,** can be made by the reaction of potassium permanganate and concentrated sulfuric acid:

$$2KMnO_4 + H_2SO_4 \longrightarrow K_2SO_4 + Mn_2O_7 + H_2O$$

It is an unstable, dark-brown, oily liquid.

Terpositive Manganese. The *manganic ion,* Mn^{+++}, is a strong oxidizing agent, and its salts are unimportant. The insoluble oxide, Mn_2O_3, and its hydrate, $MnO(OH)$, are stable. When manganous ion is precipitated as hydroxide, $Mn(OH)_2$, in the presence of air, the white precipitate is rapidly oxidized to the brown manganic compound $MnO(OH)$:

$$Mn^{++} + 2OH^- \longrightarrow \underset{\text{white}}{Mn(OH)_2} \downarrow$$

$$4Mn(OH)_2 + O_2 \longrightarrow \underset{\text{brown}}{4MnO(OH)} + 2H_2O$$

Manganous Ion and Its Salts. *Manganous ion,* Mn^{++} or $[Mn(H_2O)_6]^{++}$, is the stable cationic form of manganese. The hydrated ion is pale rose-pink in color. Representative salts are $Mn(NO_3)_2 \cdot 6H_2O$, $MnSO_4 \cdot 7H_2O$, and $MnCl_2 \cdot 4H_2O$. These salts and the mineral rhodochrosite, $MnCO_3$, are all rose-pink or rose-red. The isomorphism of rhodochrosite and calcite has been mentioned in Chapter 6.

With hydrogen sulfide manganous ion forms a flesh-colored precipitate:

$$Mn^{++} + H_2S \longrightarrow MnS \downarrow + 2H^+$$

25–5. *Acid-Forming and Base-Forming Oxides and Hydroxides*

Chromium and manganese illustrate the general rules about the acidic and basic properties of metallic oxides and hydroxides:

1. *The oxides of an element in its higher oxidation states form acids.*
2. *The lower oxides of an element form bases.*
3. *The intermediate oxides may be amphoteric; that is, they may serve either as acid-forming or as base-forming oxides.*

The highest oxide of chromium, chromic oxide, is acidic, and forms chromates and dichromates. The lowest oxide, CrO, is basic, forming the chromous ion Cr^{++} and its salts. Chromic hydroxide, $Cr(OH)_3$, representing the intermediate oxidation state, is amphoteric. With acids it forms the salts of chromic ion, such as chromic sulfate, $Cr_2(SO_4)_3$, and with strong base it dissolves to form the chromite ion, $Cr(OH)_4^-$.

Similarly, the two highest oxidation states of manganese, $+7$ and $+6$, are represented by the anions MnO_4^- and MnO_4^{--}, and the two lowest states are represented by the cations Mn^{++} and Mn^{+++}. The intermediate state $+4$ is unstable (except for the compound MnO_2), and is feebly amphoteric.

25–6. *The Congeners of Manganese*

Technetium.   No stable isotopes of element 43 exist. Minute amounts have been made, by Segré and his collaborators, who have named the element technetium, symbol Tc.

Rhenium.   The element rhenium, atomic number 75, was discovered by the German chemists Walter Noddack and Ida Tacke in 1925. The principal compound of rhenium is potassium perrhenate, $KReO_4$, a colorless substance. In other compounds all oxidation numbers from $+7$ to -1 are represented: examples are Re_2O_7, ReO_3, $ReCl_5$, ReO_2, Re_2O_3, $Re(OH)_2$.

Neptunium.   Neptunium, element 93, was first made in 1940 by E. M. McMillan and P. H. Abelson, at the University of California, by the reaction of a neutron with U^{238}, to form U^{239}, and the subsequent emission of an electron from this nucleus, increasing the atomic number by 1:

$$_{92}U^{238} + {_0}n^1 \longrightarrow {_{92}}U^{239}$$
$$_{92}U^{239} \longrightarrow e^- + {_{93}}Np^{239}$$

Neptunium is important as an intermediate in the manufacture of plutonium (Chap. 33).

25–7. *Scandium, Yttrium, Lanthanum, and the Rare-Earth Elements*

Scandium, yttrium, and lanthanum, in group IIIa of the periodic table, usually occur in nature with the fourteen rare-earth elements, from cerium (atomic number 58) to lutetium (atomic number 71).* All of these elements except promethium (which is made artificially) are found in nature in very small quantities, the principal source being the mineral *monazite*, a mixture of rare-earth phosphates containing also some thorium phosphate.

The metals themselves are very electropositive, and are accordingly difficult to prepare. Electrolytic reduction of a fused oxide-fluoride mixture may be used. An alloy containing about 70% cerium and smaller amounts of other rare-earth metals and iron is highly pyrophoric; that is, it gives sparks when scratched. This alloy, called *Mischmetall*, is widely used for cigarette lighters and gas lighters.

These elements are usually terpositive, forming salts such as $La(NO_3)_3 \cdot 6H_2O$. Cerium forms also a well-defined series of salts in which it is quadripositive. This oxidation state corresponds to its atomic number, 4 greater than that of xenon. Praseodymium, neodymium, and terbium form dioxides, but not quadrivalent salts.

The bipositive europous ion is stable, and europium forms a series of europous salts

---

* Lanthanum is often considered as one of the rare-earth elements. For convenience, the convention is adopted here of including lanthanum as a member of group IIIa, leaving fourteen elements in the rare-earth group.

as well as of europic salts. Ytterbium and samarium have a somewhat smaller tendency to form salts representing the $+2$ state of oxidation.

The ions of several of the rare earths have characteristic colors. A special glass containing rare-earth ions is used in glassblowers' goggles.

Many of the rare-earth compounds are strongly paramagnetic. Crystalline compounds of gadolinium, especially **gadolinium sulfate octahydrate,** $Gd_2(SO_4)_3 \cdot 8H_2O$, are used in the magnetic method of obtaining extremely low temperatures.

The sulfides **cerium monosulfide,** CeS, and **thorium monosulfide,** ThS, and related sulfides have been found valuable as refractory substances. The melting point of cerium monosulfide is 2,450° C.

25–8. *Titanium, Zirconium, Hafnium, and Thorium*

The elements of group IVa of the periodic system are titanium, zirconium, hafnium, and thorium.

Titanium occurs in the minerals *rutile*, TiO_2, and *ilmenite*, $FeTiO_3$. It forms compounds representing oxidation states $+2$, $+3$, and $+4$. Pure **titanium dioxide,** TiO_2, is a white substance. As a powder it has great power of scattering light, which makes it an important pigment. It is used in special paints and face powders. Crystals of titanium dioxide (rutile) colored with small amounts of other metal oxides have been made recently for use as gems. **Titanium tetrachloride,** $TiCl_4$, is a molecular liquid at room temperature. On being sprayed into air it hydrolyzes, forming hydrogen chloride and fine particles of titanium dioxide. For this reason it is sometimes used in making smoke screens. Titanium metal is very strong, light (density 4.5), refractory (melting point 1,800° C), and resistant to corrosion.

Zirconium occurs in nature principally as the mineral *zircon*, $ZrSiO_4$. Zircon crystals are found in a variety of colors—white, blue, green, and red—and because of its beauty and hardness (7.5) the mineral is used as a semi-precious stone. The principal oxidation state of zirconium is $+4$; the states $+2$ and $+3$ are represented by only a few compounds.

Hafnium is closely similar to zirconium, and natural zirconium minerals usually contain a few percent hafnium. The element was not discovered until 1923, and it has found little use.

Thorium is found in nature as the mineral *thorite*, ThO_2, and in *monazite sand*. The principal use of thorium is in the manufacture of Welsbach gas mantles, which are made by saturating cloth fabric with thorium nitrate, $Th(NO_3)_4$, and cerium nitrate, $Ce(NO_3)_4$. When the treated cloth is burned, there remains a residue of thorium dioxide and cerium dioxide, ThO_2 and CeO_2, which has the property of exhibiting a brilliant white luminescence when it is heated to a high temperature. Thorium dioxide is also used in the manufacture of laboratory crucibles, for use at temperatures as high as 2,300° C. Thorium can be made to undergo nuclear fission, and it may become an important nuclear fuel (Chap. 33).

25–9. *Vanadium, Niobium, and Tantalum*

Vanadium is the most important element of group Va. It finds extensive use in the manufacture of special steels. Vanadium steel is tough and strong, and is used in automobile crank shafts and for similar purposes. The principal ores of vanadium are *vanadinite*, $Pb_5(VO_4)_3Cl$, and *carnotite*, $K(UO_2)VO_4 \cdot \frac{3}{2}H_2O$. The latter mineral is also important as an ore of uranium.

The chemistry of vanadium is very interesting. The element forms compounds representing the oxidation states $+2$, $+3$, $+4$, and $+5$. The hydroxides of bipositive and terpositive vanadium are basic, and those of the higher oxidation states are amphoteric. The compounds of vanadium are striking for their varied colors. The bipositive ion, V^{++}, has a deep violet color; the terpositive compounds, such as **potassium vanadic alum**, $KV(SO_4)_2 \cdot 12H_2O$, are green; the dark-green substance **vanadium dioxide**, VO_2, dissolves in acid to form the blue *vanadyl ion*, VO^{++}. **Vanadium pentoxide**, V_2O_5, an orange substance, is used as a catalyst in the contact process for making sulfuric acid. An important compound of vanadium is **ammonium metavanadate**, NH_4VO_3, which forms yellow crystals from solution. It is used for making preparations of vanadic oxide for the contact process.

Niobium (columbium) and **tantalum** usually occur together, as the minerals *columbite*, $FeCb_2O_6$, and *tantalite*, $FeTa_2O_6$. Niobium finds some use as a constituent of alloy steels. **Tantalum carbide**, TaC, a very hard substance, is used in making high-speed cutting tools.

Exercises

25-1. Make a diagram listing compounds representative of the various important oxidation levels of chromium and manganese.

25-2. What reduction product is formed when dichromate ion is reduced in acidic solution? when permanganate ion is reduced in acidic solution? when permanganate ion is reduced in basic solution? Write the electron reactions for these three cases.

25-3. Write equations for the reduction of dichromate ion by (a) sulfur dioxide; (b) ethyl alcohol, C_2H_5OH, which is oxidized to acetaldehyde, H_3CCHO; (c) iodide ion, which is oxidized to iodine.

25-4. Write an equation for the chemical reaction which occurs on fusion of a mixture of chromite, potassium carbonate, and potassium chlorate (which forms potassium chloride).

25-5. Write the chemical equations for the preparation of potassium manganate and potassium permanganate from manganese dioxide, using potassium hydroxide, air, and carbon dioxide.

25-6. What property of tungsten makes it suitable for use as the filament material in electric light bulbs?

25-7. Barium chromate, $BaCrO_4$, is only extremely slightly soluble, and barium dichromate, $BaCr_2O_7$, is soluble in water. What effect will the addition of Ba^{++} ion have on the equilibrium

$$2H^+ + 2CrO_4^{--} \rightleftarrows Cr_2O_7^{--} + H_2O$$

in a solution containing both CrO_4^{--} and $Cr_2O_7^{--}$?

25-8. What chemical reactions are taking place when a violet solution of chrome alum on treatment with hydrochloric acid turns green in color?

25-9. The two most important oxidation levels of uranium are $+4$ and $+6$. Which of these levels would you expect to have the more acidic properties?

25-10. Write the equation for the reduction of chromic ion by zinc in acidic solution.

25-11. Give the name and formula of one ore of each of the following metals: chromium, manganese, molybdenum, tungsten, uranium.

25-12. Write equations for the reactions which occur when molybdenite is roasted, and the product is dissolved in ammonium hydroxide solution.

Chapter 26

Iron, Cobalt, Nickel, and the Platinum Metals

Iron, cobalt, and nickel, with atomic numbers 26, 27, and 28, lie in the center of the first long period, and are described, with their congeners, the platinum metals, as group VIII of the periodic table. They show a trend in their chemical properties, forming a transition from the metals chromium and manganese, which may assume several oxidation states, and whose higher oxides are acidic, to the more basic and less chemically versatile metals copper and zinc.

Iron can assume the oxidation states $+2$, $+3$, and $+6$, the last being represented by only a few compounds, such as potassium ferrate, K_2FeO_4. The oxidation states $+2$ and $+3$ correspond to the ferrous ion, Fe^{++}, and ferric ion, Fe^{+++}, respectively. The ferrous ion is easily oxidized to ferric ion by air or other oxidizing agents. Both ferrous and ferric ion form complexes, such as the ferrocyanide ion, $Fe(CN)_6^{----}$, and the ferricyanide ion, $Fe(CN)_6^{---}$, but they do not form complexes with ammonia.

Cobaltous and cobaltic compounds are also known; the cobaltous ion, Co^{++}, is more stable than the cobaltic ion, Co^{+++}, which is a sufficiently powerful oxidizing agent to oxidize water, liberating molecular oxygen. On the other hand, the covalent cobaltic complexes, such as the cobalticyanide ion, $Co(CN)_6^{---}$, are very stable, and the cobaltous complexes, such as the cobaltocyanide ion, $Co(CN)_6^{----}$, are unstable, being strong reducing agents.

Nickel forms only one series of salts, containing the nickelous ion, Ni^{++}. As was mentioned in Chapter 24, iron, cobalt, and nickel are sexivalent in the metals and their alloys. This high metallic valence causes the bonds to be especially strong, and confers valuable properties of strength and hardness on the alloys.

TABLE 26-1   *Some Physical Properties of Iron, Cobalt, and Nickel*

	ATOMIC NUMBER	ATOMIC WEIGHT	DENSITY	MELTING POINT	BOILING POINT	METALLIC RADIUS*
Iron	26	55.85	7.86 g/cm³	1,535° C	3,000° C	1.26 Å
Cobalt	27	58.94	8.93	1,480°	2,900°	1.25
Nickel	28	58.71	8.89	1,452°	2,900°	1.24

* For coordination number 12.

26–1. *Iron*

Pure iron is a bright silvery-white metal which tarnishes (rusts) rapidly in moist air or in water containing dissolved oxygen. It is soft, malleable, and ductile, and is strongly magnetic ("ferromagnetic"). Its melting point is 1,535° C, and its boiling point 3,000° C. Ordinary iron (α-iron) has the atomic arrangement shown in Figure 24-2 (the *body-centered arrangement*—each atom is in the center of a cube formed by the eight surrounding atoms). At 912° C α-iron undergoes a transition to another allotropic form, γ-iron, which has the *face-centered arrangement* described for copper in Chapter 2 (Figs. 2-2 and 2-3). At 1,400° C another transition occurs, to δ-iron, which has the same body-centered structure as α-iron.

Pure iron, containing only about 0.01% impurities, can be made by electrolytic reduction of iron salts. It has little use; a small amount is used in analytical chemistry, and a small amount in the treatment of anemia.* Metallic iron is greatly strengthened by the presence of a small amount of carbon, and its mechanical and chemical properties are also improved by moderate amounts of other elements, especially other transition metals.

The Ores of Iron.   The chief ores of iron are its oxides *hematite*, Fe_2O_3, and *magnetite*, Fe_3O_4, and its carbonate *siderite*, $FeCO_3$. The hydrated ferric oxides such as *limonite* are also important. The sulfide *pyrite*, FeS_2,

* See hemoglobin, Chapter 30.

is used as a source of sulfur dioxide, but the impure iron oxide left from its roasting is not satisfactory for smelting iron, because the remaining sulfur is a troublesome impurity.

The Metallurgy of Iron.   The ores of iron are usually first roasted, in order to remove water, to decompose carbonates, and to oxidize sulfides. They are then reduced with coke, in a structure called a **blast furnace** (Fig. 26-1). Ores containing limestone or magnesium carbonate are mixed with an acidic flux (containing an excess of silica), such as sand or clay, in order to make a liquid *slag*. Limestone is used as flux for ores containing an excess of silica. The mixture of ore, flux, and coke is introduced at the top of the blast furnace, and pre-heated air is blown in at the bottom through *tuyeres*.* As the solid materials slowly descend they are converted completely into gases, which escape at the top, and two liquids, molten iron and slag, which are tapped off at the bottom.

The important reactions which occur in the blast furnace are the combustion of coke to carbon monoxide, the reduction of iron oxide by the carbon monoxide, and the combination of acidic and basic oxides (the impurities of the ore and the added flux) to form slag:

$$2C + O_2 \longrightarrow 2CO$$
$$3CO + Fe_2O_3 \longrightarrow 2Fe + 3CO_2$$
$$CaCO_3 \longrightarrow CaO + CO_2$$
$$CaO + SiO_2 \longrightarrow CaSiO_3$$

The slag is a glassy silicate mixture of complex composition, idealized as calcium metasilicate, $CaSiO_3$, in the above equation.

The hot exhaust gases, which contain some unoxidized carbon monoxide, are cleaned of dust and then are mixed with air and burned in large steel structures filled with fire brick. When one of these structures, which are called *stoves*, has thus been heated to a high temperature the burning exhaust gas is shifted to another stove, and the heated stove is used to pre-heat the air for the blast furnace.

Cast Iron.   The molten iron from the blast furnace, having been in contact with coke in the lower part of the furnace, contains several percent dissolved carbon (usually about 3 or 4%), together with silicon, manganese, phosphorus, and sulfur in smaller amounts. These impurities lower its melting point from 1,535° C, that of pure iron, to about

---

* A tuyere is a nozzle through which an air-blast is delivered to a furnace, forge, or converter.

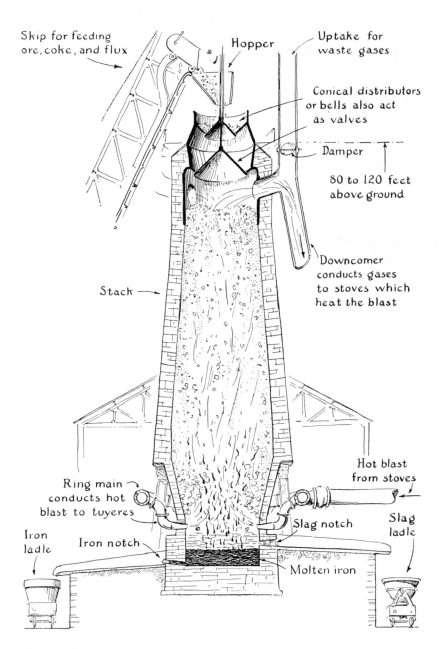

Skip for feeding
ore, coke, and flux

Hopper

Uptake for
waste gases

Conical distributors
or bells also act
as valves

Damper

80 to 120 feet
above ground

Downcomer
conducts gases
to stoves which
heat the blast

Stack

Ring main
conducts hot
blast to tuyeres

Hot blast
from stoves

Slag notch

Slag
ladle

Iron
ladle

Iron notch

Molten iron

FIG. 26-1   *A blast furnace for smelting iron ore.*

FIG. 26-2

A photomicrograph of white cast iron, consisting largely of the compound cementite, Fe₃C. Magnification 100 ×. (From Malleable Founders' Society.)

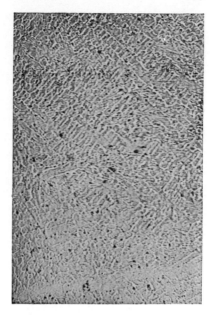

1,200° C. This iron is often cast into bars called *pigs;* the cast iron itself is called *pig iron.*

When cast iron is made by sudden cooling from the liquid state it is white in color, and is called **white cast iron.** It consists largely of the compound *cementite*, Fe₃C, a hard, brittle substance (Fig. 26-2). **Gray cast iron,** made by slow cooling, consists of crystalline grains of pure

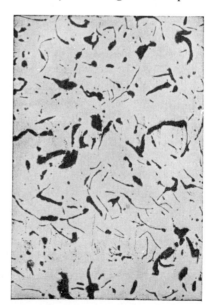

FIG. 26-3

A photomicrograph of gray cast iron, unetched. The white background is ferrite, and the black particles are flakes of graphite. Magnification 100 ×. (From Malleable Founders' Society.)

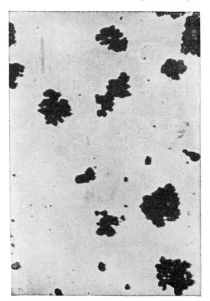

FIG. 26-4

A photomicrograph of malleable cast iron, showing ferrite (background) and globular particles of graphite. Unetched. (See Fig. 1-2 for photomicrograph of etched sample, showing grains of ferrite.) Magnification 100 ×. (From Malleable Founders' Society.)

iron (called *ferrite*) and flakes of graphite (Fig. 26-3). Both white cast iron and gray cast iron are brittle, the former because its principal constituent, cementite, is brittle, and the latter because the tougher ferrite in it is weakened by the soft flakes of graphite distributed through it.

Malleable cast iron, which is tougher and less brittle than either white or ordinary gray cast iron, is made by heat treatment of gray cast iron of suitable composition. Under this treatment the flakes of graphite coalesce into globular particles, which, because of their small cross-sectional area, weaken the ferrite less than do the flakes (Fig. 26-4).

Cast iron is the cheapest form of iron, but its usefulness is limited by its low strength. A great amount is converted into steel, and a smaller amount into wrought iron.

Wrought Iron. Wrought iron is nearly pure iron, with only 0.1% or 0.2% carbon, and all impurities amounting to less than 0.5%. It is made by melting cast iron on a bed of iron oxide in a reverberatory furnace (Fig. 26-5). As the molten cast iron is stirred, the iron oxide oxidizes the dissolved carbon to carbon monoxide, and the sulfur, phosphorus, and silicon are also oxidized and pass into the slag. As the impurities are removed the melting point of the iron rises, and the mass becomes pasty. It is then taken out of the furnace and beaten under steam hammers to force out the slag.

Wrought iron is a strong, tough metal which can be readily welded and forged. In past years it was extensively used for making chains, wire, and similar objects. It has now been largely displaced by mild steel.

26–2. *Steel*

Steel is a purified alloy of iron, carbon, and other elements which is manufactured in the liquid state. Most steels are almost free from phos-

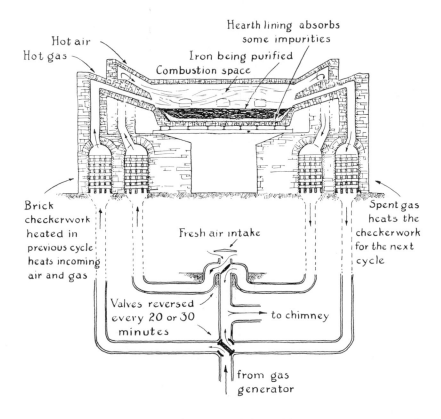

FIG. 26-5   *Reverberatory furnace, used for making wrought iron and steel.*

phorus, sulfur, and silicon, and contain between 0.1 and 1.5% carbon. *Mild steels* are low-carbon steels (less than 0.2%). They are malleable and ductile, and are used in place of wrought iron. They are not hardened by being quenched (suddenly cooled) from a red heat. *Medium steels*, containing from 0.2 to 0.6% carbon, are used for making rails and structural elements (beams, girders, etc.). Mild steels and medium steels can be forged and welded. *High-carbon steels* (0.75 to 1.50% carbon) are used for making razors, surgical instruments, drills, and other tools.

Medium steels and high-carbon steels can be hardened and tempered (see later paragraphs of this section).

Steel is made from pig iron chiefly by the *open-hearth process* (by which over 90% of that produced in the United States is made) and by the *Bessemer process*. In each process either a basic or an acidic lining may be used in the furnace or converter. A basic lining (lime, magnesia, or

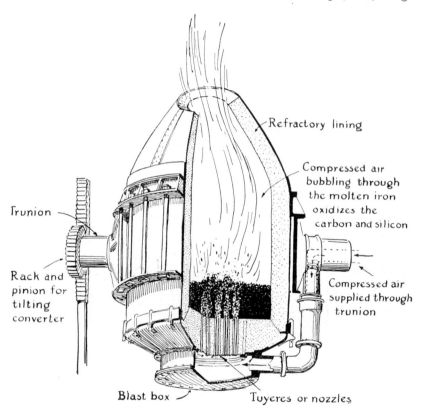

FIG. 26-6   *Bessemer converter, used for making steel from pig iron.*

a mixture of the two) is used if the pig iron contains elements, such as phosphorus, which form acidic oxides, and an acidic lining (silica) if the pig iron contains base-forming elements.

The Open-Hearth Process.   Open-hearth steel is made in a reverberatory furnace—that is, a furnace in which the flame is reflected by the roof onto the material to be heated (Fig. 26-5). Cast iron is melted with scrap steel and some hematite in a furnace heated with gas or oil fuel. The fuel and air are pre-heated by passage through a checkerwork of hot brick at one side of the furnace, and a similar checkerwork on the other side is heated by the hot outgoing gases. From time to time the direction of flow of gas is reversed. The carbon and other impurities in the molten iron are oxidized by the hematite and by excess air in the furnace gas. Analyses are made during the run, which requires about eight hours, and when almost all the carbon is oxidized the amount desired for the steel is added as coke or as a high-carbon alloy, usually ferromanganese or spiegeleisen. The molten steel is then cast into billets. Open-hearth steel of very uniform quality can be made, because the process can be closely checked by analyses during the several hours of the run.

The Bessemer Process.   The Bessemer process of making steel was invented by an American, William Kelly, in 1852 and independently by an Englishman, Henry Bessemer, in 1855. Molten pig iron is poured into an egg-shaped converter (Fig. 26-6). Air is blown up through the liquid from tuyeres in the bottom, oxidizing silicon, manganese, and other impurities and finally the carbon. In about ten minutes the reaction is nearly complete, as is seen from the change in character of the flame of burning carbon monoxide from the mouth of the converter. High-carbon alloy is then added, and the steel is poured.

The Bessemer process is inexpensive, but the steel is not so good as open-hearth steel.

The Properties of Steel.   When high-carbon steel is heated to bright redness and slowly cooled, it is comparatively soft. However, if it is

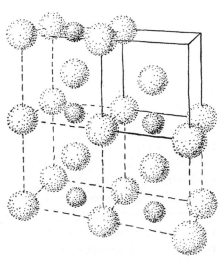

FIG. 26-7

The structure of martensite, a carbide of iron that is present in steel. The atoms of carbon (small spheres) are in the centers of the horizontal squares formed by the iron atoms, which are in a body-centered arrangement.

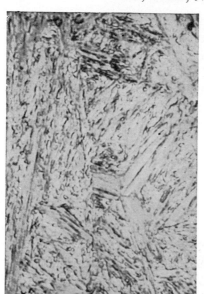

FIG. 26-8

A photomicrograph of martensite, a constituent of hardened steel. Magnification 2,000 ×. (From Dr. D. S. Clark.)

rapidly cooled, by quenching in water, oil, or mercury, it becomes harder than glass, and brittle instead of tough. This hardened steel can be "tempered" by suitable reheating, to give a product with the desired combination of hardness and toughness. Often the tempering is carried out in such a way as to leave a very hard cutting edge backed up by softer, tougher metal.

These processes of hardening and tempering can be understood by consideration of the phases which can be formed by iron and carbon. Carbon is soluble in γ-iron, the form stable above 912° C. If the steel is quenched from above this temperature there is obtained a solid solution of carbon in α-iron, with the structure shown in Figure 26-7. This material, called *martensite*, is very hard and brittle (Fig. 26-8). It confers hardness and brittleness upon hardened high-carbon steel. Martensite is not stable at room temperature, but its rate of conversion to more stable phases is so small at room temperature as to be negligible, and hardened steel containing martensite remains hard as long as it is not reheated.

When hardened steel is tempered by mild reheating, the martensite undergoes transformation to more stable phases. The changes which it undergoes are complex, but result ultimately in a mixture of grains of α-iron (ferrite) and the hard carbide Fe_3C, cementite. Steel containing 0.9% carbon (*eutectoid steel*) changes on tempering into *pearlite*, which is composed of extremely thin alternating layers of ferrite and cementite

FIG. 26-9

A photomicrograph of pearlite, showing lamellae of ferrite and cementite. Magnification 1,000 ×. (From Dr. D. S. Clark.)

(Fig. 26-9). Pearlite is strong and tough. Steel containing less than 0.9% carbon (*hypo-euctectoid steel*) changes on tempering into a microcrystalline metal consisting of grains of ferrite and grains of pearlite (Fig. 26-10), whereas that containing more than 0.9% carbon (*hyper-eutectoid steel*) on tempering yields grains of cementite and grains of pearlite.

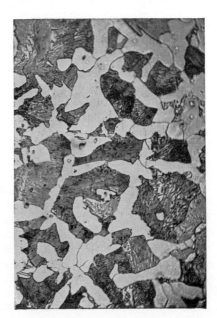

FIG. 26-10

A photomicrograph of hypo-eutectoid steel, showing grains of pearlite. Carbon content of steel 0.38%. Magnification 500 ×. (From Dr. D. S. Clark.)

Steel intended to withstand both shock and wear must be tough and strong and must also present a very hard surface. Steel objects with these properties are made by a process called **case-hardening**. Medium-carbon steel objects are heated in contact with carbon or sodium cyanide until a thin surface layer is converted into high-carbon steel, which can be hardened by suitable heat treatment. Some alloy steels are case-hardened by formation of a surface layer of metal nitrides, by heating the objects in an atmosphere of ammonia.

Alloy Steels.   Many alloy steels, steel containing considerable amounts of metals other than iron, have valuable properties and extensive industrial uses. Manganese steel (12–14% Mn) is extraordinarily hard, and crushing and grinding machines and safes are made of it. Nickel steels have many special uses. Chromium-vanadium steel (5–10% Cr, 0.15% V) is tough and elastic, and is used for automobile axles, frames, and other parts. Stainless steels usually contain chromium; a common composition is 18% Cr, 8% Ni. Molybdenum and tungsten steels are used for high-speed cutting tools.

26–3. *Interstitial Solid Solutions and Substitutional Solid Solutions*

Two clearly distinct types of solid solutions (crystalline solutions) have been recognized. In solid solutions of one type, called *interstitial solid solutions*, atoms of one element are inserted into some of the interstices in the crystal lattice formed by the atoms of a second element. Usually this results in a small increase in the lattice constant of the crystal; but usually the increase in lattice constant is not large enough to compensate for the mass of the inserted atom, and the density of the interstitial solid solution may become larger than that of the substance without the interstitial atoms. The second sort of solid solutions, called *substitutional solid solutions*, involves the replacement of atoms of one kind in the crystal lattice by atoms of a second kind.

An example of an interstitial solid solution is provided by martensite. The structure shown in Figure 26-7 is an ideal structure, corresponding to one carbon atom for every two iron atoms. It is seen from the figure that the iron atoms are arranged approximately as in α-iron—that is, in the body-centered arrangement. The carbon atoms are inserted in the centers of the horizontal faces of the unit of structure. The presence of carbon atoms in these faces, and not in the lateral faces, causes the crystal to be tetragonal in symmetry, rather than cubic. The vertical edge of the unit of structure shown in the figure is about 3% larger than the two horizontal edges. If there are not so many carbon atoms present in the phase, some of the interstitial positions in the horizontal faces are unoccupied. When the number of carbon atoms becomes smaller, the horizontal faces and the lateral faces are occupied at random by carbon atoms, and the interstitial solid solution becomes cubic, rather than tetragonal, in symmetry.

Interstitial solid solutions are usually formed when a substance with small atoms is dissolved in a substance with large atoms—the covalent radius of carbon is 0.77 Å, and the metallic radius of iron is 1.26 Å. Solid solutions composed of atoms with nearly the same size usually are substitutional solid solutions. For example, iron and nickel form substitutional solid solutions, having atoms of iron and nickel distributed at random over the positions of the body-centered structure (for compositions between 0 and about 25 atomic percent nickel) or over the face-centered positions (for compositions between 25 and 100 atomic percent nickel). The irregularity in the lattice produced by the presence of atoms of different sizes makes itself evident in an increased electric resistance; solid solutions are not such good conductors of electricity as the pure metals.

26–4. *Compounds of Iron*

Iron is an active metal, which displaces hydrogen easily from dilute acids. It burns in oxygen to produce ferrous-ferric oxide, Fe_3O_4. This oxide is also made by interaction with superheated steam. One method of preventing rusting involves the production of an adherent surface layer of this oxide on iron.

Iron becomes *passive* when it is dipped in very concentrated nitric acid. It then no longer displaces hydrogen from dilute acids. However, a sharp blow on the metal produces a change which spreads over the surface from the point struck, the metal once more becoming active. The production of passivity is due to the formation of a protective layer of oxide, and the passivity is lost when the layer is broken. Passivity is also produced by other oxidizing agents, such as chromate ion; safety razor blades kept in a solution of potassium chromate remain sharp much longer than blades kept in air.

When exposed to moist air, iron becomes oxidized, forming a loose coating of rust, which is a partially hydrated ferric oxide.

Ferrous Compounds.   The ferrous compounds, containing bipositive iron, are usually green in color. Most of the ferrous salts are easily oxidized by atmospheric oxygen.

Ferrous sulfate, $FeSO_4 \cdot 7H_2O$, is made by dissolving iron in sulfuric acid, or by allowing pyrite to oxidize in air. It is used in dyeing and in making ink. To make ink a solution of tannic acid, a complex organic acid obtained by extraction of nut-galls, is mixed with ferrous sulfate, producing ferrous tannate. On oxidation by the air a fine, black, insoluble pigment is produced.

Ferrous chloride, $FeCl_2 \cdot 4H_2O$, is made by dissolving iron in hydrochloric acid. It is pale-green in color. **Ferrous hydroxide,** $Fe(OH)_2$, is formed as a nearly white precipitate on addition of alkali to a ferrous solution. The precipitate rapidly becomes a dirty green, and finally brown, by oxidation by air. **Ferrous sulfide,** FeS, is a black compound made by heating iron filings with sulfur. It is used in making hydrogen sulfide. Ferrous sulfide is also obtained as a black precipitate by the action of sulfide ion on a ferrous salt in solution.

Ferrous carbonate, $FeCO_3$, occurs in nature as a mineral, and can be obtained as a white precipitate by the action of carbonate ion on ferrous ion in the absence of dissolved oxygen. Like calcium carbonate, ferrous carbonate is soluble in acidic waters, the bicarbonate, $Fe(HCO_3)_2$, being a soluble salt. Hard waters often contain ferrous or ferric ion.

Ferric Compounds.   The hydrated ferric ion, $Fe(H_2O)_6^{+++}$, is pale-violet in color. The ion loses protons very readily, however, and ferric salts in solution usually are yellow or brown, because of the formation of hydroxide complexes. **Ferric nitrate,** $Fe(NO_3)_3 \cdot 6H_2O$, exists as pale-violet deliquescent crystals. Anhydrous **ferric sulfate,** $Fe_2(SO_4)_3$, is obtained as a white powder by evaporation of a ferric sulfate solution. A well-crystallized ferric sulfate is **iron alum,** $KFe(SO_4)_2 \cdot 12H_2O$, which forms pale-violet octahedral crystals. **Ferric chloride,** $FeCl_3 \cdot 6H_2O$, is obtained as yellow deliquescent crystals by evaporation of a solution made by oxidation of ferrous chloride with chlorine. Solutions of ferric ion containing chloride ion are more intensely colored, yellow or brown, than nitrate or sulfate solutions because of the formation of ferric chloride complexes. **Ferric hydroxide,** $Fe(OH)_3$, is formed as a brown precipitate when alkali is added to a solution of ferric ion. When it is strongly heated, ferric hydroxide is converted into **ferric oxide,** Fe_2O_3, which, as a fine powder, is called *rouge* and, as a pigment, *Venetian red*.

Complex Cyanides of Iron.   Cyanide ion added to a solution of ferrous or ferric ion forms precipitates, which dissolve in excess cyanide to produce the complexes. Yellow crystals of **potassium ferrocyanide,** $K_4Fe(CN)_6 \cdot 3H_2O$, are made by heating organic material, such as dried blood, with iron filings and potassium carbonate. The mass produced by the heating is extracted with warm water, and the crystals are made by evaporation of the solution. **Potassium ferricyanide,** $K_3Fe(CN)_6$, is made as red crystals by oxidation of ferrocyanide.

These substances contain the complexes **ferrocyanide ion,** $Fe(CN)_6^{----}$, and **ferricyanide ion,** $Fe(CN)_6^{---}$, respectively, and the ferrocyanides and ferricyanides of other metals are easily made from them.

The pigments **Prussian blue** and **Turnbull's blue** are made by addition of ferrous ion to a ferricyanide solution or ferric ion to a ferrocyanide solution. The pigments which precipitate have the approximate composition $KFeFe(CN)_6 \cdot H_2O$. They have a brilliant blue   •

color. Ferrous ion and ferrocyanide ion produce a white precipitate of $K_2FeFe(CN)_6$, whereas ferric ion and ferricyanide ion do not form a precipitate, but only a brown solution.

26–5. *Cobalt*

Cobalt occurs in nature in the minerals *smaltite*, $CoAs_2$, and *cobaltite*, CoAsS, usually associated with nickel. The metal is obtained by reducing the oxide with aluminum.

Metallic cobalt is silvery-white, with a slight reddish tinge. It is less reactive than iron, and displaces hydrogen slowly from dilute acids. It is used in special alloys, including *Alnico*, a strongly ferromagnetic alloy of aluminum, nickel, cobalt, and iron which is used for making permanent magnets.

Cobaltous ion, $Co(H_2O)_6^{++}$, in solution and in hydrated salts is red or pink in color. **Cobaltous chloride,** $CoCl_2 \cdot 6H_2O$, forms red crystals, which when dehydrated change into a deep-blue powder. Writing made with a dilute solution of cobaltous chloride is almost invisible, but becomes blue when the paper is warmed, dehydrating the salt. **Cobaltous oxide,** CoO, is a black substance which dissolves in molten glass, to give it a blue color (*cobalt glass*).

Cobaltic ion is unstable, and an attempt to oxidize cobaltous ion usually leads to the precipitation of **cobaltic hydroxide,** $Co(OH)_3$. The covalent cobaltic compounds are very stable. The most important of these are **potassium cobaltinitrite,** $K_3Co(NO_2)_6$, and **potassium cobalticyanide,** $K_3Co(CN)_6$.

26–6. *Nickel*

Nickel occurs, with iron, in meteorites. Its principal ores are *nickelite*, NiAs, *millerite*, NiS, and *pentlandite*, (Ni,Fe)S. The metal is produced, as an alloy containing iron and other elements, by roasting the ore and reducing with carbon.

Nickel is a white metal, with a faint tinge of yellow. It is used in making alloys, including the copper-nickel alloy (75% Cu, 25% Ni) used in coinage. Iron objects are plated with nickel by electrolysis from an ammoniacal solution of **ammonium nickel sulfate,** $(NH_4)_2Ni(SO_4)_2 \cdot 6H_2O$. The metal is still less reactive than cobalt, and displaces hydrogen only very slowly from acids.

The hydrated salts of nickel such as **nickel sulfate,** $NiSO_4 \cdot 6H_2O$, and **nickel chloride,** $NiCl_2 \cdot 6H_2O$, are green in color. **Nickelous hy-**

droxide, $Ni(OH)_2$, is formed as an apple-green precipitate by addition of alkali to a solution containing nickelous ion. When heated it produces the insoluble green substance **nickelous oxide,** NiO. Nickelous hydroxide is soluble in ammonium hydroxide, forming ammonia complexes such as $Ni(NH_3)_4(H_2O)_2^{++}$ and $Ni(NH_3)_6^{++}$.

In alkaline solution nickelous hydroxide can be oxidized to a hydrated **nickelic oxide,** $NiO_2 \cdot xH_2O$. This reaction is used in the **Edison storage cell.** The electrodes of this cell are plates coated with $NiO_2 \cdot xH_2O$ and metallic iron, which are converted on discharge of the cell into nickelous hydroxide and ferrous hydroxide, respectively. The electrolyte in this cell is a solution of sodium hydroxide.

26–7. *The Platinum Metals*

The congeners of iron, cobalt, and nickel are the *palladium metals*, ruthenium, rhodium, and palladium, and the *platinum metals*, osmium, iridium, and platinum. These six metals are often referred to collectively as the platinum metals. The properties of these elements are given in Table 26-2.

TABLE 26-2   *Some Physical Properties of the Palladium and Platinum Metals*

	PALLADIUM METALS			PLATINUM METALS		
	Ru	Rh	Pd	Os	Ir	Pt
Atomic number	44	45	46	76	77	78
Atomic weight	101.1	102.91	106.4	190.2	192.2	195.09
Density (g/cm³)	12.36	12.48	12.09	22.69	22.82	21.60
Melting point (°C)	2,450°	1,985°	1,555°	2,700°	2,440°	1,755°

The palladium and platinum metals are noble metals, chemically unreactive, which are found in nature as alloys, consisting mainly of platinum.

Ruthenium and **osmium** are iron-gray metals, the other four elements being whiter in color. Ruthenium can be oxidized to RuO_2, and even to the octavalent compound RuO_4. Osmium unites with oxygen to form **osmium tetroxide,** "osmic acid," OsO_4, a white crystalline substance melting at 40° and boiling at about 100°. Osmium tetroxide has an irritating odor similar to that of chlorine. It is a very poisonous substance. Its aqueous solution is used in histology; it stains tissues through its reduction by organic matter to metallic osmium. It also hardens the material without distorting it.

Ruthenium and osmium form compounds corresponding to various states of oxidation, such as the following: $RuCl_3$, K_2RuO_4, Os_2O_3, $OsCl_4$, K_2OsO_4.

Rhodium and **iridium** are very unreactive metals, not being attacked by aqua regia (a mixture of nitric and hydrochloric acids). Iridium is alloyed with platinum to produce a very hard alloy, which is used for the tips of gold pens, surgical tools, and scientific apparatus. Representative compounds are Rh_2O_3, K_3RhCl_6, Ir_2O_3, K_3IrCl_6, and K_2IrCl_6.

Palladium is the only metal of the palladium and platinum groups which is attacked by nitric acid. Metallic palladium has an unusual ability to absorb hydrogen. At 1,000° C it absorbs enough hydrogen to correspond approximately to the formula Pd_2H.

The principal compounds of palladium are the salts of **chloropalladous acid,** H_2PdCl_4, and **chloropalladic acid,** H_2PdCl_6. The chloropalladite ion, $PdCl_4^{--}$, is a planar ion, consisting of the palladium atom with four coplanar chlorine atoms arranged about it at the corners of a square. The chloropalladate ion, $PdCl_6^{--}$, is an octahedral covalent complex ion.

Platinum is the most important of the palladium and platinum metals. It is grayish-white in color, and is very ductile. It can be welded at a red heat, and melted in an oxyhydrogen flame. Because of its very small chemical activity it is used in electrical apparatus and in making crucibles and other apparatus for use in the laboratory. Platinum is attacked by chlorine and dissolves in aqua regia. It also interacts with fused alkalies, such as potassium hydroxide, but not with alkali carbonates.

The principal compounds of platinum are the salts of **chloroplatinous acid,** H_2PtCl_4, and **chloroplatinic acid,** H_2PtCl_6. These salts are similar in structure to the corresponding palladium salts. Both palladium and platinum form many other covalent complexes, such as the **platinous ammonia complex ion,** $Pt(NH_3)_4^{++}$.

A finely divided form of metallic platinum, called *platinum sponge*, is made by strongly heating ammonium chloroplatinate, $(NH_4)_2PtCl_6$. *Platinum black* is a fine powder of metallic platinum made by adding zinc to chloroplatinic acid. These substances have very strong catalytic activity, and are used as catalysts in commercial processes, such as the oxidation of sulfur dioxide to sulfur trioxide. Platinum black causes the ignition of a mixture of illuminating gas and air or of hydrogen and air as a result of the heat developed by the rapid chemical combination of the gases in contact with the surface of the metal.

Exercises

26-1. Make a list of the known oxidation states of iron, cobalt, and nickel, naming the free ion, a complex ion, and a solid compound for each valence state, if they exist.

26-2. Compare the stability of the free cobaltic ion, Co^{+++}, with that of the cobalti-cyanide ion, $Co(CN)_6^{---}$, and explain in terms of electronic structure.

26-3. What happens to the acidity of a ferrous sulfate solution when air is bubbled through it? Write the equation.

26-4. What are the oxidation states of iron in hematite, magnetite, and siderite?

26-5. What are the chemical reactions for the conversion of hematite to cast iron?

26-6. Calculate the percentage of carbon in cementite.

26-7. What can you say about the equilibrium in the following chemical reaction, from your knowledge of the properties of steel and cast iron?

$$3Fe + C \rightleftarrows Fe_3C$$

26-8. What are the chemical reactions in the open-hearth process of making steel? in the Bessemer process?

26-9. What is the composition of stainless steel?

26-10. What is the normality of a permanganate solution, 48.0 ml of which is required to titrate 0.400 g of $(NH_4)_2Fe(SO_4)_2 \cdot 6H_2O$?

26-11. In which direction does the following chemical reaction mainly proceed?

$$Cu + Fe^{++} \rightleftarrows Fe + Cu^{++}$$

26-12. What chemical reaction do you think would take place between siderite and carbonated water?

26-13. Which do you predict would have the lower pH, an aqueous solution of ferric nitrate, or an aqueous solution of ferric chloride?

26-14. What compounds of the $Fe(CN)_6^{---}$ ion are the most strongly colored?

26-15. Write a chemical equation for the preparation of metallic cobalt. Why is not cobalt made by the same method as is used for the commercial preparation of iron?

26-16. What are the names and formulas of an ore of cobalt and an ore of nickel?

26-17. What chemical reactions take place when acidic solutions of bipositive nickel, cobalt, and iron are treated with aqueous ammonia?

26-18. Name compounds of the important oxidation states of palladium and platinum.

26-19. Devise a simple method for the separation of osmium in qualitative analysis.

26-20. What are the most important properties of platinum?

26-21. Devise a method of converting pyrite into ferrous sulfate, and write equations for the chemical reactions.

26-22. Write formulas for the following compounds, including water of crystallization:

ferrous ammonium sulfate	ferrous sulfate	ferric nitrate
Prussian blue	iron alum	potassium ferrocyanide
potassium chloroplatinate	potassium chloropalladite	nickelous hydroxide
osmium tetroxide	nickelic oxide	potassium cobaltinitrite

26-23. Write an electronic structural formula for nickel carbonyl, and discuss the arrangement of the electrons around the nickel atoms in relation to the structure of krypton. Iron forms a carbonyl, $Fe(CO)_5$, and chromium a carbonyl, $Cr(CO)_6$; discuss the electronic structures of these substances.

26-24. What substances are used for making acidic linings and for making basic linings of furnaces and converters? What conditions determine the choice between acidic linings and basic linings?

Chapter 27

Copper, Zinc, Gallium, and Germanium and Their Congeners

The chemistry of the elements copper, silver, gold, zinc, cadmium, mercury, gallium, indium, thallium, germanium, tin, and lead is discussed in the following sections.

The three metals copper, silver, and gold comprise group Ib of the periodic table. These metals all form compounds representing oxidation state $+1$, as do the alkali metals, but aside from this they show very little similarity in properties to the alkali metals. The alkali metals are very soft and light, and very reactive chemically, whereas the metals of the copper group are much harder and heavier and are rather inert, sufficiently so to occur in the free state in nature and to be easily obtainable by reducing their compounds, sometimes simply by heating.

Group IIb of the periodic table includes two very important elements, zinc and mercury, and one element, cadmium, which has found more limited use. The chemistry of these metals is simple. Zinc forms only one series of compounds, in which the metal is bipositive (Zn^{++}, ZnO, etc.). The compounds of cadmium are closely similar to those of zinc, representing only oxidation number $+2$. Mercury forms two series of compounds: the *mercuric* compounds, which contain bipositive mercury (Hg^{++}, $HgCl_2$, HgS, etc.), and the *mercurous* compounds, which contain unipositive mercury (Hg_2^{++}, Hg_2Cl_2, etc.).

The elements of group IIIb, gallium, indium, and thallium, are unimportant.

The elements of group IVb are germanium, tin, and lead. Germanium is intermediate in its properties between silicon and tin. It has recently become important as an essential constituent of the transistor. Tin and lead are very important metals. They are easily extracted from their ores, and have been known since ancient times. The metals themselves and their alloys have many uses. Germanium, tin, and lead all form compounds representing oxidation state +4, which is shown also by carbon and silicon. They form a second series of compounds, representing oxidation state +2, which is the most important oxidation state for lead, and is less important for germanium than the higher oxidation state. The hydroxides of these elements tend to be amphoteric. The acidic character is more pronounced for the quadripositive state than for the bipositive state, and is most pronounced for germanium, decreasing to tin and lead.

27–1. *Oxidation States of Copper, Silver, and Gold*

The oxidation states of copper, silver, and gold represented in their important compounds are shown in the diagram below.

The principal compounds of copper are the *cupric compounds*, containing bipositive copper. The *cupric ion*, Cu^{++} [or $Cu(H_2O)_4^{++}$], occurs in many salts. The cuprous ion, Cu^+, is unstable, and the *cuprous compounds*, except the very insoluble ones, are easily oxidized.

		Copper	Silver	Gold
+3				$\begin{cases} AuCl_3 \\ AuCl_4^- \end{cases}$
+2		$\begin{cases} Cu^{++} \\ Cu(NH_3)_4^{++} \\ CuS,\ etc. \end{cases}$		
+1		$\begin{cases} Cu_2O \\ CuCl,\ etc. \end{cases}$	$\begin{cases} Ag^+ \\ Ag_2O \\ AgCl,\ etc. \end{cases}$	$\begin{cases} AuCl \\ AuCl_2^- \end{cases}$
0		Cu	Ag	Au

The unipositive *argentous ion*, Ag^+, is stable, and forms many salts. A very few compounds have been made containing bipositive and terpositive silver. These compounds are very strong oxidizing agents. The stable oxidation state +1 shown by silver is that which might be expected from the electronic structure of the element. Silver has atomic number 47, and the ion Ag^+ contains just enough electrons to fill completely the K shell, the L shell, and the M shell. The outer shell of this ion thus contains eighteen electrons. This *eighteen-shell structure* is found to be stable for ions of other transition metals (Zn^{++}, Cd^{++}, Hg^{++}, Ga^{+++}, etc.), and this stability is in part responsible for the existence of the important oxidation states recognized in the group numbers. It is surprising that the cupric compounds are more important than the cuprous compounds.

The aurous ion, Au^+, and the auric ion, Au^{+++}, are themselves unstable in aqueous solution. The stable aurous and auric compounds contain covalent bonds, as in the complex ions $AuCl_2^-$ and $AuCl_4^-$.

27–2. *The Properties of the Metals*

Copper is a red, tough metal with a moderately high melting point. It is an excellent conductor of heat and of electricity when pure, and it finds extensive use as an electrical conductor. Pure copper which has been heated is soft, and can be drawn into wire or shaped by hammering. This "cold work" causes the metal to become hard, because the crystal grains are broken into much smaller grains, with grain boundaries which interfere with the process of deformation and thus strengthen the metal. The hardened metal can be made soft by heating ("annealing"), which permits the grains to coalesce into larger grains.

Silver is a soft, white metal, somewhat denser than copper, and with a lower melting point. It is used in coinage, jewelry, and tableware, and as a filling for teeth.

Gold is a soft, very dense metal, which is used for jewelry, coinage, dental work, and scientific and technical apparatus. Gold is bright yellow by reflected light; very thin sheets are blue or green. Its beautiful color and fine luster, which, because of its inertness, are not affected by exposure to the atmosphere, are responsible for its use for ornamental purposes. Gold is the most malleable and most ductile of all metals.

Alloys of Copper, Silver, and Gold.   The transition metals find their greatest use in alloys. Alloys are often far stronger, harder, and tougher than their constituent elementary metals. The alloys of copper and zinc are called *brass*, those of copper and tin are called *bronze*, and those of copper and aluminum are called *aluminum bronze*. Many of these alloys have valuable properties. Copper is a constituent also of

TABLE 27-1   *Some Physical Properties of Copper, Silver, and Gold*

	ATOMIC NUMBER	ATOMIC WEIGHT	DENSITY	MELTING POINT	BOILING POINT	METALLIC RADIUS	COLOR
Copper	29	63.54	8.97 g/cm^3	1,083° C	2,310° C	1.28 Å	Red
Silver	47	107.880	10.54	960.5°	1,950°	1.44	White
Gold	79	197.0	19.42	1,063°	2,600°	1.44	Yellow

other useful alloys, such as beryllium copper, coinage silver, and coinage gold.

Coinage silver in the United States contains 90% silver and 10% copper. This composition also constitutes *sterling silver* in the United States. British sterling silver is 92.5% silver and 7.5% copper.

Gold is often alloyed with copper, silver, palladium, or other metals. The amount of gold in these alloys is usually described in *carats*, the number of parts of gold in 24 parts of alloy—pure gold is 24 carat. American coinage gold is 21.6 carat (90% gold, 10% copper), and British coinage gold is 22 carat. *White gold*, used in jewelry, is usually a white alloy of gold and nickel.

27–3. Cupric Compounds

The hydrated **cupric ion,** $Cu(H_2O)_4{}^{++}$, is an ion with light-blue color which occurs in aqueous solutions of cupric salts and in some of the hydrated crystals. The most important cupric salt is **copper sulfate,** which forms blue crystals, $CuSO_4 \cdot 5H_2O$. The metal copper is not sufficiently reactive to displace hydrogen ion from dilute acids, and copper does not dissolve in acids unless an oxidizing agent is present. However, hot concentrated sulfuric acid is itself an oxidizing agent, and can dissolve the metal, and dilute sulfuric acid also slowly dissolves it in the presence of air:

$$Cu + 2H_2SO_4 + 3H_2O \longrightarrow CuSO_4 \cdot 5H_2O + SO_2$$

or

$$2Cu + 2H_2SO_4 + O_2 + 8H_2O \longrightarrow 2CuSO_4 \cdot 5H_2O$$

Copper sulfate, which has the common names *blue vitriol* and *bluestone*, is used in copper plating, in printing calico, in electric cells, to prevent algae from growing in swimming pools and reservoirs, and in the manufacture of other compounds of copper. *Bordeaux mixture,* made by adding a suspension of calcium hydroxide to a copper sulfate solution, is used to spray plants to destroy fungi.

Cupric chloride, $CuCl_2$, can be made as yellow crystals by direct union of the elements. The hydrated salt, $CuCl_2 \cdot 2H_2O$, is blue-green in color, and its solution in hydrochloric acid is green. The blue-green color of the salt is due to its existence as a complex,

$$
\begin{array}{c}
OH_2 \\
| \\
Cl-Cu-Cl \\
| \\
OH_2
\end{array}
$$

in which the chlorine atoms are bonded directly to the copper atom. The green solution contains ions $CuCl_3(H_2O)^-$ and $CuCl_4^{--}$. All of these complexes are planar, the copper atom being at the center of a square formed by the four attached groups. The planar configuration is shown also by other complexes of copper, including the deep-blue ammonia complex, $Cu(NH_3)_4^{++}$.

Cupric bromide, $CuBr_2$, is a black solid obtained by reaction of copper and bromine or by solution of cupric oxide, CuO, in hydrobromic acid. It is interesting that cupric iodide, CuI_2, does not exist; when a solution containing cupric ion is added to an iodide solution there occurs an oxidation-reduction reaction, with precipitation of cuprous iodide, CuI:

$$2Cu^{++} + 4I^- \longrightarrow 2CuI \downarrow + I_2$$

This reaction occurs because of the extraordinary stability of cuprous iodide, which is discussed in the following section. The reaction is used in a method of quantitative analysis for copper, the liberated iodine being determined by titration with sodium thiosulfate solution.

Cupric hydroxide, $Cu(OH)_2$, forms as a pale-blue gelatinous precipitate when an alkali hydroxide or ammonium hydroxide is added to a cupric solution. It dissolves very readily in excess ammonium hydroxide, forming the deep-blue complex $Cu(NH_3)_4^{++}$ (Chap. 23). Cupric hydroxide is slightly amphoteric, and dissolves to a small extent in very concentrated alkali, forming $Cu(OH)_4^{--}$.

27–4. *Cuprous Compounds*

Cuprous ion, Cu^+, is so unstable in aqueous solution that it undergoes auto-oxidation-reduction into copper and cupric ion:

$$2Cu^+ \longrightarrow Cu \downarrow + Cu^{++}$$

Very few cuprous salts of oxygen acids exist. The stable cuprous compounds are either insoluble crystals containing covalent bonds or covalent complexes.

When copper is added to a solution of cupric chloride in strong hydrochloric acid a reaction occurs which results in the formation of a colorless solution containing cuprous chloride complex ions such as $CuCl_2^-$:

$$CuCl_4^{--} + \underline{Cu} \longrightarrow 2CuCl_2^-$$

This complex ion involves two covalent bonds, its electronic structure being

$$\left[: \overset{..}{\underset{..}{Cl}} - Cu - \overset{..}{\underset{..}{Cl}} : \right]^-$$

Other cuprous complexes, $CuCl_3^{--}$ and $CuCl_4^{---}$, also exist.

If the solution is diluted with water a colorless precipitate of **cuprous chloride,** CuCl, forms. This precipitate also contains covalent bonds, each copper atom being bonded to four neighboring chlorine atoms and each chlorine atom to four neighboring copper atoms, with use of the outer electrons of the chloride ion. The structure is closely related to that of diamond, with alternating carbon atoms replaced by copper and chlorine (Fig. 10-6).

Cuprous bromide, CuBr, and **cuprous iodide,** CuI, are also colorless, insoluble substances. The covalent bonds between copper and iodine in cuprous iodide are so strong as to make cupric iodide relatively unstable, as mentioned above.

Other stable cuprous compounds are the insoluble substances cuprous oxide, Cu_2O (red), cuprous sulfide, Cu_2S (black), cuprous cyanide, CuCN (white), and cuprous thiocyanate, CuSCN (white).

27–5. The Compounds of Silver

Silver oxide, Ag_2O, is obtained as a dark-brown precipitate on the addition of sodium hydroxide to a solution of silver nitrate. It is slightly soluble, producing a weakly alkaline solution of silver hydroxide:

$$\underline{Ag_2O} + H_2O \rightleftarrows 2Ag^+ + 2OH^-$$

Silver oxide is used in inorganic chemistry to convert a soluble chloride, bromide, or iodide into the hydroxide. For example, cesium chloride solution can be converted into cesium hydroxide solution in this way:

$$2Cs^+ + 2Cl^- + \underline{Ag_2O} + H_2O \longrightarrow 2AgCl \downarrow + 2Cs^+ + 2OH^-$$

This reaction proceeds to the right because silver chloride is much less soluble than silver oxide.

The **silver halides,** AgF, AgCl, AgBr, and AgI, can be made by adding silver oxide to solutions of the corresponding halogen acids. Silver fluoride is very soluble in water, and the other halides are nearly insoluble. Silver chloride, bromide, and iodide form as curdy precipitates when the ions are mixed. They are respectively white, pale-yellow, and yellow in color, and on exposure to light they slowly turn black, through photochemical decomposition. Silver chloride and bromide dissolve in ammonium hydroxide solution, forming the **silver ammonia complex** $Ag(NH_3)_2^+$ (Chap. 23); silver iodide does not dissolve in ammonium hydroxide. These reactions are used as qualitative tests for silver ion and the halide ions.

Other complex ions formed by silver, such as the silver cyanide complex $Ag(CN)_2^-$ and the silver thiosulfate complex $Ag(S_2O_3)_2^{---}$, have been mentioned in Chapter 23.

Silver nitrate, $AgNO_3$, is a colorless, soluble salt made by dissolving silver in nitric acid. It is used to cauterize sores, and for this use it has the old name *lunar caustic* (from the alchemistic name *luna,* the moon, for silver). Silver nitrate is easily reduced to metallic silver by organic matter, such as skin or cloth, and is for this reason used in making indelible ink.

Silver ion is an excellent antiseptic, and several of the compounds of silver are used in medicine because of their germicidal power.

27–6. Photography

A photographic film is a sheet of cellulose acetate coated with a thin layer of gelatin in which very fine grains of silver bromide are suspended. This layer of gelatin and silver bromide is called the *photographic emulsion.* The silver halides are sensitive to light, and undergo photochemical decomposition. The gelatin increases this sensitivity, apparently because of the sulfur which it contains.

When the film is briefly exposed to light some of the grains of silver bromide undergo a small amount of decomposition, perhaps forming a small particle of silver sulfide on the surface of the grain. The film can then be *developed* by treatment with an alkaline solution of an organic reducing agent, such as hydroquinone, the *developer.* This causes the silver bromide grains that have been sensitized to be reduced to metallic silver, whereas the unsensitized silver bromide grains remain unchanged. By this process the developed film reproduces the pattern of the light which exposed it. This film is called the *negative*, because it is darkest (with the greatest amount of silver) in the places which were exposed to the most light.

The undeveloped grains of silver halide are next removed, by treatment with a fixing bath, which contains thiosulfate ion, $S_2O_3^{--}$ (from sodium thiosulfate, "hypo," $Na_2S_2O_3 \cdot 5H_2O$). The soluble silver thiosulfate complex is formed:

$$\underline{AgBr} + 2S_2O_3^{--} \longrightarrow Ag(S_2O_3)_2^{---} + Br^-$$

The fixed negative is then washed. Care must be taken not to transfer the negative from a used fixing bath, containing a considerable concentration of silver complex, directly to the wash water, as insoluble silver thiosulfate might precipitate in the emulsion:

$$2Ag(S_2O_3)_2^{---} \rightleftarrows Ag_2S_2O_3 \downarrow + 3S_2O_3^{--}$$

Since there are three ions on the right, and only two on the left, dilution causes the equilibrium to shift toward the right.

A positive print can be made by exposing print paper, coated with a silver halide emulsion, to light which passes through the superimposed negative, and then developing and fixing the exposed paper.

Many other very interesting chemical processes are used in photography, especially for the reproduction of color.

The Chemistry of Color Photography.   The electromagnetic waves of light of different colors have different wavelengths. In the visible spectrum these wavelengths extend from a little below 4,000 Å (violet in color) to nearly 8,000 Å (red in color). The sequence of colors in the visible region is shown in the next to the top diagram of Figure 27-1.

When white light (light containing all wavelengths in the visible region) is passed through a substance, light of certain wavelengths may be absorbed by the substance. The solar spectrum is shown in Figure 27-1. It consists of a background of white light, produced by the very hot gases in the sun, on which there are superimposed some dark lines, resulting from absorption of certain wavelengths by atoms in the cooler surface layers of the sun. It is seen that the yellow sodium lines, which occur as bright lines in the emission spectrum of sodium atoms, are shown as dark lines in the solar spectrum.

Molecules and complex ions in solution and in solid substances sometimes show sharp line spectra, but usually show rather broad absorption bands, as is indicated for the permanganate ion near the bottom of Figure 27-1. The permanganate ion has the power of absorbing light in the green region of the spectrum, permitting the blue-violet light and red light to pass through. The combination of blue-violet and red light appears magenta in color. We accordingly say that permanganate ion has a magenta color.

The human eye does not have the power of completely differentiating between light of one wavelength and that of another wavelength in the visible spectrum. Instead, it responds to three different wavelength regions in different ways. All of the colors that can be recognized by the eye can be composed from three fundamental colors. These may be taken as red-green (seen by the eye as yellow), which is complementary to blue-violet; blue-red, or magenta, which is complementary to green; and blue-green, or cyan, which is complementary to red. Three *primary colors*, such as these, need to be used in the development of any method of color photography.

The first successful method of color photography was the *Autochrome method*, developed in France about 1904. Three samples of starch, which consists of minute spherical grains, were dyed red, green, and blue, respectively. These dyed starch grains were thoroughly mixed, were scattered over the surface of a photographic plate, and were then squashed into flat discs. The plate was then exposed and developed. In a region of the plate on which red light was falling the red light would pass through the green and blue starch grains, exposing the plate behind these grains, so that after development silver would be deposited there, and light passed through the plate from behind would be absorbed. However, the red light would have been stopped by the red starch grains during the exposure, so that no silver would have been deposited behind these grains, and light passing through the exposed plate from behind would continue through the red starch grains, producing a red color in this region of the plate. Similar effects would be produced by the green and blue starch grains in green and blue light, so that the plate would reproduce approximately the colors of the incident light.

An important modern method of color photography is the *Kodachrome method*, developed by the Kodak Research Laboratories. This method is illustrated in Figure 27-2. The film consists of several layers of emulsion, superimposed on a cellulose acetate base. The uppermost layer of photographic emulsion is the ordinary photographic emulsion, which is sensitive to blue and violet light. The second layer of photographic emulsion is a green-sensitive emulsion. It consists of a photographic emulsion that has been treated with a magenta-colored dye, which absorbs green light and sensitizes the silver bromide grains, thus making the emulsion sensitive to green light as well as to blue and violet light.

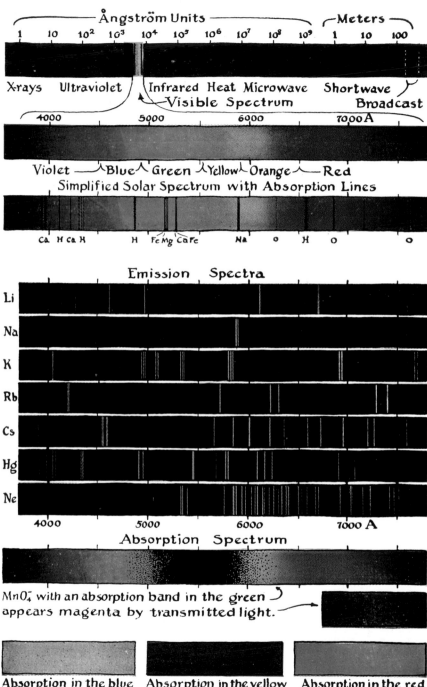

FIG. 27–1.   Emission spectra and absorption spectra.

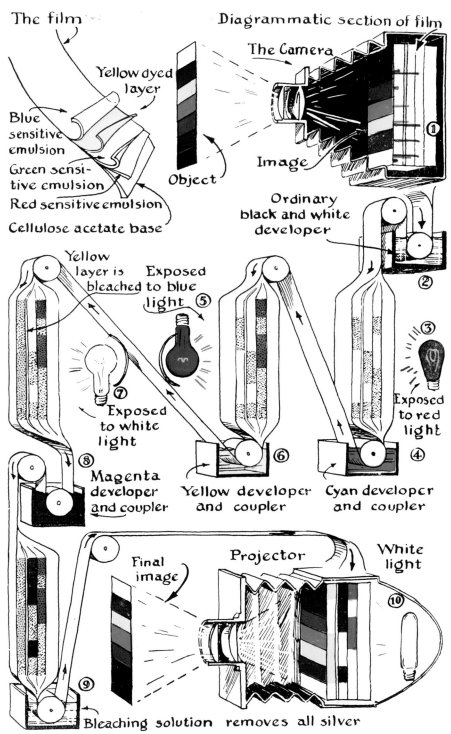

The film

Diagrammatic section of film

The Camera

Yellow dyed layer

Blue sensitive emulsion

Green sensitive emulsion

Red sensitive emulsion

Cellulose acetate base

Object

Image

①

Ordinary black and white developer

②

Yellow layer is bleached to blue light ⑤

Exposed to red light ③

④

Exposed to white light ⑦

⑥

Magenta developer and coupler ⑧

Yellow developer and coupler

Cyan developer and coupler

Final image

Projector

White light

⑩

Bleaching solution removes all silver ⑨

FIG. 27–2. The Kodachrome process of color photography.

The third photographic emulsion, red-sensitive emulsion, has been treated with a blue dye, which absorbs red light, making the emulsion sensitive to red light as well as to blue and violet (but not to green). Between the first layer and the middle layer there is a layer of yellow filter, containing a yellow dye, which during exposure prevents blue and violet light from penetrating to the lower layers. Accordingly, when such a film is exposed to light the blue-sensitive emulsion is exposed by blue light, the middle emulsion is exposed by green light, and the bottom emulsion is exposed by red light.

The exposure of the different layers of photographic emulsion in the film is illustrated diagrammatically as Process 1 in Figure 27-2.

The development of Kodachrome film involves several steps, which are represented as Processes 2 9 in Figure 27-2. First (Process 2) the Kodachrome film after exposure is developed with an ordinary black-and-white developer, which develops the silver negative in all three emulsions. Then, after simple washing in water (not shown in the figure) the film is exposed through the back to red light, which makes the previously unexposed silver bromide in the red-sensitive emulsion capable of development (Process 3). The film then passes into a special developer, called cyan developer and coupler (Process 4). This mixture of chemical substances has the power of interacting with the exposed silver bromide grains in such a way as to deposit a cyan dye in the bottom layer, at the same time that the silver bromide grains are reduced to metallic silver. The cyan dye is deposited only in the regions occupied by the sensitized silver bromide grains. The next process (Process 5) consists in exposure to blue light from the front of the negative. The blue light is absorbed by the yellow dye, and so affects only the previously unexposed grains in the first emulsion, the blue-sensitive emulsion. This emulsion is then developed in a special developer (Process 6), a yellow developer and coupler, which deposits a yellow dye in the neighborhood of these recently exposed grains. The film is then exposed to white light, to sensitize the undeveloped silver bromide grains in the middle emulsion, the yellow layer is bleached, the middle emulsion is developed with a magenta developer and coupler (Process 8), and the deposited metallic silver in all three solutions is removed by a bleaching solution (Process 9), leaving only a film containing deposited cyan, yellow, and magenta dyes in the three emulsion layers, in such a way that by transmitted light the originally incident colors are reproduced (Process 10).

The development of the Kodachrome method and other methods of color photography has been a triumph of organic chemistry. It was the organic chemists who solved the problem of the synthesis of stable dyes with the special properties required for this purpose. The photographic industry, like most industries of the modern world, is a chemical industry.

27–7. *Gold*

$KAu(CN)_2$, the potassium salt of the complex **aurous cyanide ion** $Au(CN)_2^-$, with electronic structure

$$[: N \equiv C - Au - C \equiv N :]^-$$

is an example of an aurous compound. The **aurous chloride** complex $AuCl_2^-$ has a similar structure, and the **aurous halides,** $AuCl$, $AuBr$, and AuI, resemble the corresponding halides of silver.

Gold dissolves in aqua regia (a mixture of concentrated nitric and hydrochloric acids) to form **hydrogen aurichloride,** $HAuCl_4$. This acid contains the aurichloride ion, $AuCl_4^-$, a square planar complex ion:

$$\begin{bmatrix} & \overset{\displaystyle ..}{:\overset{.}{C}l:} & \\ & | & \\ :\overset{..}{C}l- & Au & -\overset{..}{C}l: \\ & | & \\ & :\overset{.}{C}l: & \end{bmatrix}$$

Hydrogen aurichloride can be obtained as a yellow crystalline substance, which forms salts with bases. When heated it forms **auric chloride,** $AuCl_3$, and then an aurous auric chloride, Au_2Cl_4, and then aurous chloride, $AuCl$. On further heating all the chlorine is lost, and pure gold remains.

27–8. *Color and Mixed Oxidation States*

The gold halides provide examples of an interesting phenomenon—the *deep, intense color often observed in a substance which contains an element in two different oxidation states.* Aurous auric chloride, Au_2Cl_4, is intensely black, although both aurous chloride and auric chloride are yellow. Cesium aurous auric bromide, $Cs_2^+[AuBr_2]^-[AuBr_4]^-$, is deep-black in color, and both $CsAuBr_2$ and $CsAuBr_4$ are much lighter. Black mica (biotite) and black tourmaline contain both ferrous and ferric iron. Prussian blue is ferric ferrocyanide; ferrous ferrocyanide is white, and ferric ferricyanide is light yellow. When copper is added to a light-green solution of cupric chloride a deep brownish-black solution is formed, before complete conversion to the colorless cuprous chloride complex.

The theory of this phenomenon is not understood. The very strong absorption of light is presumably connected with the transfer of an electron from one atom to another of the element present in two valence states.

27-9. *The Properties and Uses of Zinc, Cadmium, and Mercury*

Zinc is a bluish-white, moderately hard metal. It is brittle at room temperature, but is malleable and ductile between 100° and 150° C, and becomes brittle again above 150°. It is an active metal, above hydrogen in the electromotive-force series, and it displaces hydrogen even from dilute acids. In moist air zinc is oxidized, and becomes coated with a tough film of basic zinc carbonate, $Zn_2CO_3(OH)_2$, which protects it from further corrosion. This behavior is responsible for its principal use, in protecting iron from rusting. Iron wire or sheet iron is *galvanized* by cleaning with sulfuric acid or a sandblast, and then dipping in molten zinc; a thin layer of zinc adheres to the iron. Galvanized iron in some shapes is made by electroplating zinc onto the iron pieces.

Zinc is also used in making alloys, the most important of which is brass (the alloy with copper), and as a reacting electrode in dry cells and wet cells.

TABLE 27-2   *Some Physical Properties of Zinc, Cadmium, and Mercury*

	ATOMIC NUMBER	ATOMIC WEIGHT	DENSITY	MELTING POINT	BOILING POINT	METALLIC RADIUS	COLOR
Zinc	30	65.38	7.14 g/cm³	419.4° C	907° C	1.38 Å	Bluish-white
Cadmium	48	112.41	8.642	320.9°	767°	1.54	Bluish-white
Mercury	80	200.61	13.546	−38.89°	356.9°	1.57	Silvery-white

Cadmium is a bluish-white metal of pleasing appearance. It has found increasing use as a protective coating for iron and steel. The cadmium plate is deposited electrolytically from a bath containing the cadmium cyanide complex ion, $Cd(CN)_4^{--}$. Cadmium is also used in some alloys, such as the low-melting alloys needed for automatic fire extinguishers. *Wood's metal*, which melts at 65.5° C, contains 50% Bi, 25% Pb, 12.5% Sn, and 12.5% Cd. Because of the toxicity of compounds of elements of this group, care must be taken not to use cadmium-plated vessels for cooking, and not to inhale fumes of zinc, cadmium, or mercury.

Mercury is the only metal which is liquid at room temperature (cesium melts at 28.5° C, and gallium at 29.8°). It is unreactive, being below hydrogen in the electromotive-force series. Because of its unreactivity, fluidity, high density, and high electric conductivity it finds extensive use in thermometers, barometers, and many special kinds of scientific apparatus.

The alloys of mercury are called *amalgams*. Amalgams of silver, gold, and tin are used in dentistry. Mercury does not wet iron, and it is usually shipped and stored in iron bottles, called *flasks*, which hold 76 pounds of the metal.

27–10. *Compounds of Zinc and Cadmium*

The **zinc ion,** $Zn(H_2O)_4^{++}$, is a colorless ion formed by solution of zinc in acid. It is poisonous to man and to bacteria, and is used as a disinfectant. It forms tetracoordinated complexes readily, such as $Zn(NH_3)_4^{++}$, $Zn(CN)_4^{--}$, and $Zn(OH)_4^{--}$. The white precipitate of **zinc hydroxide,** $Zn(OH)_2$, which forms when ammonium hydroxide is added to a solution containing zinc ion, dissolves in excess ammonium hydroxide, forming the zinc ammonia complex. The zinc hydroxide complex, $Zn(OH)_4^{--}$, which is called **zincate ion,** is similarly formed on solution of zinc hydroxide in an excess of strong base; zinc hydroxide is amphoteric.

Zinc sulfate, $ZnSO_4 \cdot 7H_2O$, is used as a disinfectant and in dyeing calico, and in making *lithopone*, which is a mixture of barium sulfate and zinc sulfide used as a white pigment in paints:

$$Ba^{++}S^{--} + Zn^{++}SO_4^{--} \longrightarrow BaSO_4 \downarrow + ZnS \downarrow$$

Zinc oxide, ZnO, is a white powder (yellow when hot) made by burning zinc vapor or by roasting zinc ores. It is used as a pigment (zinc white), as a filler in automobile tires, adhesive tape, and other articles, and as an antiseptic (zinc oxide ointment).

Zinc sulfide, ZnS, is the only white sulfide among the sulfides of the common metals. Its conditions of precipitation have been discussed in Chapter 22.

The **compounds of cadmium** are closely similar to those of zinc. **Cadmium ion,** Cd^{++}, is a colorless ion, which forms complexes $[Cd(NH_3)_4^{++}, Cd(CN)_4^{--}]$ similar to those of zinc. The cadmium hydroxide ion, $Cd(OH)_4^{--}$, is not stable, and **cadmium hydroxide,** $Cd(OH)_2$, is formed as a white precipitate by addition even of concentrated sodium hydroxide to a solution containing cadmium ion. The precipitate is soluble in ammonium hydroxide or in a solution containing cyanide ion. **Cadmium oxide,** CdO, is a brown powder obtained by heating the hydroxide or burning the metal. **Cadmium sulfide,** CdS, is a bright-yellow precipitate obtained by passing hydrogen sulfide through a solution containing cadmium ion; it is used as a pigment (*cadmium yellow*).

27–11. *Compounds of Mercury*

The **mercuric compounds,** in which mercury is bipositive, differ some-what in their properties from the corresponding compounds of zinc and cadmium. The differences are due in part to the very strong tendency of the mercuric ion, Hg^{++}, to form covalent bonds. Thus the covalent crystal **mercuric sulfide,** HgS, is far less soluble than cadmium sulfide or zinc sulfide (Chap. 22).

Mercuric nitrate, $Hg(NO_3)_2$ or $Hg(NO_3)_2 \cdot \frac{1}{2}H_2O$, is made by dis-solving mercury in hot concentrated nitric acid:

$$3Hg + 8HNO_3 \longrightarrow 3Hg(NO_3)_2 + 2NO \uparrow + 4H_2O$$

It hydrolyzes on dilution, unless a sufficient excess of acid is present, to form basic mercuric nitrates, such as $HgNO_3OH$, as a white precipitate.

Mercuric chloride (*bichloride of mercury*), $HgCl_2$, is a white crystalline substance usually made by dissolving mercury in hot concentrated sul-furic acid, and then heating the dry mercuric sulfate with sodium chloride, subliming the volatile mercuric chloride:

$$Hg + 2H_2SO_4 \longrightarrow HgSO_4 + SO_2 \uparrow + H_2O$$
$$HgSO_4 + 2NaCl \longrightarrow Na_2SO_4 + HgCl_2 \uparrow$$

A dilute solution of mercuric chloride (about 0.1%) is used as a disin-fectant. Any somewhat soluble mercuric salt would serve equally well, except for the tendency of mercuric ion to hydrolyze and to precipitate basic salts. Mercuric chloride has only a small tendency to hydrolyze because its solution contains only a small concentration of mercuric ion, the mercury being present mainly as un-ionized covalent molecules,

$: \overset{..}{\underset{..}{Cl}} \!-\! Hg \!-\! \overset{..}{\underset{..}{Cl}} :.$ The electronic structure of these molecules, which

have a linear configuration, is analogous to that of the aurous chloride complex, $AuCl_2^-$ (Fig. 27-3). The ease of sublimation of mercuric chlo-ride (old name *corrosive sublimate*, melting point 275° C, boiling point 301°) results from the stability of these molecules.

Mercuric chloride, like other soluble salts of mercury, is very poisonous when taken internally. The mercuric ion combines strongly with pro-teins; in the human body it acts especially on the tissues of the kidney, destroying the ability of this organ to remove waste products from the

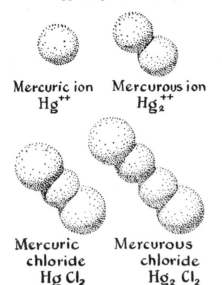

Mercuric ion   Mercurous ion
Hg^{++} Hg_2^{++}

Mercuric   Mercurous
chloride   chloride
$Hg\,Cl_2$ $Hg_2\,Cl_2$

FIG. 27-3

The structure of the mercuric ion, mercurous ion, mercuric chloride molecule, and mercurous chloride molecule. In the mercurous ion and the two molecules the atoms are held together by covalent bonds.

blood. Egg white and milk are swallowed as antidotes; their proteins precipitate the mercury in the stomach.

With ammonium hydroxide mercuric chloride forms a white precipitate, $HgNH_2Cl$:

$$HgCl_2 + 2NH_3 \longrightarrow HgNH_2Cl \downarrow + NH_4^+ + Cl^-$$

Mercuric iodide, HgI_2, is a red precipitate formed on addition of iodide ion to a solution containing mercuric ion. When heated it changes from red to yellow in color at 128° C, as it undergoes transformation to a second crystalline form. Mercuric iodide dissolves in solution containing excess iodide ion, forming the complex ion HgI_4^{--}:

$$HgI_2 + 2I^- \longrightarrow HgI_4^{--}$$

This ion in alkaline solution (*Nessler's reagent*) serves as a delicate test for ammonia (as in drinking water), giving with it a yellow or brown precipitate.

Mercuric sulfide, HgS, is formed as a black precipitate when hydrogen sulfide is passed through a solution of a mercuric salt. It can also be made by rubbing mercury and sulfur together in a mortar. The black sulfide (which also occurs in nature as the mineral *metacinnabarite*) is converted by heat into the red form (cinnabar). Mercuric sulfide is the most insoluble of metallic sulfides. It is not dissolved even by boiling concentrated nitric acid, but it does dissolve in aqua regia, under the combined action of the nitric acid, which oxidizes the sulfide to free sulfur, and hydrochloric acid, which provides chloride ion to form the stable complex $HgCl_4^{--}$:

$$3HgS + 12HCl + 2HNO_3 \longrightarrow 3HgCl_4^{--} + 6H^+ + 3S \downarrow$$
$$+ 2NO \uparrow + 4H_2O$$

Mercuric oxide, HgO, is formed as a yellow precipitate by adding a base to a solution of mercuric nitrate or as a red powder by heating dry mercuric nitrate or, slowly, by heating mercury in air. The yellow and red forms seem to differ only in grain size; it is a common phenomenon that red crystals (such as potassium dichromate or potassium ferricyanide) form a yellow powder when they are ground up. Mercuric oxide liberates oxygen when it is strongly heated.

Mercuric fulminate, $Hg(CNO)_2$, is made by dissolving mercury in nitric acid and adding ethyl alcohol, C_2H_5OH. It is a very unstable substance, which detonates when it is struck or heated, and it is used for making detonators and percussion caps.

Mercurous nitrate, $Hg_2(NO_3)_2$, is formed by reduction of a mercuric nitrate solution with mercury:

$$Hg^{++} + \underline{Hg} \longrightarrow Hg_2^{++}$$

The solution contains the **mercurous ion,** Hg_2^{++}, a colorless ion which has a unique structure; it consists of two mercuric ions plus two electrons, which form a covalent bond between them (Fig. 27-3):

$$2Hg^{++} + 2e^- \longrightarrow [Hg:Hg]^{++} \text{ or } [Hg\text{---}Hg]^{++}$$

Mercurous chloride, Hg_2Cl_2, is an insoluble, white, crystalline substance obtained by adding a solution containing chloride ion to a mercurous nitrate solution:

$$Hg_2^{++} + 2Cl^- \longrightarrow Hg_2Cl_2 \downarrow$$

It is used in medicine under the name *calomel*. The mercurous chloride

molecule has the linear covalent structure $: \overset{..}{\underset{..}{Cl}}\text{---}Hg\text{---}Hg\text{---}\overset{..}{\underset{..}{Cl}} :$ (Fig. 27-3).

The precipitation of mercurous chloride and its change in color from white to black on addition of ammonium hydroxide are used as the test for mercurous mercury in qualitative analysis. The effect of ammonium hydroxide is due to the formation of finely divided mercury (black) and mercuric aminochloride (white) by an auto-oxidation-reduction reaction:

$$Hg_2Cl_2 + 2NH_3 \longrightarrow Hg \downarrow + HgNH_2Cl \downarrow + NH_4^+ + Cl^-$$

Mercurous sulfide, Hg_2S, is unstable, and when formed as a brownish-black precipitate by action of sulfide ion on mercurous ion it immediately decomposes into mercury and mercuric sulfide:

$$Hg_2{}^{++} + S^{--} \longrightarrow Hg_2S \downarrow \longrightarrow Hg \downarrow + HgS \downarrow$$

27–12. *Gallium, Indium, and Thallium*

The elements of group IIIb, gallium, indium, and thallium, are very rare and have small practical importance. Their principal compounds represent oxidation state +3; thallium also forms thallous compounds, in which it has oxidation number +1. Gallium is liquid from 29° C, its melting point, to 1,700° C, its boiling point. It has found use as the liquid in quartz-tube thermometers, which can be used to above 1,200° C.

27–13. *Germanium*

The chemistry of germanium, a moderately rare and unimportant element, is similar to that of silicon, which is discussed in Chapter 30. Most of the compounds of germanium correspond to oxidation number +4; examples are germanium tetrachloride, $GeCl_4$, a colorless liquid with boiling point 83° C, and germanium dioxide, GeO_2, a colorless crystalline substance melting at 1,086° C.

The compounds of germanium have found little use. The element itself, a gray metalloid, is a poor conductor of electricity. It has the property, when alloyed with very small amounts of other elements, of permitting an electric current to pass only one way through its surface, in contact with a small metal wire. This rectifying power, which is superior to that of other crystals, has caused the substance to find much use in recent years in special pieces of apparatus, such as radar. It is also the basis of the transistor, a simple apparatus for amplifying minute currents of electricity, which can replace the ordinary vacuum tube for such purposes.

27–14. *Tin*

Tin is a silvery-white metal, with great malleability, permitting it to be hammered into thin sheets, called tin foil. Ordinary *white tin*, with metallic properties, has the unique crystal structure shown in Figure 25-3, in which each atom is surrounded by six nearest neighbors. White tin slowly changes at temperatures below 18° C to a non-metallic allotropic modification, *gray tin*, which has the diamond structure, each atom having four neighbors, to which it is held by single covalent bonds. At very low temperatures, around −50° C, the speed of this conversion is sufficiently great so that metallic tin objects sometimes fall into a powder of gray tin. This phenomenon has been called the "tin pest."

Tin finds extensive use as a protective layer for mild steel. Tin plating is done by dipping clean sheets of mild steel into molten tin, or by electrolytic deposition. Copper and other metals are sometimes also coated with tin.

The principal alloys of tin are *bronze* (tin and copper), *soft solder* (50% tin and 50% lead), *pewter* (75% tin and 25% lead), and *britannia metal* (tin with small amounts of antimony and copper).

Tin is reactive enough to displace hydrogen from dilute acids, but it does not tarnish in moist air. It reacts with warm hydrochloric acid to produce stannous chloride, $SnCl_2$, and hydrogen, and with hot concentrated sulfuric acid to produce stannous sulfate, $SnSO_4$, and sulfur dioxide, the equations for these reactions being

$$Sn + 2HCl \longrightarrow SnCl_2 + H_2 \uparrow$$

and

$$Sn + 2H_2SO_4 \longrightarrow SnSO_4 + SO_2 \uparrow + 2H_2O$$

With cold dilute nitric acid it forms stannous nitrate, and with concentrated nitric acid it is oxidized to a hydrated stannic acid, H_2SnO_3.

Compounds of Tin.   Stannous chloride, made by solution of tin in hydrochloric acid, forms colorless crystals, $SnCl_2 \cdot H_2O$, on evaporation of the solution. In neutral solution the substance hydrolyzes, forming a precipitate of **stannous hydroxychloride,** $Sn(OH)Cl$. The hydrolysis in solution may be prevented by the presence of an excess of acid. Stannous chloride solution is used as a mordant in dyeing cloth.

The stannous ion is an active reducing agent, which is easily oxidized to **stannic chloride,** $SnCl_4$, or, in the presence of excess chloride ion, to the complex **chlorostannate ion,** $SnCl_6^{--}$.

Stannic chloride, $SnCl_4$, is a colorless liquid (boiling point 114°), which fumes very strongly in moist air, producing hydrochloric acid and **stannic acid,** $H_2Sn(OH)_6$. **Sodium stannate,** $Na_2Sn(OH)_6$, contains the octahedral *hexahydroxystannate ion* (stannate ion). This complex ion is similar in structure to the chlorostannate ion. Sodium stannate is used as a mordant, and in preparing fireproof cotton cloth and weighting silk. The cloth is soaked in the sodium stannate solution, dried, and treated with ammonium sulfate solution. This treatment causes hydrated stannic oxide to be deposited in the fibers.

Stannous hydroxide, $Sn(OH)_2$, is formed by adding dilute sodium hydroxide solution to stannous chloride. It is readily soluble in excess alkali, producing the *stannite ion*, $Sn(OH)_3^-$. When a solution containing stannite ion is boiled an auto-oxidation-reduction reaction occurs, with deposition of metallic tin and production of the stannate ion, $Sn(OH)_6^{--}$:

$$2Sn(OH)_3^- \longrightarrow Sn \downarrow + Sn(OH)_6^{--}$$

Stannous sulfide, SnS, is obtained as a dark-brown precipitate by addition of hydrogen sulfide or sulfide ion to a solution of a stannous salt. **Stannic sulfide,** SnS_2, is formed in the same way from stannic solution; it is yellow in color. Stannic sulfide is soluble in solutions of ammonium sulfide or sodium sulfide, producing the *sulfostannate ion*, SnS_4^{----}. Stannous sulfide is not soluble in sulfide solution, but is easily oxidized in the presence of polysulfide solutions to the sulfostannate ion. These properties are used in the scheme of qualitative analysis.

27–15. *Lead*

Lead is a soft, heavy, dull-gray metal with low tensile strength. It is used in making type, for covering electric cables, and in many alloys. The organic lead compound **lead tetraethyl,** $Pb(C_2H_5)_4$, is added to gasoline to prevent knock in automobile engines.

Lead forms a thin surface layer of oxide in air. This oxide slowly changes to a basic carbonate. Hard water forms a similar coating on lead, which protects the water from contamination with soluble lead compounds. Soft water dissolves appreciable amounts of lead, which is poisonous; for this reason lead pipes cannot be used to carry drinking water.

There are several oxides of lead, of which the most important are **lead monoxide** (*litharge*), PbO, **minium** or **red lead,** Pb_3O_4, and **lead dioxide,** PbO_2.

Litharge is made by heating lead in air. It is a yellow powder or yellowish-red crystalline material, used in making lead glass and for preparing compounds of lead. It is amphoteric, dissolving in warm sodium hydroxide solution to produce the *plumbite ion*, $Pb(OH)_4^{--}$. Red lead, Pb_3O_4, can be made by heating lead in oxygen. It is used in glass-making, and for making a red paint for protecting iron and steel structures.

Lead dioxide, PbO_2, is a brown substance made by oxidizing a solution of sodium plumbite, $Na_2Pb(OH)_4$, with hypochlorite ion, or by anodic oxidation of lead sulfate. It is soluble in sodium hydroxide and potassium hydroxide, forming the *hexahydroxyplumbate ion*, $Pb(OH)_6^{--}$. The principal use of lead dioxide is in the lead storage battery (Chap. 13).

Lead nitrate, $Pb(NO_3)_2$, is a white crystalline substance made by dissolving lead, lead monoxide, or lead carbonate in nitric acid. **Lead carbonate,** $PbCO_3$, occurs in nature as the mineral *cerussite*. It appears as a precipitate when a solution containing the hydrogen carbonate ion, HCO_3^-, is added to lead nitrate solution. With a more basic carbonate solution a basic carbonate of lead, $Pb_3(OH)_2(CO_3)_2$, is deposited. This basic salt, called **white lead,** is used as a white pigment in paint

For this use it is manufactured by methods involving the oxidation of lead by air, the formation of a basic acetate by interaction with vinegar or acetic acid, and the decomposition of this salt by carbon dioxide. **Lead chromate,** $PbCrO_4$, is also used as a pigment, under the name *chrome yellow.*

Lead sulfate, $PbSO_4$, is a white, nearly insoluble substance. Its precipitation is used as a test for either lead ion or sulfate ion in analytical chemistry.

Exercises

27-1. What is the electronic structure of the Ag^+ ion? of the Cu^{++} ion?

27-2. What are the constituents of brass? of bronze?

27-3. In which form does copper exist in a cupric sulfate solution? in a strong hydrochloric acid solution? in an ammoniacal solution? added as cupric sulfate to a solution of potassium iodide? in a solution of potassium cyanide?

27-4. Under what conditions can cuprous compounds or solutions be prepared?

27-5. Under what conditions can dilute sulfuric acid dissolve copper? Write an equation for the reaction.

27-6. Describe a simple test to show that silver iodide is less soluble than silver chloride.

27-7. What is the structure of the complexes of univalent silver and gold?

27-8. How can you prepare a compound of tervalent gold?

27-9. What is the weight of gold in an 18-carat gold ring weighing 10 g?

27-10. What weight of copper would be deposited from a cupric sulfate solution by the passage of 3,214 coulombs of electricity?

27-11. Write the equation for the formation of hydrogen aurichloride by solution of gold in aqua regia, assuming that nitric oxide, NO, is also produced. What four products are successively formed as hydrogen aurichloride is heated?

27-12. Compare the electronegative character of zinc, cadmium, mercury, and the alkaline-earth metals.

27-13. Discuss the change in properties in the sequence zinc, cadmium, mercury for all properties about which there is information in this chapter.

27-14. Suggest possible procedures for separating (a) an amalgam containing zinc and cadmium, (b) a nitric acid solution of Zn^{++}, Cd^{++}, and Hg^{++} into the pure constituents.

27-15. Is mercuric nitrate soluble in pure water?

27-16. Compare the properties of NaCl, $HgCl_2$, and CCl_4.

27-17. What would happen if mercury were shaken with a solution of mercuric chloride?

27-18. What would happen if mercury were shaken with a dilute solution of sulfuric acid?

27-19. Compare the stabilities of zinc oxide and mercuric oxide.

27-20. Write the equation for the reaction of zinc in moist air, to form a film of basic zinc carbonate, $Zn_2CO_3(OH)_2$.

27-21. A sample of mercuric oxide weighing 2.000 g is strongly heated in a test tube and the volume of oxygen evolved is measured. What would be the predicted volume of the evolved gas if the atmospheric pressure was 745 mm of mercury, the temperature was 23.5° C, and the gas was collected over water?

27-22. Describe the electronic structure of the mercurous ion, the mercuric ion, the mercurous chloride molecule, and the mercuric chloride molecule. Compare the total number of electrons surrounding each mercury atom with the number in the nearest noble gas.

27-23. Write the equation for the reaction of zinc with hydrochloric acid. Would you expect zinc to dissolve in a concentrated solution of sodium hydroxide? If so, write the equation for this reaction.

27-24. How is the occurrence of "tin pest" related to the position of tin in the periodic system?

27-25. How would you prepare K_2SnCl_6 from an aqueous solution of $SnCl_2$?

27-26. Complete and balance the chemical reaction

$$SnS + S^{--} + O_2^{--} \longrightarrow$$

27-27. Compare the amphoteric properties of the bivalent and the quadrivalent states of tin and lead.

27-28. Compare the relative stabilities of the bivalent and the quadrivalent states of tin and lead; of the zero-valent and quadrivalent states.

27-29. What chemical reaction takes place when tin is treated with hot nitric acid? with hot sulfuric acid? with hot hydrochloric acid? Which of these acids do you suppose will react with lead?

27-30. How would you prepare $K_2Pb(OH)_6$ from an aqueous solution of lead chloride?

Chapter 28

Organic Chemistry

28–1. *The Nature and Extent of Organic Chemistry*

Organic chemistry is the chemistry of the compounds of carbon. It is a very great subject—nearly half a million different organic compounds have already been reported and described in the chemical literature. Many of these substances have been isolated from living matter, and many more have been synthesized (manufactured) by chemists in the laboratory.

In this chapter and the following chapter (dealing with biochemistry) we shall discuss a few of these compounds. Several large parts of organic chemistry will not be discussed at all; these include the methods of isolation and purification of naturally occurring compounds, the methods of analysis and determination of structure, and the methods of synthesis used in organic chemistry.

There are two principal ways in which organic chemists work. One of these ways is to begin the investigation of some natural material, such as a plant, which is known to have special properties. This plant might, for example, have been found by the natives of a tropical region to be beneficial in the treatment of malaria. The chemist then proceeds to make an extract from the plant, with use of a solvent such as alcohol or ether, and, by various methods of separation, to divide the extract into fractions. After each fractionation a study is made to see which fraction still contains the active substance. Finally this process may be carried so far that a pure crystalline active substance is obtained. The chemist then analyzes the substance, and determines its molecular weight, in order to find out what atoms are contained in the molecule of the substance. He next investigates the chemical properties of the substance, splitting its molecules into smaller molecules of known substances, in order to determine its molecular structure. When the structure has been determined, he attempts to synthesize the substance; if he is successful, the active material may be made available in large quantity and at low cost.

The other way in which organic chemists work involves the synthesis and study of a large number of organic compounds, and the continued effort to correlate the empirical facts by means of theoretical principles. Often a knowledge of the structure and properties of natural substances is valuable in indicating the general nature of the compounds that are worth investigation. The ultimate goal of this branch of organic chemistry is the complete understanding of the physical and chemical properties, and also the physiological properties, of substances in terms of their molecular structure. At the present time chemists have obtained a remarkable insight into the dependence of the physical and chemical properties of substances on the structure of their molecules. So far, however, only a small beginning has been made in attacking the great problem of the relation between structure and physiological activity. This problem remains one of the greatest and most important problems of science, challenging the new generation of scientists.

28–2. *The Simplest Organic Compounds: the Hydrocarbons*

The hydrocarbons are compounds containing only carbon and hydrogen atoms. The simplest hydrocarbon is **methane,** CH_4. Its molecules are tetrahedral, the four hydrogen atoms lying at the corners of a regular tetrahedron around the carbon atom, and connected with the carbon atom by single bonds. Methane is a gas, which occurs in natural gas, and is used as a fuel. It is also used in large quantities for the manufacture of *carbon black*, by combustion with a limited supply of air:

$$CH_4 + O_2 \longrightarrow 2H_2O + C$$

The methane burns to form water, and the carbon is deposited as very finely divided carbon, which finds extensive use as a filler for rubber for automobile tires.

Methane is the first member of a series of hydrocarbons having the general formula C_nH_{2n+2}, called the **methane series** or **paraffin series.** The first members of this series are listed below:

Methane Series, C_nH_{2n+2}
    Methane, CH_4
    Ethane, C_2H_6
    Propane, C_3H_8

Butane, C_4H_{10}
Pentane, C_5H_{12}
Hexane, C_6H_{14}
Heptane, C_7H_{16}
Octane, C_8H_{18}, etc.

The name "paraffin" means "having little affinity." The compounds of this series are not very reactive chemically. They occur in the complex mixtures called petroleum. The molecules heavier than ethane are characterized by containing carbon atoms attached to one another

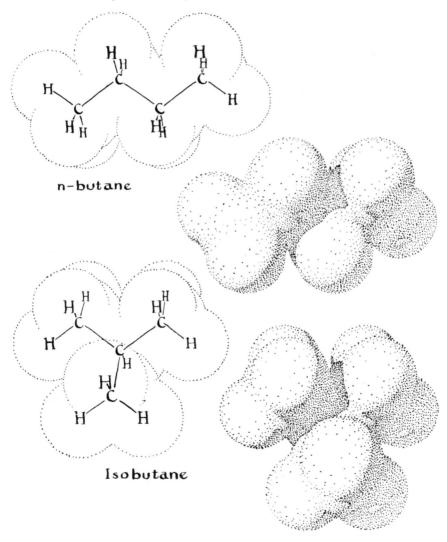

FIG. 28-1   *The structure of the isomers normal butane and isobutane.*

by single bonds. **Ethane** has the structure 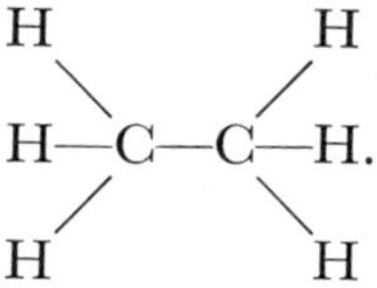 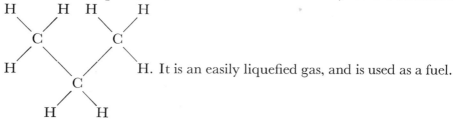. It is a gas

(b.p. $-88°$ C), which occurs in large amounts in natural gas from some wells. **Propane,** the third member of the series, has the structure

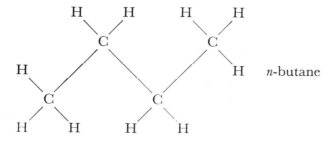 H. It is an easily liquefied gas, and is used as a fuel.

The lighter members of the paraffin series are gases, the intermediate members are liquids, and the heavier members are solid substances. The common name *petroleum ether* refers to the pentane-hexane-heptane mixture, used as a solvent and in dry cleaning. *Gasoline* is the heptane-to-nonane mixture (C_7H_{16} to C_9H_{20}), and *kerosene* the decane-to-hexadecane mixture ($C_{10}H_{22}$ to $C_{16}H_{34}$). *Heavy fuel oil* is a mixture of paraffins containing twenty or more carbon atoms per molecule. The *lubricating oils, petroleum jelly* ("vaseline"), and *solid paraffin* are mixtures of still larger paraffin molecules.

The phenomenon of **isomerism** is shown first in the paraffin series by **butane,** C_4H_{10}. Isomerism is the existence of two or more substances having the same composition but different properties. The d fference in properties is usually the result of difference in the structure of the molecule—that is, in the way the atoms are bonded together. There are two isomers of butane, called *normal butane* (*n*-butane) and *isobutane*. These substances have the structures shown below and in Figure 28-1; normal butane is a "straight chain" (actually, of course, the carbon chain is a zigzag chain, because of the tetrahedral nature of the carbon atom), and the isobutane molecule contains a branched chain:

n-butane

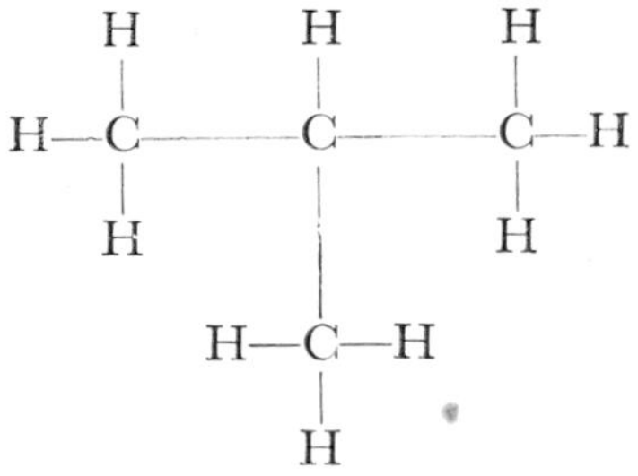

$$H-\overset{\overset{\displaystyle H}{|}}{\underset{\underset{\displaystyle H}{|}}{C}}----\overset{\overset{\displaystyle H}{|}}{\underset{\underset{\displaystyle |}{|}}{C}}----\overset{\overset{\displaystyle H}{|}}{\underset{\underset{\displaystyle H}{|}}{C}}-H$$

isobutane

$$H-\overset{\overset{\displaystyle |}{}}{\underset{\underset{\displaystyle H}{|}}{C}}-H$$

The large hydrocarbons have great numbers of isomers.

Hydrocarbons Containing Double Bonds. The substance **ethylene,**

C_2H_4, consists of molecules 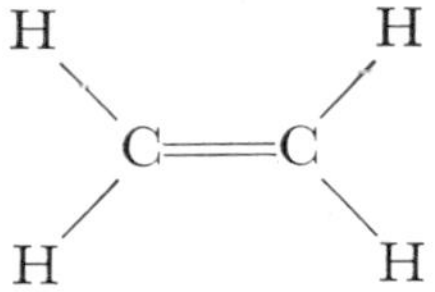
$$\overset{\displaystyle H}{\diagdown}\overset{\displaystyle H}{\diagup}$$
$$C\!\!=\!\!C$$
$$\overset{\displaystyle }{\diagup}\overset{\displaystyle }{\diagdown}$$
$$H\qquad H$$
, in which there is a

double bond between the two carbon atoms. This double bond confers upon the molecule the property of much greater chemical reactivity than is possessed by the paraffins. For example, whereas chlorine, bromine, and iodine do not attack the paraffin hydrocarbons, they easily react with ethylene, in the way described as "adding on" to the double bonds. That is, the chlorine molecule reacts with an ethylene molecule to form the substance dichloroethane,

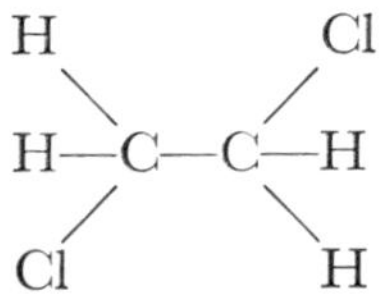

$$\overset{\displaystyle H}{\diagdown}\qquad\overset{\displaystyle Cl}{\diagup}$$
$$H-C-C-H$$
$$\overset{\displaystyle }{\diagup}\qquad\overset{\displaystyle }{\diagdown}$$
$$Cl\qquad H$$

Because of this property of readily combining with other substances such as the halogens, ethylene and related hydrocarbons are said to be *unsaturated.* Ethylene is the first member of a homologous series of hydrocarbons, called the *ethylene series.*

Ethylene has the interesting property of causing green fruit to ripen, and it is used commercially for this purpose.

Hydrocarbons Containing Several Double Bonds. Some important natural products are hydrocarbons containing several double bonds. For example, the red coloring matter of tomatoes, called *lycopene,* is an unsaturated hydrocarbon, $C_{40}H_{56}$, with the structure shown in Figure 28-2.

The molecule of this substance contains thirteen double bonds. It is seen that eleven of these double bonds are related to one another in a

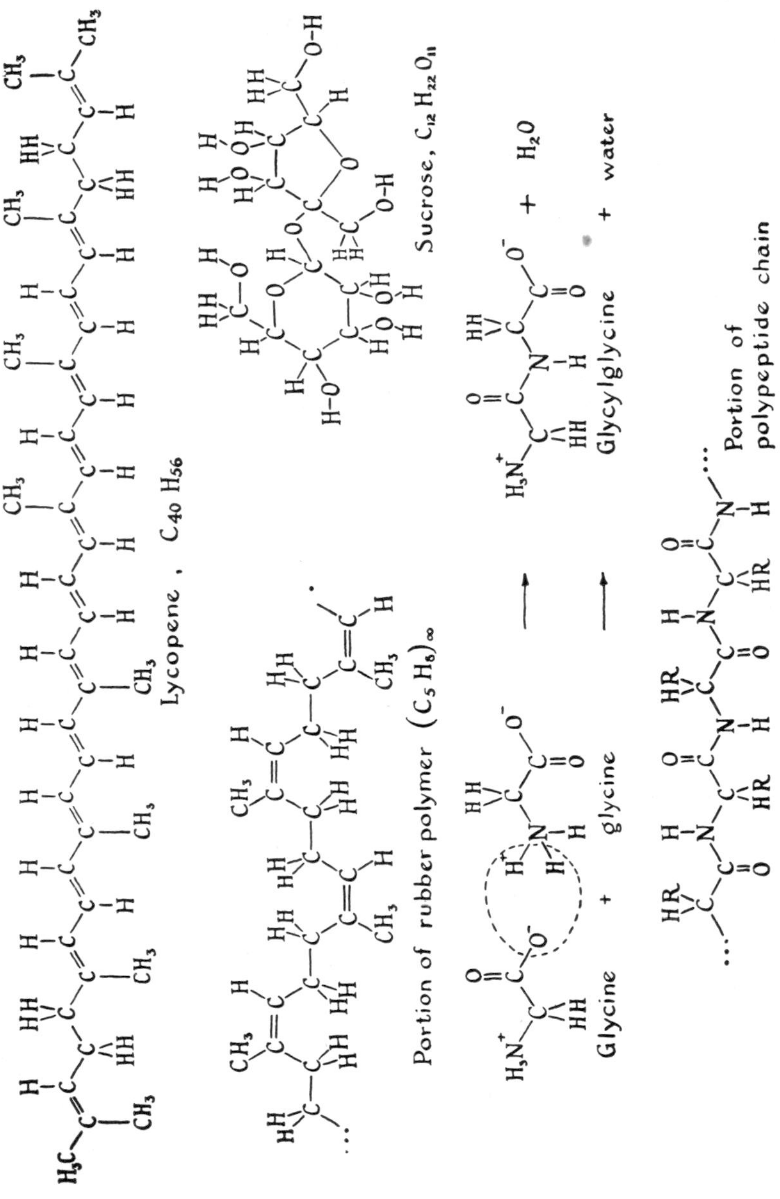

FIG. 28-2 *Structural formulas of some organic molecules.*

special way—they alternate regularly with single bonds. A regular alternation of double bonds and single bonds in a hydrocarbon chain is called a *conjugated system of double bonds.* The existence of this structural feature in a molecule confers upon the molecule special properties, such as the power of absorbing visible light, causing the substance to be colored.

Other yellow and red substances, isomers of lycopene, with the same formula $C_{40}H_{56}$, are called α-**carotene,** β-**carotene,** and similar names. These substances occur in butter, milk, green leafy vegetables, eggs, cod-liver oil, halibut-liver oil, carrots, tomatoes, and other vegetables and fruits. They are important substances because they serve in the human body as a source of Vitamin A (see Chap. 29).

The Acetylene Series. **Acetylene,** which has the structural formula H—C≡C—H, is the first member of a homologous series of hydrocarbons containing triple bonds. Aside from acetylene, these substances have not found wide use, except for the manufacture of other chemicals.

Acetylene is a colorless gas, with a characteristic garlic-like odor. It is liable to explode when compressed in the pure state, and is usually kept in solution under pressure in acetone. It is used as a fuel, in the oxy-acetylene torch and the acetylene lamp.

Cyclic Hydrocarbons. A hydrocarbon whose molecule contains a ring of carbon atoms is called a *cyclic hydrocarbon.* **Cyclohexane,** C_6H_{12}, with

the structure

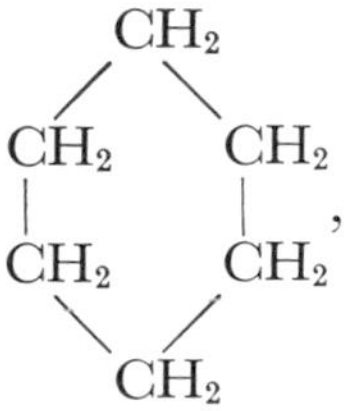

$$
\begin{array}{ccc}
 & CH_2 & \\
 \diagup & & \diagdown \\
CH_2 & & CH_2 \\
| & & | \\
CH_2 & & CH_2 \\
 \diagdown & & \diagup \\
 & CH_2 &
\end{array}
$$

, is representative of this class of substances.

It is a volatile liquid, closely similar to normal hexane (gasoline) in its properties.

Many important substances exist whose molecules contain two or more rings, fused together. One of these substances is **pinene,** $C_{10}H_{16}$, which is the principal constituent of *turpentine.* Turpentine is an oil obtained by distilling a semi-fluid resinous material that exudes from pine trees. The pinene molecule has the following structure:

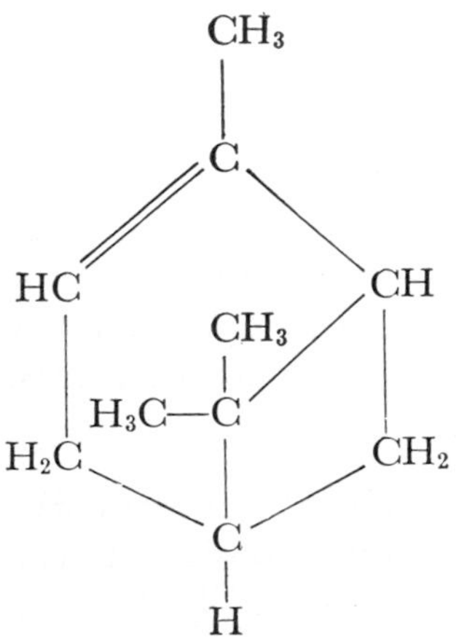

Another interesting polycyclic substance is **camphor,** obtained by steam distillation of the wood of the camphor tree, or, in recent years, by a synthetic process starting with pinene. The molecule of camphor

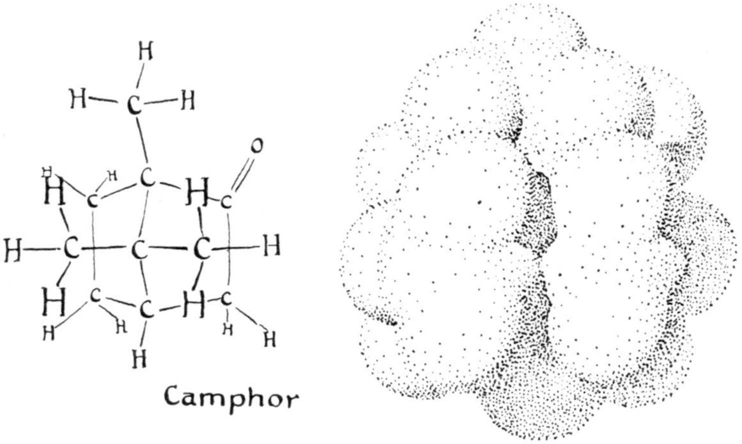

Camphor

FIG. 28-3 *The structure of the camphor molecule.*

is roughly spherical in shape—it is a sort of "cage" molecule. Its structure is shown in Figure 28-3. It is to be noted that camphor is not a hydrocarbon, but contains one oxygen atom, its formula being $C_{10}H_{16}O$:

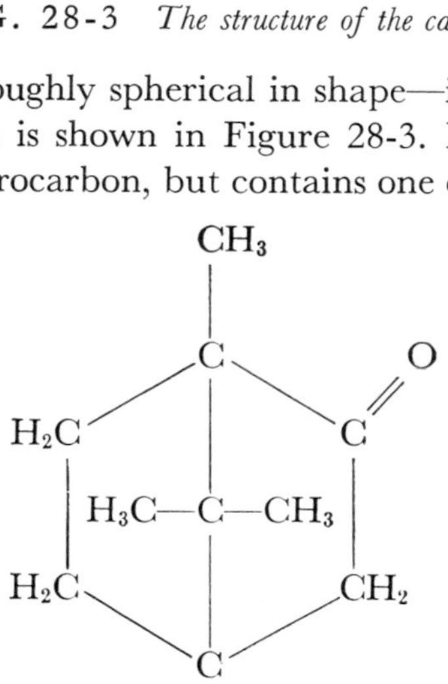

A hydrocarbon is obtained by replacing the oxygen atom by two hydrogen atoms, producing the substance called *camphane.* Camphor is used in medicine and in the manufacture of plastics. Ordinary *celluloid* consists of nitrocellulose plasticized with camphor.

Rubber. Rubber is an organic substance, obtained mainly from the sap of the rubber tree, *Hevea brasiliensis.* Rubber consists of very long molecules, which are polymers of *isoprene*, C_5H_8. The structure of iso-prene is

H—C
 H
 |
 C
 |
 CH₃

C
 H
 |
 C—H
 |
 H

and that of the rubber polymer, as produced in the plant, is shown in Figure 28-2.

The characteristic properties of rubber are due to the fact that it is an aggregate of very long molecules, intertwined with one another in a rather random way. The structure of the molecules is such that they do not tend to align themselves side by side in a regular way (that is, to crystallize), but instead tend to retain an irregular arrangement.

It is interesting to note that the rubber molecule contains a large number of double bonds, one for each C_5H_8 residue. In natural rubber the configuration about the double bonds is the *cis* configuration,* as shown in the structural formula in Figure 28-2. **Gutta percha,** a similar product which does not have the elasticity of rubber, contains the same molecules, with, however, the *trans* configuration around the double bonds. This difference in configuration permits the molecules of gutta percha to crystallize more readily than those of rubber.

Ordinary unvulcanized rubber is sticky, as a result of a tendency for the molecules to pull away from one another, a portion of the rubber thus adhering to any material with which it comes in contact. The stickiness is eliminated by the process of *vulcanization*, which consists in heating rubber with sulfur. During this process sulfur molecules, S_8, open up and combine with the double bonds of rubber molecules, forming bridges of sulfur chains from one rubber molecule to another rubber molecule. These sulfur bridges bind the aggregate of rubber molecules together into a large molecular framework, extending through the whole sample of rubber. Vulcanization with a small amount of sulfur leads to a soft product, such as that in rubber bands or (with a filler, carbon black or zinc oxide) in automobile tires. A much harder

---

* This *cis* configuration about the double bond can be represented by the formula

X   X
 \   /
  C=C   , and the *trans* configuration by
 /   \
H   H

X   H
 \   /
  C=C   .
 /   \
H   X

material, called vulcanite, is obtained by using a larger amount of sulfur.

The modern materials called **"synthetic rubber"** are not really synthetic rubber, since they are not identical with the natural product. They are, rather, substitutes for rubber—materials with properties and structure similar to but not identical with those of natural rubber. For example, the substance **chloroprene,** C_4H_5Cl, with the structure

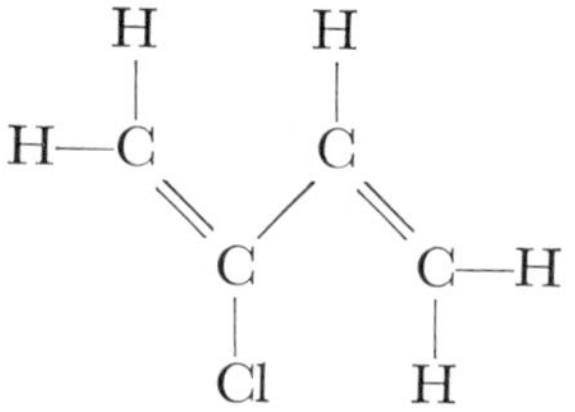

is similar to isoprene except for the replacement of a methyl group by a chlorine atom. Chloroprene polymerizes to a rubber called *chloroprene rubber*. It and other synthetic rubbers have found extensive uses, and are superior to natural rubber for some purposes.

Benzene and Other Aromatic Hydrocarbons.   An important hydrocarbon is **benzene,** which has the formula C_6H_6. It is a volatile liquid (b.p. 80° C), which has an aromatic odor. Benzene and other hydrocarbons similar to it in structure are called the *aromatic hydrocarbons*. Benzene itself was first obtained by Faraday, by the distillation of coal.

For many years there was discussion about the structure of the benzene molecule. The German chemist August Kekulé suggested that the six carbon atoms form a regular planar hexagon in space, the six hydrogen atoms being bonded to the carbon atoms, and forming a larger hexagon. Kekulé suggested that, in order for a carbon atom to show its normal quadrivalence, the ring contains three single bonds and three double bonds in alternate positions, as shown below. A structure of this sort is called a Kekulé structure.

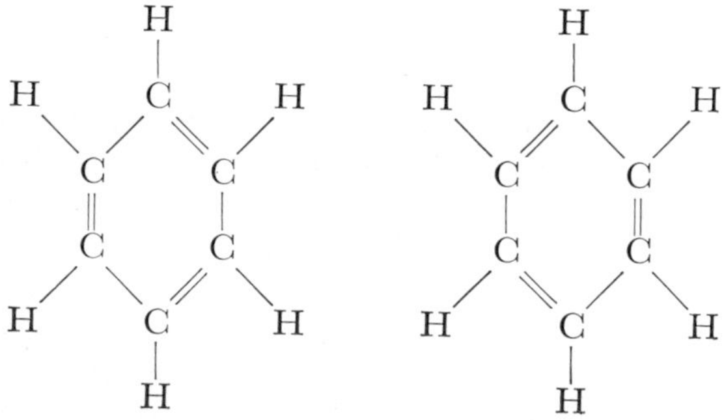

Other hydrocarbons, derivatives of benzene, can be obtained by replacing the hydrogen atoms by methyl groups or similar groups. Coal tar and petroleum contain substances of this sort, such as **toluene,** C_7H_8, and the three **xylenes,** C_8H_{10}. These formulas are usually written $C_6H_5CH_3$ and $C_6H_4(CH_3)_2$, to indicate the structural formulas, as shown below.

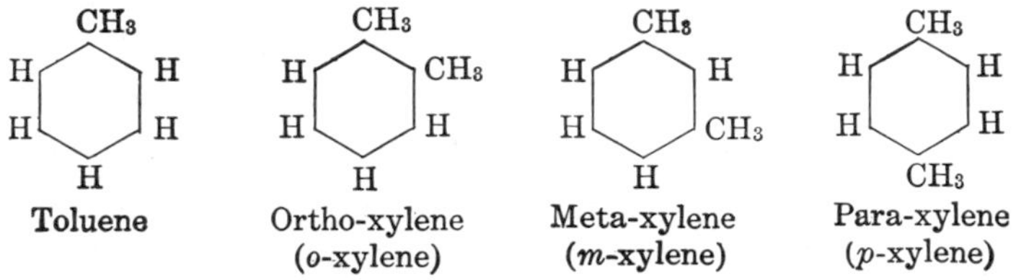

| Toluene | Ortho-xylene (o-xylene) | Meta-xylene (m-xylene) | Para-xylene (p-xylene) |

In these formulas the benzene ring of six carbon atoms is shown simply as a hexagon. This convention is used by organic chemists, who often also do not show the hydrogen atoms, but only other groups attached to the ring.

It is to be noted that we can draw two Kekulé structures for benzene and its derivatives. For example, for ortho-xylene the two Kekulé structures are

In the first structure there is a double bond between the carbon atoms to which methyl groups are attached, and in the second there is a single bond in this position. The organic chemists of a century ago found it impossible, however, to separate two substances, isomers, corresponding to these formulas. In order to explain this apparent impossibility of separation Kekulé suggested that the molecule does not retain one Kekulé structure, but rather slips easily from one to the other. The modern theory of molecular structure says that these two structures do not correspond to separate forms of ortho-xylene, and that neither one alone represents the molecule satisfactorily; instead, the actual structure of the ortho-xylene molecule is a hybrid of these two structures, with each bond between two carbon atoms in the ring intermediate in character between a single bond and a double bond. Even though this *resonance structure* is accepted for benzene and related compounds, it is often convenient simply to draw one of the Kekulé structures, or just a hexagon, to represent a benzene molecule.

Benzene and its derivatives are extremely important substances. They are used in the manufacture of drugs, explosives, photographic developers, plastics, synthetic dyes, and many other substances. For example, the substance **trinitrotoluene,** $C_6H_2(CH_3)(NO_2)_3$, is an important explosive (TNT). The structure of this substance is

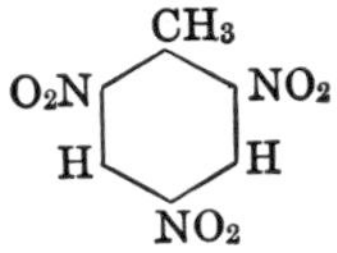

$$\begin{array}{c} CH_3 \\ O_2N \overbrace{} NO_2 \\ H \underbrace{} H \\ NO_2 \end{array}$$

In addition to benzene and its derivatives, there exist other aromatic hydrocarbons, containing two or more rings of carbon atoms. **Naphthalene,** $C_{10}H_8$, is a solid substance with a characteristic odor; it is used as a constituent of moth balls, and in the manufacture of dyes and other organic compounds. **Anthracene,** $C_{14}H_{10}$, and **phenanthrene,** $C_{14}H_{10}$, are isomeric substances containing three rings fused together. These substances are also used in making dyes, and derivatives of them are important biological substances (cholesterol, sex hormones; see Chap. 29). The structures of naphthalene, anthracene, and phenanthrene are the following:

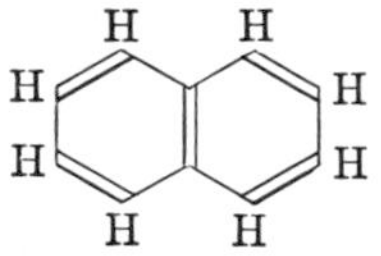

Naphthalene 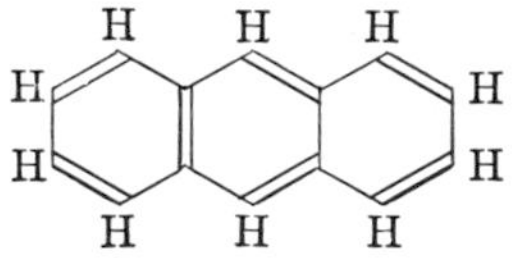   Anthracene

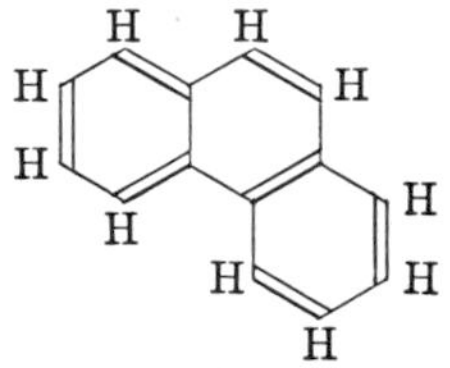

Phenanthrene

These molecules also have hybrid structures: the structures shown do not represent the molecules completely, but are analogous to one Kekulé structure for benzene.

28–3. *Alcohols and Ethers*

An *alcohol* is obtained from a hydrocarbon by replacing one hydrogen atom by a hydroxyl group, —OH. Thus methane, CH_4, gives **methyl alcohol,** CH_3OH, and ethane, C_2H_6, gives **ethyl alcohol,** C_2H_5OH. The names of the alcohols are often written by using the ending *ol*; methyl alcohol is called *methanol*, and ethyl alcohol *ethanol*.

Methyl alcohol is made by the destructive distillation of wood; it is sometimes called wood alcohol. It is a poisonous substance which on ingestion causes blindness and death. It is used as a solvent, and for the preparation of other organic compounds.

The most important method of making ethyl alcohol is by the fermentation of sugars with yeast. Grains and molasses are the usual raw materials for this purpose.

Alcohols containing two or more hydroxyl groups attached to different carbon atoms can be made. **Diethylene glycol,** CH_2OH, is used

$$| \\ CH_2OH$$

as a solvent and as an anti-freeze material for automobile radiators. **Glycerol** (glycerin), $C_3H_5(OH)_3$, is a trihydroxypropane, with the structure

$$\begin{array}{c} H \\ | \\ H\!-\!C\!-\!OH \\ | \\ H\!-\!C\!-\!OH \\ | \\ H\!-\!C\!-\!OH \\ | \\ H \end{array}$$

The *ethers* are compounds obtained by condensation of alcohols, with elimination of water. The most important ether is **diethyl ether** (ordinary ether), $(C_2H_5)_2O$. It is made by treating ethanol with concentrated sulfuric acid, which serves as a dehydrating agent:

$$2C_2H_5OH \longrightarrow C_2H_5OC_2H_5 + H_2O$$

It is used as a general anesthetic, and as a solvent.

An important aromatic alcohol is **phenol,** C_6H_5OH, obtained from benzene by replacing one hydrogen atom by a hydroxyl group. It is a bactericidal agent, used as a disinfectant (carbolic acid).

28–4. *Aldehydes and Ketones*

The alcohols and ethers represent the first stage of oxidation of hydrocarbons. Further oxidation leads to substances called *aldehydes* and *ketones*.

The aldehydes contain the group $-C{\Large\diagup}^{H}_{\diagdown O}$, and the ketones contain the

carbonyl group, ${\diagdown\atop\diagup}C{=}O$. The simplest aldehyde is **formaldehyde,** which can be made by passing methyl alcohol vapor and air over a heated metal catalyst:

$$2CH_3OH + O_2 \longrightarrow 2HCHO + 2H_2O$$

The structural formula of formaldehyde is $\underset{H}{\overset{H}{\diagdown}} C{=}O$. This substance is a gas with a sharp irritating odor. It is used as a disinfectant and antiseptic, and in the manufacture of plastics and of leather and artificial silk.

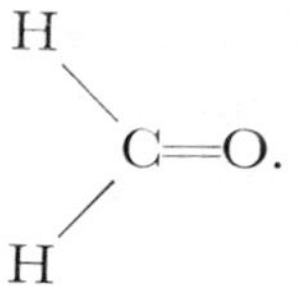

Acetaldehyde, CH_3CHO, is a similar substance made from ethyl alcohol.

The ketones are closely similar in structure: whereas an aldehyde contains a carbonyl group with an alkyl group and a hydrogen atom attached (or two hydrogen atoms, in the case of formaldehyde), the ketones contain a carbonyl group with two hydrocarbon groups attached. The ketones are effective solvents for organic compounds, and are extensively used in chemical industry for this purpose. **Acetone,** $(CH_3)_2CO$, which is dimethyl ketone, is the simplest and most important of these substances. It is a good solvent for nitrocellulose.

28–5. *The Organic Acids and Their Esters*

The *organic acids* represent a still higher stage of oxidation of hydrocarbons than the aldehydes and ketones—namely, the stage of oxidation to a molecule containing a group $-C{\overset{\displaystyle O}{\underset{\displaystyle OH}{\Big\langle}}}$. This group is called the *carboxyl group*. It has the properties of a weak acid; the extent of ionization of the carboxyl group in most organic acids is such as to correspond to an equilibrium constant (acid constant) of about 1×10^{-4} or 1×10^{-5}.

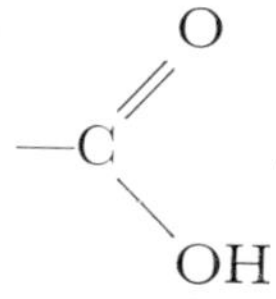

The simplest organic acid is **formic acid,** $HCOOH$. It can be made by distilling ants, and its name is from the Latin word for ant.

Acetic acid, the second member of the homologous series of carboxylic acids, has the formula CH_3COOH and the following structure:

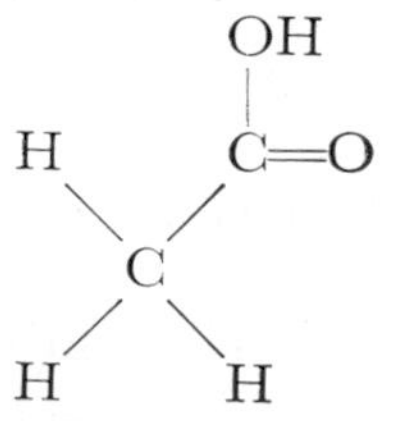

$$\underset{\underset{\displaystyle H}{\diagup}\overset{}{\underset{\displaystyle}{}}\overset{}{\diagdown}\underset{\displaystyle H}{\diagdown}}{\overset{\overset{\displaystyle OH}{\big|}}{\underset{\displaystyle C}{\overset{\displaystyle H \diagdown \quad \diagup C{=}O}{}}}}$$

It is the acidic constituent of vinegar. Vinegar is produced by the atmospheric oxidation of the ethyl alcohol present in hard cider, under the catalytic influence of enzymes produced by appropriate bacteria.

The next two acids in the series are **propionic acid,** CH_3CH_2COOH, and **butyric acid,** $CH_3CH_2CH_2COOH$. Butyric acid is the principal odorous substance in rancid butter.

Some of the important organic acids occurring in nature are those in which there is a carboxyl group at the end of a long hydrocarbon chain. **Palmitic acid,** $C_{15}H_{31}COOH$, and **stearic acid,** $C_{17}H_{35}COOH$, have structures of this sort. **Oleic acid,** $C_{17}H_{33}COOH$, is similar to stearic acid except that it contains a double bond between two of the carbon atoms in the chain.

Oxalic acid, $(COOH)_2$, is a poisonous substance which occurs in some plants. Its molecule consists of two carboxyl groups bonded together:

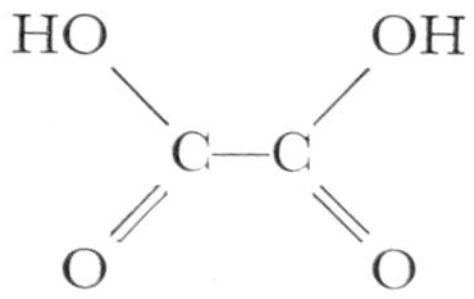

$$
\begin{array}{ccc}
HO & & OH \\
\diagdown & & \diagup \\
& C\!-\!C & \\
\diagup & & \diagdown \\
O & & O
\end{array}
$$

Lactic acid, having the structural formula 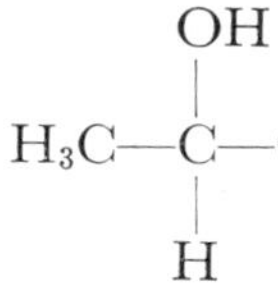
$$
H_3C\!-\!\underset{\underset{H}{|}}{\overset{\overset{OH}{|}}{C}}\!-\!COOH,
$$
contains a hydroxyl group as well as a carboxyl group; it is a hydroxypropionic acid. It is formed when milk sours and when cabbage ferments, and it gives the sour taste to sour milk and sauerkraut. **Tartaric acid,** which occurs in grapes, is a dihydroxydicarboxylic acid, with the structural formula

$$
\begin{array}{l}
\quad\;\; H \\
\quad\;\; | \\
HO\!-\!C\!-\!COOH \\
\quad\;\; | \\
HO\!-\!C\!-\!COOH \\
\quad\;\; | \\
\quad\;\; H
\end{array}
$$

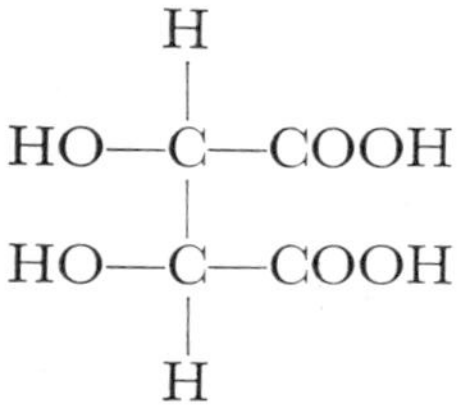

Citric acid, which occurs in the citrus fruits, is a hydroxytricarboxylic acid, with the formula

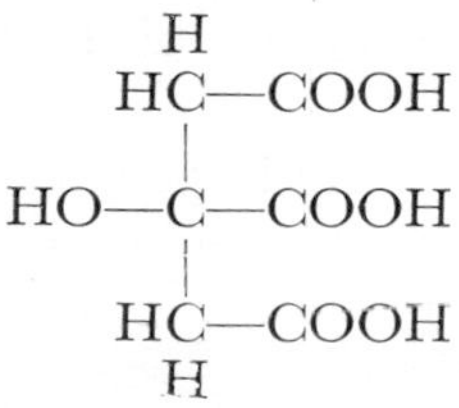

$$
\begin{array}{l}
\quad\;\; H \\
\quad\; HC\!-\!COOH \\
\quad\;\; | \\
HO\!-\!C\!-\!COOH \\
\quad\;\; | \\
\quad\; HC\!-\!COOH \\
\quad\;\; H
\end{array}
$$

Esters are the products of reaction of acids and alcohols. For example, ethyl alcohol and acetic acid react with the elimination of water to produce **ethyl acetate:**

$$C_2H_5OH + CH_3COOH \longrightarrow H_2O + CH_3COOC_2H_5$$

Ethyl acetate is a volatile liquid with a pleasing, fruity odor. It is used as a solvent, especially in lacquers.

Many of the esters have pleasant odors, and are used in perfumes and flavorings. The esters are the principal flavorful and odorous constituents of fruits and flowers.

The natural *fats* and *oils* are also esters, principally of the trihydroxy alcohol glycerol. Animal fats consist mainly of the glyceryl esters of palmitic acid and stearic acid. **Glyceryl oleate,** the glyceryl ester of oleic acid, is found in olive oil, whale oil, and the fats of cold-blooded animals; these fats tend to remain liquid at ordinary temperatures, whereas **glyceryl palmitate** and **glyceryl stearate** form the solid fats.

Esters can be decomposed by boiling with strong alkali, such as sodium hydroxide. This treatment forms the alcohol and the sodium salt of the carboxylic acid. When fat is boiled with sodium hydroxide, glycerol and sodium salts of the fatty acids, sodium palmitate, sodium stearate, and sodium oleate, are formed. These sodium salts of the fatty acids are called *soap*. Soap made from wood ashes and fat (*soft soap*) contains the potassium salts of the fatty acids.

28–6. *Amines and Other Organic Compounds*

The amines are derivatives of ammonia, NH_3, obtained by replacing one or more of the hydrogen atoms by organic radicals. The lighter amines, such as **methylamine,** CH_3NH_2, **dimethylamine,** $(CH_3)_2NH$, and **trimethylamine,** $(CH_3)_3N$, are gases. Trimethylamine has a pronounced fishy odor, and many other amines also have disagreeable odors.

Aniline is aminobenzene, $C_6H_5NH_2$. It is a colorless, oily liquid, which on standing becomes dark in color, because of oxidation to highly colored derivatives. It is used in the manufacture of dyes and other chemicals.

The halogen derivatives of hydrocarbons have some important uses. Four chlorine derivatives of methane can be made, by replacement of successive hydrogen atoms by the halogen:

$$\begin{array}{cc}
\text{H} & \text{Cl} \\
 & \text{C} \\
\text{H} & \text{H}
\end{array}
\qquad
\begin{array}{cc}
\text{H} & \text{Cl} \\
 & \text{C} \\
\text{H} & \text{Cl}
\end{array}
\qquad
\begin{array}{cc}
\text{H} & \text{Cl} \\
 & \text{C} \\
\text{Cl} & \text{Cl}
\end{array}
\qquad
\begin{array}{cc}
\text{Cl} & \text{Cl} \\
 & \text{C} \\
\text{Cl} & \text{Cl}
\end{array}$$

Monochloromethane or methyl chloride | Dichloromethane or methylene chloride | Trichloromethane or chloroform | Tetrachloromethane or carbon tetrachloride

Chloroform and **carbon tetrachloride** are used as solvents; carbon tetrachloride is an important dry-cleaning agent. Chloroform is also used as a general anesthetic.

Care must be taken in the use of carbon tetrachloride that no large amount of its vapor is inhaled, because it damages the liver.

The compound **iodoform**, CHI_3, is a yellow solid substance which finds some use as a disinfectant and antiseptic, especially for the treatment of burns.

Many substances which occur in plant and animal tissues are compounds of nitrogen. One of these, **urea,** is the principal nitrogenous product of metabolism in the animal body (Chap. 29). Urea has the formula $(NH_2)_2CO$, its structural formula being

$$\begin{array}{c}
H_2N \\
\qquad\diagdown \\
\qquad\qquad C{=}O \\
\qquad\diagup \\
H_2N
\end{array}$$

Carbohydrates, Sugars, Polysaccharides.   The *carbohydrates* are substances with the general formula $C_x(H_2O)_y$. They occur widely in nature. The simpler carbohydrates are called *sugars,* and the complex ones, consisting of very large molecules, are called *polysaccharides* (see Chap. 29).

A common simple sugar is **D-glucose** (also called *dextrose* and *grape sugar*), $C_6H_{12}O_6$. It occurs in many fruits, and is present in the blood of animals. Its structural formula (not showing the spatial configuration of bonds around the four central carbon atoms) is

$$\begin{array}{cccccc}
H_2C & \!\!-\!\!-CH & \!\!-\!\!-CH & \!\!-\!\!-CH & \!\!-\!\!-CH & \!\!-\!\!-CH \\
| & | & | & | & | & \| \\
OH & OH & OH & OH & OH & O
\end{array}$$

The molecule thus contains five hydroxyl groups and one aldehyde group.

Ordinary sugar, obtained from sugar cane and sugar beets, is **sucrose,** $C_{12}H_{22}O_{11}$. The molecules of sucrose have a complex structure, consisting of two rings (each containing one oxygen atom), held together by bonds to an oxygen atom as shown in Figure 28-2.

Many other simple carbohydrates occur in nature. These include *fructose* (fruit sugar), *maltose* (malt sugar), and *lactose* (milk sugar).

Important polysaccharides include *starch, glycogen,* and *cellulose.* Starch, $(C_6H_{10}O_5)_x$, occurs in plants, mainly in their seeds or tubers. It is an important constituent of foods. Glycogen, $(C_6H_{10}O_5)_x$, is a substance similar to starch which occurs in the blood and the internal organs, especially the liver, of animals. Glycogen serves as a reservoir of readily available food for the body; whenever the concentration of glucose in the blood becomes low, glycogen is rapidly hydrolyzed into glucose.

Cellulose, which also has the formula $(C_6H_{10}O_5)_x$, is a stable polysaccharide which serves as a structural element for plants, forming the walls of cells. Like starch and glycogen, cellulose consists of long molecules which contain rings of atoms held together by oxygen atoms, in the way shown in Figure 28-2 for the two rings of sucrose.

The sugars have the properties of dissolving readily in water and of crystallizing in rather hard crystals. These properties are attributed to the presence of a number of hydroxyl groups in these molecules, which form hydrogen bonds with water molecules and (in the crystals) with each other.

28–7. Fibers and Plastics

Silk and wool are protein fibers, consisting of long polypeptide chains (see Chap. 29). Cotton and linen are polysaccharides (carbohydrates), with composition $(C_6H_{10}O_5)_x$. These fibers consist of long chains made from carbon, hydrogen, and oxygen atoms, with no nitrogen atoms present.

In recent years synthetic fibers have been made, by synthesizing long molecules in the laboratory. One of these, which has valuable properties, is **nylon.** It is the product of condensation of adipic acid and diaminohexane. These two substances have the following structures:

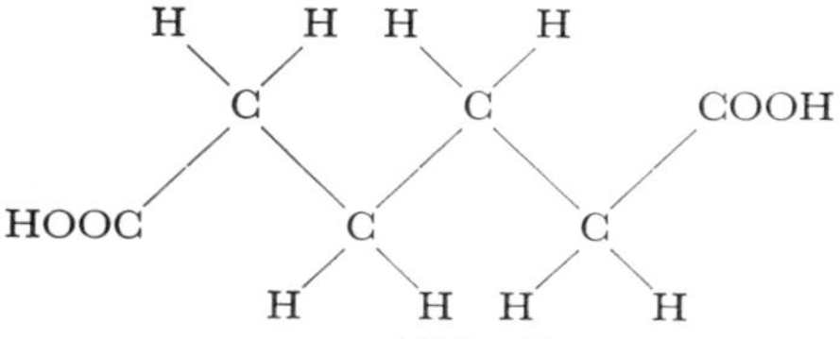

Adipic acid is a chain of four methylene groups with a carboxyl group at each end, and diaminohexane is a similar chain of six methylene groups with an amino group at each end. A molecule of adipic acid can react with a molecule of diaminohexane in the following way:

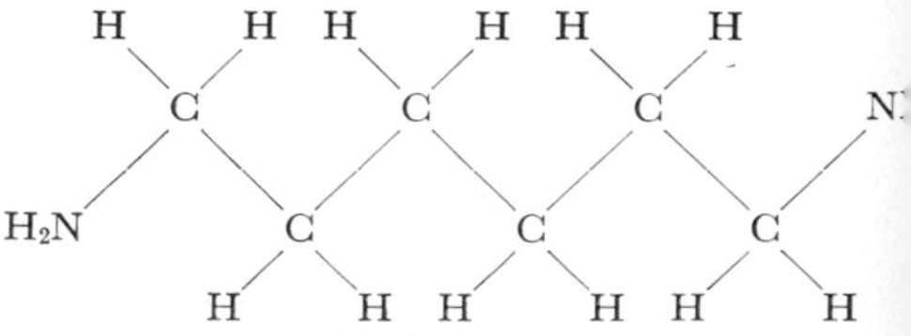

If this process is continued, a very long molecule can be made, in which the adipic acid residues alternate with the diaminohexane residues. Nylon is a fibrous material which consists of these long molecules in approximately parallel orientation.

Other artificial fibers and plastics are made by similar condensation reactions. A *thermolabile plastic* usually is an aggregate of long molecules of this sort which softens upon heating, and can be molded into shape. A *thermosetting plastic* is an aggregate of long molecules containing some reactive groups, capable of further condensation. When this material is molded and heated, these groups react in such a way as to tie the molecules together into a three-dimensional framework, producing a plastic material which cannot be further molded.

With a great number of substances available for use as his starting materials, the chemist has succeeded in making fibers and plastics which are for many purposes superior to natural materials. This field of chemistry, that of synthetic giant molecules, is still a new field, and we may look forward to further great progress in it in the coming years.

Exercises

28-1. What is the difference in the structures of the saturated and the unsaturated hydrocarbons?

28-2. How many isomers of pentane, C_5H_{12}, can you draw?

28-3. What do you suppose the structure of cyclopentane, C_5H_{10}, is? How many isomers of this substance can you draw?

28-4. How does a study of the properties of ortho-xylene pertain to the question of the structure of benzene?

28-5. What is the oxidation number of carbon in each of the following compounds: CH_4, CH_3OH, CH_3OCH_3, H_2CO, $HCOOH$, CO_2? Name these compounds, and draw their structural formulas.

28-6. Which do you think is the more soluble in water, sodium palmitate or ethyl palmitate? in benzene?

28-7. Which do you think is the more soluble in water, acetic acid or stearic acid?

28-8. In what ways does the reaction

$$C_2H_5OH + CH_3COOH \longrightarrow H_2O + CH_3COOC_2H_5$$

differ from the neutralization of acetic acid with sodium hydroxide?

28-9.   Write the chemical reaction for the preparation of soap.

28-10.   What relation is there between sugar, glycogen, and starch?

Books on Organic Chemistry

J. B. Conant, *Organic Chemistry: A Brief Introductive Course*, The Macmillan Co., New York, **1936.**

L. F. and M. Fieser, *Organic Chemistry*, D. C. Heath and Co., Boston, **1950.**

R. C. Fuson and H. R. Snyder, *Organic Chemistry*, John Wiley and Sons, New York, **1942.**

H. J. Lucas, *Organic Chemistry*, American Book Co., New York, **1935.**

Roger J. Williams and Lewis F. Hatch, *An Introduction to Organic Chemistry*, D. Van Nostrand Co., New York, **1948.**

Chapter 29

Biochemistry

Biochemistry is the study of the chemical composition and structure of the human body and other living organisms, of the chemical reactions that take place within these organisms, and of the drugs and other substances that interact with them.

During the past century biochemistry has developed into an important branch of science. We shall not be able in the limited space of the present chapter to give a general survey of this interesting subject, but shall instead have to content ourselves with a simple introductory discussion of a few of its aspects.

29–1. *The Nature of Life*

All of our ideas about life involve chemical reactions. What is it that distinguishes a living organism,* such as a man or some other animal or a plant, from an inanimate object, such as a piece of granite? We recognize that the plant or animal may have several attributes that are not possessed by the rock. The plant or animal has, in general, the power of **reproduction**—the power of having progeny, which are sufficiently similar to itself to be recognized as belonging to the same species of living organisms. The process of reproduction involves chemical reactions, the reactions that take place during the growth of the progeny. The growth of the new organism may occur only during a small fraction of the total lifetime of the animal, or may continue throughout its lifetime.

A plant or animal in general has the ability of ingesting certain

---

* The word *organism* is used to refer to anything that lives or has ever been living—we speak of dead organisms, as well as of living organisms.

materials, foods, subjecting them to chemical reactions, which usually involve the release of energy, and secreting (eliminating) some of the products of the reactions. This process, by which the organism makes use of the food which it ingests by subjecting it to chemical reaction, is called **metabolism.**

Most plants and animals have the ability to respond to their environment. A plant may grow toward the direction from which a beam of light is coming, in response to the stimulus of the beam of light, and an animal may walk or run in a direction indicated by increasing intensity of the odor of a palatable food.

In order to illustrate the difficulty of defining a living organism, let us consider the simplest kinds of matter that have been thought to be alive. These are the *plant viruses*, such as the tomato bushy stunt virus, of which an electron micrograph has been shown as Figure 2-20. These viruses have the power of reproducing themselves when in the appropriate environment. A single molecule (individual organism) of tomato bushy stunt virus, when placed on the leaf of a tomato plant, can cause the material in the cells of the leaf to be in large part converted into replicas of itself. This power of reproduction seems, however, to be the only characteristic of living organisms possessed by the virus. After the particles are formed, they do not grow. They do not ingest food nor carry on any metabolic processes. So far as can be told by use of the electron microscope and by other methods of investigation, the individual particles of the virus are identical with one another, and show no change with time—there is no phenomenon of aging, of growing old. The virus particles seem to have no means of locomotion, and seem not to respond to external stimuli in the way that large living organisms do. But they do have the power of reproducing themselves.

Considering these facts, should we say that a virus is a living organism, or that it is not? At the present time scientists do not agree about the answer to this question—indeed, the question may not be a scientific one at all, but simply a matter of the definition of words. If we were to define a living organism as a material structure with the power of reproducing itself, then we would include the plant viruses among the living organisms. If, however, we require that living organisms also have the property of carrying on some metabolic reactions, then the plant viruses would be described simply as molecules (with molecular weight of the order of magnitude of 10,000,000) which have such a molecular structure as to permit them to catalyze, in a proper medium, a chemical reaction or reactions leading to the synthesis of molecules identical with themselves.

29–2. *The Structure of Living Organisms*

Chemical investigation of the plant viruses has shown that they consist largely of the materials called **proteins,** the nature of which is discussed in the following section. The giant virus particles or molecules, with molecular weight of the order of magnitude of 10,000,000, may perhaps be described as aggregates of smaller molecules, tied together in a definite way. However, very little is known about the nature of these structures. Investigation with the electron microscope has shown that the plant-virus molecules have definite size and shape, but has not given any evidence about their internal structure.

On the other hand, the animal viruses—viruses which grow on animal tissues—arc seen in the electron microscope to have a definite structure. These viruses are in general considerably larger than the plant viruses, their molecular weight being of the order of 1,000,000,000. The vaccinia virus (cowpox virus, used for vaccination against smallpox) is shown by the electron microscope to have roughly the shape of a rectangular box, in the interior of which there are some round particles of material that absorb the beam of electrons more strongly than the remaining material.

Many micro-organisms, such as molds and bacteria, consist of single **cells.** These cells may be just big enough to be seen with an ordinary microscope, having a diameter around 10,000 Å (10^{-4} cm), or they may be much bigger, as large as a millimeter or more in diameter. The cells have a well-organized structure, consisting of a *cell wall*, a few hundred Ångströms in thickness, within which is enclosed a semi-fluid material called *cytoplasm*, and often other structures that can be seen by the microscope. Other plants and animals consist largely of aggregates of cells, which may be of many different kinds in one organism. The muscles, blood-vessel and lymph-vessel walls, tendons, connective tissues, nerves, skin, and other parts of the body of a man consist of cells attached to one another to constitute a well-defined structure. In addition, there are many cells that are not attached to this structure, but float around in the body fluids. Most numerous among these cells are the *red corpuscles* of the blood. The red corpuscles in man are flattened disks, about 70,000 Å in diameter and 10,000 Å thick. The number of red cells in a human adult is very large. There are about 5 million red cells per cubic millimeter of blood, and a man contains about 5 liters of blood— that is, 5 million cubic millimeters of blood. Accordingly, there are 25×10^{12} red cells in his body. In addition, thcre are many other cells, some of them small, like the red cells, and some somewhat larger—a single nerve cell may be about 10,000 Å in diameter and 100 centimeters long, extending from the toe to the spinal cord. The total number of cells in the human body is about 10^{14}. The amount of *organization* in the human organism is accordingly very great.

The human body does not consist of cells alone. In addition there are the *bones*, which have been laid down as excretions of bone-making cells. The bones consist of inorganic constituents, calcium hydroxyphosphate, $Ca_5(PO_4)_3OH$, and calcium carbonate, and an organic constituent, *collagen*, which is a protein. The body also contains the body fluids blood and lymph, as well as fluids which are secreted by special organs, such as saliva and the digestive juices. Very many different chemical substances are present in these fluids.

The structure of cells is determined by their framework materials, which constitute the cell walls and, in some cases, reinforcing frameworks within the cells. In plants the carbohydrate cellulose, described in the preceding chapter, is the most important constituent of the cell walls. In animals the framework materials are proteins. Moreover, the cell contents consist largely of proteins. For example, a red cell is a thin membrane enclosing a medium which consists of 60% water, 5% miscellaneous materials, and 35% **hemoglobin,** an iron-containing protein, which has molecular weight 68,000, and has the power of combining reversibly with oxygen. It is this power that permits the blood to combine with a large amount of oxygen in the lungs, and to carry it to the tissues, making it available there for oxidation of foodstuffs and body constituents. It has been mentioned earlier in this section that the simplest forms of matter with the power of reproducing themselves, the viruses, consist largely of proteins, as do also the most complex living organisms.

29–3. *Amino Acids and Proteins*

Proteins may well be considered the most important of all the substances present in plants and animals. Proteins occur either as separate molecules, usually with very large molecular weight, ranging from about 10,000 to many millions, or as reticular constituents of cells, constituting their structural framework (Fig. 29-1). The human body contains many thousands of different proteins, which have special structures that permit them to carry out specific tasks.

All proteins are nitrogenous substances, containing approximately 16% nitrogen, together with carbon, hydrogen, oxygen, and often other elements such as sulfur, phosphorus, iron (four atoms of iron are present in each molecule of hemoglobin), and copper.

Amino Acids. When proteins are heated in acidic or basic solution they undergo hydrolysis, producing substances called amino acids. Amino acids are carboxylic acids in which one hydrogen atom has been replaced by an amino group, —NH_2. The amino acids which are obtained from proteins are *alpha* amino acids, with the amino group attached to the carbon atom next to the carboxyl group (this carbon atom is called the alpha carbon atom). The simplest of these amino acids is **glycine,** $CH_2(NH_2)COOH$. The other natural amino acids contain another group, usually called R, in place of one of the hydrogen atoms on the alpha carbon atom, their general formula thus being $CHR(NH_2)COOH$.

The amino group is sufficiently basic and the carboxyl group is sufficiently acidic so that in solution in water the proton is transferred from the carboxyl group to the amino group. The carboxyl group is thus converted into a carboxyl ion, and the amino group into a substituted ammonium ion. The structure of glycine and of the other amino acids in aqueous solution is accordingly the following:

FIG. 29-1

Electron micrograph of an edestin crystal, showing individual molecules in the octahedral face (magnification 200,000 ✕). Within the circumscribed area, and in other places where the surface has not been disturbed during preparation, the molecules form a hexagonal pattern. The molecules are about 80 Å in diameter, and the molecular weight is 300,000. Note the molecular layers growing out over the supporting film from the edges of the crystal. Edestin is a protein found in wheat, corn, and other seeds. Reference: C. E. Hall, J. Am. Chem. Soc., 71, 2915 (1949).

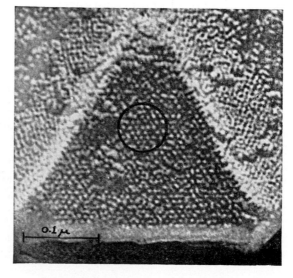

o.1 µ

The amino groups and carboxyl groups of most substances dissolved in animal or plant liquids, which usually have *p*H about 7, are internally ionized in this way, to form an ammonium ion group and a carboxyl ion group within the same molecule.

There are twenty-four amino acids that have been recognized as important constituents of proteins. Their names are given in Table 29-1, together with the formulas of the characteristic group R. Some of the amino acids have an extra carboxyl group or an extra amino group. There is one double amino acid, *cystine*, which is closely related to a simple amino acid, *cysteine*. Four of the amino acids contain *heterocyclic rings*—rings of carbon atoms and one or more other atoms, in this case nitrogen atoms. Two of the amino acids given in the table, *asparagine* and *glutamine*, are closely related to two others, *aspartic acid* and *glutamic acid*, differing from them only in having the extra carboxyl group

$$\text{changed into an amide group,} \quad -C \overset{\displaystyle O}{\underset{\displaystyle NH_2}{\big\langle}}$$

Proteins are important constituents of foods. They are digested by the digestive juices in the stomach and intestines, being split in the process of digestion into small molecules, probably mainly the amino acids themselves. These small molecules are able to pass through the walls of the stomach and intestines into the blood stream, by which they are carried around into the tissues, where they may then serve as building stones for the manufacture of the body proteins. Sometimes people who are ill and cannot digest foods satisfactorily are fed by the injection of a solution of amino acids directly into the blood stream. A solution of amino acids for this purpose is usually obtained by hydrolyzing proteins.

Although all of the amino acids listed in Table 29-1 are present in the proteins of the human body, not all of them need to be in the food. Experiments have been carried out which show that nine of the amino acids are essential to man. These nine **essential amino acids** are *histidine, lysine, tryptophan, phenylalanine, leucine, isoleucine, threonine, methionine,* and *valine.* The human body seems to be able to manufacture the others, which are called the non-essential amino acids. Some organisms that we usually consider to be simpler than man have greater powers than the human organism, in that they are able to manufacture all of the amino acids from inorganic constituents. The red bread mold, *Neurospora,* has this power.

TABLE 29-1   *The Principal Amino Acids Occurring in Proteins*

MONOAMINOMONOCARBOXYLIC ACIDS

Glycine, aminoacetic acid — $-R = -H$

Alanine, α-aminopropionic acid — $-CH_3$

Serine, α-amino-β-hydroxypropionic acid — $-CH_2OH$

Threonine, α-amino-β-hydroxybutyric acid — $-CH{\Large<}^{CH_3}_{OH}$

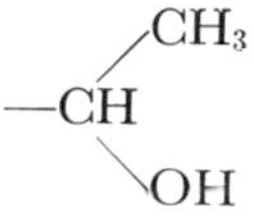

Methionine, α-amino-γ-methylmercaptobutyric acid — $-CH_2-CH_2-S-CH_3$

Valine, α-amino-isovaleric acid — $-CH{\Large<}^{CH_3}_{CH_3}$

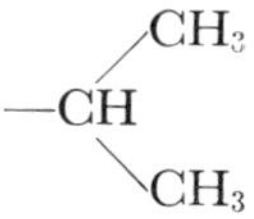

Norvaline, α-aminovaleric acid — $-CH_2-CH_2-CH_3$

Leucine, α-amino-isocaproic acid — $-CH_2-CH{\Large<}^{CH_3}_{CH_3}$

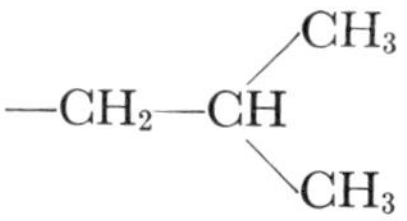

Isoleucine, α-amino-β-methylvaleric acid — $-CH{\Large<}^{CH_2-CH_3}_{CH_3}$

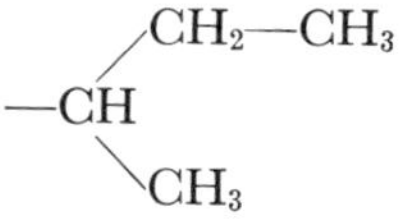

Phenylalanine, α-amino-β-phenylpropionic acid — $-CH_2-$ (benzene ring)

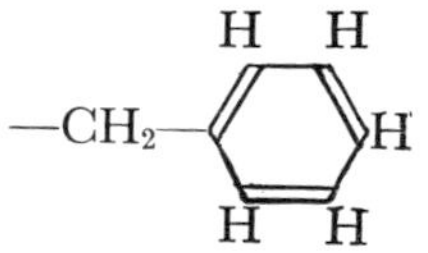

Tyrosine, α-amino-β-(para-hydroxyphenyl)propionic acid — $-CH_2-$ (para-hydroxyphenyl ring) OH

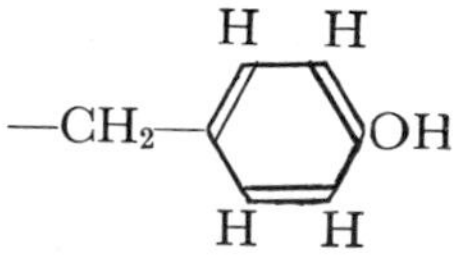

Cysteine, α-amino-β-sulfhydrylpropionic acid — $-CH_2-SH$

MONOAMINODICARBOXYLIC ACIDS

Aspartic acid, aminosuccinic acid — $-CH_2-COOH$

Glutamic acid, α-aminoglutaric acid — $-CH_2-CH_2-COOH$

TABLE 29-1 (*continued*)

Hydroxyglutamic acid, α-amino-β-hydroxyglutaric acid

$$-CH \begin{cases} CH_2-COOH \\ OH \end{cases}$$

DIAMINOMONOCARBOXYLIC ACIDS

Arginine, α-amino-δ-guanidinevaleric acid

$$-CH_2-CH_2-CH_2-NH-C \begin{cases} NH \\ NH_2 \end{cases}$$

Lysine, α,ϵ-diaminocaproic acid

$$-CH_2-CH_2-CH_2-CH_2-NH_2$$

DIAMINODICARBOXYLIC ACID

Cystine, di-β-thio-α-aminopropionic acid

$$-CH_2-S-S-CH_2-$$

AMINO ACIDS CONTAINING HETEROCYCLIC RINGS

Histidine, α-amino-β-imidazolepropionic acid

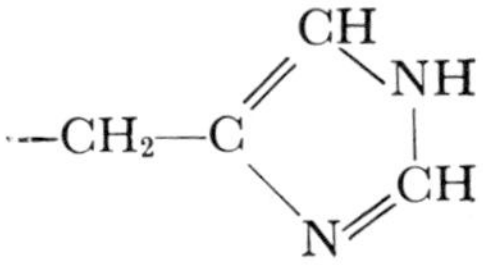

Proline, 2-pyrrolidinecarboxylic acid*

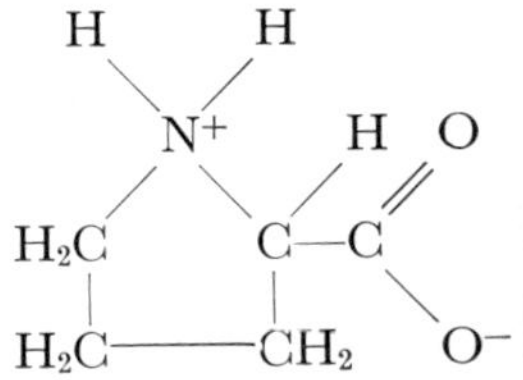

Hydroxyproline, 4-hydroxy-2-pyrrolidinecarboxylic acid*

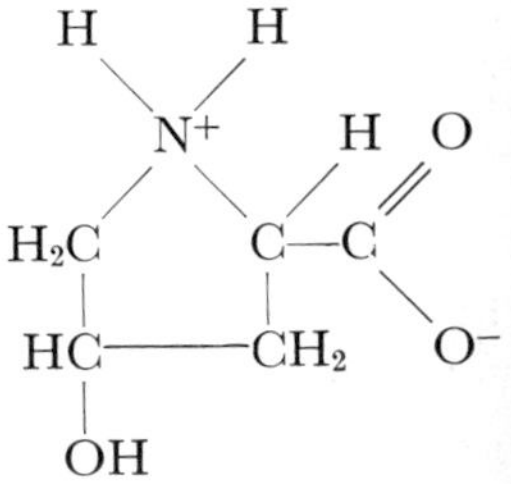

Tryptophan, α-amino-β-indolepropionic acid†

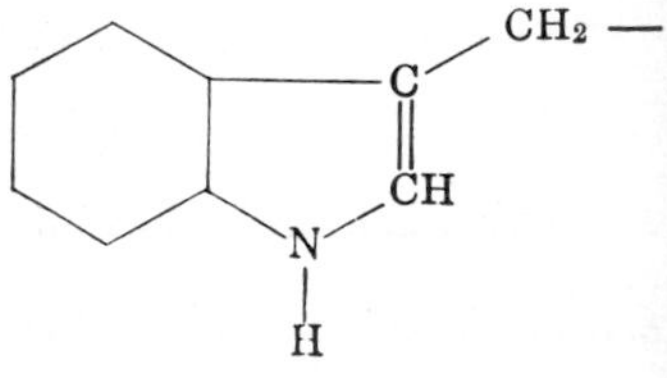

TABLE 29-1 (*continued*)

AMINO ACIDS CONTAINING AN AMIDE GROUP

Asparagine, aminosuccinic acid monoamide

$$-CH_2-C\overset{O}{\underset{NH_2}{}}$$

Glutamine, α-aminoglutaric acid monoamide

$$-CH_2-CH_2-C\overset{O}{\underset{NH_2}{}}$$

---

* The formulas given for proline and hydroxyproline are those of the complete molecules, and not just of the groups R.

† The hexagon represents a benzene ring.

Protein foods for man may be classed as *good protein foods*, those that contain all of the essential amino acids, and *poor protein foods*, those that are lacking in one or more of the essential amino acids. *Casein*, the principal protein in milk, is a good protein, from this point of view, whereas *gelatin*, a protein obtained by boiling bones, skin, and tendons (partial hydrolysis of the insoluble protein collagen produces gelatin) is a poor protein. Gelatin contains no tryptophan and little or no threonine.

Right-handed and Left-handed Molecules.   Every amino acid except glycine can exist in two isomeric forms. These two forms, called L (levo) and D (dextro) forms, are identical with one another except for the arrangement in space of the four groups attached to the α-carbon atom. The two molecules are *mirror images* of one another—one can be called the left-handed molecule, and the other the right-handed molecule.* Figure 29-2 shows the two isomers of the amino acid alanine, in which R is the methyl group, CH_3.

A most extraordinary fact is that only one of the two isomers of each of the twenty-four amino acids has been found to occur in plant and animal proteins, and that this isomer has the same configuration for all of these amino acids; that is, the hydrogen atom, carboxyl ion group, and ammonium ion group occupy the same position relative to the group R around the alpha carbon atom. This configuration is called the L configuration—*proteins are built entirely of L-amino acids.*

This is a very puzzling fact. Nobody knows why it is that we are

* The term *optical isomers* is used to describe right-handed and left-handed molecules of this sort, because these isomers have the power of rotating the plane of polarization of polarized light. Two optical isomers rotate the plane of polarization by equal amounts in opposite directions. The isomers are also called *stereoisomers*.

built of L-amino acid molecules, rather than of D-amino acid molecules. All the proteins that have been investigated, obtained from animals and from plants, from higher organisms and from very simple organisms—bacteria, molds, even viruses—are found to have been made of L-amino acids. Now right-handed molecules and left-handed molecules have exactly the same properties, so far as their interaction with ordinary substances is concerned—they differ in their properties only when they interact with other right-handed or left-handed molecules. The earth might just as well be populated with living organisms made of

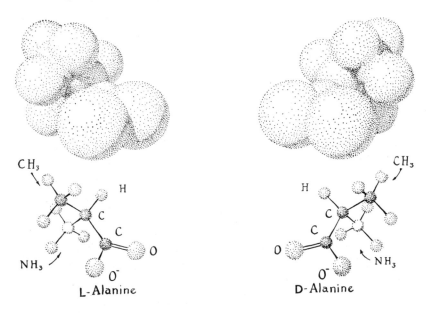

L-Alanine   D-Alanine

FIG. 29-2   *The two stereoisomers of the amino acid alanine.*

D-amino acids as with those made of L-amino acids. A man who was suddenly converted into an exact mirror image of himself would not at first know that anything had changed about him, except that he would write with his left hand, instead of his right, his hair would be parted on the right side instead of the left, his heartbeat would show his heart to be on the right side, and so on; he could drink water, inhale air and use the oxygen in it for combustion, exhale carbon dioxide, and carry on other bodily functions just as well as ever—so long as he did not eat any ordinary food. If he were to eat ordinary plant or animal food, he would find that he could not digest it. He could be kept alive only on a diet containing synthetic D-amino acids, made in the chemical laboratory. He could not have any children, unless he could find a wife who had been subjected to the same process of reflection into a mirror image of her original self. We see that there is the possibility that the earth might have been populated with two completely independent kinds of life—plants, animals, human beings of two kinds, who could not use one another's food, could not produce hybrid progeny.

No one knows why living organisms are constructed of L-amino acids. We have no strong reason to believe that molecules resembling proteins could not be built up of equal numbers of right-handed and left-handed amino-acid molecules. Perhaps the protein molecules that are made of amino-acid molecules of one sort only are especially suited to the construction of a living organism—but if this is so, we do not know why. Nor do we know why it is that living organisms have evolved in the L-system rather than in the D-system. The suggestion has been made that the first living organism happened by chance to make use of a few molecules with the L configuration, which were present with D molecules in equal number; and that all succeeding forms of life that have evolved have continued to use L-amino acid molecules through inheritance of the character from the original form of life. Perhaps a better explanation than this can be found—but I do not know what it is.

The Structure of Proteins.   During the past century much effort has been devoted by scientists to the problem of the structure of proteins. This is a very important problem; if it were to be solved, we should have a much better understanding than at present of the nature of physiological reactions, and the knowledge of the structure of protein molecules would probably help in the attack on important medical problems, such as the problem of the control of heart disease, cancer, and other diseases.

In the period between 1900 and 1910 strong evidence was obtained by the German chemist Emil Fischer (1852–1919) to indicate that the amino acids in proteins are combined into long chains, called *polypeptide chains*. For example, two molecules of glycine can be condensed together, with elimination of water, to form the double molecule glycylglycine, shown in Figure 28-2. The bond formed in this way is called a *peptide bond*. The process of forming these bonds can be continued, resulting in the production of a long chain containing many amino-acid residues, as shown in Figure 28-2.

Chemical methods have been developed to determine how many polypeptide chains there are in a protein molecule. These methods involve the use of a reagent (fluorodinitrobenzene) which combines with the free α-amino group of the amino-acid residue at the end of the polypeptide chain, to form a colored complex, which can be isolated and identified after the protein has been hydrolyzed into its constituent amino acids (and the end amino acid with the colored group attached). For example, lysozyme, a protein in tears and in egg white which has the power of destroying bacteria, has been found by use of the ultra-centrifuge to have molecular weight about 14,000, and to consist of about 125 amino-acid residues. Application of the chemical method mentioned above has shown that there is only one free α-amino group, and accordingly it has been concluded that the molecule consists of a single polypeptide chain. If this polypeptide chain were to be stretched out it would be about 450 Å long. However, it has been found, by use of the ultracentrifuge, X-ray diffraction, and other methods of investigation, that the lysozyme molecule is approximately spherical in shape, with diameter about 25 Å. Hence the polypeptide chain cannot be stretched out, but must be folded back and forth, to produce the globular molecule.

The order of amino-acid residues in the polypeptide chains has only recently been determined, for a single protein, insulin. The insulin molecule has molecular weight about 12,000. It consists of four poly-peptide chains, of which two contain 21 amino-acid residues apiece, and the other two contain 30. The sequence of amino acids in the short chains and in the long chains was determined, in the years between 1945 and 1952, by the English biochemist F. Sanger and his collaborators. The four chains in the molecule are attached to one another by sulfur-sulfur bonds, between the halves of cystine residues (see Table 29-1).

Considering their structure, we see that the existence of a great number of different proteins (perhaps 50,000 different proteins in one human being) is not surprising. Protein molecules might differ from one another not only in the numbers of residues of different amino acids, but also in the order of the residues in the polypeptide chains, and the way in which the chains are folded. The number of possible structures is extremely great.

Proteins such as lysozyme, insulin, and hemoglobin have certain special properties that make them valuable to the organism. Lysozyme helps to protect the organism against infection, through its power of causing some bacteria to split open. Insulin is a hormone that assists in the process of oxidation of sugar in the body. Hemoglobin has the power of combining reversibly with oxygen, permitting it to attach oxygen molecules to itself in the lungs, and to liberate them in the tissues. Moreover, when hemoglobin combines with oxygen it becomes a stronger acid than before. There are eight acidic groups in the hemo-globin molecule which interact with the iron atom in such a way that when the four oxygen molecules are attached to the four iron atoms the acidic groups become stronger: the blood that comes to the lungs is loaded down with carbon dioxide, in the form of hydrogen carbonate ion, and the increase in acidity of these groups when oxygen combines with the hemoglobin helps the hydrogen carbonate ion to be decomposed into carbon dioxide, which then escapes into the air that is to be exhaled. These well-defined properties show that the protein molecules have very definite structures.

A protein that retains its characteristic properties is called a *native protein:* hemoglobin as it exists in the red cell or in a carefully prepared hemoglobin solution, in which it still has the power of combining reversibly with oxygen, is called native hemoglobin. Many proteins lose their characteristic properties very easily. They are then said to have been *denatured*. Hemoglobin can be denatured simply by heating its solution to 65° C. It then coagulates, to form a brick-red insoluble coagulum of denatured hemoglobin. Most other proteins are also denatured by heating to approximately this temperature. Egg white, for example, is a solution consisting mainly of the protein *ovalbumin*, with molecular weight 43,000. Ovalbumin is a soluble protein. When its solution is heated for a little while at about 65° C the ovalbumin is denatured, forming an insoluble white coagulum of denatured ovalbumin. This phenomenon is observed when an egg is cooked.

It is believed that the process of denaturation involves uncoiling the polypeptide chains from the characteristic structure of the native protein. In the coagulum of denatured hemoglobin or denatured ovalbumin the uncoiled polypeptide chains of different molecules of the protein have become tangled up with one another in such a way that they cannot be separated; hence the denatured protein is insoluble. Some chemical agents, including strong acid, strong alkali, and alcohol, are good denaturing agents.

The principal method of folding polypeptide chains in proteins has recently been discovered, through application of the X-ray diffraction technique. The polypeptide chain is folded into a helix, as shown in Figure 29-3. There are about 3.6 amino-acid residues per turn of the helix—about 18 residues in 5 turns. Each residue is linked to residues in the preceding and following turns by hydrogen bonds between the N—H groups and the oxygen atom of the C=O group. The side chains R of the different residues project radially from the helix; there is plenty of room for them, so that the sequence of residues can be an arbitrary one. This configuration is called the α helix.

Many fibrous proteins, including hair, fingernails, horn, and muscle, consist of polypeptide chains with the configuration of the α helix, arranged approximately parallel to one another, with the axis of the helix in the direction of the fiber. In some of these proteins the polypeptide chains, with the configuration of the α helix, are twisted about one another, to form cables or ropes (Fig. 29-4). Hair and horn can be stretched out to over twice their normal length; this process involves breaking the hydrogen bonds of the α helix, and forcing the polypeptide chains into a stretched configuration. Silk fibers consist of polypeptide chains with the stretched configuration, attached to one another by hydrogen bonds that extend laterally.

It has been found that lysozyme, insulin, hemoglobin, and many

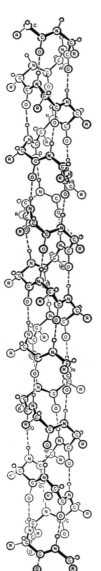

FIG. 29-3

A drawing of the α helix, a hydrogen-bonded helical configuration of the polypeptide chain present in many proteins. The polypeptide chain is coiled into the configuration of a left-handed screw, with about 3.6 amino-acid residues per turn of the helix. The circles labeled R represent the side chains of the various amino-acid residues.

FIG. 29-4 *A drawing representing the molecular structure of hair, fingernail, muscle, and related fibrous proteins. The protein molecules have the configuration of the α helix (Fig. 29-3); each molecule is represented in this drawing as a rod with circular cross section. These fibrous proteins contain seven-strand cables, consisting of a central α helix and six others which are twisted about it, in the direction of a right-handed screw. The spaces between these cables are filled with additional α helixes.*

other soluble proteins also have polypeptide chains folded into the configuration of the α helix. In these molecules an individual polypeptide chain does not form a single helix, but instead coils into a short segment, with the configuration of the α helix—perhaps half a dozen turns of the helix—and then bridges over to another helical segment.

29–4. *Metabolic Processes; Enzymes and Their Action*

The chemical reactions that take place in a living organism are called *metabolic processes* (Greek *metabole*, change). These reactions are of very many kinds. Let us consider what happens to food that is ingested. The food may contain complex carbohydrates, especially starch, that are split up into simple sugars in the process of digestion, and then pass through the walls of the digestive tract into the blood stream. The sugars may then be converted, in the liver, into glycogen (animal starch), which has the same formula as starch, $(C_6H_{10}O_5)_x$, where x is a large number. Glycogen and other polysaccharides constitute one of the important sources of energy for animals. They combine with oxygen to form carbon dioxide and water, with liberation of energy, part of which can be used for doing work, and part to keep the body warm.

We have mentioned before that proteins in foodstuffs are split in the stomach and intestines into amino acids or simple peptides, which pass through the walls into the blood stream, and then may be built up into the special proteins needed by the organism. A process of tearing down the proteins of the body also takes place. For example, red cells have a lifetime of a few weeks, at the end of which they are destroyed, being replaced by newly formed red cells. The nitrogen of the protein molecules that are torn down is eliminated in the urine, as urea, $CO(NH_2)_2$.

Fats that are ingested are also decomposed in the process of digestion into simpler substances, which then are used by the body for fuel and as structural material.

Some of the chemical reactions that take place in the body can also be made to take place in beakers or flasks in the laboratory. For example, a protein can be decomposed into amino acids in the laboratory by adding strong acids to it and boiling for a long time. Similarly, sugar can be oxidized to carbon dioxide and water; if a little cigarette ash or other solid material is rubbed onto a cube of sugar, the sugar can be lighted by a match, and it will then burn in air, producing carbon dioxide and water:

$$C_{12}H_{22}O_{11} + 12O_2 \longrightarrow 12CO_2 + 11H_2O$$

However, it has not been found possible to cause these chemical reactions to take place in the laboratory at the temperature of the human body, except in the presence of special substances obtained from plants or animals. These substances, which are called **enzymes,** are proteins that have a catalytic power for certain reactions. Thus the saliva contains a special protein, an enzyme called *salivary amylase* or *ptyalin*, which has the power of catalyzing the decomposition of starch into a sugar, maltose, $C_{12}H_{22}O_{11}$. The reaction that is catalyzed by salivary amylase is

$$(C_6H_{10}O_5)_x + \frac{x}{2} H_2O \longrightarrow \frac{x}{2} C_{12}H_{22}O_{11}$$

Saliva is mixed with a food, such as potato, while the food is being chewed, and during the first few minutes that the food is in the stomach the salivary amylase causes the conversion of the starch into maltose to take place.

Similarly, there is an enzyme in the stomach, *pepsin*, which has the power of serving as a very effective catalyst for the reaction of hydrolysis of proteins into amino acids—that is, for splitting the peptide bond by reaction with water, to form an amino group and a carboxyl group. Pepsin does its work most effectively in a somewhat acidic solution. Gastric juice is, in fact, rather strongly acidic, its *p*H being about 0.8— it is hence somewhat more strongly acidic than 0.1 *F* hydrochloric acid.

The stomach also contains an enzyme, *rennin*, which assists in the digestion of milk, and another enzyme, *lipase*, which catalyzes the decomposition of fats into simpler substances. Additional enzymes involved in the digestion of polysaccharides, proteins, and fats take part in the continuation of the digestion in the intestines; these enzymes are contained in the intestinal juice, pancreatic juice, and bile.

The chemical reactions that take place in the blood and in the cells of the body are also in general catalyzed by enzymes. For example, the process of oxidation of sugar is a complicated one, involving a number of steps, and it is believed that a special enzyme is present to catalyze each of these steps. It has been estimated that there may be twenty thousand or thirty thousand different enzymes in the human body, each constructed in such a way as to permit it to serve as an effective catalyst for a particular chemical reaction useful to the organism.

In recent years many enzymes have been isolated and purified. Many have, indeed, been crystallized. A great deal of work has been done in an effort to discover the mechanism of the catalytic activity of enzymes. So far, however, no one has succeeded in determining the structure of any enzyme, nor in finding out how the enzyme does its job. This general problem is one of the most important of all of the problems of biochemistry.

29–5. *Vitamins*

It was mentioned above that man requires nine amino acids in his diet in order to keep in good health. It is not enough, however, that the diet contain proteins that provide these nine amino acids, and a sufficient supply of carbohydrates and fats to provide energy. Other substances, both inorganic and organic, are also essential to health.

Among the inorganic constituents that must be present in foods in order that a human being be kept in good health we may mention sodium ion, chloride ion, potassium ion, calcium ion, magnesium ion, iodide ion, phosphorus (which may be ingested as phosphate), and several of the transition metals. Iron is necessary for the synthesis of hemoglobin and of some other protein molecules in the body which serve as enzymes; in the absence of sufficient iron in the diet anemia will develop. Copper is also required; it seems to be involved in the process of manufacture of hemoglobin and the other iron-containing compounds in the body.

The organic compounds other than the essential amino acids which are required for health are called *vitamins*. Man is known to require at least thirteen vitamins: vitamin A, B_1 (thiamine), B_2 (riboflavin), B_6 (pyridoxin), B_{12}, C (ascorbic acid), D, K, niacin, pantothenic acid, inositol, para-aminobenzoic acid, and biotin.

Although it has been recognized for over a century that certain diseases occur when the diet is restricted, and can be prevented by additions to the diet (such as lime juice for the prevention of scurvy), the identification of the essential food factors as chemical substances was not made until a few years ago. Progress in the isolation of these substances and in the determination of their structure has been rapid in recent years, and many of the vitamins are now being made synthetically, for use as dietary supplements. It is usually possible for a diet to be obtained that provides all of the essential food substances in satisfactory amounts, but in some cases it is wise to have the diet supplemented by vitamin preparations.

Vitamin A has the formula $C_{20}H_{29}OH$, and the structure

$$\begin{array}{ccccccc}
H_3C \quad CH_3 & & CH_3 & & CH_3 & & \\
\diagdown\diagup & & | & & | & & \\
C \quad CH & C & CH & C & CH_2 & \\
\diagup\diagdown\diagup\diagdown & \diagup\diagdown & \diagup\diagdown & \diagup\diagdown & \diagup\diagdown & \\
H_2C \quad C \quad CH & CH & CH & CH & OH \\
| \quad \| & & & & & \\
H_2C \quad C & & & & & \\
\diagdown\diagup\diagdown & & & & & \\
CH_2 \quad CH_3 & & & & &
\end{array}$$

It is a yellow, oily substance, which occurs in nature in butter fat and fish oils. Lack of vitamin A in the diet causes a scaly condition of the eyes, and similar abnormality of the skin in general, together with a decreased resistance to infection of the eyes and skin. In addition there occurs a decreased ability to see at night, called *night-blindness*. There are two mechanisms for vision, one situated in the cones of the retina of the eye, which are especially concentrated in the neighborhood of the fovea (the center of vision), and the other situated in the rods of the retina. Color vision, which is the ordinary vision, used when the intensity of light is normal, involves the retinal cones. Night vision, which operates when the intensity of light is very small, involves the rods; it is not associated with a recognition of color. It has been found that a certain protein, *visual purple*, which occurs in the rods, takes part in the process of night vision. Vitamin A is the prosthetic group of the visual purple molecule, and a deficiency in this vitamin leads for this reason to a decrease in the ability to see at night.

A protein such as visual purple which has a characteristic chemical group other than the amino-acid residues as part of its structure is called a *conjugated protein*. Such a characteristic group in a conjugated protein is called a *prosthetic group* (Greek *prosthesis*, an addition). Hemoglobin is another example of a conjugated protein. Each hemoglobin molecule consists of a simple protein called globin to which there are attached four prosthetic groups called *heme groups*. The formula of the heme group is $C_{34}H_{32}O_4N_4Fe$.

It is not essential that vitamin A itself be present in food in order to prevent the vitamin A deficiency symptoms. Certain hydrocarbons, the *carotenes*, with formula $C_{40}H_{56}$ (similar in structure to lycopene, Fig. 28-2), can be converted into vitamin A in the body. These substances, which are designated by the name *provitamin A*, are red and yellow substances which are found in carrots, tomatoes, and other vegetables and fruits, as well as in butter, milk, green leafy vegetables, and eggs.

Thiamine, vitamin B$_1$, has the following formula (that shown is for thiamine chloride):

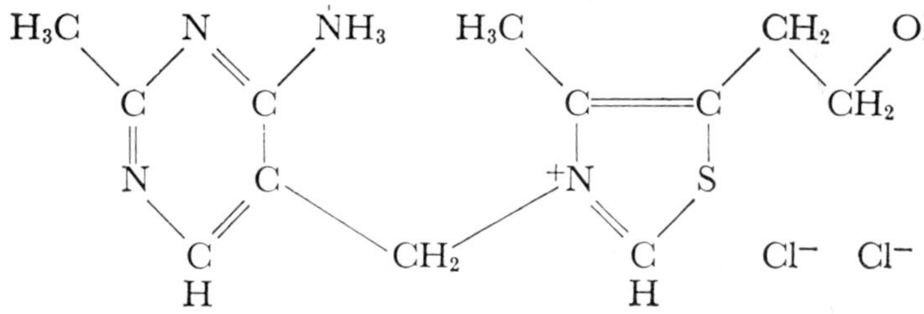
H₃C
N
NH₃
H₃C
CH₂
OH
C
C
C
C
CH₂
N
C
+N
S
C
H
CH₂
C
H
Cl⁻ Cl⁻

A lack of thiamine in the diet causes the disease beri-beri, a nerve disease which in past years was common in the Orient. Just before 1900 it was found by Eijkman in Java that beri-beri occurred as a consequence of a diet consisting largely of polished rice, and that it could be cured by adding the rice polishings to the diet. In 1911 Casimir Funk assumed that beri-beri and similar diseases were due to a substance present in a satisfactory diet and missing from a deficient diet, and he attempted to isolate the substance the lack of which was responsible for beri-beri. He coined the name "vitamin" for substances of this sort (he spelled it "vitamine" because he thought that the substances were amines). The structure of vitamin B$_1$, thiamine, was determined by R. R. Williams, E. R. Buchman, and their collaborators in 1936.

Thiamine seems to be important for metabolic processes in the cells of the body, but the exact way in which it operates is not known. There is some evidence that it is the prosthetic group for an enzyme involved in the oxidation of carbohydrates. The vitamin is present in potatoes, whole cereals, milk, pork, eggs, and other vegetables and meats.

Riboflavin (vitamin B$_2$) has the following structure:

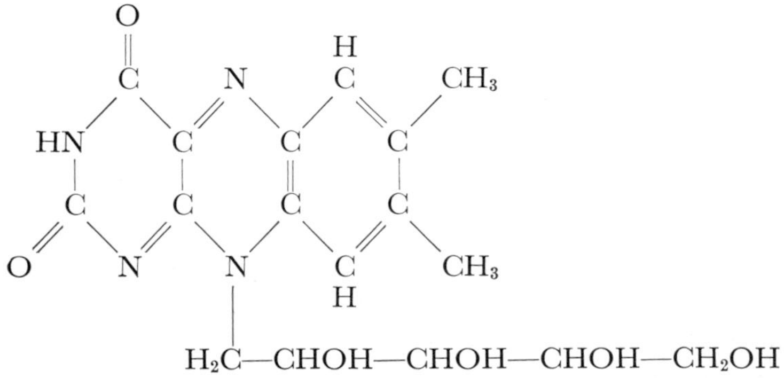
O
H
C
N
C
CH₃
HN
C
C
C
C
C
C
C
O
N
N
C
CH₃
H
H₂C—CHOH—CHOH—CHOH—CH₂OH

It seems to be essential for growth and for a healthy condition of the skin. Riboflavin is known to be the prosthetic group of an enzyme, called *yellow enzyme*, which catalyzes the oxidation of glucose and certain other substances in the animal body.

Vitamin B$_6$ (pyridoxin) has the formula

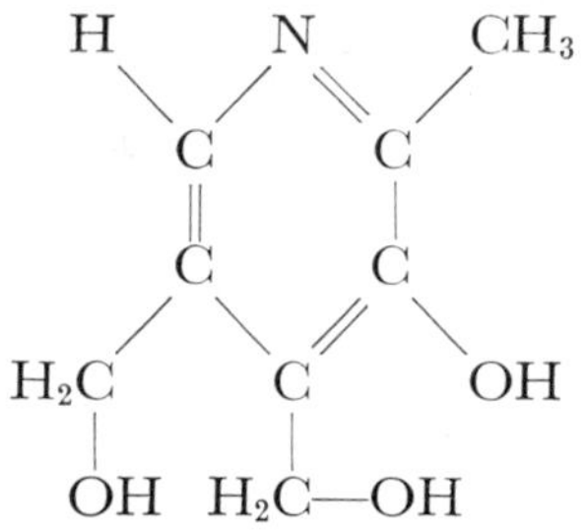

It is present in yeast, liver, rice polishings, and other plant and animal foods, and is also produced synthetically. It has the power of stimulating growth, and of preventing skin eruptions (dermatitis).

Vitamin B$_{12}$ is involved in the manufacture of the red corpuscles of the blood. It can be used for the treatment of pernicious anemia, and it is perhaps the most potent substance known in its physiological activity: 1 microgram per day (1×10^{-6} g) of vitamin B$_{12}$ is effective in the control of the disease. The vitamin can be isolated from liver tissue, and is also produced by molds and other micro-organisms. The structure of the molecule of vitamin B$_{12}$ has not yet been determined. It is known that the molecular weight is about 1,400, and that each molecule contains one cobalt atom. This is the only compound of cobalt that is known to be present in the human body.

Ascorbic acid, vitamin C, is a water-soluble vitamin of great importance. It has the following formula:

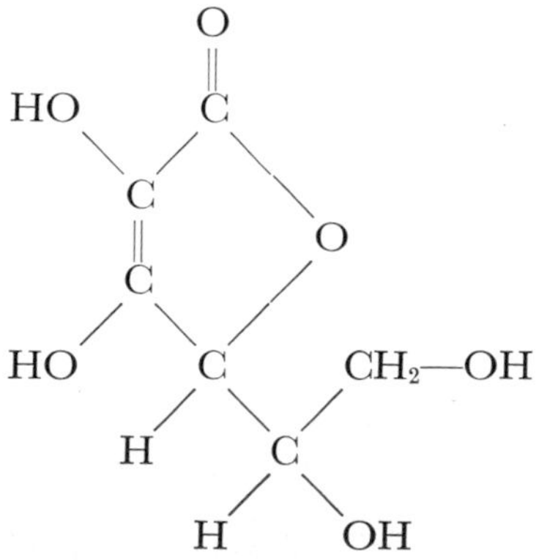

A deficiency of vitamin C in the diet leads to scurvy, a disease characterized by loss of weight, general weakness, hemorrhagic condition of the gums and skin, loosening of the teeth, and other symptoms. Sound tooth development seems to depend upon a satisfactory supply of this vitamin, and a deficiency is thought to cause a tendency to incidence of a number of diseases.

The vitamin is present in many foods, especially fresh green peppers, turnip greens, parsnip greens, spinach, orange juice, and tomato juice. The daily requirement of vitamin C is about 60 mg.

Vitamin D is necessary in the diet for the prevention of rickets, a disease involving malformation of the bones and unsatisfactory development of the teeth. There are several substances with anti-rachitic activity. The form that occurs in oils from fish livers is called vitamin D_3; it has the following chemical structure:

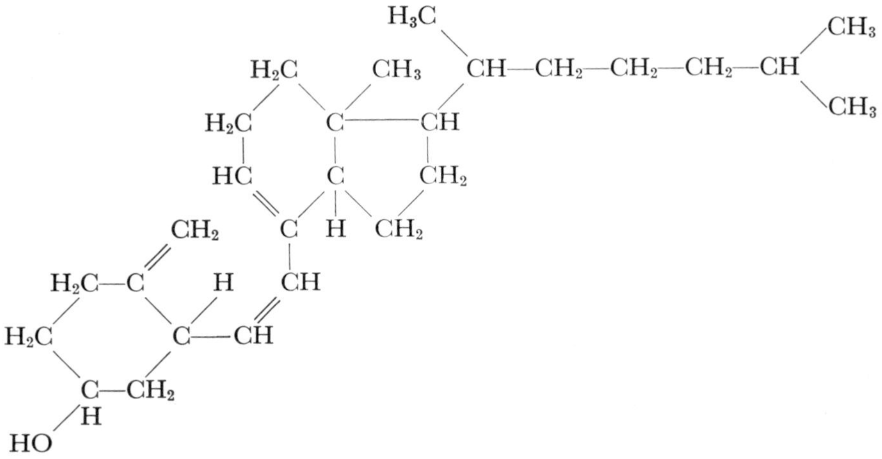

Only a very small amount of vitamin D is necessary for health— approximately 0.01 mg per day. The vitamin is a fat-soluble vitamin, occurring in cod-liver oil, egg yolks, milk, and in very small amounts in other foods. Cereals, yeast, and milk acquire an added vitamin D potency when irradiated with ultraviolet light. The radiation converts a fatty substance (a *lipid*) that is present in the food, a substance called *ergosterol*, into another substance, *calciferol* (vitamin D_2), which has vitamin D activity. The structure of calciferol is closely related to that of vitamin D_3.

Whereas most vitamins are harmless even when large quantities are ingested, vitamin D is harmful when taken in large amounts.

Vitamin E, while not necessary for health, seems to be required for the reproduction and lactation of animals. Niacin, a member of the B group of vitamins, is necessary for the prevention of the deficiency disease pellagra. Pantothenic acid, inositol, *p*-amino-benzoic acid, and biotin are substances involved in the process of normal growth. Vitamin K is a vitamin that prevents bleeding, by assisting in the process of clotting of the blood.

It is interesting that many "simpler organisms" do not require so many substances for growth as does man. It was mentioned above that the red bread mold, *Neurospora*, can synthesize all of the amino acids present in proteins, whereas man is unable to synthesize nine of them, but must obtain them in his diet. The red bread mold is also able to manufacture other substances that man requires as vitamins. The only organic growth substance required by this organism is biotin. Similarly, the food requirements of the rat, while greater than those of *Neurospora*, are not so great as those of man. The rat, for example, does not require ascorbic acid (vitamin C) in its diet, but is able to synthesize this substance, which is present as an important constituent in the tissues of the animal.

29–6. *Hormones*

Another class of substances of importance in the activity of the human body consists of the *hormones*, which are substances that serve as messengers from one part of the body to another, moving by way of the blood stream. The hormones control various physiological processes. For example, when a man is suddenly frightened a substance called *epinephrine* (also called adrenalin) is secreted by the suprarenal glands, small glands which lie just above the kidneys. The formula of epinephrine is

When epinephrine is introduced into the blood stream it speeds up the action of the heart, causes the blood vessels to contract, thus increasing the blood pressure, and causes glucose to be released from the liver, providing an immediate source of extra energy.

Thyroxin is a secretion of the thyroid gland which controls metabolism. *Insulin* is a secretion of the pancreas which controls the combustion of carbohydrates. Both of these hormones are proteins, thyroxin having a prosthetic group which contains iodine. Many other hormones are known, some of which are proteins and some simpler chemical substances.

It has been recognized that diseases (such as goiter) affecting the thyroid gland may arise from a deficient production of thyroxin, which can be remedied by the introduction of added iodide ion into the diet. The disease *diabetes mellitus*, characterized by the appearance of sugar in the urine and perhaps due to a deficient production of the hormone insulin, has in recent decades been treated by the injection of insulin, obtained from the pancreatic glands of animals. The hormones *cortisone* and *ACTH* (adrenocorticotropic hormone) have been shown recently to have strong therapeutic activity toward rheumatoid arthritis and some other diseases.

29–7. *Chemistry and Medicine*

From the earliest times chemicals have been used in the treatment of disease. The substances that were first used as drugs were natural products from the leaves, branches, and roots of plants. As the alchemists discovered or made new chemical substances, these substances were tried out to see if they had physiological activity, and many of them were introduced into early medical practice. For example, both mercuric chloride, $HgCl_2$, and mercurous chloride, Hg_2Cl_2, were used in medicine, mercuric chloride as an antiseptic, and mercurous chloride, taken internally, as a cathartic and general medicament.

The modern period of *chemotherapy*, the treatment of disease by use of chemical substances, began with the work of Paul Ehrlich (1854–1915). It was known at the beginning of the present century that certain organic compounds of arsenic would kill protozoa, parasitic micro-organisms responsible for certain diseases, and Ehrlich set himself the task of synthesizing a large number of arsenic compounds, in an effort to find one which would be at the same time toxic (poisonous) to protozoa in the human body and non-toxic to the human host of the micro-organism. After preparing many compounds he synthesized *arsphenamine*, which has the following structure:

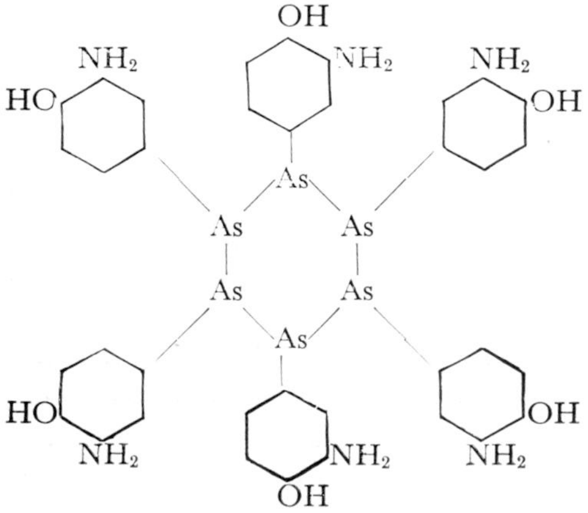

This compound used to be called 606; the name is said to have resulted from the fact that it was the 606th compound of arsenic synthesized by Ehrlich in his investigation.

Arsphenamine has been found to be extremely valuable. Its greatest use is in the treatment of syphilis; the drug attacks the micro-organism responsible for this disease, *Spirocheta pallida*. It has also been useful in the treatment of some other diseases. At the present time it seems to be in the process of being superseded by penicillin (which we shall discuss below) in the treatment of syphilis.

Ehrlich later synthesized another compound, *neoarsphenamine*, which is somewhat superior to arsphenamine for the treatment of syphilis. It is closely related in structure, differing only in having a more complicated side chain in place of three of the amino groups of the molecule.

Since Ehrlich's time there has been continual progress in the development of new chemotherapeutic agents. Fifteen years ago the infectious diseases constituted the principal cause of death; now most of these diseases are under effective control by chemotherapeutic agents, some of which have been synthesized in the laboratory and some of which have been isolated from micro-organisms. At the present time only a few of the infectious diseases, especially certain viral diseases, such as poliomyelitis, constitute major hazards to the health of man, and we may confidently anticipate that the control of these diseases by chemotherapeutic agents will be achieved in a few years.

The recent period of rapid progress began with the discovery of the **sulfa drugs** by Gerhard Domagk. In 1935 Domagk discovered that the compound prontosil, a derivative of *sulfanilamide*, was effective in the control of streptococcus infections. It was soon found by other workers that sulfanilamide itself is just as effective in the treatment of these diseases, and that it can be administered by mouth. The formula of sulfanilamide is given in Table 29-2. Sulfanilamide is effective against hemolytic streptococcic infections and meningococcic infections. As soon as the value of sulfanilamide was recognized chemists synthesized hundreds of related substances, and investigations were made of their usefulness as bacteriostatic agents (agents with the power of controlling the spread of bacterial infections). It was found that many of these related substances are valuable, and their use is now an important part of medical practice. *Sulfapyridine* has been found valuable for the control of pneumococcic pneumonia (pneumonia due to the *Pneumococcus* micro-organisms), as well as of other pneumococcic infections and gonorrhea. *Sulfathiazole* is used for these infections and also for the control of staphylococcic infections, which occur especially in carbuncles and eruptions of the skin. These and other sulfa drugs are all derivatives of sulfanilamide itself, obtained by replacing one of the hydrogen atoms of the amide group (the NH_2 bonded to the sulfur atom) by some other group (Table 29-2).

The introduction of **penicillin** into medical treatment was the next great step forward. In 1929 Professor Alexander Fleming, a bacteriologist working in the University of London, noticed that bacteria that he was growing in a dish in his laboratory were not able to grow in the region immediately surrounding a bit of mold that had accidentally begun to develop. He surmised that the mold was able to produce a

TABLE 29-2   *Structural Formulas of Sulfa Drugs and Related Substances*

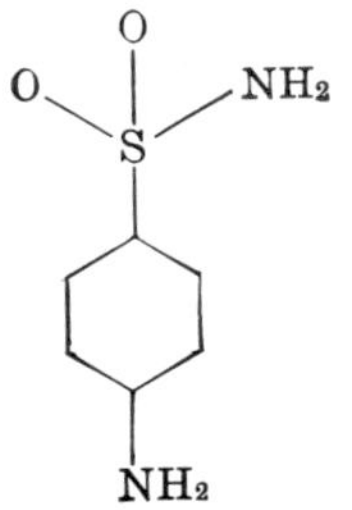

Sulfanilamide

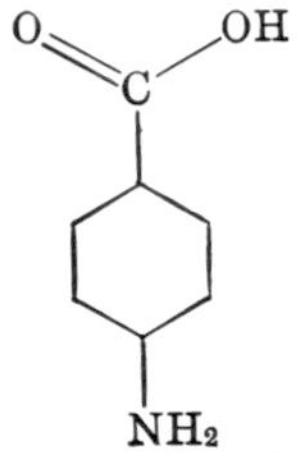

Para-aminobenzoic acid

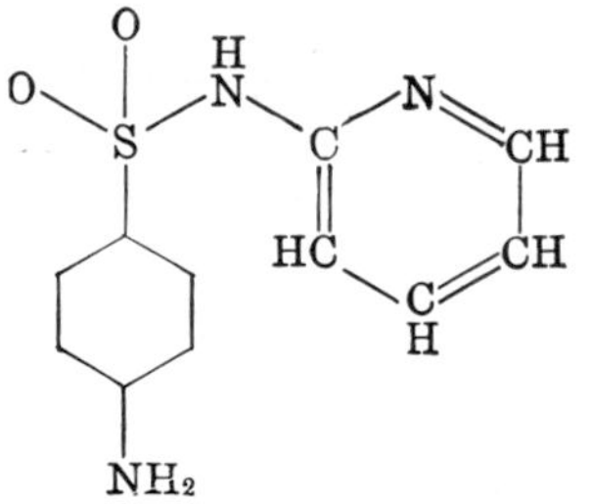

Sulfapyridine

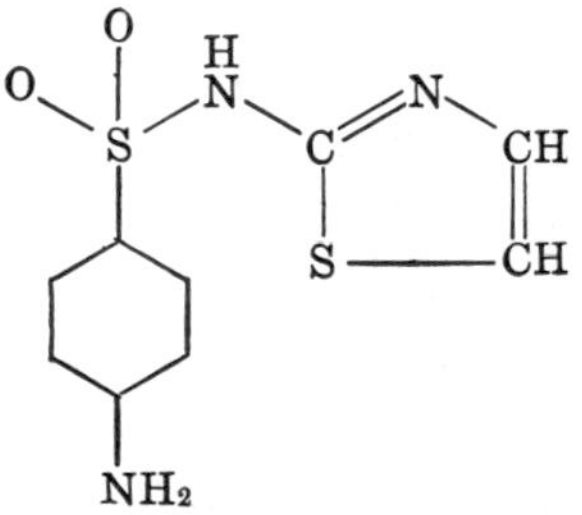

Sulfathiazole

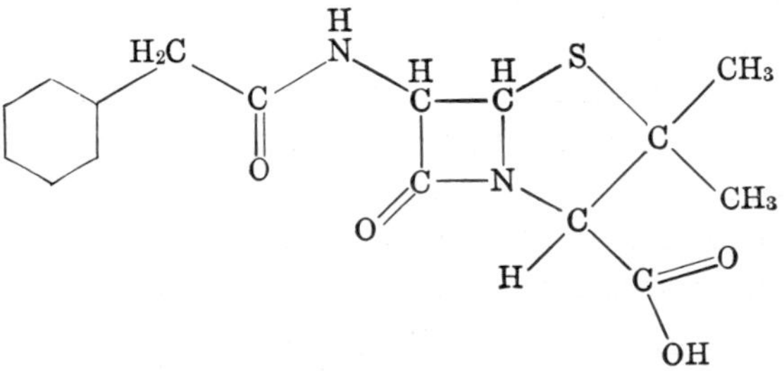

Penicillin G

chemical substance that had bacteriostatic activity, and he made a preliminary investigation of the nature of this substance. Ten years later,
spurred on by the successful use of the sulfa drugs in medicine, Professor
Howard Florey of Oxford University decided to make a careful study of
the antibacterial substances that had been reported in order to see
whether they would be similarly useful in the treatment of disease. When
he tested the bacteriostatic power of the liquid in which the mold
Penicillium notatum that had been observed by Fleming was growing, he
found it to be very great, and within a few months the new antibiotic
substance penicillin was being used in the treatment of patients. Through
the cooperative effort of many investigators in the United States and
England, rapid progress was made during the next two or three years in
the determination of the structure of penicillin, the development of
methods of manufacturing it in large quantities, and the investigation
of the diseases that could be effectively treated by use of it. Within less
than a decade this new antibiotic agent became the most valuable of all
drugs. It provides an effective therapeutic treatment of many diseases.

The structure of penicillin is shown in Table 29-2. The substance
has been synthesized, but no cheap method of synthesizing it has been
developed, and the large amount of penicillin that is being manufactured and used in the treatment of disease is made by growing the mold
penicillium in a suitable medium and then extracting the penicillin
from the medium. Important forward steps in the introduction of penicillin into medical treatment were the development of strains of the
mold which produce the desired penicillin in large quantities, and the
discovery of the best medium on which to grow the mold.

It is interesting that a number of slightly different penicillins are
formed in nature by different strains of the mold. The formula in
Table 29-2 represents benzyl penicillin (penicillin G), which is the
product that is now manufactured and used. Other naturally occurring
penicillins differ from benzyl penicillin only with respect to the part
of the molecule that is shown on the left side of the structure. In benzyl
penicillin there is indicated a benzyl group, C_6H_5—CH_2—, in this position. Penicillin K contains the normal heptyl group in this position, the
hydrocarbon chain $CH_3CH_2CH_2CH_2CH_2CH_2CH_2$—. It is not so effective as penicillin G in the treatment of infections. Scores of other penicillins have been made and investigated.

The spectacular success of penicillin as a chemotherapeutic agent has
led to the search for other antibiotic products of living organisms.
Streptomycin, which is produced by the mold *Actinomyces griseus*, has been
found to be valuable in the treatment of diseases that are not effectively

controlled by penicillin, and some other bacteriostatic agents also have been found to have significant value.

Another very great step forward has been made during the past two years by the discovery of substances which can control the development of viral infections. Penicillin, streptomycin, and the sulfa drugs are effective against bacteria but not against viruses. It has recently been found, however, that *chloramphenicol* (Chloromycetin) and *aureomycin*, both of which are substances manufactured by molds (the molds *Streptomyces venezuele* and *Streptomyces aureofaciens* respectively), have the power of controlling certain viral infections.

The Relation Between the Molecular Structure of Substances and Their Physiological Activity. No one knows what the relation between the molecular structure of substances and their physiological activity is. We know the structural formulas of many drugs, vitamins, and hormones—some of these formulas have been given in the preceding sections. It is probable, however, that most of these substances produce their physiological action by interacting with or combining with proteins in the human body or in the bacterium or virus that they counteract, and little is known as yet about the structure of these proteins.

Ten years ago a suggestion was made about the way in which the sulfa drugs exercise their bacteriostatic action. It seems probable that this suggestion is essentially correct. It was found that a concentration of sulfanilamide or other sulfa drug that would prevent bacterial cultures from growing under ordinary circumstances lost this power when some para-aminobenzoic acid was added. The amount of para-aminobenzoic acid required to permit the bacteria to increase in number was found to be approximately proportional to the excess of the amount of the sulfa drug over the minimum that would produce bacteriostatic action. This *competition* between the sulfa drug and para-aminobenzoic acid can be given a reasonable explanation. Let us assume that the bacteria need to have some para-aminobenzoic acid in order to grow—that is, that para-aminobenzoic acid is a vitamin for the bacteria. Probably it serves as a vitamin by combining with a protein to form an essential enzyme; presumably it serves as the prosthetic group of this enzyme. It is likely that the bacterium synthesizes a protein molecule which has a small region, a cavity, on one side of itself into which the para-aminobenzoic acid molecule just fits. The sulfanilamide molecule is closely similar in structure to the para-aminobenzoic molecule (see Table 29-2). Each of the molecules contains a benzene ring, an amino group ($-NH_2$) attached to one of the carbon atoms of the benzene ring, and another group attached to the opposite carbon atom. It seems not unlikely that the sulfanilamide molecule can fit into the cavity on the protein, thus preventing the para-aminobenzoic molecule from getting into this place. If it is further assumed that the sulfanilamide molecule is not able to function in such a way as to make its complex with the protein able to act as an enzyme, then the explanation of the action of sulfanilamide is complete. It is thought that the protein fits tightly around the benzene ring and the amino group, but not around the other end of the molecule. The evidence for this is that derivatives of sulfanilamide in which various other groups are attached to the sulfur atom are effective as bacteriostatic agents, whereas compounds in which other groups are attached to the benzene ring or the amino group are not effective.

Nobody knows why penicillin is able to control many bacterial infections, nor why chloramphenicol and aureomycin attack viruses; but we may hope that further studies will lead to the solution of this great problem of the molecular basis of the action of drugs, and we may then expect great further progress to occur in medical research. When the mechanism of the action of drugs has been understood, it will be possible for investigators to attack the problem presented by a new disease in a logical and systematic way; new chemotherapeutic agents can then be developed by logical, scientific procedures, rather than by chance.

Exercises

29-1. What is meant by "metabolism"? by "power of reproduction"? Discuss the differentiation between a living organism and an inanimate object with use of these terms.

29-2. What are the properties of a virus?

29-3. What is the formula of glycine, in aqueous solution? of alanine? of some other amino acid?

29-4. What is meant by the statement that all of the natural amino acids except glycine have the L configuration? Why is glycine an exception?

29-5. Histidine, lysine, tryptophan, phenylalanine, leucine, isoleucine, threonine, methionine, and valine are said to be the essential amino acids for man. What is meant by this statement? What is the relation of the human body to other amino acids? Why is casein described as a good protein and gelatin as a poor protein?

29-6. Describe the structure of hair.

29-7. Discuss briefly the role of enzymes in metabolism.

29-8. What are vitamins? Why is it important to have a good supply of vitamin A, of vitamin B_1, of vitamin B_{12}, of vitamin C, of vitamin D?

29-9.   What are hormones?

29-10. Discuss briefly the use in medicine of sulfanilamide, penicillin, and streptomycin. What can you say about the mechanism of pharmacological action of these
substances?

Reference Books

Garrett Hardin, *Biology, Its Human Implications*, W. H. Freeman and Co., San Francisco,
1952.

Roger J. Williams and Ernest Beerstecher, Jr., *An Introduction to Biochemistry*, D. Van
Nostrand Co., New York, **1948.**

W. Gortner and R. A. Gortner, Jr., *Outlines of Biochemistry*, John Wiley and Sons, New
York, **1949.**

J. H. Northrop, *Crystalline Enzymes*, Columbia University Press, New York, **1949.**

M. Bodansky, *Introduction to Physiological Chemistry*, John Wiley and Sons, New York,
1938.

H. C. Sherman, *Chemistry of Food and Nutrition*, The Macmilian Co., New York, **1941.**

Chapter 30

The Chemistry
of Silicon

Silicon (from Latin *silex*, flint), the fourteenth element in the periodic table, is a congener of carbon, in group IV. Silicon plays an important part in the inorganic world, similar to that played by carbon in the organic world. Most of the rocks that constitute the earth's crust are composed of the silicate minerals, of which silicon is the most important elementary constituent.

The importance of carbon in organic chemistry results from its ability to form carbon-carbon bonds, permitting complex molecu'es, with the most varied properties, to exist. The importance of silicon in the inorganic world results from a different property of the element—a few compounds are known in which silicon atoms are connected to one another by covalent bonds, but these compounds are relatively unimportant. The characteristic feature of the silicate minerals is the existence of chains and more complex structures (layers, three-dimensional frameworks) in which the silicon atoms are not bonded directly to one another but are connected by oxygen atoms. The nature of these structures is described briefly in later sections of this chapter.

30–1. *Silicon and Its Simpler Compounds*

Elementary Silicon and Silicon Alloys. Silicon is a brittle steel-gray metalloid, with m.p. 1,420° C, b.p. 2,600° C, and density 2.42 g/cm³. It can be made by the reduction of silicon tetrachloride by sodium:

$$SiCl_4 + 4Na \longrightarrow Si + 4NaCl$$

The element has the same crystal structure as diamond, each silicon atom forming single covalent bonds with four adjacent silicon atoms which surround it tetrahedrally.

Silicon contaminated with carbon can be obtained by reduction of silica, SiO_2, with carbon in an electric furnace. An alloy of iron and silicon, called *ferrosilicon*, is obtained by reducing a mixture of iron oxide and silica with carbon.

Ferrosilicon, which has composition approximately FeSi, is used in the manufacture of acid-resisting alloys, such as *duriron*, which contains about 15% silicon. Duriron is used in chemical laboratories and manufacturing plants. A mild steel containing a few percent silicon may be made which has a high magnetic permeability, and is used for the cores of electric transformers. In recent years a special process has been used in making the metal for transformer cores. An iron-silicon alloy of suitable composition is heat-treated and rolled in such a way as to orient the small crystal grains so that the direction of maximum magnetic permeability coincides with the direction of the magnetic field due to the transformer winding, thus increasing the magnetic effectiveness of the metal.

Silicides.   Many metals form compounds with silicon, called *silicides*. These compounds include Mg_2Si, Fe_2Si, $FeSi$, $CoSi$, $NiSi$, $CaSi_2$, $Cu_{15}Si_4$, and $CoSi_2$. **Calcium silicide,** $CaSi_2$, is made by heating a mixture of lime, silica, and carbon in an electric furnace. It is a powerful reducing agent, and is used for removing oxygen from molten steel in the process of manufacture of steel.

The Hydrides of Silicon.   The hydrides of silicon, called the *silicanes* or *silanes*, have the general formula Si_nH_{2n+2}, analogous to that of the paraffin series in organic chemistry. The silanes are made by reaction of metallic silicides with water or acid; for example, magnesium silicide with acid produces **monosilane,** SiH_4:

$$Mg_2Si + 4H^+ \longrightarrow 2Mg^{++} + SiH_4$$

The silanes are reactive substances, which inflame spontaneously in air at room temperature, and hydrolyze readily with water.

Silicon Carbide.   Silicon carbide, SiC, is made by heating a mixture of carbon and sand in a special electric furnace:

$$SiO_2 + 3C \longrightarrow SiC + 2CO$$

The structure of this substance is similar to that of diamond, with carbon and silicon atoms alternating; each carbon atom is surrounded by a tetrahedron of silicon atoms, and each silicon atom by a tetrahedron of carbon atoms. The covalent bonds connecting all of the atoms in this structure make silicon carbide very hard (hardness on the Mohs scale about $9\frac{1}{2}$). The substance is used as an abrasive.

30–2. *Silicon Dioxide*

Silicon dioxide (*silica*), SiO_2, occurs in nature in three different crystal forms, as the minerals *quartz* (hexagonal), *cristobalite* (cubic), and *tridymite* (hexagonal). Quartz is the most widespread of these minerals; it occurs in many deposits as well-formed hexagonal crystals, and also as a crystalline constituent of many rocks, such as granite. It is a hard, colorless substance, with hardness 7 on the Mohs scale.

The structure of quartz is closely related to that of *silicic acid*, H_4SiO_4. In silicic acid silicon has coordination number 4, the silicon atom being surrounded by a tetrahedron of four oxygen atoms, with one hydrogen atom attached to each oxygen atom. Silicic acid, which is a very weak acid, has the property of undergoing condensation very readily, with elimination of water (see the last section of Chap. 21). If each of the four hydroxyl groups of a silicic acid molecule condenses with a similar hydroxyl group of an adjacent molecule, eliminating water, a structure is obtained in which the silicon atom is bonded to four surrounding silicon atoms by silicon-oxygen-silicon bonds. This process leads to a condensation product with formula SiO_2, since each silicon atom is surrounded by four oxygen atoms, and each oxygen atom serves as a neighbor to two silicon atoms. The structure of quartz and of the other forms of silica may be described as consisting of SiO_4 tetrahedra, with each oxygen atom serving as the corner of two of these tetrahedra. In order to break a crystal of quartz it is necessary to break some silicon-oxygen bonds. In this way the structure of quartz accounts for the hardness of the mineral.

Cristobalite and tridymite are similarly made from SiO_4 tetrahedra fused together by sharing oxygen atoms, with, however, different arrangements of the tetrahedra in space than that of quartz.

Silica Glass.   If any of the forms of silica is melted (m.p. about 1,600° C) and the molten material is then cooled, it usually does not crystallize at the original melting point, but the liquid becomes more viscous as the temperature is lowered, until, at about 1,500° C, it is so stiff that it cannot flow. The material obtained in this way is not crystalline, but is a *supercooled liquid*, or *glass*. It is called *silica glass* (or sometimes *quartz glass* or *fused quartz*). Silica glass does not have the properties of a crystal —it does not cleave, nor form crystal faces, nor show other differences in properties in different directions. The reason for this is that the atoms which constitute it are not arranged in a completely regular manner in space, but show a randomness in arrangement similar to that of the liquid. The structure of silica glass is very similar in its general nature to that of quartz and the other crystalline forms of silica. Nearly every silicon atom is surrounded by a tetrahedron of four oxygen atoms, and nearly every oxygen atom serves as the common element of two of these tetrahedra. However, the arrangement of the framework of tetrahedra in the glass is not regular, as it is in the crystalline forms of silica, but is irregular, so that a very small region may resemble right-handed or left-handed quartz, and an adjacent region may resemble cristobalite or tridymite, in the same way that liquid silica, above the melting point of the crystalline forms, would show some resemblance to the structures of the crystals.

Silica glass is used for making chemical apparatus and scientific instruments. The coefficient of thermal expansion of silica glass is very small, so that vessels made of the material do not break readily on sudden heating or cooling. Silica is transparent to ultraviolet light, and because of this property it is used in making mercury-vapor ultraviolet lamps and optical instruments for use with ultraviolet light.

30–3. *Sodium Silicate and Other Silicates*

Silicic acid (orthosilicic acid), H_4SiO_4, cannot be made by the hydration of silica. The sodium and potassium salts of silicic acid are soluble in water, however, and can be made by boiling silica with a solution of sodium hydroxide or potassium hydroxide, in which it slowly dissolves. A concentrated solution of **sodium silicate,** called *water glass*, is available commercially and is used for fireproofing wood and cloth, as an adhesive, and for preserving eggs. This solution is not sodium orthosilicate, Na_4SiO_4, but is a mixture of the sodium salts of various condensed silicic acids, such as $H_6Si_2O_7$, $H_4Si_3O_8$, and $(H_2SiO_3)_x$.

A gelatinous precipitate of condensed silicic acids $(SiO_2 \cdot xH_2O)$ is obtained when an ordinary acid, such as hydrochloric acid, is added to a solution of sodium silicate. When this precipitate is partially dehydrated it forms a porous product called *silica gel*. This material has great powers of adsorption for water and other molecules and is used as a drying agent and decolorizing agent.

Except for the alkali silicates, most silicates are insoluble in water. Many occur in nature, as ores and minerals.

30–4. *The Silicate Minerals*

Most of the minerals which constitute rocks and soil are silicates. Many of these minerals have complex formulas, corresponding to the complex condensed silicic acids from which they are derived. These minerals can be divided into three principal classes, the *framework minerals* (hard minerals similar in their properties to quartz), the *layer minerals* (such as mica), and the *fibrous minerals* (such as asbestos).

The Framework Minerals.   A crystal of quartz may be described as a single giant molecule, in which every atom is linked to the rest of the structure by silicon-oxygen bonds. This crystal is hard and strong because any fracture requires that many of these chemical bonds be broken. The entire crystal may be described as made up of SiO_4 tetrahedra which are condensed together by sharing corners—that is, oxygen atoms—with one another; the crystal has a tetrahedral framework structure.

Many of the silicate minerals have similar framework structures. If a silicon ion in the center of one of the silicate tetrahedra is replaced by an aluminum ion, Al^{+++} instead of Si^{++++}, the tetrahedral framework remains essentially the same, but another positive ion must be present in the crystal in order that it retain electric neutrality. Many silicate minerals have tetrahedral framework structures in which some of the tetrahedra are AlO_4 tetrahedra instead of SiO_4 tetrahedra. These minerals have structures somewhat resembling that of quartz, with additional ions, usually alkali or alkaline-earth ions, introduced in the larger openings in the framework structure. Ordinary *feldspar (orthoclase)*, $KAlSi_3O_8$, is an example of a tetrahedral aluminosilicate mineral. The tetrahedral framework, $(AlSi_3O_8^-)_\infty$, extends throughout the entire crystal, giving it hardness nearly as great as that of quartz (6 on the Mohs scale, with quartz 7).

A characteristic feature of these tetrahedral framework minerals is that the number of oxygen atoms is just twice the sum of the number of aluminum and silicon atoms. In some of these minerals the framework is an open one, through which corridors run which are sufficiently large to permit ions to move in and out. The *zeolite minerals*, used for softening water, are of this nature. As the hard water, containing Ca^{++} and Fe^{+++} ions, passes around the grains of the mineral, these cations enter the mineral, replacing an equivalent number of sodium ions.

Some of the zeolite minerals contain water molecules in the corridors and chambers within the aluminosilicate framework, as well as alkali

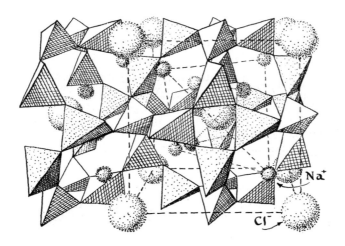

FIG. 30-1   *The structure of the mineral sodalite,* $Na_4Al_3Si_3O_{12}Cl$. *The framework consists of* AlO_4 *tetrahedra and* SiO_4 *tetrahedra, which share corners with one another. In the spaces formed by this framework there are large chloride ions and the smaller sodium ions, represented in the drawing by spheres. The mineral lazulite has the same structure, except that the chloride ions are replaced by polysulfide groups.*

and alkaline-earth ions. When a crystal of one of these minerals, such as chabazite, $CaAl_2Si_4O_{12} \cdot 6H_2O$, is heated, the water molecules are driven out of the structure. The crystal does not collapse, however, but retains essentially its original size and shape, the spaces within the framework formerly occupied by water molecules remaining unoccupied. This dehydrated chabazite has a strong attraction for water molecules, and for molecules of other vapors, and can be used as a drying agent or adsorbing agent for them. The structure of silica gel, mentioned above as a drying agent, is similar in nature.

Some of the important minerals in soil are aluminosilicate minerals which have the property of base exchange, and which, because of this property, serve a useful function in the nutrition of plants.

An interesting framework mineral is *lazulite*, or *lapis lazuli*, a mineral with a beautiful blue color. When ground into a powder, this mineral constitutes the pigment called *ultramarine*. Lazulite has the formula $Na_8Al_6Si_6O_{24}(S_x)$. It consists of an aluminosilicate framework in which there are sodium ions (some of which neutralize the charge of the framework) and anions S_x^{--}, such as S_2^{--} and S_3^{--} (Fig. 30-1). These poly-

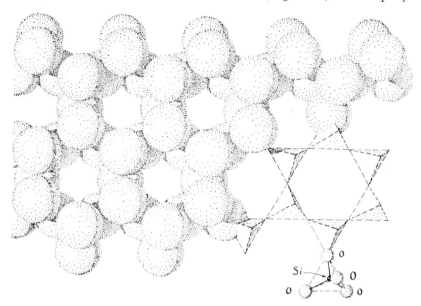

FIG. 30-2   *A portion of an infinite layer of silicate tetrahedra, as present in talc and other minerals with layer structures.*

sulfide ions are responsible for the color of the pigment. It was discovered at the beginning of the eighteenth century that a synthetic ultramarine can be made by melting together a suitable sodium aluminosilicate mixture with sulfur. Similar stable pigments with different colors can also be made by replacing the sulfur by selenium and the sodium ion by other cations.

Many of the framework minerals contain frameworks of SiO_4 tetrahedra condensed with AlO_6 octahedra, or with octahedra formed by other cations. The understanding of the structure of these minerals has constituted an important part of modern mineralogy.

Minerals with Layer Structures.   By a condensation reaction involving three of the four hydroxyl groups of each silicic acid molecule, a condensed silicic acid can be made, with composition $(H_2Si_2O_5)_\infty$, which has the form of an infinite layer, as shown in Figure 30-2. The mineral *hydrargillite*, $Al(OH)_3$, has a similar layer structure which involves AlO_6 octahedra (Fig. 30-3). More complex layers involving both tetrahedra and octahedra are present in other layer minerals, such as *talc*, *kaolinite* (clay), and *mica*. In talc and kaolinite, with formulas $Mg_3Si_4O_{10}(OH)_2$ and $Al_2Si_2O_5(OH)_4$, respectively, the layers are electrically neutral, and

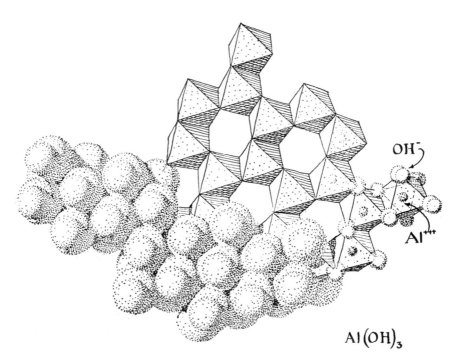

FIG. 30-3 *The crystal structure of aluminum hydroxide, Al(OH)$_3$. This substance crystallizes in layers, consisting of octahedra of oxygen atoms (hydroxide ions) about the aluminum atom. Each oxygen atom serves as a corner for two aluminum octahedra. One layer is shown in this drawing.*

they are loosely superimposed on one another to form the crystalline material. These layers slide over one another very readily, which gives to these minerals their characteristic properties (softness, easy cleavage, soapy feel). In mica, $KAl_3Si_3O_{10}(OH)_2$, the aluminosilicate layers are negatively charged, and positive ions, usually potassium ions, must be present between the layers in order to give the mineral electric neutrality. The electrostatic forces between these positive ions and the negatively charged layers make mica considerably harder than kaolinite and talc, but its layer structure is still evident in its perfect basic cleavage, which permits the mineral to be split into very thin sheets. These sheets of mica are used for windows in stoves and furnaces, and for electrical insulation in machines and instruments.

Other layer minerals, such as *montmorillonite*, with formula approximately $AlSi_2O_5(OH) \cdot xH_2O$, are important constituents of soils, and have also found industrial uses, as catalysts in the conversion of long-chain hydrocarbons into branched-chain hydrocarbons (to make high-octane gasoline), and for other special purposes. *Vermiculite* is a similar mineral which has the property of exfoliating when it is strongly heated. The water of crystallization in the mineral is turned into steam, the pressure of which causes the silicate layers to separate from one another. In this way a small grain, perhaps a quarter of an inch in diameter and a sixteenth of an inch thick, expands into a large grain, with the same diameter but with thickness many times greater, so great as to cause the grain to resemble a worm. The name "vermiculite" is from the Latin *vermiculus*, a little worm. Exfoliated vermiculite is used, in place of sawdust, as a packing material. It has also been used as insulation for houses,

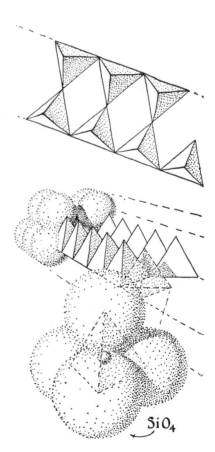

FIG. 30-4

A double chain of silicate tetrahedra, extending from one end of an asbestos crystal to the other end. This double chain, called the tremolite chain, has the composition $(Si_4O_{11})_\infty$.

and, in place of the gravel of ordinary concrete, for the manufacture of a light-weight concrete.

The Fibrous Minerals.   The fibrous minerals contain very long silicate ions in the form of tetrahedra condensed into a chain, as shown in Figure 30-4. These crystals can be cleaved readily in directions parallel to the silicate chains, but not in the directions which cut the chains. Accordingly, crystals of these minerals show the extraordinary property of being easily unraveled into fibers. The principal minerals of this sort, *tremolite*, $Ca_2Mg_5Si_8O_{22}(OH)_2$, and *chrysotile*, $Mg_6Si_4O_{11}(OH)_6 \cdot H_2O$, are called *asbestos*. Deposits of these minerals are found in South Africa in layers several inches thick. These minerals are shredded into fibers, which are then spun or felted into asbestos yarn, fabric, and board for use for thermal insulation and as a heat-resistant structural material.

30–5. *Glass*

Silicate materials with important uses include glass, porcelain, glazes and enamels, and cement. Ordinary glass is a mixture of silicates in the form of a supercooled liquid. It is made by melting a mixture of sodium carbonate (or sodium sulfate), limestone, and sand, usually with some scrap glass of the same grade to serve as a flux. After the bubbles of gas have been expelled, the clear melt is poured into molds or stamped with dies to produce pressed glass ware, or a lump of the semi-fluid material on the end of a hollow tube is blown, sometimes in a mold, to produce hollow ware, such as bottles and flasks. *Plate glass* is made by pouring liquid glass on to a flat table and rolling it into a sheet. The sheet is then ground flat and polished on both sides.

Ordinary glass (soda-lime glass, soft glass) contains about 10% sodium, 5% calcium, and 1% aluminum, the remainder being silicon and oxygen. It consists of an aluminosilicate tetrahedral framework, within which are embedded sodium ions and calcium ions and some smaller complex anions. Soda-lime glass softens over a range of temperatures beginning at a dull-red heat, and can be conveniently worked in this temperature range.

Boric acid easily forms highly condensed acids, similar to those of silicic acid, and borate glasses, such as those made by heating borax with metal oxides ("borax beads," Chap. 6), are similar to silicate glasses in their properties. **Pyrex glass,** used for chemical glassware and baking dishes, is a boro-aluminosilicate glass containing only about 4% alkali and alkaline-earth metal ions. This glass is not so soluble in water as is soft glass, and it also has a smaller coefficient of thermal expansion than soft glass, so that it does not break readily when it is suddenly heated or cooled.

Glazes on chinaware and pottery and **enamels** on iron kitchen utensils and bathtubs consist of easily fusible glass containing pigments or white fillers such as titanium oxide and stannic oxide.

30–6. Cement

Portland cement is an aluminosilicate powder which sets to a solid mass on treatment with water. It is usually manufactured by grinding lime-stone and clay to a fine powder, mixing with water to form a slurry, and burning the mixture, with a flame of gas, oil, or coal dust, in a long rotary kiln. At the hot end of the kiln, where the temperature is about 1,500° C, the aluminosilicate mixture is sintered together into small round marbles, called "clinker." The clinker is ground to a fine powder in a ball mill (a rotating cylindrical mill filled with steel balls), to produce the final product.

Portland cement before treatment with water consists of a mixture of calcium silicates, mainly Ca_2SiO_4 and Ca_3SiO_5, and calcium alumi-nate, $Ca_3Al_2O_6$. When treated with water the calcium aluminate hydro-lyzes, forming calcium hydroxide and aluminum hydroxide, and these substances react further with the calcium silicates to produce calcium aluminosilicates, in the form of intermeshed crystals.

Ordinary *mortar* for laying bricks is made by mixing sand with slacked lime. This mortar slowly becomes hard through reaction with carbon dioxide of the air, forming calcium carbonate. A stronger mortar is made by mixing sand with Portland cement. The amount of cement needed for a construction job is greatly reduced by mixing sand and crushed stone or gravel with the cement, forming the material called *concrete*. Concrete is a very valuable building material. It does not require carbon dioxide from the air in order to harden, and it will set under water or in very large masses.

30–7. The Silicones

When we consider the variety of structures represented by the silicate minerals, and their resultant characteristic and useful properties, we might well expect chemists to synthesize many new and valuable silicon

compounds. In recent years this has been done; many silicon compounds
of the class called *silicones* have been found to have valuable properties.

The simplest silicones are the methyl silicones. These substances
exist as oils, resins, and elastomers (rubber-like substances). Methyl
silicone oil consists of long molecules, each of which is a silicon-oxygen
chain with methyl groups attached to the silicon atoms. A short silicone
molecule would have the following structure:

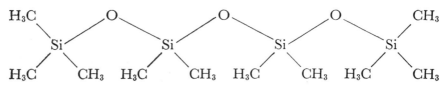

A *silicone oil* for use as a lubricating oil or in hydraulic systems contains
molecules with an average of about ten silicon atoms per molecule.

The valuable properties of the silicone oils are their very low coefficient of viscosity with temperature, ability to withstand high temperature without decomposition, and chemical inertness to metals and
most reagents. A typical silicone oil increases only about sevenfold in
viscosity on cooling from 100° F to −35° F, whereas a hydrocarbon oil
with the same viscosity at 100° F increases about 1,800-fold in viscosity
on cooling through the same range.

Resinous silicones can be made by polymerizing silicones into cross-
linked molecules. These resinous materials are used for electrical insulation. They have excellent dielectric properties and are stable at
operating temperatures at which the usual organic insulating materials decompose rapidly. The use of these materials permits electrical
machines to be operated with increased loads.

Silicones may be polymerized to molecules containing 2,000 or more
$(CH_3)_2SiO$ units, and then milled with inorganic fillers (such as zinc
oxide or carbon black, used also for ordinary rubber), and "vulcanized," by heating to cause cross-links to form between the molecules,
bonding them into an insoluble, infusible three-dimensional framework. The resultant elastomers (*silicone rubber*) may be used for electrical
insulation and for other purposes for which rubber is needed, especially
at high temperature.

Similar silicones with ethyl groups or other organic groups in place
of the methyl groups are also used.

The coating of materials with a water-repellent film has been achieved
by use of the **methylchlorosilanes.** A piece of cotton cloth exposed for a
second or two to the vapor of *trimethylchlorosilane*, $(CH_3)_3SiCl$, becomes

coated with a layer of

$$
\begin{array}{c}
CH_3 \\
H_3C \quad | \quad CH_3 \\
\diagdown \; | \; \diagup \\
Si \\
| \\
O \\
\diagup \\
R
\end{array}
$$

groups, through reaction with

hydroxyl groups of the cellulose:

$$(CH_3)_3SiCl + HOR \longrightarrow (CH_3)_3SiOR + HCl$$

The exposed methyl groups repel water in the way that a hydrocarbon film such as lubricating oil would. Paper, wool, silk, glass, porcelain, and other materials can be treated in this way. The treatment has been found especially useful for ceramic insulators.

Exercises

30-1. What is the electronic structure of elementary silicon? of silicon carbide?

30-2. What is the oxidation number of Si in Mg_2Si? in $CaSi_2$?

30-3. Write a chemical equation for the preparation of calcium silicide in the electric furnace.

30-4. Write the chemical equation underlying the use of calcium silicide in the steel industry.

30-5. Write the structural formulas of the simpler silicanes. How are these substances prepared?

30-6. Compare the properties of silica glass and crystalline quartz. What properties of a glass, as distinct from a crystal, are important in the uses of glass?

30-7. To how many silicon or aluminum atoms is each oxygen atom bonded in a framework?

30-8. Write a general formula for an anhydrous sodium aluminosilicate which is a framework mineral, containing only tetrahedrally coordinated aluminum and silicon.

30-9. Can you suggest an explanation of the fact that silicon dioxide does not form a fibrous mineral with the structure shown below?

$$
\begin{array}{ccccccc}
& O & & O & & O & \\
\diagdown & \diagup & \diagdown & \diagup & \diagdown & \diagup & \diagdown \\
Si & & Si & & Si & & Si \\
\diagup & \diagdown & \diagup & \diagdown & \diagup & \diagdown & \\
& O & & O & & O &
\end{array}
$$

Silicon disulfide does form fibrous crystals of this sort.

30-10. Compare the properties of talc and mica, and explain their differences in terms of their structure.

30-11. What is Portland cement? What happens when it sets?

30-12. What is the formula of a simple silicone? What is the difference in structure of silicone oil, silicone resin, and silicone rubber?

30-13. What is the structure of the linear polymer $(CH_3)_{16}Si.O_6$?

30-14. What do you think is the structure of the silicone with the molecular formula $(CH_3)_6Si_3O_3$ and the name hexamethylcyclotrisiloxane? What would you predict as to its properties?

30-15. Draw possible structures for portions of the cross-linked polymer prepared by "co-hydrolysis" of $(CH_3)_2SiCl_2$ and CH_3SiCl_3 (disregard the problem of the end of the molecule and represent units in its middle).

30-16. Describe the process for preparing a silicone rubber.

References

Linus Pauling, *The Nature of the Chemical Bond*, Cornell University Press, Ithaca, **1940,** Chapter 10.

E. G. Rochow, *An Introduction to the Chemistry of the Silicones*, John Wiley and Sons, New York, **1951.**

Chapter 31

Thermochemistry

In earlier chapters mention has been made that some chemical reactions (exothermic) take place with the evolution of heat, and some (endothermic) with the absorption of heat. Of course, any reaction that is exothermic when it takes place in one direction is endothermic when it takes place in the reverse direction.

The branch of chemistry dealing with heats of reaction and closely related subjects is called *thermochemistry*. The more general study of the relations between energy and chemical change, including such questions as the electric potential that can be obtained from an electrolytic cell and the amount of work that can be done by chemical means, is called *thermodynamic chemistry*. Thermochemistry and thermodynamic chemistry are a part of physical chemistry.

31–1. *Heat of Reaction*

The heat of a chemical reaction is the quantity of heat which is evolved when the reaction takes place at constant temperature and constant pressure. The symbol Q may be used to represent the heat of reaction. If heat is evolved (that is, if the reaction is exothermic) Q is a positive quantity, and if heat is absorbed by the reaction, the reaction being endothermic, Q is a negative quantity.

We can tell whether a chemical reaction is exothermic or endothermic by causing the reactants, at room temperature, say, to undergo reaction, and then by determining the temperature of the products. If the products are warmer than the reactants were, the reaction is exothermic, and if they are colder, the reaction is endothermic. For example, we know that when a fuel burns in air the products are very hot. This reaction, the combustion of a fuel, is a strongly exothermic reaction. On the other hand, when common salt is dissolved in water the solution is cooled somewhat below room temperature. This reaction, the solution of salt in water, is endothermic.

Measuring the Heat of a Reaction.   An instrument used to measure the heat of a reaction is called a *calorimeter*. Calorimeters are made of various designs, corresponding to the nature of the reaction to be studied. A calorimeter of simple design is shown in Figure 31-1. This calorimeter consists of a reaction vessel, which may be built to withstand considerable pressure, in the center of a larger vessel filled with water, and provided with a stirrer and a sensitive thermometer. The larger vessel is surrounded by insulating material.

If it is desired to obtain the heat of a reaction such as the combustion of carbon, a weighed quantity of carbon is placed in the reaction vessel, and oxygen gas is forced into the vessel under pressure. A reaction vessel for this purpose is strongly built of steel, to stand high pressure; it is called a *combustion bomb*. The temperature of the surrounding water is recorded, and the sample of carbon is ignited by passing an electric

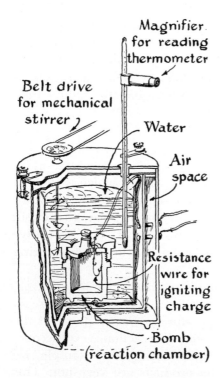

FIG. 31-1

A bomb calorimeter.

current through a wire embedded in it. The heat liberated by the reaction causes the entire system inside of the insulating material to increase in temperature. After enough time has elapsed to permit the temperature of this material to become uniform, the temperature is again recorded. From the rise in temperature and the total water equivalent of the calorimeter (that is, the weight of water that would require the same amount of heat to cause the temperature to rise one degree as is required to cause a rise in temperature of one degree of the total material of the calorimeter inside of the insulation), the amount of heat liberated in the reaction can be calculated. A correction must, of course, be made for the amount of heat introduced by the electric current that produced the ignition.

It has been found by experiments of this sort that the heat of combustion of carbon in the form of graphite to carbon dioxide is 94,230 calories per gram atom of carbon. That is, the value of Q for the reaction

$$C_{gr} + O_2 \longrightarrow CO_2$$

is 94,230 cal. The heat of the reaction may be expressed by including the value of Q in the equation:

$$C_{gr} + O_2 \longrightarrow CO_2 + 94{,}230 \text{ cal}$$

The heat of solution of sodium chloride in water might be determined by use of a calorimeter similar to that shown in Figure 31-1, but provided with a central container in which water is placed, with a little bucket of salt crystals arranged in such a way as to permit the bucket to be dropped into the water during the experiment. A stirrer for the salt solution would also be needed in order to cause the salt to dissolve sufficiently rapidly. When this experiment is carried out, it is found that the process of solution of 1 gram formula weight of sodium chloride in water is accompanied by the absorption of approximately 1,200 cal. The heat of the reaction depends slightly on the concentration of the solution that is produced. We may express this heat effect by the following equation:

$$NaCl(c) + aq \longrightarrow Na^+(aq) + Cl^-(aq) - 1{,}200 \text{ cal}$$

The Heat Content of a Substance.   It has been found by experiment that it is possible to assign to every chemical substance at standard conditions a numerical value of its *heat content*, such that the heat liberated during a chemical reaction can be found by subtracting the heat contents of the products from the heat contents of the reactants. (The word *enthalpy* is often used for heat content.) It is customary to place the heat contents of the elements equal to zero. The heat content of carbon dioxide is then $-94,230$ calories per mole, since the amount of heat 94,230 calories is liberated when 1 gram atom of carbon combines with 1 mole of oxygen to form 1 mole of carbon dioxide. We see that the heat content of a compound is just equal to the heat of formation of the compound from its component elements, but with opposite sign. Thus a compound such as carbon dioxide which is formed from the elements by an exothermic reaction has a negative heat content.

It is evident that it is not necessary to determine the heat of a particular reaction by experiment. If the heat of formation of every compound involved in the reaction is known, the heat of the reaction can be calculated. Values of heats of formation of compounds from elements in their standard states are given in the chemical handbooks and other reference books. The standard reference books are F. R. Bichowsky and F. D. Rossini, *The Thermochemistry of Chemical Substances*, Reinhold Publishing Corp., New York, **1936,** and F. D. Rossini, D. D. Wagman, W. H. Evans, S. Levine, and I. Jaffe, *Selected Values of Chemical Thermodynamic Properties*, Circular of the National Bureau of Standards 500, U.S. Government Printing Office, Washington, D.C., **1952.**

For example, suppose that we want to know the heat of reaction of carbon monoxide and oxygen to form carbon dioxide. The heat of formation of carbon monoxide from carbon and oxygen has been found by experiment to be 26,840 calories per mole of carbon monoxide. We may express this by the following equation:

$$C + \tfrac{1}{2}O_2 \longrightarrow CO + 26,840 \text{ cal}$$

In this equation we have written $\tfrac{1}{2}O_2$, instead of multiplying by 2 throughout the equation, in order that the product should be 1 mole of carbon monoxide. The heats of formation given in tables always refer to 1 mole of the compound.

The heat of formation of carbon dioxide from carbon in its standard state (diamond) and oxygen is 94,450 cal/mole:

$$C + O_2 \longrightarrow CO_2 + 94,450 \text{ cal}$$

By subtracting the first equation from the second, we obtain the result

$$CO + \tfrac{1}{2}O_2 \longrightarrow CO_2 + 67,610 \text{ cal}$$

Hence we have found that the heat of reaction of carbon monoxide (1 mole) with oxygen to form carbon dioxide is 67,610 calories.

31–2. *Heats of Ionic Reactions*

The theory of the complete ionization of strong electrolytes requires that the properties of dilute solutions of these electrolytes be determined completely by the individual ions; for example, the properties of a dilute solution of hydrochloric acid are the properties of a solution of hydrogen ion and chloride ion. Thermochemical properties are of especial interest. Thus the sum of the heats of formation of $HCl(aq)$ and $NaNO_3(aq)$ is equal to that of $NaCl(aq)$ and $HNO_3(aq)$ (all in dilute solution), since in each case the products are really $H^+(aq)$, $Na^+(aq)$, $Cl^-(aq)$, $NO_3^-(aq)$. For the same reason the heat of mixing of dilute solutions of strong electrolytes is zero, unless one of the products is not a strong electrolyte.

Example.   The experimental data (heats of formation) for the above case are the following:

$HCl(aq)$	39.56	$HNO_3(aq)$	49.80 kcal
$NaNO_3(aq)$	107.33	$NaCl(aq)$	97.08
	146.89		146.88

The sums are equal. For another set of pairs they are unequal:

$2HCl(aq)$	79.12	$2HNO_3(aq)$	99.60
$Hg(NO_3)_2(aq)$	58.10	$HgCl_2(aq)$	50.11
	137.22		149.71

This lack of equality results from the fact that in 0.02 F solution (to which the data refer) mercuric chloride is only slightly ionized, and the heat of formation of $HgCl_2(aq)$ molecules is greater than that of the ions $Hg^{++}(aq) + 2Cl^-(aq)$. The data, in fact, show that the heat of the reaction $Hg^{++}(aq) + 2Cl^-(aq) \longrightarrow HgCl_2(aq)$ is 12.49 kcal per mole.

An interesting special application of these considerations is to the reaction of *neutralization of an acid by a base*. It is found experimentally that the heat of neutralization in dilute solution of any strong acid [HCl, HBr, HI, HNO_3, H_2SO_4 (first hydrogen), $HClO_4$] and any strong base [$NaOH$, KOH, $Ba(OH)_2$] is 13.71 kcal per equivalent. The reason for this constancy of heat of neutralization is that the neutralization reaction for any strong acid and any strong base is the same,

$$H^+ + OH^- \longrightarrow H_2O$$

or, writing the symbol for hydronium ion explicitly,

$$H_3O^+ + OH^- \longrightarrow 2H_2O$$

and 13.71 kcal is the molar heat of this reaction. The heat of neutralization of a weak acid or weak base is different, as illustrated by the following experimental values:

$$NH_4OH + H^+ = NH_4^+ + H_2O + 12.3 \text{ kcal}$$
$$H_2S + OH^- = HS^- + H_2O + 7.7 \text{ kcal}$$

31–3. *Heat Capacity; Heats of Fusion, Vaporization, and Transition*

The amount of heat required to raise the temperature of unit quantity
(1 mole or 1 gram) of a substance by 1° C without change in phase is
called the *heat capacity* (sometimes called *specific heat*) of the substance.
Values of the heat capacity of substances are given in tables which may
be found in reference books.

Some general rules exist, such as that the molar heat capacity (at
constant pressure) of any monatomic gas is approximately 5 cal deg^{-1}
mole^{-1}, except at very low temperatures. The most useful rule (*Kopp's
rule*) is that *the molar heat capacity of a solid substance is the sum of its atomic
heat capacities, with the value about 6.2 for all atoms except the light ones*, for
which values used are

H	Be	B	C	N	O	F
2.5	3.0	2.5	2.0	3.0	4.0	5.0

The examples in Table 31-1 illustrate the agreement of this rule with
experiment; the experimental values are for room temperature.

TABLE 31-1

SUBSTANCE	HEAT CAPACITY CAL DEG^{-1} G^{-1}	MOLAR HEAT CAPACITY	SUM OF ATOMIC VALUES FROM RULE
C, graphite	0.160	1.9	2.0 cal deg^{-1} mole^{-1}
Pb	.0305	6.3	6.2
CuI	.066	12.5	12.4
NH$_4$Br	.210	20.6	19.2
CaCO$_3$	.208	20.8	20.2
CaSO$_4$.2H$_2$O	.265	45.7	46.4
H$_2$O (ice)	.50	9.0	9.0

The *rule of Dulong and Petit*, dealing with the relation between the heat capacity of an element and its atomic weight, has been mentioned in Chapter 14. It is closely related to Kopp's rule.

The heat capacity of a liquid substance is usually somewhat larger than that of a solid. Water has an unusually large heat capacity.

Heat of Fusion. A definite amount of heat is required to convert a crystal into the liquid at the melting point; this is called the *heat of fusion*. The heat of fusion of ice is 79.7 cal/g or 1,436 cal/mole.

Heat of Vaporization. The heat absorbed on vaporization at the boiling point is the *heat of vaporization;* for water its value is 539.6 cal/g or 9,710 cal/mole.

For most substances a rough value of the heat of vaporization can be predicted from *Trouton's rule*, which states that the quotient of the molar heat of vaporization by the absolute boiling point has a constant value, about 21. For example, this rule predicts that the molar heat of vaporization of carbon disulfide, b.p. 319.3° A, be 21 × 319.8 = 6,700 cal; the experimental value is 6,391 cal. The heats of vaporization of water and alcohol are larger than expected from Trouton's rule, apparently because of the strong intermolecular forces in the liquids, due to the action of hydrogen bonds.

Heat of Transition. The transition of a substance from one crystalline modification to another crystalline modification stable in a higher temperature range is accompanied by the absorption of the *heat of transition*. The value of this quantity for the transition of white phosphorus to red phosphorus, for example, is 3,700 cal/mole, and for red mercuric iodide to yellow mercuric iodide it is 3,000 cal/mole.

The use of these thermal quantities in calculations is illustrated below.

Example 1. What product would result from adding 100 ml of water to 56 g of powdered lime, CaO, in an insulated vessel of small heat capacity? The heat of the reaction $CaO + H_2O(l) \longrightarrow Ca(OH)_2$ is 16.0 kcal/mole.

    Solution. The product is 1 mole of $Ca(OH)_2$, with heat capacity (Kopp's rule) 19.2 cal/deg, plus 82 ml of water, with heat capacity 82 cal/deg. The heat required to raise this system from 20° (room temperature) to 100° is 80 × 101.2 = 8,096 cal. There remains available 16.0 − 8.1 = 7.9 kcal. The heat of vaporization of water is 540 cal/g; hence about 7.9/0.54 = 14.6 g of water will be boiled away, leaving as the product a mixture of 74 g of slacked lime and 67 g of water at 100° C.

In working this problem we have assumed that the vessel is open, and that the reaction is taking place under atmospheric pressure.

31–4. *Heats of Formation and Relative Electronegativity of Atoms*

In Chapter 10 it was pointed out that in general strong bonds are formed between atoms which differ in electronegativity, and weaker bonds between atoms with a smaller electronegativity difference.

The most electronegative element is fluorine, in the upper right corner of the periodic table, and the electronegativity of elements decreases toward the left and toward the bottom of the table. Hydrogen and iodine, although quite different in general, are approximately equal in electronegativity. In the molecule H—$\overset{\cdot\cdot}{\underset{\cdot\cdot}{I}}$ the two atoms attract the shared electron pair which constitutes the covalent bond between them about equally. This bond is accordingly much like the covalent bonds in the elementary molecules H—H and $\overset{\cdot\cdot}{\underset{\cdot\cdot}{I}}$—$\overset{\cdot\cdot}{\underset{\cdot\cdot}{I}}$. It is hence not surprising that the energy of the H—I bond is very nearly the average of the energies of the H—H bond and the I—I bond. The heat of formation of HI is only 1.5 kcal/mole:

$$\tfrac{1}{2}H_2 + \tfrac{1}{2}I_2 \longrightarrow HI + 1.5 \text{ kcal}$$

On the other hand, hydrogen and chlorine differ considerably in electronegativity, and we may assume the covalent bond in HCl to have considerable ionic character, with the chlorine attracting the bonding electrons (resonance between H $\overset{\cdot\cdot}{\underset{\cdot\cdot}{:}}$ Cl $\overset{\cdot\cdot}{:}$ and H$^+$ $\overset{\cdot\cdot}{\underset{\cdot\cdot}{:}}$ Cl $\overset{\cdot\cdot}{:}$ $^-$). This *partial ionic character* of the bond stabilizes the molecule, and causes hydrogen and chlorine to unite vigorously to form hydrogen chloride, which has the value 22 kcal/mole for its heat of formation:

$$\tfrac{1}{2}H_2 + \tfrac{1}{2}Cl_2 \longrightarrow HCl + 22 \text{ kcal/mole}$$

The following statement may be repeated from Chapter 10: *The greater the separation of two elements on the electronegativity scale, the greater is the strength of the bond between them.* The electronegativity scale of the elements, given in Figure 10-11, was formulated largely from the observed heats of formation of substances.

The electronegativity scale is useful mainly in drawing roughly quantitative conclusions. Compounds between elements close together on the scale have small heats of formation, and tend to be unstable. Examples are NCl_3, CI_4, SI_2, PH_3, AsH_3, SiH_4. Compounds between metals and non-metals, which are far apart on the scale, are in general stable, and have large heats of formation. The heats of formation of the alkali halides, such as NaCl, lie between 70 and 150 kcal/mole.

The quantitative relation between bond energy and electronegativity difference may be expressed by an equation. For a single covalent bond between two atoms A and B the extra energy due to the partial ionic character is approximately $23(x_A - x_B)^2$ kcal/mole; that is, it is proportional to the square of the difference in electronegativity of the two atoms, and the proportionality constant has the value 23 kcal/mole. For example, chlorine and fluorine have electronegativity values differing by 1 (Fig. 10-11); hence the heat of formation of ClF (containing one Cl—F bond) is predicted to be 23 kcal/mole. The observed heat of formation of ClF is 25.7 kcal/mole. The agreement between the predicted and observed heat of formation is only approximate. There seem to be other factors than electronegativity affecting the heats of formation of substances, and it is for this reason that the values of the electronegativity are given only to one decimal place in Figure 10-11.

Heats of formation calculated in this way would refer to elements in states in which the atoms form single bonds, as they do in the molecules P_4 and S_8. Nitrogen (N_2) and oxygen (O_2) contain multiple bonds, and the nitrogen and oxygen molecules are more stable, by 110 kcal/mole and 48 kcal/mole, respectively, than they would be if the molecules contained single bonds (as in P_4 and S_8). Hence we must correct for this extra stability, by using the equation

$$Q = \text{heat of formation (in kcal/mole)} = 23\Sigma(x_A - x_B)^2 - 55n_N - 24n_O$$

Here the summation indicated by Σ is to be taken over all the bonds represented by the formula of the compound. The symbol n_N means the number of nitrogen atoms in the formula, and n_O the number of oxygen atoms.

As an example, we may consider the substance nitrogen trichloride, $N\begin{smallmatrix}\nearrow Cl \\ -Cl \\ \searrow Cl\end{smallmatrix}$.

Nitrogen and chlorine have the same electronegativity; hence the first term contributes nothing. There is one nitrogen atom in the molecule. Hence $Q = -55$ kcal/mole. The minus sign shows that the substance is unstable, and that heat is liberated when it decomposes. Nitrogen trichloride is, in fact, an oil which explodes easily, with great violence:

$$2NCl_3 \longrightarrow N_2 + 3Cl_2 + 110 \text{ kcal}$$

31–5. *Heats of Combustion*

Thermochemical data for organic substances are usually obtained experimentally by burning the substances in oxygen and measuring the amounts of heat evolved. These *heats of combustion* of the substances are reported in tables in the standard reference books.

The method of determining heats of combustion has been described above, for carbon. This method, with use of a bomb calorimeter, is the customary basis for determining the value of a fuel, such as coal or oil. A weighed sample of the fuel is placed in the bomb calorimeter, the bomb is filled with oxygen, and the fuel is burned. The fuel value or calorific value of the fuel is considered to be measured by its heat of combustion, and when large amounts of fuel are purchased the price may be determined by the result of tests in a bomb calorimeter.

In reporting the calorific value of fuels it is customary to use the *British thermal unit* (B.T.U.) instead of the calorie as the unit of heat.

The British thermal unit is the amount of heat required to raise the temperature of 1 pound of water by 1 degree Fahrenheit. Since a pound is 453 g, and 1 degree F is 5/9 degrees C, the British thermal unit is equal to $5/9 \times 453 = 252$ cal. The calorific value of a fuel expressed in B.T.U. per pound of fuel has a numerical value 9/5 as great as that expressed in calories per gram.

Example 2.   The heat of combustion of ethylene, C_2H_4, is 331.6 kcal/ mole, and that of ethane, C_2H_6, is 368.4 kcal/mole. What is the heat of hydrogenation of ethylene to ethane?

   Solution.   We are given the equations

$$C_2H_4 + 3O_2 \longrightarrow 2CO_2 + 2H_2O(l) + 331.6 \text{ kcal}$$
$$C_2H_6 + 3\tfrac{1}{2}O_2 \longrightarrow 2CO_2 + 3H_2O(l) + 368.4 \text{ kcal}$$

By subtracting the second equation from the first, we obtain

$$C_2H_4 + H_2O(l) \longrightarrow C_2H_6 + \tfrac{1}{2}O_2 - 36.8 \text{ kcal}$$

It is necessary to know the value of the heat of formation of water (given in the handbooks) in order to solve this problem:

$$H_2 + \tfrac{1}{2}O_2 \longrightarrow H_2O(l) + 68.4 \text{ kcal}$$

By adding this equation to the previous one we obtain the result

$$C_2H_4 + H_2 \longrightarrow C_2H_6 + 31.6 \text{ kcal}$$

Accordingly, the reaction of combination of ethylene with hydrogen to form ethane must be exothermic, the molar heat of hydrogenation of ethylene being **31.6 kcal.**

   It is interesting to note that the heat of this reduction can be found without having to carry out the particular reaction at all—it can be obtained, as shown by the calculation we have just made, from measurement of the heat of combustion of ethylene, the heat of combustion of ethane, and the heat of combustion of hydrogen. Heats of combustion are ordinarily reliable to about 0.5%, which in this case would be ±2 kcal. The molar heat of hydrogenation of ethylene has been determined directly by carrying out the hydrogenation reaction (in the presence of a catalyst) in a calorimeter. The value 32.8 ± 0.1 kcal was obtained by this direct method.

Heat Values of Foods.   One important use of foods is to serve as a source of energy, permitting work to be done, and of heat, keeping the body warm. Foods serve in this way through their oxidation within the body by oxygen which is extracted from the air in the lungs and is carried to the tissues by the hemoglobin of the blood. The ultimate products of oxidation of most of the hydrogen and carbon in foods are water and carbon dioxide. The nitrogen is for the most part converted into urea, $CO(NH_2)_2$, which is eliminated in the urine.

Heats of combustion of foods and their relation to dietary requirements have been thoroughly studied. The food ingested daily by a healthy man of average size doing a moderate amount of muscular work should have a total heat of combustion of about 3,000 kcal. About 90% of this is made available as work and heat by digestion and metabolism of the food.

Fats and carbohydrates are the principal sources of energy in foods. Pure fat has a caloric value (heat of combustion) of 4,080 kcal per pound, and pure carbohydrate (sugar) a caloric value of about 1,860 kcal per pound. The caloric values of foods are obtained by use of a bomb calorimeter, just as was described above for fuels. The third main constituent of food, protein, is needed primarily for growth and for the repair of tissues. About 50 g of protein is the daily requirement for an adult of average size. Usually about twice this amount of protein is ingested. This amount, 100 g, has a caloric value of only about 400 kcal, the heat of combustion of protein being about 2,000 kcal per pound. Accordingly, fat and carbohydrate must provide about 2,600 kcal of the 3,000 kcal required daily.

Exercises

31-1. A 3% solution (by weight) of hydrogen peroxide in an insulated bottle is caused to decompose by adding a small amount of a catalyst (MnO_2). How warm does the solution become? Use data given in this chapter.

31-2. What relation exists between the heat liberated or absorbed in a dry cell in its operation and the heat of the reaction

$$Zn + 2NH_4^+ + 2MnO_2 \longrightarrow Zn(NH_3)_2^{++} + 2MnO(OH)$$

31-3. The molar heat of formation of zinc chloride is 99.55 kcal and its molar heat of solution is 15.72 kcal; the corresponding values for hydrogen chloride are 22.03 kcal/mole and 17.44 kcal/mole. How much heat is evolved by the reaction of zinc and aqueous hydrochloric acid?

31-4. The heat capacity of $ZnCl_2$ is 0.14 cal deg^{-1} g^{-1}, and its melting point is 365° C. Could the heat of combustion of zinc in chlorine raise the temperature to the melting point of the salt?

31-5. The heat of formation of $H_2O(g)$ is 57.80 kcal/mole, and the heat capacity of steam varies from 0.48 cal/g at 100° C to 0.50 at 500° C. What is the maximum temperature that could be expected from an oxygen-hydrogen flame?

31-6. The molar heats of formation of NO and NO_2 are -21.5 kcal and -7.43 kcal, respectively. Is the reaction $2NO + O_2 \longrightarrow 2NO_2$ exothermic or endothermic? What is the heat of the reaction?

31-7. A person with a distaste for exercise and dieting decided to lose weight by drinking a gallon of ice water a day. His normal daily diet had a caloric value of 3,000 kcal; what fraction of this did he use up in warming the ice water (body temperature $= 37°$ C)?

31-8. What is the minimum amount of food (fat, say) which must be used by a 220-lb. man in climbing a 1,000-foot hill?

31-9. From data given in this chapter and the following table of composition of foods, calculate the calorific value of the foods:

	PERCENT BY WEIGHT		
	PROTEIN	FAT	CARBOHYDRATE
American cheese..	28.8	35.9	9.3
Whole milk......	3.3	4.0	5.0
White bread.....	9.3	1.2	52.2
Butter..........	1.0	85.0	
Potatoes........	2.5	0.1	20.3

31-10. Calculate the exact atomic weight of an element which has (as the solid elementary substance) a heat capacity of 0.092 cal/g and whose oxide contains 11.18% oxygen.

31-11. A piece of metal weighing 100 g and at temperature $120°$ C was dropped in a liter of water at temperature $20.00°$ C. The final temperature was $20.53°$ C. What is the approximate atomic weight of the metal?

31-12. The heat of solution of gaseous phosgene in excess base is 104.5 kcal/mole:

$$COCl_2(g) + 4OH^- \longrightarrow 2Cl^- + CO_3^{--} + 2H_2O + 104.5 \text{ kcal}$$

The heat of solution of gaseous carbon dioxide in excess base is 25.1 kcal/mole. The heat of formation of hydrogen chloride gas is 22.0 kcal/mole, and its heat of solution in water is 17.4 kcal/mole. Calculate the heat of formation of phosgene.

31-13. What is the heat of hydrogenation of methyl alcohol to methane? The heats of combustion of methyl alcohol and methane are 182.6 and 213.0 kcal/mole, respectively.

Chapter 32

Oxidation-Reduction Equilibria

What makes a chemical reaction go? This is a question which chemists and students have asked ever since chemical reactions began to be investigated. At the beginning of the nineteenth century the question was answered by saying that two substances react if they have a "chemical affinity" for each other. This answer, of course, had no value until some quantitative meaning was given to "chemical affinity," and some way was found for measuring or predicting it.

It might be thought that the heat of a reaction is its driving force, and that a reaction will proceed if it evolves heat, and not proceed if it would absorb heat. This idea, however, is wrong; many reactions proceed even though they absorb heat. For example, when mercuric oxide is heated it decomposes into mercury and oxygen, with absorption of heat. Other endothermic processes are the solution of sodium chloride in water, and the evaporation of a volatile liquid, such as ether. Sodium chloride dissolves in water until its solution becomes saturated, even though the process requires heat to be absorbed, and liquid ether evaporates, with absorption of heat, until the partial pressure of its vapor reaches the equilibrium value.

Before entering upon the detailed discussion of what makes a chemical reaction go, we shall, in the following section, discuss the relation between heat and work, and the problem of producing low temperatures. We shall find in the discussion of this problem that the equilibrium between a gas and a liquid involves not only the difference in energy of the molecules of gas and liquid, but also the difference in their probability. These factors are important also in chemical equilibria; together they constitute the driving force of a chemical reaction.

32–1. *Heat and Work*

The relation between heat and work is treated in courses in physics, and may be briefly reviewed here. Work is done by a directed force acting through a distance; the amount of work done by a force of one dyne acting through a distance of one centimeter is called one erg. If this amount of work is done in putting an object initially at rest into motion, we say that the moving object has a *kinetic energy* of 1 erg. All of this kinetic energy may be used to do work, as the moving object is slowed down to rest; for example, a string attached to the moving object might serve to lift a small weight to a certain height above its original position.

Another way in which the moving object can be slowed down to rest is through *friction*. The process which then occurs is that the kinetic energy of the directed motion of the moving body is converted into energy of randomly directed motion of the molecules of the bodies between which friction occurs. This increase in vigor of molecular motion corresponds to an increase in temperature of the bodies. We say that heat has been added to the bodies, causing their temperatures to rise. Thus, if one of the bodies was 1 g of water, and if its temperature rose by 1°, we would say that 1 cal of heat had entered it.

The question at once arises as to how much work must be done to produce this much heat. This question was answered by experiments carried out in Manchester, England, between 1840 and 1878 by James Prescott Joule (1818–1889), after Count Rumford (Benjamin Thompson, 1753–1814) had shown in 1798 that the friction of a blunt borer in a cannon caused an increase in temperature of the cannon. Joule's work led to a value close to the more precise value now accepted for the mechanical equivalent of heat—that is, the relation between heat and work:

1 cal = 4.185 joules = 4.185 × 10⁷ ergs

The large unit of energy introduced here, the **joule,** is 1×10^7 ergs. One joule is equal to the work done by the flow of one coulomb of electricity through a potential difference of one volt, and hence it is also equal to 1 watt second:

1 joule = 1 volt coulomb = 1 watt sec

It is interesting to note that 1 cal is a large amount of energy. Since the force of gravity on 1 g of water is 980 dynes, the water would have to fall through a height of $4.185 \times 10^7/980 = 42,690$ cm, or 1,400 feet, to get enough kinetic energy to raise its temperature by 1° C when converted into heat.

The Production of Low Temperatures.   It is not very hard to achieve high temperatures. A strongly exothermic chemical reaction can be made to take place rapidly, in such a way as to allow the energy that is given out to be used to heat a system that it is desired to have at a high temperature. Temperatures as high as 2,800° C can be reached by use of the oxy-hydrogen torch and as high as 3,500° C by use of the oxy-acetylene torch. Still higher temperatures can be reached by pouring electric energy into a system. The temperature in an electric arc is between 5,000° and 6,000° C. The highest temperature that has been produced by man except by the detonation of an atomic bomb is about 20,000° C. This very high temperature was obtained by passing the electricity stored in a large electric condenser through a fine wire; the great amount of electric energy passing through the wire causes it to explode, and heats the metallic vapor to about 20,000°. The temperature at the center of a detonating atomic bomb is extremely high—of the order of magnitude of 50,000,000°.

The problem of removing energy from a portion of matter, and taking it to a lower temperature, is not so easy. It would be fine if some strongly endothermic reaction could be found which would proceed rapidly, and would thus cool a system to lower and lower temperatures. However, it is difficult to find a reaction of this kind.

The usual method of achieving low temperatures involves the evaporation of a liquid. This process, the change of a substance from the liquid state at the boiling point to the gaseous state at the boiling point, is an endothermic reaction. An amount of heat equal to the heat of vaporization is absorbed in the process. For example, the heat of vaporization of water is 10,571 calories per mole. When 18 grams of water is made to evaporate at room temperature, by blowing a current of air over it in order to carry away the water vapor, 10,571 calories of heat is absorbed, and the system is cooled by this amount. Water is not so effective for use in this way as are some other substances, such as diethyl ether, $(C H_5)_2O$, and ethyl chloride, C_2H_5Cl. These substances are sometimes used to freeze a small portion of the body for a minor surgical operation.

Ammonia, NH_3, is usually used as the refrigerant in the manufacture of ice. The way in which a commercial ice plant operates is indicated by Figure 32-1. Ammonia gas, which can be made to condense to a liquid at room temperature by compressing it, is passed through a mechanical compressor, indicated at the left of the figure. The compressed gas liquefies, giving out a quantity of heat equal to the heat of vaporization. This causes the liquid ammonia to be at a temperature considerably above room temperature. The warm liquid is passed through cooling coils, and heat is transferred to the cooling water,

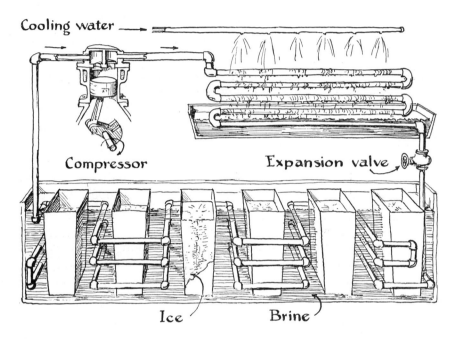

FIG. 32-1   *The manufacture of ice with ammonia as the refrigerant.*

reducing the temperature of the liquid ammonia to room temperature. The liquid is then allowed to pass through an expansion valve, into a region of low pressure. The liquid evaporates in this region of low pressure, forming ammonia gas, and absorbing an amount of heat equal to the heat of vaporization. This absorption of heat cools a brine bath in which the tanks of water to be frozen to blocks of ice are contained, and the gaseous ammonia is then ready to be compressed again.

Ordinary domestic refrigerators operate in the same way. Instead of ammonia, other substances are usually used in domestic refrigerators; methyl chloride (CH_3Cl), sulfur dioxide (SO_2), and dichlorodifluoromethane (CCl_2F_2) are the common ones. The last of these substances, dichlorodifluoromethane, is a popular refrigerant because it is not toxic, and there is no danger in case that some of it escapes from the refrigerating system.

It is interesting to ask why the evaporation of the liquid takes place, even though this reaction is endothermic. The explanation of this phenomenon is given by the consideration of *probability*. Let us consider a large flask, with volume 10 liters, into which some water molecules are introduced. We might well think that it would be equally probable that a particular water molecule would be in any place in the flask—that the probability would be 1 in 10,000 that the molecule would occupy any particular milliliter of volume within the flask. If enough water has been introduced into the flask, however, some of the water will liquefy, the rest remaining as water vapor. Let us suppose that there is 1 ml of liquid water present in a little puddle at the bottom of the flask. At room temperature most of the water-substance present in the flask will be in this puddle of liquid water, only a fraction of the water molecules being present as water vapor. Now, although it seems very improbable that a water molecule should stay in the small volume, 1 milliliter, occupied by the liquid water, instead of occupying the remaining 9,999 milliliters of space, we know that the reason that the water vapor condenses to liquid water is that liquid water is the more stable state, and that condensation proceeds until the rate at which gas molecules strike the surface of the liquid and stick is just equal to the rate at which molecules of the liquid leave the surface and escape into the gas. This is the equilibrium state. We see that the equilibrium state involves a balance between the effect of *energy*, which tends to concentrate the molecules into the liquid phase, and the effect of *probability*, which tends to change the liquid into the gas. If the volume of the flask were five times as great, making the probability for the gas phase 49,999 to 1 instead of 9,999 to 1, five times as many molecules would leave the liquid phase and move to the gaseous phase.

Accordingly, we see that this effect of probability can be made to cause more of the liquid to evaporate, simply by increasing the volume of the system. This is the explanation of the process of refrigeration described above. When the total volume is reduced, by use of a compressor, more of the substance changes to the liquid phase; and when the volume is increased, by allowing the substance to pass through the reducing valve from the region of high pressure to the region of low pressure, more of the substance evaporates.

In the branch of science called thermodynamic chemistry a more detailed consideration is given to the relative effects of energy and probability. It has been found that the effect of probability can be described quantitatively by a new property of substances. This new property, which represents the probability of a substance in various states, is called *entropy*.

32–2. *The Driving Force of Chemical Reactions*

We now are ready to discuss the question of the nature of the driving force of chemical reactions.

In the preceding section we have pointed out that, in addition to the energy change taking place during a reaction, there is another important factor involved, the *probability* of the states represented by the reactants and the products. This probability factor is described by the quantity called the *entropy*. Whereas the energy change that accompanies a chemical reaction does not depend very much on the pressures of the gases or the concentrations of the solutes involved in the reaction, the entropy change does depend on these partial pressures and concentrations. In general, a system held at constant temperature will reach a steady state, called the state of equilibrium. In this state of the system the reaction has no preferential tendency to proceed either forward or backward; it has no driving force in either direction. If, however, the concentration of one of the reactants (a solute or a gas) is increased, a driving force comes into existence which causes the reaction to go in the forward direction until the equilibrium expression, involving the concentrations or partial pressures of reactants and products, again becomes equal to the equilibrium constant for the reaction.

It is clear from these considerations that *the driving force of a reaction depends not only on the chemical formulas of the reactants, and the structure of their molecules, but also on the concentrations of the reactants and of the products.*

A great step forward was made around the end of the last century when it was found that an energy quantity called its **free energy** can be assigned to each substance, such that a reaction in a system held at constant temperature tends to proceed if it is accompanied by a decrease in free energy—that is, if the free energy of the reactants is greater than that of the products. *The free energy of a substance is a property that expresses the resultant of the energy (heat content) of the substance and its inherent probability (entropy).* If the substances whose formulas are written on the left of the double arrow in a chemical equation and those whose formulas are written on the right have the same entropy (probability), the reaction will proceed in the direction that leads to the evolution of heat—that is, in the exothermic direction. If the substances on the left and those on the right have the same energy, the reaction will proceed from the substances with the smaller probability (entropy) toward the substances with the greater probability (entropy). At equilibrium, when a reaction has no preferential tendency to go in either the forward or the backward direction, the free energy of the substances on the left side is exactly equal to that of the substances on the right side. *At equilibrium the driving force of the heat-content change (enthalpy change) accompanying a reaction is exactly balanced by the driving force of the probability change (entropy change).*

The discovery of the relation between equilibrium constant and free energy has simplified the task of systematizing chemical reactions. Chemists might determine, at 25° C, say, the value of the equilibrium constant of each reaction in which they are interested. This would be a great task. It would be far simpler to determine the standard free-energy value at 25° C for each of a large number of chemical substances. Then, by combining these values, the free-energy change for any chemical reaction involving these substances as reactants and products could be calculated, and from it the equilibrium constant for the reaction could be found. The great simplification introduced by this procedure can be seen by examining Table 32-1, given in the next section. This table contains only 57 entries, which correspond to 57 different electron reactions. By combining any two of these electron reactions the equation for an ordinary oxidation-reduction reaction can be written. There are $57 \times 56/2$, or 1,596, of these oxidation-reduction reactions which can be formed from the 57 electron reactions. The 57 numbers in the table can be combined in such a way as to give the 1,596 values of their equilibrium constants; accordingly, this small table permits a prediction to be made as to whether any one of these 1,596 reactions will tend to go in the forward direction or the reverse direction. A similar table given in the book on oxidation potentials written by W. M. Latimer occupies nine pages; the information given on these nine pages permits one to calculate values of the equilibrium constants for about 85,000 reactions. A table giving the equilibrium constants for these 85,000 reactions would occupy 1,750 pages of the same size as the pages in Professor Latimer's book; and, moreover, it is evident that if the equilibrium constants were independent of one another, and had to be determined by separate experiments, we would not have been able to gather nearly so much information about these reactions.

The study of the free energy of substances constitutes a complex subject, and only a bare introduction to it can be given in a course in general chemistry. The following section deals with free-energy changes accompanying oxidation-reduction reactions; a similar treatment can also be given to other reactions.

32–3. *The Table of Standard Oxidation-Reduction Potentials*

In the discussion of oxidation-reduction reactions in Chapter 11 a brief table was given of oxidation-reduction couples arranged according to strength, the couple with the strongest reducing agent being at the top of the table and that with the strongest oxidizing agent at the bottom.

Table 32-1 is a more extensive table of this kind.

TABLE 32-1   *Standard Oxidation-Reduction Potentials and Equilibrium Constants* (The values apply to temperature 25° C, with standard concentration for aqueous solutions 1 M and standard pressure of gases 1 atm.)

	E^0	K
$Li = Li^+ + e^-$	3.02	4×10^{50}
$Cs = Cs^+ + e^-$	3.02	4×10^{50}
$Rb = Rb^+ + e^-$	2.99	2×10^{50}
$K = K^+ + e^-$	2.92	1×10^{49}
$\frac{1}{2}Ba = \frac{1}{2}Ba^{++} + e^-$	2.90	5×10^{48}
$\frac{1}{2}Sr = \frac{1}{2}Sr^{++} + e^-$	2.89	4×10^{48}
$\frac{1}{2}Ca = \frac{1}{2}Ca^{++} + e^-$	2.87	2×10^{48}
$Na = Na^+ + e^-$	2.712	4.0×10^{45}
$\frac{1}{3}Al + \frac{4}{3}OH^- = \frac{1}{3}Al(OH)_4^- + e^-$	2.35	3×10^{39}
$\frac{1}{2}Mg = \frac{1}{2}Mg^{++} + e^-$	2.34	2×10^{39}
$\frac{1}{2}Be = \frac{1}{2}Be^{++} + e^-$	1.70	4×10^{28}
$\frac{1}{3}Al = \frac{1}{3}Al^{+++} + e^-$	1.67	1×10^{28}
$\frac{1}{2}Zn + 2OH^- = \frac{1}{2}Zn(OH)_4^{--} + e^-$	1.216	2.7×10^{20}
$\frac{1}{2}Mn = \frac{1}{2}Mn^{++} + e^-$	1.05	4×10^{17}
$\frac{1}{2}Zn + 2NH_3 = \frac{1}{2}Zn(NH_3)_4^{++} + e^-$	1.03	2×10^{17}
$Co(CN)_6^{----} = Co(CN)_6^{---} + e^-$	0.83	1×10^{14}
$\frac{1}{2}Zn = \frac{1}{2}Zn^{++} + e^-$	.762	6.5×10^{12}
$\frac{1}{2}H_2C_2O_4(aq) = CO_2 + H^+ + e^-$	.49	2×10^8
$\frac{1}{2}Fe = \frac{1}{2}Fe^{++} + e^-$	.440	2.5×10^7
$\frac{1}{2}Cd = \frac{1}{2}Cd^{++} + e^-$	.402	5.7×10^6
$\frac{1}{2}Co = \frac{1}{2}Co^{++} + e^-$	.277	4.5×10^4
$\frac{1}{2}Ni = \frac{1}{2}Ni^{++} + e^-$	.250	1.6×10^4
$I^- + Cu = CuI(s) + e^-$	.187	1.4×10^3
$\frac{1}{2}Sn = \frac{1}{2}Sn^{++} + e^-$	.136	1.9×10^2
$\frac{1}{2}Pb = \frac{1}{2}Pb^{++} + e^-$	.126	1.3×10^2
$\frac{1}{2}H_2 = H^+ + e^-$	.000	1
$\frac{1}{2}H_2S = \frac{1}{2}S + H^+ + e^-$	−0.141	4.3×10^{-3}

From this table we see that of the substances listed lithium metal is the strongest reducing agent, and fluoride ion is the weakest; and conversely fluorine is the strongest oxidizing agent and lithium ion the weakest.

There is given for each couple the value of the standard potential E^0. This is the potential developed by the electric cell formed by the couple under consideration and the standard hydrogen couple $\frac{1}{2}H_2 \rightleftarrows H^+ + e^-$; this standard hydrogen couple has been selected as the reference point, with $E^0 = 0$.

TABLE 32-1 (*continued*)

	E^0	K
$Cu^+ = Cu^{++} + e^-$	-0.167	1.6×10^{-3}
$\frac{1}{2}H_2O + \frac{1}{2}H_2SO_3 = \frac{1}{2}SO_4^{--} + 2H^+ + e^-$	-0.20	4×10^{-4}
$\frac{1}{2}Cu = \frac{1}{2}Cu^{++} + e^-$	-0.345	1.6×10^{-6}
$Fe(CN)_6^{----} = Fe(CN)_6^{---} + e^-$	-0.36	9×10^{-7}
$2OH^- + \frac{1}{2}Cl_2 = ClO^- + H_2O + e^-$	-0.52	2×10^{-9}
$I^- = \frac{1}{2}I_2(s) + e^-$	-0.53	1×10^{-9}
$MnO_4^{--} = MnO_4^- + e^-$	-0.54	1×10^{-9}
$\frac{4}{3}OH^- + \frac{1}{3}MnO_2 = \frac{1}{3}MnO_4^- + \frac{2}{3}H_2O + e^-$	-0.57	3×10^{-10}
$OH^- + \frac{1}{2}ClO^- = \frac{1}{2}ClO_2^- + \frac{1}{2}H_2O + e^-$	-0.59	1×10^{-10}
$\frac{1}{2}H_2O_2 = \frac{1}{2}O_2 + H^+ + e^-$	-0.682	3.5×10^{-12}
$Fe^{++} = Fe^{+++} + e^-$	-0.771	1.1×10^{-13}
$Hg = \frac{1}{2}Hg_2^{++} + e^-$	-0.799	3.7×10^{-14}
$Ag = Ag^+ + e^-$	-0.800	3.5×10^{-14}
$H_2O + NO_2 = NO_3^- + 2H^+ + e^-$	-0.81	3×10^{-14}
$\frac{1}{2}Hg = \frac{1}{2}Hg^{++} + e^-$	-0.854	4.5×10^{-15}
$\frac{1}{2}Hg_2^{++} = Hg^{++} + e^-$	-0.910	5.0×10^{-16}
$\frac{1}{2}HNO_2 + \frac{1}{2}H_2O = \frac{1}{2}NO_3^- + \frac{3}{2}H^+ + e^-$	-0.94	2×10^{-16}
$NO + H_2O = HNO_2 + H^+ + e^-$	-0.99	2×10^{-17}
$\frac{1}{2}ClO_3^- + \frac{1}{2}H_2O = \frac{1}{2}ClO_4^- + H^+ + e^-$	-1.00	2×10^{-17}
$Br^- = \frac{1}{2}Br_2(l) + e^-$	-1.065	1.3×10^{-18}
$H_2O + \frac{1}{2}Mn^{++} = \frac{1}{2}MnO_2 + 2H^+ + e^-$	-1.28	3×10^{-22}
$Cl^- = \frac{1}{2}Cl_2 + e^-$	-1.358	1.5×10^{-23}
$\frac{7}{6}H_2O + \frac{1}{3}Cr^{+++} = \frac{1}{6}Cr_2O_7^{--} + \frac{7}{3}H^+ + e^-$	-1.36	1×10^{-23}
$\frac{1}{3}Au = \frac{1}{3}Au^{+++} + e^-$	-1.42	1×10^{-24}
$\frac{1}{2}H_2O + \frac{1}{6}Cl^- = \frac{1}{6}ClO_3^- + H^+ + e^-$	-1.45	4×10^{-25}
$\frac{4}{5}H_2O + \frac{1}{5}Mn^{++} = \frac{1}{5}MnO_4^- + \frac{8}{5}H^+ + e^-$	-1.52	3×10^{-23}
$\frac{1}{2}Cl_2 + H_2O = HClO + H^+ + e^-$	-1.63	4×10^{-28}
$H_2O = \frac{1}{2}H_2O_2 + H^+ + e^-$	-1.77	2×10^{-30}
$Co^{++} = Co^{+++} + e^-$	-1.84	1×10^{-31}
$F^- = \frac{1}{2}F_2 + e^-$	-2.85	1×10^{-48}

For example, a cell made with a strip of zinc as one electrode, in contact with a solution 1 M in Zn^{++}, and a piece of platinum over which bubbles of hydrogen are passing as the other electrode (Fig. 11-4) would develop the potential 0.762 volt, this being the value given in the table for the couple $\frac{1}{2}Zn = \frac{1}{2}Zn^{++} + e^-$.

The potential of a cell depends on the concentrations or partial pressures of the reacting substances. The standard concentrations of the dissolved substances in Table 32-1 are taken to be approximately 1 M (more accurately, unit activity, correction being made for deviation from the perfect-solution law), and the standard pressure for gases is 1 atm (corrected in very accurate work for deviation from the perfect-gas law)

32–4. *Equilibrium Constants for Oxidation-Reduction Couples*

The zinc-hydrogen cell develops a large electric potential, 0.762 v, because the over-all reaction

$$\tfrac{1}{2}Zn + H^+ \rightleftarrows \tfrac{1}{2}Zn^{++} + \tfrac{1}{2}H_2$$

which represents the reduction of hydrogen ion by zinc metal, has a strong tendency to go to the right, and in a cell so built that the electron reactions occur at separate electrodes this tendency results in electrons being forced into one electrode by the electrode reaction and pulled out of the other. It is clear that the equilibrium constant

$$K = \frac{[Zn^{++}]^{\frac{1}{2}}p_{H_2}^{\frac{1}{2}}}{[H^+]}$$

for the over-all reaction must have a large numerical value, corresponding to the tendency of the reaction to proceed to the right.

Half a century ago it was shown by physical chemists from the laws of thermodynamics that the equilibrium constant of the over-all cell reaction can be calculated from the potential of the cell. In fact, we can calculate from standard potentials of the couples, as given in Table 32-1, values of equilibrium constants for the couples; these values are also given in the table.

The relation between the equilibrium constant and the standard potential is

$$RT \ln K = E^0 F$$

where R is the gas constant, T the absolute temperature, and F the faraday. At 25° C this reduces to

$$\log K = 16.8 \, E^0$$

The quantity E^0F (product of potential and quantity of electricity) is an energy quantity—namely, the amount of electric energy produced by the cell on reaction of one gram equivalent weight of substance at each electrode. This energy quantity is the amount of work which the cell can do (the electric energy can be completely used in doing work). It is, moreover, exactly equal to the free-energy decrease accompanying the reaction—*free energy is the power to do work.*

The study of relations such as this is part of the important subject of chemical thermodynamics, which is a branch of physical chemistry. In recent years great progress has been made in formulating a system of chemical thermodynamics by means of which prediction can be made of the extent to which a possible chemical reaction may take place and the conditions which favor the reaction. Part of this progress has been made by the direct study of chemical equilibria and the determination of cell potentials, and part by experiments which give information about molecular structure, such as electron diffraction and spectroscopy.

The meaning of the equilibrium constants of the oxidation-reduction couples can be made clear by the discussion of some examples. For the couple

$$\tfrac{1}{2}Zn \rightleftharpoons \tfrac{1}{2}Zn^{++} + e^-$$

the constant is given as $K = 6.5 \times 10^{12}$. For this reaction the equilibrium expression is written according to the convention adopted in Chapter 20 as

$$K = [Zn^{++}]^{\frac{1}{2}}[e^-]$$

(The term $[Zn]$ does not appear in the denominator because the activity of a crystalline substance is constant [at a given temperature] and is conventionally taken equal to unity.) It is this product which has the value 6.5×10^{12}.

This is, however, not of use until the quantity $[e^-]$, the electron concentration, has been evaluated or eliminated. It can be eliminated by combining the couple with another couple. Thus for the reaction

$$\tfrac{1}{2}H_2 \rightleftharpoons H^+ + e^-$$

we have K given in the table as 1 (corresponding to $E^0 = 0$), which leads to

$$\frac{[H^+][e^-]}{p_{H_2}^{\frac{1}{2}}} = 1$$

By dividing this into the above equation we obtain

$$\frac{[Zn^{++}]^{\frac{1}{2}}[e^-]}{[H^+][e^-]/p_{H_2}^{\frac{1}{2}}} = \frac{6.5 \times 10^{12}}{1}$$

We now cancel the term $[e^-]$ and obtain the result

$$\frac{[Zn^{++}]^{\frac{1}{2}}p_{H_2}^{\frac{1}{2}}}{[H^+]} = 6.5 \times 10^{12}$$

This is the equilibrium equation corresponding to the reaction

$$\tfrac{1}{2}Zn + H^+ \rightleftarrows \tfrac{1}{2}Zn^{++} + \tfrac{1}{2}H_2$$

We may for convenience square the equilibrium expression, obtaining

$$\frac{[Zn^{++}]p_{H_2}}{[H^+]^2} = 42 \times 10^{24}$$

corresponding to the reaction

$$Zn + 2H^+ \rightleftarrows Zn^{++} + H_2$$

This tells us that the equilibrium pressure of hydrogen for the reaction of zinc with acid is extremely great; the reaction cannot be stopped by increasing the pressure of hydrogen, but will proceed until all of the zinc is dissolved.

On the other hand, for tin the equilibrium expression is

$$\frac{[Sn^{++}]p_{H_2}}{[H^+]^2} = (1.9 \times 10^2)^2 = 3.6 \times 10^4$$

Hence equilibrium would be reached, for example, by having $[Sn^{++}] = 1$, $p_{H_2} = 3.6$ atm, and $[H^+] = 0.01$.

Additional illustrations of the use of the table are given in the following sections.

You will have noticed that the electron reactions are all written in Table 32-1 so as to produce one electron. This is done for convenience; with this convention the ratio of two values of K gives the equilibrium constant for the reaction obtained by subtracting the equation for one couple from that for another. It is sometimes desirable to clear the equation of fractions by multiplying by a suitable factor; as we have seen from the examples given above, and as we know from the definition of equilibrium constant, this involves raising the equilibrium constant to the power equal to this factor.

The Combination of Two Related Couples to Form a Third Couple. Two couples which have a substance in common can be combined to form a third couple, and the position of this couple in the oxidation-reduction table can be found from the data for the other two.

In making such a calculation do not try to learn new rules about how to use oxidation-reduction potentials; instead, make use of the knowledge that you already have about equilibrium constants in general to derive anything that you need. For example, suppose that you were asked to find the equilibrium constant for a reaction involving the oxidation of metallic copper to cuprous ion, with use of data from Table 32-1, which does not give the potential for the electron reaction

$$Cu \rightleftarrows Cu^+ + e^-$$

You would notice that the table includes the two related electron reactions

$$\tfrac{1}{2}Cu \rightleftarrows \tfrac{1}{2}Cu^{++} + e^-$$

and

$$Cu^+ \rightleftarrows Cu^{++} + e^-$$

with the respective equilibrium expressions

$$[Cu^{++}]^{\frac{1}{2}} [e^-] = 1.6 \times 10^{-6}$$

and

$$\frac{[Cu^{++}][e^-]}{[Cu^+]} = 1.6 \times 10^{-3}$$

By squaring the first equation we obtain

$$[Cu^{++}][e^-]^2 = 2.6 \times 10^{-12}$$

Dividing this by the second we get as the desired expression

$$\frac{[Cu^{++}][e^-]^2[Cu^+]}{[Cu^{++}][e^-]} = \frac{2.6 \times 10^{-12}}{1.6 \times 10^{-3}}$$

or

$$[Cu^+][e^-] = 1.6 \times 10^{-9}$$

This is the equilibrium expression corresponding to the reaction

$$Cu \rightleftarrows Cu^+ + e^-$$

which results from multiplying the copper–cupric-ion equation as written above by the factor 2 and subtracting the cuprous-ion–cupric-ion equation.

32–5. *Examples Illustrating the Use of Standard Oxidation-Reduction Potentials*

Many questions about chemical reactions can be answered by reference to a table of standard oxidation-reduction potentials. In particular it can be determined whether or not a given oxidizing agent and a given reducing agent can possibly react to an appreciable extent, and the extent of possible reaction can be predicted. It cannot be said, however, that the reaction will necessarily proceed at a significant rate under given conditions; *the table gives information only about the state of chemical equilibrium and not about the rate at which equilibrium is approached.* For this reason the most valuable use of the table is in connection with reactions which are known to take place, to answer questions as to the extent of reaction; but the table is also valuable in telling whether or not it is worth while to try to make a reaction go by changing conditions.

Some ways in which the table can be used are illustrated below.

Question 1. Is ferricyanide ion a stronger or a weaker oxidizing agent than ferric ion?

Answer.   We see from the table that the ferrocyanide-ferricyanide potential is larger than the ferrous-ferric potential; hence ferrocyanide ion is a stronger reducing agent than ferrous ion, and ferricyanide ion is a weaker oxidizing agent than ferric ion.

Question 2.   Would you expect reaction to occur on mixing solutions of ferrous sulfate and mercuric sulfate?

Answer.   The ferrous-ferric couple has potential -0.771 v and the mercurous-mercuric couple -0.910 v; hence the latter couple is the stronger oxidizing of the two, and the reaction

$$2Fe^{++} + 2Hg^{++} = 2Fe^{+++} + Hg_2^{++}$$

would occur, and proceed well toward completion.

Question 3.   What would you expect to occur on mixing solutions of ferrous sulfate and mercuric chloride?

Answer.   The above oxidation-reduction reaction would take place; in addition, when the solubility product of the very slightly soluble salt Hg_2Cl_2 is reached, this substance would precipitate, keeping the concentration $[Hg_2^{++}]$ low and causing the oxidation-reduction reaction to go further toward completion than in the previous case.

Question 4.   In the manufacture of potassium permanganate a solution containing manganate ion is oxidized by chlorine. Would bromine or iodine be as good?

Answer.   From the table we see that the values of E^0 and K are the following:

		E^0	K
MnO_4^{--}	$= MnO_4^- + e^-$	-0.54	1×10^{-9}
Cl^-	$= \frac{1}{2}Cl_2 + e^-$	-1.358	1.5×10^{-23}
Br^-	$= \frac{1}{2}Br_2(l) + e^-$	-1.065	1.3×10^{-18}
I^-	$= \frac{1}{2}I_2(s) + e^-$	-0.53	1×10^{-9}

The value for iodine is so close to that for manganate-permanganate that effective oxidation by iodine (approaching completion) would not occur; hence iodine would be unsatisfactory. Bromine would produce essentially complete reaction, and in this respect would be as good as chlorine; but it costs ten times as much, and so should not be used.

Question 5.   Analysis for copper is sometimes made by adding iodide ion, which reacts with cupric ion to form cuprous iodide and iodine. Is this not incompatible with the location of the cuprous-ion–cupric-ion couple above the iodide-ion–iodine couple in the table?

   Answer.   According to the table cupric ion should not oxidize iodine very much, the equilibrium of the reaction favoring the reactants:

$$Cu^{++} + I^- \rightleftarrows Cu^+ + \tfrac{1}{2}I_2(s)$$

The equilibrium expression is, in fact,

$$\frac{[Cu^+]}{[Cu^{++}][I^-]} = 6 \times 10^{-7}$$

But cuprous iodide is very slightly soluble, with solubility product

$$K_{SP} = [Cu^+][I^-] = 4 \times 10^{-12}$$

Hence by precipitation of CuI the concentration of cuprous ion is made very small, causing the oxidation-reduction reaction to go essentially to completion. The equilibrium constant for the reaction

$$Cu^{++} + 2I^- \rightleftarrows CuI(s) + \tfrac{1}{2}I_2(s)$$

is seen to be

$$\frac{1}{[Cu^{++}][I^-]^2} = \frac{6}{4} \times 10^5$$

or

$$[Cu^{++}] = \frac{7 \times 10^{-6}}{[I^-]^2}$$

which shows that if there is a reasonable concentration of iodide ion present the reaction continues until the cupric ion concentration becomes negligibly small.

Exercises

32-1.   What oxidizing agents might be selected to oxidize manganous ion to permanganate ion?

32-2.   What pressures of hydrogen are necessary to cause lead to precipitate from a 1 M Pb^{++} solution at pH 0, 1, and 2?

32-3.   Calculate the equilibrium constant for the reaction

$$Ni + Cd^{++} \rightleftarrows Ni^{++} + Cd$$

32-4.   Calculate the equilibrium constant for the decomposition of hydrogen peroxide into oxygen and water.

32-5.   Compare the numerical values of the free energy of decomposition and the heat of decomposition of hydrogen peroxide into oxygen and water.

32-6.   What concentration of sulfurous acid is necessary to cause the precipitation of metallic copper from a 1 F $CuSO_4$ solution? from a 0.01 F $CuSO_4$ solution? Assume pH 0 in each case.

32-7.   If some mercury were allowed to stand in contact with a 0.1 F solution of ferric sulfate until equilibrium were attained, what would be the concentrations of all ionic species in the solution?

32-8.   Do you think that cadmium could replace zinc for reducing ferric ion to the ferrous state preliminary to permanganate titration? Could metallic iron itself be used as the reducing agent for this purpose?

32-9.   Why is the standard potential for the zinc–zincate-ion couple larger than that for the zinc–zinc-ion couple?

32-10. Is aluminum a stronger or a weaker reducing agent in use with basic solution (pH 14) than with acidic solution (pH 0)?

32-11. Would chlorine be liberated if a solution of hypochlorous acid and one of hydrochloric acid were mixed? if a solution of sodium hypochlorite and one of sodium chloride were mixed? Explain.

32-12. Calculate the acid constant of HOCl from the data of Table 32-1. Compare with the value quoted in a previous chapter.

32-13. Calculate the potential of an Hg-Hg$_2$Cl$_2$ electrode in 1 F KCl from the data of Table 32-1 and the value of K_{SP} (2×10^{-18}) of Hg$_2$Cl$_2$.

32-14. Can H$_2$S reduce ferric ion in acid solution? cupric ion? mercuric ion?

32-15. What would be the ratio of concentrations of bromide ion and iodide ion in an aqueous solution saturated with bromine and iodine?

32-16. What happens when permanganate ion is added to manganous ion in acid solution?

32-17. Calculate the potential of the oxygen electrode in 1 N acid and at pH 7, using the data on hydrogen peroxide of Table 32-1.

32-18. Using the data of Exercise 32-17, decide how much chlorine can be formed by bubbling oxygen through 1 N HCl; through 1 N KCl.

32-19. What chemical reaction is possible between MnO_2 and H_2O_2 in acid solution? What chemical reaction is possible between Mn^{++} and H_2O_2 in acid solution? Can you suggest a reason why MnO_2 is a catalyst for the decomposition of H_2O_2? In what part of Table 32-1 are other catalysts for this decomposition likely to occur?

Reference Books

W. M. Latimer and J. H. Hildebrand, *The Reference Book of Inorganic Chemistry*, The Macmillan Co., New York, **1951.**

W. M. Latimer, *The Oxidation States of the Elements and Their Potentials in Aqueous Solutions*, Prentice-Hall, New York, **1952;** a very valuable and useful survey of oxidation potentials and equilibrium constants.

Chapter 33

Nuclear Chemistry

The field of science dealing with the nature and reactions of the fundamental particles and of atomic nuclei has developed more rapidly during the past twenty years than any other field. Work in this branch of science has been carried out by both physicists and chemists, and the field itself may be properly considered to be a borderline field between physics and chemistry. The discussion of nuclear science in the present chapter, under the title "Nuclear Chemistry," is designed to cover the whole subject, but with special emphasis on its chemical aspects.

Nuclear chemistry has now become a large and very important branch of science. Over four hundred radioactive nuclides (isotopes) have been made in the laboratory, whereas only about three hundred stable nuclides have been detected in nature. Three elements—technetium (43), astatine (85), and promethium (61)—as well as some trans-uranium elements, seem not to occur in nature, and are available only as products of artificial transmutation. The use of radioactive isotopes as "tracers" has become a valuable technique in scientific and medical research. The controlled release of nuclear energy promises to lead us into a new world, in which the achievement of man is no longer severely limited by the supply of energy available to him.

33–1. *Natural Radioactivity*

After their discovery of polonium and radium in 1896, the Curies found that radium chloride could be separated from barium chloride by fractional precipitation of the aqueous solution by addition of alcohol, and by 1902 Madame Curie had prepared 0.1 g of nearly pure radium chloride, with radioactivity about 3,000,000 times that of uranium.

Within a few years it had been found that natural radioactive materials emit three kinds of rays capable of sensitizing the photographic plate (Chap. 3). These rays, called α rays, β rays, and γ rays, are affected differently by a magnetic field (Fig. 3-17). Alpha rays are the nuclei of helium atoms, moving at high speeds; β rays are electrons, also moving at high speeds; and γ rays are photons, with very short wavelengths.

It was soon discovered that the rays from radium (and other radioactive elements) cause regression of cancerous growths. These rays also

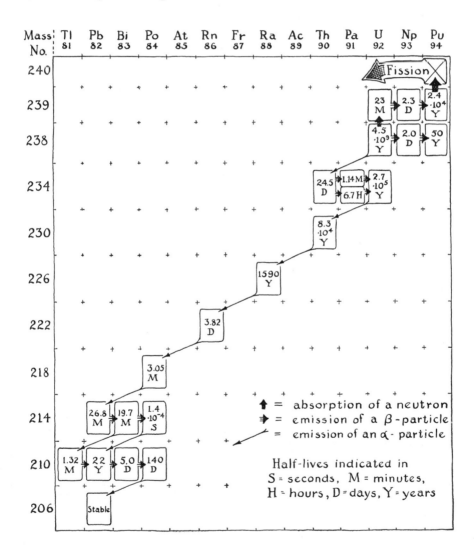

FIG. 33-1 *The uranium-radium series.*

affect normal cells, "radium burns" being caused by overexposure; but often the cancerous cells are more sensitive to radiation than normal cells, and can be killed by suitable treatment without serious injury to normal tissues. The medical use in the treatment of cancer is the main use for radium, which now costs about $20,000 per gram. Since about

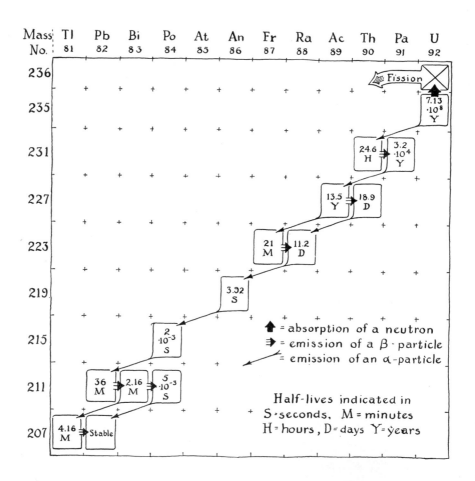

FIG. 33-2 *The uranium-actinium series.*

1950 considerable use has also been made of the artificial radioactive isotope cobalt 60 as a substitute for radium (Sec. 33-4).

Through the efforts of many investigators the chemistry of the radio-active elements of the uranium series and the thorium series was unraveled during the first two decades of the twentieth century, and that of the neptunium series during a few years from 1939 on.

The Uranium Series of Radioactive Disintegrations.   When an α particle (He^{++}) is emitted by an atomic nucleus the nuclear charge decreases by two units; the element hence is transmuted into the element two columns to the left in the periodic table. Its mass number (atomic weight) decreases by 4, the mass of the α particle. When a β particle (e^-) is emitted by a nucleus the nuclear charge is increased by 1 unit, with no change in mass number (only a very small decrease in atomic weight); the element is transmuted into the element one col-

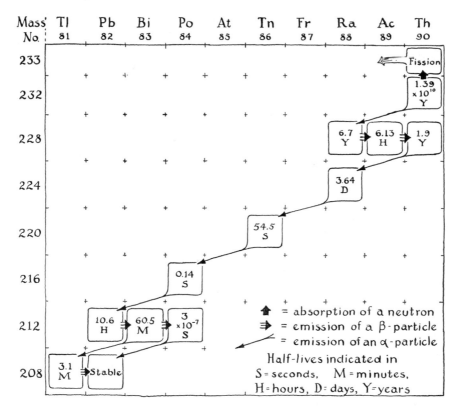

FIG. 33-3   *The thorium series.*

umn to its right. No change in atomic number or atomic weight is caused by emission of a γ ray.

The nuclear reactions in the **uranium-radium series** are shown in Figure 33-1. The principal isotope of uranium, U^{238}, constitutes 99.28% of the natural element. This isotope has a half-life of 4,500,000,000 years. It decomposes by emitting an α particle and forming Th^{234}. This isotope of thorium undergoes decomposition with β emission,* forming Pa^{234},

* It is interesting to note that two isotopes Pa^{234} exist, with different half-lives.

which in turn forms U^{234}. Five successive α emissions then occur, giving Pb^{214}, which ultimately changes to Pb^{206}, a stable isotope of lead.

It is interesting that some nuclides can decompose in two ways, by the emission of an α particle and by the emission of a β particle. An ex-

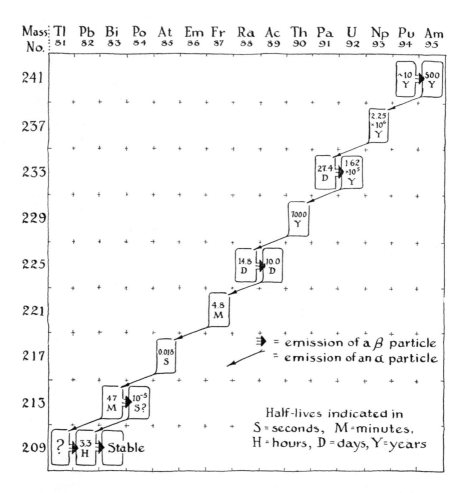

FIG. 33-4 *The neptunium series.*

ample is Bi^{214}, which by the emission of an α particle can form Tl^{210} or by the emission of a β particle can form Po^{214}.

The **uranium-actinium series,** shown in Figure 33-2, is a similar series beginning with U^{235}, which occurs to the extent of 0.71% in natural uranium. This series leads, through the emission of seven α particles and four β particles, to the stable isotope Pb^{207}.

The Thorium Series.   The third natural radioactive series begins with the long-lived naturally occurring isotope of thorium, Th^{232}, which has half-life 1.39×10^{10} years (Fig. 33-3). It leads to another stable isotope of lead, Pb^{208}.

The Neptunium Series.   During the last war the fourth radioactive series was discovered. This series (Fig. 33-4) is named after its longest-lived member, which is Np^{237}. The neptunium series was discovered through the artificial production of the members of the chain (Sec. 33-4), and for several years it was thought that none of the members of the chain existed in detectable concentration in nature except the final stable product, Bi^{209}. Recently, however, careful studies have led to the detection of Np^{237} in uranium ores.

The nature of radioactive disintegration within each of the four series —the emission of β particles, with mass nearly zero, or of α particles, with mass 4—is such that all the members of a series have mass numbers differing by a multiple of 4. The four series can hence be classified as follows (n being integral):

the $4n$ series = the thorium series
the $4n + 1$ series = the neptunium series
the $4n + 2$ series = the uranium-radium series
the $4n + 3$ series = the uranium-actinium series

33–2. *The Age of the Earth*

Measurements made on rocks containing radioactive elements can be interpreted to provide rough values of the time that has elapsed since the rocks were formed. For example, one gram of U^{238} would in its half-life of 4.5 billion years decompose to leave 0.5000 g of U^{238} and to produce 0.0674 g of helium and 0.4326 g of Pb^{206}. (Each atom of U^{238} which decomposes forms eight atoms of helium, with total mass 32, leaving one atom of Pb^{206}.) Analyses of the amount of helium gas entrapped in uranium ores have shown somewhat smaller ratios of helium to uranium than 0.0674/0.5000; the ratios found indicate, however, that the rocks are very old, up to a maximum of 2.8 billion years.

Values of about 2×10^9 years for the age of ores of thorium have also been estimated from the excess of Pb^{208} found in the lead in these ores, and similar values have been obtained for rocks by determination of the isotopic composition of strontium and potassium in the rocks.

Calculations based upon the observed amounts of isotopes have also been made which indicate that the solar system has an age of about 3.3×10^9 years.

33–3. *The Fundamental Particles*

All of the particles that exist in nature have been found to undergo reactions in which they are converted into or obtained from other particles or radiation. There are, then, no particles which are immutable, and which can be said to be truly fundamental.

For example, two photons which together have energy equivalent to the mass of an electron and a positron (see the following paragraphs) can disappear at the same time that an electron and a positron are produced; also, an electron and a positron can disappear at the same time that two high-energy photons are produced.

The fourteen particles mentioned in Table 33-1 are the simplest known particles.* These particles can be considered to serve as the building units for more complicated forms of matter. Thus the deuteron, the nucleus of H^2, can be considered to be built up from a proton and a neutron.

The **electron** has been discussed throughout this book. It was the first of the simple particles to be recognized. The electron is a stable particle—it can be destroyed only by reaction with other particles.

The **proton,** the nucleus of the ordinary hydrogen atom, was observed as positively charged rays in a discharge tube in 1886, by the German physicist Eugen Goldstein. The nature of the rays was not at first understood. In 1898 the German physicist Wilhelm Wien determined their ratio of charge to mass, and more accurate measurements of this sort, which verified the existence of protons as independent particles in a tube containing ionized hydrogen at low pressure, were made by J. J. Thomson in 1906. The proton is a stable particle.

The next simple particle to be discovered was the **positron,** found in 1932 by Carl Anderson (born 1905). Positrons were found among the particles produced by the interaction of cosmic rays with matter.† They seem to be identical with electrons except that their charge is $+e$ instead of $-e$. The positron is classed as a stable particle, because positrons have not been observed to be destroyed spontaneously. However, the span of life of positrons when under observation is very short.

---

* We have included the photon and the neutrino in this table of particles, although they are somewhat different from other particles, in that they do not have any rest mass, and move only with the speed of light. (The value of the rest mass of the neutrino is uncertain, but it is probably zero.)

† Cosmic rays are discussed in a later section.

TABLE 33-1   *The Simplest Known Particles*

Masses are rest masses in units equal to the mass of the electron, 9.1072×10^{-28} g.

The half-lives refer to spontaneous destruction of the particle, and not to reaction with other particles. A particle described as stable has not been observed to decompose spontaneously.

In addition to these particles, several others probably exist, including mesons with mass about 900 (τ mesons), 1,240, and 500.

POSITIVE PARTICLES ELECTRIC CHARGE e	NEUTRAL PARTICLES CHARGE 0	NEGATIVE PARTICLES CHARGE $-e$
Positron Mass 1 Stable Discovered 1932		Electron Mass 1 Stable Discovered 1896
Proton Mass 1,836.14 Stable Discovered $\sim$ 1900	Neutron Mass 1,839.0 Half-life 15 min. Discovered 1932	(Negative proton not known)
Positive μ meson Mass 210 Half-life 2×10^{-6} sec. Discovered 1936	(Neutral μ meson not known)	Negative μ meson Mass 210 Half-life 2×10^{-6} sec. Discovered 1936
Positive π meson Mass 275 Half-life 1×10^{-8} sec. Discovered 1947	Neutral π meson Mass 263 Half-life 1×10^{-14} sec. Discovered 1950	Negative π meson Mass 275 Half-life 1×10^{-8} sec. Discovered 1947
Positive V particle Mass $\sim$ 2,200 Half-life 10^{-10} sec. Discovered 1947	Neutral V particle Mass 2,200 Half-life 2×10^{-10} sec. Discovered 1947	Negative V particle Mass $\sim$ 2,200 Half-life 10^{-10} sec. Discovered 1947
	Photon Rest mass 0 Stable	
	Neutrino Rest mass 0 Stable Discovered 1931	

The concentration of electrons under ordinary conditions on the earth's surface is such that positrons have an average lifetime while under observation of about 10^{-9} sec. The reaction that destroys positrons is the combination of a positron and an electron with neutralization of their electric charges, $+e$ and $-e$, and the production of two photons. The two photons that are produced have about the same energy (the same frequency and wavelength), and they are emitted in opposite directions, in accordance with the principle of conservation of momentum. The reaction of destruction of a positron and an electron (destruction of a *positron-electron pair*) can be written in the following way:

$$e^+ + e^- \longrightarrow h\nu + h\nu \tag{33-1}$$

Here the symbol $h\nu$ is used to represent a photon. By use of the Einstein equation for the relation between mass and energy and the Planck-Einstein equation for the relation between energy of a light quantum and its frequency or wavelength, it can be calculated that each of the photons has the wavelength 0.0242 Å. Under some circumstances all or nearly all of the mass of the positron-electron pair might be converted into the energy of a single light quantum, which would have wavelength* about 0.0121 Å. It has been found by experiment that when positrons disappear photons with wavelengths about 0.024 Å and 0.012 Å are produced. This provides striking direct evidence for the concept of the equivalence of mass and energy, as given by the Einstein mass-energy equation. It has also been observed that γ rays with energy greater than 1.02 Mev (1.02 Mev is 1.02 million electron volts, the amount of energy equivalent to the mass of a positron-electron pair) can produce positron-electron pairs. In the production of pairs in this way the extra energy of the photon, above the amount required to produce the rest mass of the positron and the electron, is converted into kinetic energy. Measurements of the kinetic energy of the positron and the electron have shown that there is conservation of mass-energy, with the relation between mass and energy as given by the Einstein equation.

The **neutron** was discovered by the English physicist James Chadwick, also in the year 1932. Neutrons are particles with mass only slightly larger than that of the proton, and with zero electric charge. Because they have no electric charge, neutrons interact with other forms of matter only very weakly, and it is accordingly hard to prove their existence by direct methods. On passage through solid substances they

---

* When a single photon is produced, it is probable that the destruction of the positron-electron pair has taken place in the neighborhood of some other particle, such as the nucleus of an atom, which has received some energy and momentum from the reaction.

undergo deflection only when they approach extremely closely to nuclei. Because neutrons and nuclei are very small (about 10^{-12} cm), the chance of collision is very small, and neutrons are accordingly able to penetrate through great thicknesses of heavy elements. Neutrons interact with many atomic nuclei, as discussed in the following section (Sec. 33-4). The neutron also undergoes spontaneous destruction, with the formation of a proton and an electron, according to the reaction

$$n^1 \longrightarrow p^+ + e^- \tag{33-2}$$

The symbol n^1 is used to represent the neutron.

Mesons are particles with mass intermediate between the electron mass and the proton mass (the word *meson* means *intermediate particle*, from the Greek *mesos*, intermediate, in between). Five mesons are listed in Table 33-1; there is some evidence that several other mesons also exist.

The **positive μ meson** and the **negative μ meson,** also called the *positive muon* and the *negative muon*, were discovered in 1936 by the American physicists Carl Anderson and Seth Neddermeyer. They are produced by interaction of cosmic rays with matter. The electric charges of μ mesons are equal to those of the positron and the electron, respectively. The mass of the positive μ meson and the negative μ meson is 210. These mesons spontaneously decompose, with half-life about 2×10^{-6} sec, into a positron and two neutrinos or an electron and two neutrinos (the neutrino is discussed in a later paragraph in this section). The reaction for spontaneous destruction of a μ meson is

$$\left. \begin{array}{l} \mu^+ \longrightarrow e^+ + \nu + \nu \\ \mu^- \longrightarrow e^- + \nu + \nu \end{array} \right\} \tag{33-3}$$

The symbol ν is used for the neutrino; care should be taken not to confuse it with the symbol $h\nu$ for a photon.

The **positive π meson** and the **negative π meson** (also called the *positive pion* and the *negative pion*), which also are produced by interaction of cosmic rays with matter, were discovered in 1947 by the British physicist C. F. Powell (born 1903) and his collaborators. They have electric charges equal to those of the positron and electron, respectively, and have mass 275. They undergo spontaneous destruction, with half-life of 1×10^{-8} sec, according to the reactions

$$\left. \begin{array}{l} \pi^+ \longrightarrow \mu^+ + \nu \\ \pi^- \longrightarrow \mu^- + \nu \end{array} \right\} \tag{33-4}$$

The π mesons are of especial interest because of the belief generally held by theoretical physicists at the present time that they are involved in holding nucleons (protons and neutrons) together in atomic nuclei. In 1935 the Japanese theoretical physicist Hideki Yukawa (born 1907) published a theory of nuclear structure based upon the idea that the forces operating between nucleons are associated with the continued formation and destruction of particles. On the basis of the theory he concluded that the particles would have to have mass about 200 times the mass of the electron. When Yukawa propounded his theory no such particles were known. After μ mesons had been discovered, experiments were made to determine the strength of their interactions with protons and neutrons, and also with compound nuclei, and it was found that the interactions are too weak for the μ mesons to serve as the source of the forces holding nuclei together. However, when π mesons were discovered, twelve years after the formulation of Yukawa's theory, it was found that they interact with nucleons and nuclei in the way postulated by Yukawa in the development of his theory. It is accordingly probable that π mesons are involved in holding nucleons together in the heavier nuclei. It is interesting that the investigations made by Powell and his collaborators have shown that cosmic rays interact with nuclei to produce π mesons directly, and that the μ mesons, observed earlier by Anderson and Neddermeyer, are then formed, by the spontaneous decomposition of π mesons into μ mesons and photons. The symbol π was chosen for these particles by Powell and his collaborators to represent the word primary—the π mesons are primary products of interaction of cosmic rays and nuclei.

The **neutral π meson** (neutral pion) was discovered in 1950. Its mass, 263, is somewhat less than that of the positive and negative π mesons. Its half-life, about 1×10^{-14} sec, is very short; it is destroyed by spontaneous decomposition into two photons:

$$\pi^0 \longrightarrow h\nu + h\nu \tag{33-5}$$

The **V particles,** discovered in 1947 through cosmic-ray investigations, have masses greater than the mass of the proton. A positive V particle, a negative V particle, and a neutral V particle have been observed. Each of them has mass approximately 2,200. It is probable that each of them decomposes into a proton (or possibly a negative proton) and a π meson. There may also exist some heavier V particles.

The **photon** or light quantum has been discussed in Chapter 8. It may be mentioned here, in review, that photons travel always with the speed of light, that they have no rest mass, and that the energy of a photon is proportional to its frequency, being equal to the product $h\nu$ of Planck's constant h and the frequency ν.

The **neutrino** is a particle with zero rest mass (or possibly a finite rest mass very small in comparison with that of the electron), and with no electric charge. Its existence was first suggested, by Wolfgang Pauli, in 1931. It had been observed that some radioactive nuclides that undergo β decomposition produce β particles with a range of values of kinetic energy; inasmuch as the energy of the decomposing nuclide should be equal to the energy of the products, there seemed to be a contradiction with the law of conservation of energy. Pauli suggested that the decomposition involves the production of two particles, the β particle and another particle, the neutrino, which is produced with enough energy to make up the discrepancy. Since then many reactions have been observed which can be understood easily only if it is assumed that neutrinos are involved—several of these reactions are discussed in the preceding paragraphs. Although the direct study of the neutrino has been found difficult, it is now generally accepted as one of the simple particles.

The existence of several simple particles in symmetric pairs, one with a positive charge $+e$ and one with a negative charge $-e$, strongly suggests that it should be possible to make negative protons, and it would not be surprising if a report of the observation of negative protons were to be made before long.

Also, it might be surmised from Table 33-1 that a neutral μ meson and a neutral particle with mass approximately equal to that of the electron are capable of existence. However, the neutral π meson is considerably less stable than the positive and negative π mesons, and it is possible that the neutral μ meson and the neutral particle with mass one (the neutrelectron) are so unstable that they will elude observation for a long time.

Cosmic Rays.   Cosmic rays are particles of very high energy which reach the earth from interstellar space or other parts of the cosmos, or which are produced in the earth's atmosphere by the rays from outer space. The discovery that ionizing radiation on the earth's surface comes from outer space was made by the Austrian physicist Victor Hess (born 1883), who made measurements of ionization during balloon ascents to a height of 15,000 feet in 1911 and 1912. Many discoveries, in particular the discovery of most of the particles described in Table 33-1, have been made in the course of studies of cosmic rays.

At the present time it is believed that the cosmic rays which impinge on the outer part of the earth's atmosphere consist of protons and the nuclei of heavier atoms, moving with very great speeds. The cosmic rays that reach the earth's surface consist in large part of mesons, positrons, electrons, and photons, produced by reaction of the fast protons and other atomic nuclei with particles (mainly atomic nuclei) in the earth's atmosphere.

Some of the phenomena produced by cosmic rays can be explained only if it is assumed that particles are present with energy in the range from 10^{15} to 10^{17} ev. The great accelerators (cyclotron, synchrotron, bevatron) which have been, or are being, built (see the following section) produce or will produce particles with energies in the range from 10^6 to 10^9 ev. There is no way known at present to accelerate particles to energies as great as those of the fastest particles in cosmic rays, and the study of cosmic rays will probably continue to yield information about the world that cannot be obtained in any other way.

33–4. *Artificial Radioactivity*

Stable atoms can be converted into radioactive atoms by the collision
of particles traveling at high speeds. In the early work the high-speed
particles used were α particles from Bi^{83} (called radium C). The first
nuclear reaction produced in the laboratory was that between α particles
and nitrogen, carried out by Lord Rutherford and his collaborators in
1919. The nuclear reaction which occurs when nitrogen is bombarded
with α particles is the following:

$$N^{14} + He^4 \longrightarrow O^{17} + H^1 \tag{33-6}$$

In this reaction a nitrogen nucleus reacts with a helium nucleus which
strikes it with considerable energy, to form two new nuclei, an O^{17}
nucleus and a proton.

The O^{17} nucleus is stable, so that this nuclear reaction does not lead
to the production of artificial radioactivity. Many other elements, however, undergo similar reactions with the production of unstable nuclei,
which then undergo radioactive decomposition.

Sources of High-Speed Particles.   In recent years great progress has
been made in the laboratory production of high-speed particles. The
first efforts to accomplish this involved the use of transformers. Different
investigators built transformers which produced voltages as high as
3 million volts, to operate vacuum tubes in which protons, deuterons,
and helium nuclei could be accelerated. In 1931 an electrostatic generator was developed by R. J. Van de Graaff, an American physicist,
in which an electric charge was carried to the high-potential electrode
on a moving insulated belt. Several Van de Graaff generators have
been built and operated to produce potential differences of from
2 million to over 5 million volts.

The *cyclotron* was invented by an American physicist, E. O. Lawrence,
in 1929. In the cyclotron positive ions (usually protons or deuterons)
are given successive accelerations by falling through a potential difference of a few thousand volts. The charged particles are caused to move
in circular paths by a magnetic field, produced by a large magnet between whose pole pieces the apparatus is placed (Fig. 33-5). The 37-inch
cyclotron at Berkeley, California, produces deuterons with as much
energy as they would gain by falling through a single potential drop of
7 million volts, and the 60-inch cyclotron produces 20-million-volt
deuterons. The 184-inch cyclotron at Berkeley yields 200-million-volt
deuterons.

A new accelerator, the *synchrotron*, was proposed by V. Veksler in Russia in 1945, and independently, a few months later, by E. M. McMillan of the University of California. Several synchrotrons are now under construction, and they are expected to yield particles with en-

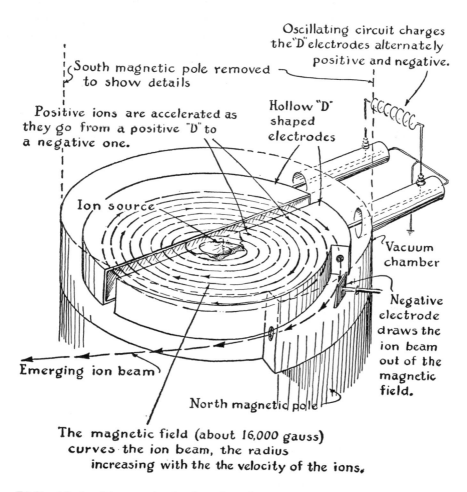

The magnetic field (about 16,000 gauss) curves the ion beam, the radius increasing with the the velocity of the ions.

FIG. 33-5   *Diagram showing how the cyclotron works.*

ergies of from 1 billion to 6 billion electron volts. The name *bevatron* (from the initials of billion electron volts) is used for these accelerators.

The Kinds of Nuclear Reactions.   Many different kinds of nuclear reactions have been studied. Spontaneous radioactivity is a nuclear reaction in which the reactant is a single nucleus. Other known nuclear reactions involve a proton, a deuteron, an α particle, a neutron, or a photon (usually a γ ray) interacting with the nucleus of an atom. The products of a nuclear reaction may be a heavy nucleus and a proton, an electron, a deuteron, an α particle, a neutron, two or more neutrons, or a photon. In addition, there occurs the very important type of nuclear reaction in which a very heavy nucleus, made unstable by the addition of a neutron, breaks up into two parts of comparable size, plus several neutrons. This process of fission has been mentioned in earlier chapters and is described in a later section of the present chapter.

Many nuclear reactions result from the interaction of nuclei and neutrons. The early experiments with neutrons were carried out by use of a mixture of radon, Rn^{222}, and beryllium metal. The α particles from radon react with the beryllium isotope Be^9 to produce neutrons in the following ways:

$$Be^9 + He^4 \longrightarrow C^{12} + n^1$$
$$Be^9 + He^4 \longrightarrow 3He^4 + n^1$$

Neutrons are also made by reactions in the cyclotron and in uranium piles.

Hundreds of radioactive nuclides have been made, by use of different nuclear reactions. The radioactive isotope Co^{60} of cobalt, which has half-life 5.3 years, is important as a substitute for radium in the treatment of cancer. It can be made from ordinary cobalt, which consists of a single stable nuclide, Co^{59}, by reaction with slow neutrons. Needles consisting of pure cobalt or of an alloy of nickel and cobalt are irradiated with neutrons which have been produced in a uranium pile. The reaction involved is the following:

$$Co^{59} + n^1 \longrightarrow Co^{60}$$

Radioactive phosphorus, P^{32}, is valuable as a tracer in biological investigations, such as studies of the fate of phosphate fertilizers in affecting the growth of plants. This nuclide is made by bombardment of ordinary phosphorus, P^{31}, with 10-million-volt deuterons from a cyclotron. The reaction is

$$P^{31} + H^2 \longrightarrow P^{32} + H^1$$

The P^{32} isotope decomposes with emission of electrons, its half-life being 14.3 days.

Manufacture of the Trans-uranium Elements.   The first trans-uranium element to be made was a neptunium isotope, Np^{239}. This nuclide was made by E. M. McMillan and P. H. Abelson in 1940, by bombarding uranium with high-speed deuterons:

$$U^{238} + H^2 \longrightarrow U^{239} + H^1$$
$$U^{239} \longrightarrow Np^{239} + e^-$$

The first isotope of plutonium to be made was Pu^{238}, by the reactions

$$U^{238} + H^2 \longrightarrow Np^{238} + 2n^1$$
$$Np^{238} \longrightarrow Pu^{238} + e^-$$

The Np^{238} decomposes spontaneously, emitting electrons. Its half-life is 2.0 days.

During and since World War II some quantity of the nuclide Pu^{239} has been manufactured. This nuclide is relatively stable; it has a half-life of about 24,000 years. It slowly decomposes with the emission of α particles. It is made by the reaction of the principal isotope of uranium, U^{238}, with a neutron, to form U^{239}, which then undergoes spontaneous radioactive decomposition with emission of an electron to form Np^{239}, which in turn emits an electron spontaneously to form Pu^{239} (see Fig. 33-1):

$$U^{238} + n^1 \longrightarrow U^{239}$$
$$U^{239} \longrightarrow Np^{239} + e^-$$
$$Np^{239} \longrightarrow Pu^{239} + e^-$$

Plutonium and the four heavier trans-uranium elements whose existence has been reported, americium, curium, berkelium, and californium, were discovered by Professor G. T. Seaborg and his collaborators at the University of California in Berkeley. Americium has been made as the isotope Am^{241} by the following reactions:

$$U^{238} + He^4 \longrightarrow Pu^{241} + n^1$$
$$Pu^{241} \longrightarrow Am^{241} + e^-$$

This nuclide slowly undergoes radioactive decomposition, with emission of α particles. Its half-life is 500 years. Curium is made from plutonium 239 by bombardment with helium ions accelerated in the cyclotron:

$$Pu^{239} + He^4 \longrightarrow Cm^{242} + n^1$$

The isotope Cm^{242} is an α-particle emitter, with half-life about 5 months. Another isotope of curium has also been made. It is Cm^{240}, made by bombarding plutonium, Pu^{239}, with high-speed helium ions:

$$Pu^{239} + He^4 \longrightarrow Cm^{240} + 3n^1$$

Berkelium and californium were made by the following reactions:

$$Am^{241} + He^4 \longrightarrow Bk^{243} + 2n^1$$
$$Cm^{242} + He^4 \longrightarrow Cf^{244} + 2n^1$$

Using only very small quantities of the substances, Seaborg and his collaborators succeeded in obtaining a considerable amount of information about the chemical properties of the trans-uranium elements. They have found that, whereas uranium is similar to tungsten in its properties, in that it has a pronounced tendency to assume oxidation state $+6$, the succeeding elements are not similar to rhenium, osmium, iridium, and platinum, but show an increasing tendency to form ionic compounds in which their oxidation number is $+3$. This behavior is similar to that of the rare-earth metals. In the periodic table given in Chapter 5 these facts were taken into consideration and the trans-uranium metals were shown in two places, one directly to the right of uranium, and the other below the corresponding rare-earth metals. It seems probable that the elements with atomic numbers greater than 98 will be closely similar to the rare-earth metals until the $5f$ shell of electrons has been completely filled.

33–5. *The Use of Radioactive Elements as Tracers*

A valuable technique for research that has been developed in recent years is the use of both radioactive and non-radioactive nuclides as tracers. By the use of these nuclides an element can be observed in the presence of large quantities of the same element. For example, one of the earliest uses of tracers was the experimental determination of the rate at which lead atoms move through a crystalline sample of the metal lead. This phenomenon is called *self-diffusion*. If some radioactive lead is placed as a surface layer on a sheet of lead, and the sample is allowed to stand for a while, it can then be cut up into thin sections parallel to the original surface layer, and the radioactivity present in each section can be measured. The presence of radioactivity in layers other than the original surface layer shows that lead atoms from the surface layer have diffused through the metal.

In the discussion of chemical equilibrium in Chapter 20 it was pointed out that a system in chemical equilibrium is not static, but that instead chemical reactions may be proceeding in the forward direction and the reverse direction at equal rates, so that the amounts of different substances present remain constant. At first thought it would seem to be impossible to determine experimentally the rates at which different chemical reactions are proceeding at equilibrium. However, it has now been found possible to make experiments of this sort, with the use of isotopes as tracers. For example, a solution of arsenious acid containing some radioactive arsenic was mixed with a solution of arsenic acid, iodide ion, and triiodide ion, in such proportions that the mixture was in chemical equilibrium. After it had stood for some time the solution was mixed with a solution containing magnesium ion and ammonium ion, to precipitate magnesium ammonium arsenate, $MgNH_4AsO_4 \cdot 12H_2O$. The precipitate was washed and dried, and the amount of its radioactivity was determined, in order to find out how much radioactive arsenic was now present as arsenic acid. The equilibrium under consideration is the following:

$$H_2O + H_3AsO_3 + I_3^- \rightleftarrows H_3AsO_4 + 2H^+ + 3I^-$$

It was found in this way that the rate of oxidation of arsenious ion by triiodide ion under equilibrium conditions is the same as the rate obtained when triiodide ion is mixed with arsenious ion and the rate of formation of arsenic acid is determined directly as the equilibrium is being approached.

The arsenic isotope used in this work was As^{76}, with half-life 26.8 hours. It is made from As^{75}, which is the only isotope of ordinary arsenic, by treatment with slow neutrons:

$$As^{75} + n^1 \longrightarrow As^{76}$$

Non-radioactive isotopes have also been used as tracers. The amounts of the added non-radioactive isotopes in a material may be determined by use of a mass spectrograph. The most useful nuclides for this purpose are H^2, C^{13}, N^{15}, and O^{18}.

Perhaps the greatest use for isotopes as tracers will be in the field of biology and medicine. The human body contains such large amounts of the elements carbon, hydrogen, nitrogen, oxygen, sulfur, etc., that it is difficult to analyze for a small amount of some organic material in the body. An organic compound containing a radioactive isotope, however, can be traced through the body by measuring its radioactivity. An especially useful radioactive isotope for these purposes is carbon 14. This isotope of carbon has a half-life of about 5,568 years. It undergoes slow decomposition with emission of β rays, and the amount of the isotope present in a sample can be followed by measuring the β activity. Large quantities of C^{14} can be readily made in a uranium pile, by the action of slow neutrons on nitrogen:

$$N^{14} + n^1 \longrightarrow C^{14} + H^1$$

The process can be carried out by running a solution of ammonium nitrate into the uranium pile, where it is exposed to neutrons. The carbon which is made in this way is in the form of the hydrogen carbonate ion, HCO_3^-, and it can be precipitated as barium carbonate by adding barium hydroxide solution. The samples of radioactive carbon are very strongly radioactive, containing as much as 5% radioactive isotope.

The Unit of Radioactivity, the Curie.   It has been found convenient to introduce a special unit in which to measure amounts of radioactive material. The unit of radioactivity is called the *curie*. One curie of any radioactive substance is an amount of the substance such that 3.70×10^{10} atoms of the substance undergo radioactive disintegration per second.

The curie is a rather large unit. One curie of radium is approximately one gram of the element (the curie was originally defined in such a way as to make a curie of radium equal to exactly one gram, but because of improvement in technique it has been found convenient to define it instead in the way given above).

It is interesting to point out that in a disintegration chain of radioactive elements in a steady state all of the radioactive elements are present in the same radioactive amounts. For example, let us consider one gram of the element radium, in a steady state with the first product of its decomposition, radon (Rn^{222}), and the successive products of disintegration (see Fig. 33-1). The rate at which radon is being produced is proportional to the amount of radium present, one atom of radon being produced for each atom of radium which undergoes decomposition. The number of atoms of radium which undergo decomposition in unit time is proportional to the number of atoms of radium present; the decomposition of radium is a unimolecular reaction. When the system has reached a steady state the number of atoms of radon present remains unchanged, so that the rate at which radon is itself undergoing radioactive decomposition must be equal to the rate at which it is being formed from radium. Hence the radon present in a steady state with one curie of radium itself amounts to one curie.

The amount of radon present in a steady state with one gram of radium (one curie of radium) can be calculated by consideration of the first-order reaction-rate equations given in Chapter 19. The reaction-rate constant for the decomposition of radium is inversely proportional to its half-life. Hence, when a steady state exists, and the number of radium atoms undergoing decomposition is equal to the number of radon atoms undergoing decomposition, the ratio of the numbers of radon atoms and radium atoms present must be equal to the ratio of their half-lives.

33–6. *Dating Objects by Use of Carbon 14*

One of the most interesting recent applications of radioactivity is the determination of the age of carbonaceous materials (materials containing carbon) by measurement of their radioactivity due to carbon 14. This technique of radiocarbon dating, which was developed by an American physical chemist, Willard F. Libby, of the Institute for Nuclear Studies of the University of Chicago, permits the dating of samples containing carbon with accuracy of around 200 years. At the present time the method can be applied to materials that are not over about 20,000 years old.

Carbon 14 is being made at a steady rate in the upper atmosphere. Cosmic-ray neutrons transmute nitrogen into carbon 14, by the reaction given in the preceding section. The radiocarbon is oxidized to carbon dioxide, which is thoroughly mixed with the non-radioactive carbon dioxide in the atmosphere, through the action of winds. The steady-state concentration of carbon 14 built up in the atmosphere by cosmic rays is about 1×10^{-12}—that is, one atom of radioactive carbon to 10^{12} atoms of ordinary carbon. The carbon dioxide, radioactive and non-radioactive alike, is absorbed by plants, which fix the carbon in their tissues. Animals that eat the plants also similarly fix the carbon, containing 1×10^{-12} part radiocarbon, in their tissues. When a plant or animal dies, the amount of radioactivity of the carbon in its tissues is determined by the amount of radiocarbon present, which is the amount corresponding to the steady state in the atmosphere. After 5,568 years (the half-life of carbon 14), however, half of the carbon 14 has undergone decomposition, and the radioactivity of the material is only half as great. After 11,136 years only one-quarter of the original radioactivity is left, and so on. Accordingly, by determining the radioactivity of a sample of carbon from wood, flesh, charcoal, skin, horn, or other plant or animal remains, the number of years that have gone by since the carbon was originally extracted from the atmosphere can be determined.

In applying the method of radiocarbon dating, a sample of material containing about 30 g of carbon (about 1 ounce) is burned to carbon dioxide, which is then reduced to elementary carbon, in the form of lamp black. The β-ray activity of the elementary carbon is then determined, with the use of Geiger counters, and compared with the β-ray activity of recent carbon. The age of the sample is then calculated by the use of the equation for a first-order reaction. The method was checked by measurement of carbon from the heartwood of a giant sequoia tree, for which the number of tree rings showed that 3,000 years had passed since the wood was laid down. This check was satisfactory.

The method of radiocarbon dating has now been applied to several hundred samples. One of the interesting conclusions that have been reached is that the last glaciation of the northern hemisphere occurred about 11,000 years ago. Specimens of wood from a buried forest in Wisconsin, in which all of the tree trunks are lying in the same direction as though pushed over by a glacier, were found to have an age of

11,400 ± 700 years. The age of specimens of organic materials laid down during the last period of glaciation in Europe was found to be 10,800 ± 1,200 years. Many samples of organic matter, charcoal, and other carbonaceous material from human camp sites in the western hemisphere have been dated as extending to, but not beyond, 10,000 years ago. The eruption of Mt. Mazama in southern Oregon, which formed the crater now called Crater Lake, was determined to have occurred 6,453 ± 250 years ago, by the dating of charcoal from a tree killed by the eruption. Several pairs of woven rope sandals found in Fort Rock Cave, which had been covered by an earlier eruption, were found to be 9,053 ± 350 years old; these are the oldest human artifacts measured on the American continents. The Lascaux Cave near Montignac, France, contains some remarkable paintings made by prehistoric man; charcoal from campfires in this cave was found to have the age 15,516 ± 900 years. Linen wrappings from the Dead Sea scrolls of the Book of Isaiah, recently found in a cave in Palestine and thought to be from about the first or second century B.C., were dated 1,917 + 200 years old.

33–7. *The Properties of Nuclides*

Most of the known isotopes of the first twenty-five elements are listed in Table 33-2, together with some of their properties (p. 691). The masses given in column 3 of this table refer to the physicists' atomic-weight scale, in which $O^{16} = 16.00000$.

Except for the elements which form part of the natural radioactive series, the distribution of isotopes for an element has been found to be nearly the same for all natural occurrences. This distribution is given in the fourth column of the table.

Some striking regularities in the properties of nuclides are evident, especially for the heavier elements. The elements of odd atomic number have only one or two natural (that is, stable) nuclides, whereas those of even atomic number are much richer in isotopes, many having eight or more. It is also found that the odd elements are much rarer in nature than the even elements. The elements with no stable isotopes (technetium, astatine) have odd atomic numbers.

The Packing Fraction. Consideration of the masses of the nuclides shows that they are not directly proportional to the mass number (the sum of the number of protons and the number of neutrons in the nucleus). Thus the mass of the ordinary hydrogen atom is 1.00813, and that of the neutron is 1.00897: if the helium atom were made from two hydrogen atoms and two neutrons without change in mass, its mass would be 4.03420, but it is, in fact, less, only 4.00386. The masses of the heavier atoms are also less than they would be if they were composed of hydrogen atoms and neutrons without change in mass.

The loss in mass accompanying the formation of a heavier atom from hydrogen atoms and neutrons results from the fact that these reactions are strongly exothermic. A very large amount of energy is evolved in the formation of the heavier atoms from hydrogen atoms and neutrons,

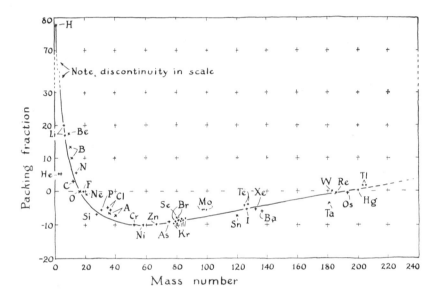

FIG. 33-6   *The mass packing fractions of the elements.*

so large an amount that the mass of the energy, as given by the Einstein equation $E = mc^2$, is significant. The more stable the heavy nucleus, the larger is the decrease in mass from that of the neutrons and protons from which the nucleus may be considered to be made.

It is customary to describe the decrease in mass by means of a quantity called the "packing fraction." This is the difference from unity of the mass per nucleon (proton or neutron) in the nucleus, relative to O^{16} as standard. An isotope which has atomic mass on the O^{16} scale equal exactly to its mass number is said to have zero packing fraction.

The packing fractions for the elements are shown in Figure 33-6. It is seen that the elements of the first long group of the periodic table, between chromium and zinc, lie at the minimum of the curve, and can accordingly be considered to be the most stable of all the elements. If one of these elements were to be converted into other elements, the total mass of the other elements would be somewhat greater than that of the reactants, and accordingly energy would have to be added in order to cause the reaction to occur. On the other hand, either the heavier or the lighter elements could undergo nuclear reactions to form the elements with mass numbers in the neighborhood of 60, and these nuclear reactions would be accompanied by the evolution of a large amount of energy.

The Structure of Atomic Nuclei.   At the present time physicists are gathering together a great body of information about the properties of

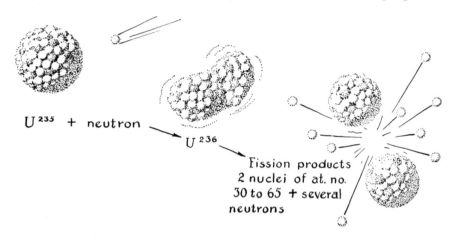

FIG. 33-7   *The process of nuclear fission (linear magnification about 10^{12}).*

nuclei, some of which is given in Table 33-2, and are attempting to interpret this information by a theory of the structure of the nucleus. However, they have not as yet succeeded—no one knows just what the structure of any nucleus is, in terms of simpler particles. Pictures of nuclei, such as Figure 33-7, are imaginative. It seems likely that the heavier nuclei are built of protons and neutrons, with π mesons forming bonds between them, and also there is some evidence that the protons and neutrons are arranged in concentric shells, somewhat similar to the electron shells in atoms, but a thorough understanding of the structure of nuclei has not as yet been obtained.

The lack of knowledge of the structure of nuclei makes nuclear science a very interesting field at the present time. Every year new facts are discovered, and we may expect that before another decade has gone by a sound theory of the nucleus will have been developed, permitting us to discuss the structure of the nucleus as confidently as we now discuss the atomic structure of molecules and crystals and the electronic struc-ture of atoms.

33–8. *Nuclear Fission and Nuclear Fusion*

The instability of the heavy elements relative to those of mass number around 60, as shown by the packing-fraction curve, suggests the possi-bility of spontaneous decomposition of the heavy elements into fragments of approximately half size (atomic masses 70 to 160, atomic numbers 30 to 65). This fission has been accomplished. A brief statement has been made about it in Chapter 11, in the discussion of uranium, and also in Chapter 1.

It was reported on 6 January 1939 by the German physicists Otto Hahn and F. Strassmann that barium, lanthanum, cerium, and krypton seemed to be present in substances containing uranium which had been exposed to neutrons. Within two months more than forty papers were then published on the fission of uranium. It was verified by direct calorimetric measurement that a very large amount of energy is lib-erated by fission, over 5×10^{12} calories per mole. Since a pound of uranium contains about two gram-atoms, the complete fission of one pound of this element, or a similar heavy element, produces about 10×10^{12} calories. This may be compared with the heat of combustion of one pound of coal, which is approximately 4×10^6 calories. Thus uranium as a source of energy may be 2.5 million times more valuable than coal.

Uranium 235 and plutonium 239, which can be made from uranium 238, are capable of undergoing fission when exposed to slow neutrons. It was also shown by the Japanese physicist Nishina in 1939 that the thorium isotope Th^{232} undergoes fission under the influence of fast neutrons. It seems likely that all of the elements with atomic number 90 or greater can be made to undergo this reaction. Uranium and thorium may well become important sources of heat and energy in the world of the future. There are large amounts of these elements available—the amount of uranium in the earth's crust has been estimated as four parts per million and the amount of thorium as twelve parts per million. The deposits are distributed all over the world.

The fission reactions can be chain reactions. These reactions are initiated by neutrons. A nucleus U^{235}, for example, may combine with a neutron to form U^{236}. This nuclide is unstable, and undergoes spontaneous fission into two particles of roughly equal atomic number; that is, the protons in the U^{236} nucleus are divided between the two daughter nuclei (Fig. 33-7). These daughter nuclei also contain some of the neutrons originally present in the U^{236} nucleus. Since, however, the ratio of neutrons to protons is greater in the heavier nuclei than in those of intermediate mass, the fission is also accompanied by the liberation of several free neutrons (and also of positrons). The neutrons which are thus liberated may then combine with other U^{235} nuclei, forming additional U^{236} nuclei which themselves undergo fission. A reaction of this sort, the products of which cause the reaction to continue, is called a *chain reaction*, or an *autocatalytic reaction*.

If a sample of U^{235} or Pu^{239} weighing a few pounds is suddenly compressed (within about one-millionth of a second) into a smaller volume, the autocatalytic fission of the nuclei occurs nearly completely, and an amount of energy is released equal to that accompanying the detonation of about twenty thousand tons of a high explosive such as TNT (trinitrotoluene). An ordinary *atomic bomb* consists of a few pounds of U^{235} or Pu^{239} and a mechanism for compressing it suddenly into a small volume; this mechanism consists of molded pieces of a high explosive, arranged about the sample of fissionable material in such a way that the force of detonation of the high explosive compresses the material. Improved atomic bombs detonate with release of energy equal to that accompanying the detonation of about 100,000 tons of TNT.

The process of *nuclear fusion* also may liberate energy. We see from the packing-fraction diagram (Fig. 33-6) that the fission of a very heavy nucleus converts about 0.1% of its mass into energy. Still larger fractions of the mass of very light nuclei are converted into energy by their fusion into heavier nuclei. The process $4H \longrightarrow He$, which is the principal source of the energy of the sun, involves a change in mass from 4×1.00813 to 4.00386, and hence a conversion of 0.7% of the mass into energy. The similar reaction of a deuteron and a triton to form a helium nucleus and a neutron is accompanied by the conversion of 0.4% of the mass into energy:

$$H^2 + H^3 \longrightarrow He^4 + n^1$$

It has been found by experiment that a mixture of these materials (say 200 pounds of deuterium and 300 pounds of tritium) surrounding an ordinary atomic bomb will undergo reaction at the temperature of many millions of degrees produced by the detonation of the bomb. In this way *hydrogen bombs* can be made, which may be one thousand times as powerful as an ordinary atomic bomb—that is, may release energy equal to that accompanying the detonation of twenty million tons of TNT. One of these hydrogen bombs could destroy any city in the world.

The *manufacture of plutonium* is carried out by a controlled chain reaction. A piece of ordinary uranium contains 0.71% U^{235}. An occasional neutron, produced by cosmic rays, strikes one of these atoms, causing it to undergo fission and to release a number of neutrons. These neutrons give rise to further reaction; the autocatalytic reaction does not build up, however, if the piece of uranium is small, because some of the neutrons escape, or may be absorbed by impurities, such as cadmium, the nuclei of which combine very readily with neutrons.

However, if a large enough sample of uranium is taken, nearly all of the neutrons which are formed by the fission remain within the sample of uranium, and either cause other U^{235} nuclei to undergo fission or are absorbed by U^{238}, converting it into U^{239}, which then undergoes spontaneous change to Pu^{239}. This is the process used in practice for the manufacture of plutonium. A large number of lumps of uranium are piled together, alternately with bricks of graphite,* in a structure called a reactor, or pile. The first uranium pile ever constructed, built at the University of Chicago and put into operation on 2 December 1942, contained 12,400 pounds of uranium metal. Cadmium rods are held in readiness to be introduced into cavities in the pile, to arrest the reaction, by absorbing neutrons, whenever there is danger of its getting out of hand.

The large reactors which were put into operation in September 1944, at Hanford, Washington, were of such size as to permit the fission reaction to proceed at the rate corresponding to an output of energy amounting to 1,500,000 kilowatts.

Deuterium for a hydrogen bomb can be made by the fractionation of ordinary water. Tritium can be made by a process involving neutrons produced by a uranium pile. For example, tritium is formed by the reaction of slow neutrons with lithium 6:

$$Li^6 + n^1 \longrightarrow H^3 + He^4$$

Inasmuch as neutrons are required for this reaction, the manufacture of tritium can be carried out only at the expense of the world's supply of fissionable material. Plutonium 239 prepared in a pile is stable: its half-life is 24,000 years, and it could at any time after its manufacture be used as a source of energy—in 350 years only 1% of the energy stored

---

* Heavy water may be used instead of graphite. The purpose of the graphite or heavy water is to slow down the fast neutrons produced by fission.

up in the plutonium will have been lost. Tritium, however, has a short half-life, about twelve years. Accordingly, a supply of tritium that has been made at great expense, and through the using up of a portion of the world's supply of fissionable material, is reduced to half of its value if it is stored for twelve years.

The significance of the uranium reactor as a source of radioactive material can be made clear by a comparison with the supply of radium now in use. Since the discovery of radium about 1,000 curies (1,000 grams) of radium has been separated from its ores and put into use, mainly for medical treatment. The rate of operation mentioned above for the reactors at Hanford represents the fission of about 5×10^{20} nuclei per second, forming about 10×10^{20} radioactive atoms. The concentration of these radioactive atoms will build up until they are undergoing decomposition at the rate at which they are being formed. Since 1 curie corresponds to 3.70×10^{10} disintegrating atoms per second, these reactors develop a radioactivity of approximately 3×10^{10} curies—that is, about thirty million times the radioactivity of all the radium which has been so far isolated from its ores.

The foregoing calculation illustrates the great significance of the fissionable elements as a source of radioactive material. Their significance as a source of energy has also been pointed out, by the statement that 1 pound of uranium or thorium is equivalent to 2.5 million pounds of coal. When we remember that uranium and thorium are not rare elements, but are among the more common elements—the amount of uranium and thorium in the earth's crust being about the same as that of the common element lead*—we begin to understand the promise of nuclear energy for the world of the future, and the possibilities of its contribution to human welfare. The discovery of the controlled fission of atomic nuclei and controlled release of atomic energy is the greatest discovery that has been made since the controlled use of fire was discovered by primitive man.

Exercises

33-1. Describe the difference in behavior of α rays, β rays, and γ rays in a magnetic field. How would rays of positrons behave? of neutrons?

33-2. What is the position in the periodic table, relative to the position of the original atom, of the product of a radioactive decomposition involving the emission of an α particle? of a β particle? of a γ ray? What change in atomic weight occurs during a radioactive decomposition involving each of these rays?

* Although uranium and thorium are not rare elements, they tend to be widely distributed in very small concentrations, and not many rich deposits have been discovered.

33-3. Natural radioactive decompositions involve the production of an α particle, a β particle, or a γ ray. Some unstable nuclides produced artificially decompose spontaneously with the production of a positron. What change in position in the periodic table accompanies this decomposition? What change in atomic weight?

33-4. An ore of uranium is found on analysis to contain Pb^{206} and U^{238} in the ratio by weight 0.3472/1.0000. Assuming that all of the lead isotope has been formed by decomposition of uranium, and that the half-life of U^{238} is 4.5×10^9 years, calculate the age of the rock. How much helium would have been formed for this amount of Pb^{206} during this period?

33-5. It is stated in the text that if an electron and a positron undergo annihilation with the production of a single photon, the wavelength of the photon is 0.0121 Å, and if two photons are produced, with equal energy, their wavelength is calculated to be 0.0242 Å. (Photons with these wavelengths are observed when positrons disappear in the presence of ordinary matter, which contains electrons.) Verify these wavelengths by calculation, using the Einstein mass-energy equation.

33-6. Discuss the argument used by Pauli in suggesting that neutrinos exist.

33-7. It is stated in the text that a neutral pion, with mass 263, is destroyed by spontaneous decomposition into two photons. Assuming the photons to have the same energy, calculate their wavelength.

33-8. What are cosmic rays?

33-9. What is the reaction between α particles and nitrogen nuclei, observed by Rutherford in 1919, which is considered to be the first nuclear reaction to have been produced by man? Using the values of the nuclear masses given in Table 33-2, calculate the energy liberated during this reaction.

33-10. Describe the structure and method of operation of the cyclotron.

33-11. Why is it easier to produce nuclear reactions in the laboratory by bombarding nuclei with neutrons than by bombarding nuclei with protons?

33-12. A sample of 25 g of carbon from woven rope sandals found in a cave under a lava flow in Oregon was observed to produce 31% as many β-ray counts in a Geiger counter as are produced by a 25-g sample of carbon from a recent sample of wood, after correction of the counts for the background due to cosmic rays and other constant sources. Using the value 5,568 years for the half-life of carbon 14, calculate from this information the age of the sandals.

33-13. If nuclear reactions were to continue until the most stable products had been formed, what elements would be present in largest amount in the universe?

33-14. One suggestion that has been made about the structure of heavy nuclei is that a nucleus consists of neutrons and protons packed together, with all of the protons (and some neutrons) in the outer layer, the core being just neutrons. What forces would you expect to operate to make this structure stable?

33-15. It is stated in the text that the reaction of a deuteron and a triton to form a helium nucleus and a neutron is accompanied by the conversion of 0.4% of the mass into energy. Using data from Table 33-2, evaluate this quantity to one additional decimal place.

33-16.   Assuming that all of the energy of the reaction of β-ray emission of a carbon
14 nucleus is converted into kinetic energy of the β ray, calculate its velocity.

References on Nuclear Chemistry

H. D. Smyth, *Atomic Energy for Military Purposes*, Princeton University Press, **1945.**

G. Friedlander and J. W. Kennedy, *Introduction to Radiochemistry*, John Wiley and Sons, New York, **1949.**

L. N. Ridenour, "The Hydrogen Bomb," *Scientific American*, **182,** 11 (March 1950).

K. K. Darrow, *Atomic Energy*, John Wiley and Sons, New York, **1948.**

Articles on the hydrogen bomb by Thirring, Einstein, and many others, *Bulletin of the Atomic Scientists*, early issues in 1950 (published by the Educational Foundation for Nuclear Science, 956 East 58th St., Chicago 37).

W. F. Libby, *Radiocarbon Dating*, University of Chicago Press, Chicago, **1952.**

E. S. Deevey, Jr., "Radiocarbon Dating," *Scientific American*, **186,** 24 (1952).

J. R. Arnold and W. F. Libby, "Radiocarbon Dates," *Science,* **113,** 111 (1951).

W. F. Libby, "Radiocarbon Dates, II," *Science,* **114,** 291 (1951).

P. J. Lovewell, "The Uses of Fission Products," *Scientific American*, **186,** 19 (June 1952).

R. E. Marshak, "The Multiplicity of Particles," *Scientific American*, **186,** 22 (January 1952).

P. Morrison and E. Morrison, "The Neutron," *Scientific American*, **185,** 44 (October 1951).

M. G. Mayer, "The Structure of the Nucleus," *Scientific American*, **184,** 42 (March 1951).

J. F. Flagg and E. L. Zebroski, "Atomic Pile Chemistry," *Scientific American*, **187,** 62 (July 1952).

L. R. Hafstad, "Reactors," *Scientific American*, **184,** 43 (April 1951).

L. P. Smith, "The Bevatron," *Scientific American*, **184,** 20 (February 1951).

E. D. Courant, "A 100-Billion-Volt Accelerator," *Scientific American*, **188,** 40 (May 1953).

R. E. Marshak, "The Energy of Stars," *Scientific American*, **182,** 42 (January 1950).

I. Perlman and G. T. Seaborg, "The Synthetic Elements," *Scientific American*, **182,** 38 (April 1950).

K. Way, L. Fano, M. R. Scott, and K. Thew, *Nuclear Data: A Collection of Experimental Values of Half-lives, Radiation Energies, Relative Isotopic Abundances, Nuclear Moments, and Cross Sections*, Circular of the National Bureau of Standards 499, U. S. Government Printing Office, Washington, D. C., **1950.**

TABLE 33-2   *Table of Principal Isotopes of the Lighter Elements*

ELEMENT NAME	Z	MASS	PERCENT ABUNDANCE	HALF-LIFE	RADIA-TION
0 Electron.............	0	0.000548			
0 Neutron.............	1	1.00897			
1 Proton.............	1	1.007582			
1 Hydrogen............	1	1.008130	99.984		
	2	2.014722	0.016		
	3	3.01705		12.4 Y	e^-
2 Alpha...............	4	4.002764			
2 Helium..............	3	3.01699	10^{-9}		
	4	4.00386	100		
	6			0.8 S	e^-
3 Lithium..............	6	6.01684	7.3		
	7	7.01818	92.7		
	8	8.0251		0.88 S	e^-
4 Beryllium............	7	7.01908		54 D	γ
	9	9.01494	100		
	10	10.01671		2.7×10^6 Y	e^-, γ
5 Boron...............	10	10.01633	18.83		
	11	11.01295	81.17		
	12	12.019		0.024 S	e^-
6 Carbon..............	10	10.01833		19.1 S	e^+
	11	11.01499		20.4 M	e^+
	12	12.00386	98.89		
	13	13.00766	1.11		
	14	14.00780		5,568 Y	e^-
7 Nitrogen.............	13	13.01005		10.1 M	e^+
	14	14.00756	99.64		
	15	15.00495	0.36		
	16	16.011		7.4 S	e^-
8 Oxygen..............	15	15.0078		1.97 M	e^+
	16	16.000	99.76		
	17	17.00449	0.04		
	18	18.00369	0.20		
	19			29.4 S	e^-
9 Fluorine..............	17	17.0076		72 S	e^+
	18	18.0056		1.87 H	e^+
	19	19.00452	100		
	20	20.0063		12 S	e^-, γ
10 Neon...............	19			18.2 S	e^+
	20	19.99896	90.0		
	21	20.99968	0.30		
	22	21.99864	9.73		
	23	23.0005		40 S	e^-

TABLE 33-2 (*continued*)

ELEMENT NAME	Z	MASS	PERCENT ABUNDANCE	HALF-LIFE	RADIA-TION
11 Sodium.............	21			23 S	
	22	22.0002		3 Y	e^+, γ
	23	22.9968	100		
	24	23.9974		14.9 H	e^-, γ
	25			62 S	e^-, γ
12 Magnesium...........	23			11.6 S	e^+
	24	23.99189	79.0		
	25	24.99277	10.0		
	26	25.99062	11.0		
	27	26.9921		9.6 M	e^-, γ
13 Aluminum............	26	25.9929		7.0 S	e^+
	27	26.9916	100		
	28	27.9903		2.4 M	e^-, γ
	29	28.9904		6.7 M	e^-, γ
14 Silicon..............	27	26.9931		4.92 S	e^+
	28	27.9866	92.18		
	29	28.9864	4.70		
	30	29.9832	3.12		
	31	30.9862		2.62 H	e^-
15 Phosphorus...........	29			4.6 S	e^+
	30	29.9882		2.2 M	e^+, γ
	31	30.9839	100		
	32	31.9841		14.3 D	e^-
16 Sulfur...............	31			3.18 S	e^+
	32	31.9823	95.1		
	33	32.9818	0.74		
	34	33.978	4.2		
	35			88 D	e^-
	36		0.016		
17 Chlorine.............	33			2.8 S	e^+
	34	33.981		33 M	e^+, γ
	35	34.97903	75.4		
	36			4×10^5 Y	e^-
	37	36.97786	24.6		
	38	37.981		38 M	e^-, γ
18 Argon...............	35			1.91 S	e^+
	36	35.9785	0.34		
	37			34 D	
	38	37.9751	0.061		
	39			4.0 M	e^-
	40	39.97564	99.60		
	41	40.9770		1.8 0H	e^-, γ

TABLE 33-2 (*continued*)

ELEMENT NAME	Z	MASS	PERCENT ABUNDANCE	HALF-LIFE	RADIA-TION
19 Potassium............	38			7.7 M	e^+, γ
	39	38.97518	93.1		
	40	39.975	0.011	15×10^8 Y	e^-, γ
	41	40.9739	6.9		
	42			12.4 H	e^-, γ
	43			22 H	e^-, γ
20 Calcium.............	39			1.0 S	e^+
	40	39.9745	96.97		
	41				e^-, γ
	42	41.9711	0.64		
	43	42.9723	0.14		
	44		2.06		
	45			152 D	e^-
	46		0.0033		
	48		0.185		
	49			8.5 M	e^-, γ
21 Scandium............	41			0.87 S	e^+
	43			4 H	e^+, γ
	44			52 H	e^-, γ
	44			4 H	e^+, γ
	45	44.9701	100		
	46			85 D	e^-, γ
	47			63 H	e^-, γ
	48			44 H	e^-, γ
	49			57 M	e^-
22 Titanium.............	45			3.1 H	e^+, γ
	46	45.9678	7.94		
	47		7.75		
	48	47.9651	73.45		
	49	48.9664	5.52		
	50	49.963	5.34		
	51			6 M	e^-, γ
23 Vanadium............	47			33 M	e^+, γ
	48			16 D	e^+, γ
	49			600 D	
	50		0.2		
	51	50.9587	99.8		
	52			3.7 M	e^-, γ

TABLE 33-2 (*continued*)

ELEMENT NAME	Z	MASS	PERCENT ABUNDANCE	HALF-LIFE	RADIA-TION
24 Chromium............	49			41.9 M	e^+, γ
	50		4.49		
	51			26.5 D	e^-, γ
	52	51.9582	83.78		
	53	52.9572	9.43		
	54	53.960	2.30		
	55			2 H	
25 Manganese..........	51			46 M	e^+
	52			21 M	e^+, γ
	52			6.0 D	e^+, γ
	54			310 D	γ
	55	54.965	100		
	56			2.59 H	e^-, γ

Appendix I

Probable Values of Some Physical and Chemical Constants (Chemists' Scale)

The probable values of physical and chemical constants change from time to time, as new experiments designed to determine them are carried out. The values below are those selected by J. W. M. DuMond and E. R. Cohen, *Least-squares Adjusted Values of the Atomic Constants*, Technical Report, California Institute of Technology, November 1952; values given by DuMond and Cohen on the physicists' scale [with $N = (0.602472 \pm 0.000036) \times 10^{24}$] have been converted to the chemists' scale by use of the assumed factor 1.000272. Slightly different values given in some places in the text may be either older or newer than these 1952 values.

Avogadro's number
$$N = (0.602308 \pm 0.000036) \times 10^{24}$$

Electronic charge
$$e = (1.60207 \pm 0.00007) \times 10^{-19} \text{ coulomb}$$
$$= (4.80288 \pm 0.00021) \times 10^{-10} \text{ statcoulomb}$$

Mass of electron
$$m = (9.1085 \pm 0.0006) \times 10^{-28} \text{ g}$$

Liter
$$1 \text{ liter} = 1,000.028 \pm 0.002 \text{ cm}^3$$

Ice point on absolute scale
$$0° \text{ C} = 273.16 \pm 0.01° \text{ K}$$

Standard molar gas volume
$$(RT)_{0°\text{C}} = 22.4140 \pm 0.0006 \text{ l atm mole}^{-1}$$

Gas constant
$$R = 0.08205447 \pm 0.0000037 \text{ l atm deg}^{-1} \text{ mole}^{-1}$$

Boltzmann's constant
$$k = R/N = (1.38042 \pm 0.00010) \times 10^{-16} \text{ erg/deg}$$

Faraday
$$F = 96,494 \pm 3 \text{ coulombs/mole}$$

Ratio of physical to chemical atomic weights
     $r = 1.000272$ (assumed)

Velocity of light
     $c = (2.997929 \pm 0.000008) \times 10^{10}$ cm/sec

Planck's constant
     $h = (6.6252 \pm 0.0005) \times 10^{-27}$ erg sec

Energy in ergs of one electron volt
     $(1.60207 \pm 0.00007) \times 10^{-12}$ erg

Energy in calories per mole for one electron volt per molecule
     $23,052.85 \pm 3.2$ cal/mole

Energy in cm^{-1} (wave number of a photon) of one electron volt per molecule
     $8,082.6$ cm^{-1}

Wavelength of photon with energy one electron volt
     $12,372.2 \pm 0.04$ Å

Appendix II

The Vapor Pressure of Water
at Different Temperatures

TEMPERATURE (° C)	VAPOR PRESSURE (MM OF MERCURY)	TEMPERATURE (° C)	VAPOR PRESSURE (MM OF MERCURY)
−10 (ice)......	1.0	27.........	26.7
−5 "	3.0	28.........	28.3
0.........	4.6	29.........	30.0
5.........	6.5	30.........	31.8
10.........	9.2	35.........	42.2
15.........	12.8	40.........	55.3
16.........	13.6	45.........	71.9
17.........	14.5	50.........	92.5
18.........	15.5	60.........	149.4
19.........	16.5	70.........	233.7
20.........	17.5	80.........	355.1
21.........	18.6	90.........	525.8
22.........	19.8	100.........	760.0
23.........	21.1	110.........	1,074.6
24.........	22.4	150.........	3,570.5
25.........	23.8	200.........	11,659.2
26.........	25.2	300.........	64,432.8

Index